Contemporary Problems in Statistics

Contemporary Problems
in Statistics

A BOOK OF READINGS
FOR THE BEHAVIORAL SCIENCES

EDITED BY
BERNHARDT LIEBERMAN
Professor of Social Psychology
in the Departments of Sociology and Psychology
University of Pittsburgh

New York
OXFORD UNIVERSITY PRESS
London   Toronto   1971

Copyright © 1971 by Oxford University Press, Inc.
Library of Congress Catalogue Card Number: 74-122520
Printed in the United States of America

Preface

This book is the product of my belief that students, as early as possible, should be introduced to the uncertainties, complexities, and confusions that characterize our knowledge. As behavioral scientists we strive to order our knowledge about human behavior, yet we know that there is much disorder, and there is disagreement among us. Too frequently we try to spare our students the true picture; what we often do is give a picture of our methods, results, and theories that emphasizes the order and neglects much of the disorder. It is not surprising, then, that some students remain intellectually naïve and unable to make intellectual work a personal activity. When we fail to teach, explicitly, the disorder and confusion present in our disciplines we are doing our students a disservice, for if a student is to become a serious investigator of any topic—language, history, chemistry, or psychology—he must accept the disorder and complexity of his discipline and then proceed to create his own personal order.

When we teach statistics the complexities and imperfections of our own knowledge become clear. Many students are troubled when they study statistics, partly because they are not experienced and at ease with mathematical and statistical language, but also because the study of statistics makes clear the contrast between precision and confusion that is very much a part of behavioral science. Mathematical statisticians have provided us with a number of statistical techniques that derive from probabilistic models which have some precisely defined characteristics—the assumptions of the model. If we were to use the techniques given to us with complete rigor we would need data that satisfy the precisely defined characteristics, the assumptions, of the statistical model.

But this is frequently not the case; the curiosity and need of the behavioral scientist lead him to ask questions that stimulate investigations producing data that do not conform to the limitations and assumptions of the statistical models available for his use. Behavioral scientists faced with these problems continue their work, and make use of the most appropriate statistical techniques they can find. Since criticism is an inherent and most important part of the scientific process, the methodologically sophisticated discover the violations of rigorous procedure, which are quite apparent to the initiated, and criticize the questionable (and sometimes inevitable) practices of the investigator. One should not wonder that dispute and disagreement result; it is sometimes difficult to distinguish the incompetent from the competent victim of the complexities.

When the student of statistics discovers this perplexing situation he is often rightfully disturbed; some students become discouraged, and some fear that statistics can never be used appropriately.

We find ourselves in a peculiar situation for people who are striving for rigorous knowledge. Some of our data satisfy the assumptions of a particular, appropriate statistical model. On the other hand, sometimes we think it best to use a statistical technique even when it is not completely appropriate; and at other times we are faced with the work of less competent investigators who have used a statistical technique that we see as clearly inappropriate. Sometimes it is difficult to tell which is the case.

What is the student to do then? He must do what sophisticated investigators have done in the past; he must learn the details and the complexities so that he can make an intelligent, trained judgment. Many of the complexities and controversies that have concerned behavioral scientists in the past twenty years are exhibited, in all their detail, in this volume.

This book is designed to be used together with one of the many standard statistics textbooks. Textbooks are supposed to give the student an understanding of the fundamental properties of statistical models, and to give the student practice in the use of statistical techniques. Some of the standard texts discuss many of the issues discussed in the readings in this book, but none of them present the details and arguments as these original sources do. It is essential that the serious student be exposed to the detailed arguments contained in them. In attempting to master the complexities, the student will learn the fundamental principles. More important, he will be convinced that statistical questions —indeed all our attempts to obtain rigorous knowledge—produce confusions, disagreements, and complexities. The student should learn that his own uncertainty, if it is combined with a modicum of mastery of the basic notions of statistics, is not a sign of weakness but of a developing maturity, and that he *is* learning statistics. When he debates the use of the one-tailed or two-tailed test, and when he debates whether he can use a *t*-test with ordinal data, he can then know he is learning what one must to use statistics competently. When he discovers that mature investigators question the appropriateness of the use of

Neyman-Pearson hypothesis testing, for example, he discovers that his confusion and uncertainties are not unique and are shared by many mature investigators.

Not all our students are hesitant and uncertain when learning statistics. There are some who are comfortable with and know some mathematics. These students are the ones who will benefit most from these readings; they will readily understand the properties of the models and recognize the properties of the data that do not conform to the models. The issues and disagreements discussed in these readings should be clear to them immediately, and their professional development should be facilitated.

Pittsburgh, Pennsylvania   B.L.
July 1970

Acknowledgments

This book could not have been produced without the efforts and help of many people, and I would like to acknowledge my debts. Lloyd Humphreys and Edgar Borgatta made a number of helpful suggestions about the plan and contents of the book. William Halpin of the Oxford University Press has been a thoughtful and generous editor who shared my view that undergraduate and graduate students should have the opportunity to read the selections in this volume with the convenience this book offers. I am especially indebted to Mary Catherine Skoog for proofreading the book and preparing its index.

I am most indebted, of course, to the authors of the articles included in the volume, for the book really consists of their ideas. Perhaps they will get some satisfaction from the knowledge that the publication of this book will make it possible for many students (who otherwise would not have the opportunity) to become familiar with their ideas.

I am also indebted to the editors and publishers of the journals and books the articles were originally printed in, for the permissions to reprint. The book publishers are John Wiley and Sons, The Macmillan Company, Hafner Publishing Company, McGraw-Hill Book Company, and Houghton Mifflin Company. The journals are *Science, Psychometrika, Psychological Bulletin, Psychological Review, Synthese,* and *Educational and Psychological Measurement.*

Contents

SECTION 2
INFERENCE AND NULL-HYPOTHESIS TESTING

SECTION 3
THE ONE-TAIL, TWO-TAIL CONTROVERSY

SECTION 4
BAYESIAN STATISTICS

SECTION 5
THE USE AND MISUSE OF CHI-SQUARE

General Introduction

The readings in this book have been selected from the behavioral-statistical literature so that the reader will become familiar with and, it is to be hoped, master the basic issues and controversies that behavioral scientists are currently, or have been recently, involved in. The articles in it discuss a variety of topics: types of measurement and scales, and the statistics appropriate to use with various types of measurement; the merits and disadvantages of null-hypothesis testing procedures and, alternately, Bayesian procedures; the chi-square controversy; and others.

The serious student of the use of statistics in the behavioral sciences needs a thorough knowledge of these topics, because what is the correct method to use is not a simple question to answer. Much of the data the behavioral scientist collects does not conform precisely to the requirements of any one model. In fact, the data is often more or less appropriate for use with two or three models, so that deciding on the model that is most appropriate is often simply a matter of individual judgment and, thus, disagreement among behavioral scientists.

Once the student has mastered the rudiments of calculating the various statistical techniques available to him, has had some experience understanding the significance of descriptive statistics, and has been introduced to the basic ideas of inference, he must master the complexities involved in the sophisticated use of statistical models.

Many mature and competent investigators have difficulty when they attempt to employ a statistical technique. This difficulty stems from the complexities discussed in the Preface, as well as from other causes. Investigators have different tastes, preferences, and habits, and there are genuine, defensible differences in beliefs about what are important problems to study and what research procedures should be employed to solve the problems thought to be worthwhile. The mature investigator imposes some personal order on this confusion of purposes and methods. He develops a style of work that helps him answer questions he and a group of similar investigators believe warrant answers, and he accepts the limitations on the statements he can make, limitations which are imposed by the difficulties involved in employing a statistical model.

The student who wishes to understand the proper use of statistics by behavioral scientists or who wishes to master the use of statistics, then, must impose some similar personal order. The first step in this process is to become familiar with the complexities, problems, and controversies that the behavioral scientist faces. The readings in this book will help him do just that. They have been organized into seven sections: (1) Measurement and Scales, (2) Inference and Null-Hypothesis Testing, (3) The One-tail, Two-tail Controversy, (4) Bayesian Statistics, (5) The Use and Misuse of Chi-Square, (6) Violations of Assumptions, (7) Current Interpretations. A few brief preliminary remarks may be helpful at this point.

(1) Measurement and Scales—This section deals with fundamental problems of measurement—the types of scales (nominal, ordinal, interval, ratio, etc.) and the statistics appropriate for use with each scale. The papers range from Stevens's early work to his most recent paper.

(2) Inference and Null-Hypothesis Testing—This section contains discussions of the fundamental ideas of null-hypothesis testing procedures and the criticisms of the weaknesses of these procedures.

(3) The One-tail, Two-tail Controversy—Behavioral scientists, particularly psychologists, often do empirical or experimental studies in which they expect to find statistical differences between two groups of subjects. The predictions they make can be of two kinds: they may predict that the mean of group 1 will be greater than the mean of group 2, or they may predict the two means will be significantly different. The first prediction is called a one-tailed (or one-sided) hypothesis, the second, a two-tailed hypothesis. Some investigators believe one should always, or nearly always, use a two-tailed hypothesis, whereas others believe one should, wherever possible, make a one-tailed prediction. The merits and disadvantages of both the one-tailed and two-tailed tests are discussed in some detail, and a familiarity with this controversy will do much to deepen the student's understanding of the null-hypothesis decision procedures.

(4) Bayesian Statistics—Some statisticians believe that null-hypothesis decision procedures have such serious deficiencies that for certain problems alternative statistical and logical models should be used. Bayesian statistical procedures, which have their origin in the work of Thomas Bayes, are suggested. Although it is not yet completely clear just how the psychologist or sociologist should actually use these techniques, there is a considerable

amount of work currently being done by statisticians and behavioral scientists, and the serious student should be familiar with these ideas.

(5) The Use and Misuse of Chi-Square—The chi-square statistical test is one that is used frequently by behavioral scientists, for, if the assumptions of the model are met, it is useful, and the calculations necessary for its use are simple—it is an approximation of an exact multinominal test.

(6) Violations of Assumptions—This section contains articles which examine the consequences of using a statistical procedure when the assumptions of that model are not satisfied. The articles consider the consequences of using the F and t tests when assumptions of normality and heterogeneity of variance are not met.

(7) Current Interpretations—The three articles of this section reflect some current concerns of psychologists. Correlation, regression, multiple regression, analysis of variance, and analyses of covariance are subjected to analyses which are frequently not considered by some behavioral scientists.

The articles are discussed in greater detail in the introductions to each section.

Contemporary Problems in Statistics

SECTION 1

Measurement and Scales

The group of readings included in this section will introduce the student to questions that deal with the logic of measurement. Measurement considerations may be said to be of two kinds: the fundamental questions discussed in this section, and questions involving specific measurement techniques—content analysis, questionnaires, psychophysical measures, etc. The student of a behavioral science must familiarize himself with specific measuring instruments and master their use, but he must also be cognizant of the fundamental questions that underlie their use. Each measuring technique produces a set of scores that lie on some kind of scale, and the serious student must be aware of, and understand, the properties of the scale he is employing. What is the significance of the numbers he has obtained? What transformations may he apply to these scores? What statistics may he appropriately use with these scores so that the statements he makes are meaningful and valid?

The first article by S. S. Stevens introduces the student to the notions of nominal, ordinal, interval, and ratio scales. This article is a most important one, for it has been recognized to be a contribution not only to the behavioral sciences but also to the physical sciences. The discussion of measurement by B. Andreas, while it is not rigorous, is an extremely useful and lucid presentation of some of the basic ideas.

The article by N. Anderson, "Scales and Statistics: Parametric and Nonparametric," discusses the relationship of the scale type to the statistic that can be appropriately employed. Anderson argues that parametric statistics should be the standard tool of the psychologist, and that the scale type has little relevance to the question of whether one should use a parametric or nonparametric test.

The chapter by P. Suppes and J. Zinnes, "Basic Measurement Theory," is a very ambitious attempt to remove the questions of the appropriate use of statistics and the definition of scale type from the domain of catechism and controversy to the plane of rigorous mathematical argument and proof. Suppes and Zinnes attempted to use rigorous mathematics—the requirement of the formal proof—to make statements about basic measurement problems. They argue that the problems that Stevens posed, and partially solved, must be treated like any other mathematical statement—without formal proofs our statements are incomplete and inadequate. To get satisfactory measurement, two problems must be solved—the problems of representation and uniqueness. The representation problem is solved when the formal properties of the empirical operations and relations are character- ized, and it is shown that these operations and relations correspond to an appropriately chosen numerical system. The uniqueness problem is solved when the scale type (ordinal, interval, ratio, etc.) is determined and defined precisely—using the full, rigorous, mathe- matical proof. The remaining articles of this section discuss these, and other related issues. The final article by Stevens is the most recent statement of his views.

S. S. STEVENS

1 On the Theory of Scales of Measurement

For seven years a committee of the British Association for the Advancement of Science debated the problem of measurement. Appointed in 1932 to represent Section A (Mathematical and Physical Sciences) and Section J (Psychology), the committee was instructed to consider and report upon the possibility of "quantitative estimates of sensory events"—meaning simply: Is it possible to measure human sensation? Deliberation led only to disagreement, mainly about what is meant by the term measurement. An interim report in 1938 found one member complaining that his colleagues "came out by that same door as they went in," and in order to have another try at agreement, the committee begged to be continued for another year.

For its final report (1940) the committee chose a common bone for its contentions, directing its arguments at a concrete example

of a sensory scale. This was the Sone scale of loudness (S. S. Stevens and H. Davis. *Hearing.* New York: Wiley, 1938), which purports to measure the subjective magnitude of an auditory sensation against a scale having the formal properties of other basic scales, such as those used to measure length and weight. Again the 19 members of the committee came out by the routes they entered, and their views ranged widely between two extremes. One member submitted "that any law purporting to express a quantitative relation between sensation intensity and stimulus intensity is not merely false but is in fact meaningless unless and until a meaning can be given to the concept of addition as applied to sensation" (Final Report, p. 245).

It is plain from this and from other statements by the committee that the real issue is the meaning of measurement. This, to be sure,

Science, Vol. 103, June 7, 1946, pp. 677–80. Reprinted by permission of the American Association for the Advancement of Science.

is a semantic issue, but one susceptible of orderly discussion. Perhaps agreement can better be achieved if we recognize that measurement exists in a variety of forms and that scales of measurement fall into certain definite classes. These classes are determined both by the empirical operations invoked in the process of "measuring" and by the formal (mathematical) properties of the scales. Furthermore—and this is of great concern to several of the sciences—the statistical manipulations that can legitimately be applied to empirical data depend upon the type of scale against which the data are ordered.

A Classification of Scales of Measurement

Paraphrasing N. R. Campbell (Final Report, p. 340), we may say that measurement, in the broadest sense, is defined as the assignment of numerals to objects or events according to rules. The fact that numerals can be assigned under different rules leads to different kinds of scales and different kinds of measurement. The problem then becomes that of making explicit (a) the various rules for the assignment of numerals, (b) the mathematical properties (or group structure) of the resulting scales, and (c) the statistical operations applicable to measurements made with each type of scale.

Scales are possible in the first place only because there is a certain isomorphism between what we can do with the aspects of objects and the properties of the numeral series. In dealing with the aspects of objects we invoke empirical operations for determining equality (classifying), for rank-ordering, and for determining when differences and when ratios between the aspects of objects are equal. The conventional series of numerals yields to analogous operations: We can identify the members of a numeral series and classify them. We know their order as given by convention. We can determine equal differences, as $8-6 = 4-2$, and equal ratios, as $8/4 = 6/3$. The isomorphism between these properties of the numeral series and certain empirical operations which

we perform with objects permits the use of the series as a *model* to represent aspects of the empirical world.

The type of scale achieved depends upon the character of the basic empirical operations performed. These operations are limited ordinarily by the nature of the thing being scaled and by our choice of procedures, but, once selected, the operations determine that there will eventuate one or another of the scales listed in Table 1.[1]

The decision to discard the scale names commonly encountered in writings on measurement is based on the ambiguity of such terms as "intensive" and "extensive." Both ordinal and interval scales have at times been called intensive, and both interval and ratio scales have sometimes been labeled extensive.

It will be noted that the column listing the basic operations needed to create each type of scale is cumulative: to an operation listed opposite a particular scale must be added all those operations preceding it. Thus, an interval scale can be erected only provided we have an operation for determining equality of intervals, for determining greater or less, and for determining equality (not greater and not less). To these operations must be added a method for ascertaining equality of ratios if a ratio scale is to be achieved.

In the column which records the group structure of each scale are listed the mathematical transformations which leave the scale-form invariant. Thus, any numeral, x, on a scale can be replaced by another numeral, x', where x' is the function of x listed in this column. Each mathematical group in the column is contained in the group immediately above it.

The last column presents examples of the type of statistical operations appropriate to each scale. This column is cumulative in that *all* statistics listed are admissible for data

1. A classification essentially equivalent to that contained in this table was presented before the International Congress for the Unity of Science, September 1941. The writer is indebted to the late Prof. G. D. Birkhoff for a stimulating discussion which led to the completion of the table in essentially its present form.

Table 1

Scale	Basic Empirical Operations	Mathematical Group Structure	Permissible Statistics (invariantive)
Nominal	Determination of equality	*Permutation group* $x' = f(x)$ $f(x)$ means any one-to-one substitution	Number of cases Mode Contingency correlation
Ordinal	Determination of greater or less	*Isotonic group* $x' = f(x)$ $f(x)$ means any monotonic increasing function	Median Percentiles
Interval	Determination of equality of intervals or differences	*General linear group* $x' = ax + b$	Mean Standard deviation Rank-order correlation Product-moment correlation
Ratio	Determination of equality of ratios	*Similarity group* $x' = ax$	Coefficient of variation

scaled against a ratio scale. The criterion for the appropriateness of a statistic is *invariance* under the transformations in Column 3. Thus, the case that stands at the median (mid-point) of a distribution maintains its position under all transformations which preserve order (isotonic group), but an item located at the mean remains at the mean only under transformations as restricted as those of the linear group. The ratio expressed by the coefficient of variation remains invariant only under the similarity transformation (multiplication by a constant). (The rank-order correlation coefficient is usually deemed appropriate to an ordinal scale, but actually this statistic assumes equal intervals between successive ranks and therefore calls for an interval scale.)

Let us now consider each scale in turn.

Nominal Scale

The *nominal scale* represents the most unrestricted assignment of numerals. The numerals are used only as labels or type numbers, and words or letters would serve as well. Two types of nominal assignments are sometimes distinguished, as illustrated (a) by the "numbering" of football players for the identification of the individuals, and (b) by the "numbering" of types or classes, where each member of a class is assigned the same numeral. Actually, the first is a special case of the second, for when we label our football players we are dealing with unit classes of one member each. Since the purpose is just as well served when any two designating numerals are interchanged, this scale form remains invariant under the general substitution or permutation group (sometimes called the symmetric group of transformations). The only statistic relevant to nominal scales of Type A is the number of cases, e.g. the number of players assigned numerals. But once classes containing several individuals have been formed (Type B), we can determine the most numerous class (the mode), and under certain conditions we can test, by the contingency methods, hypotheses regarding the distribution of cases among the classes.

The nominal scale is a primitive form, and quite naturally there are many who will urge that it is absurd to attribute to this process of assigning numerals the dignity implied by the term measurement. Certainly there can be no quarrel with this objection, for the naming of things is an arbitrary business. However we christen it, the use of numerals as names for classes is an example of the "assignment of numerals according to rule." The rule is: Do not assign the same numeral to different classes or different numerals to the same class. Beyond that, anything goes with the nominal scale.

Ordinal Scale

The *ordinal scale* arises from the operation of rank-ordering. Since any "order-preserving" transformation will leave the scale form invariant, this scale has the structure of what may be called the isotonic or order-preserving group. A classic example of an ordinal scale is the scale of hardness of minerals. Other instances are found among scales of intelligence, personality traits, grade or quality of leather, etc.

As a matter of fact, most of the scales used widely and effectively by psychologists are ordinal scales. In the strictest propriety the ordinary statistics involving means and standard deviations ought not to be used with these scales, for these statistics imply a knowledge of something more than the relative rank-order of data. On the other hand, for this "illegal" statisticizing there can be invoked a kind of pragmatic sanction: In numerous instances it leads to fruitful results. While the outlawing of this procedure would probably serve no good purpose, it is proper to point out that means and standard deviations computed on an ordinal scale are in error to the extent that the successive intervals on the scale are unequal in size. When only the rank-order of data is known, we should proceed cautiously with our statistics, and especially with the conclusions we draw from them.

Even in applying those statistics that are normally appropriate for ordinal scales, we sometimes find rigor compromised. Thus, although it is indicated in Table 1 that percentile measures may be applied to rank-ordered data, it should be pointed out that the customary procedure of assigning a value to a percentile by interpolating linearly within a class interval is, in all strictness, wholly out of bounds. Likewise, it is not strictly proper to determine the mid-point of a class interval by linear interpolation, because the linearity of an ordinal scale is precisely the property which is open to question.

Interval Scale

With the *interval scale* we come to a form that is "quantitative" in the ordinary sense of the word. Almost all the usual statistical measures are applicable here, unless they are the kinds that imply a knowledge of a "true" zero point. The zero point on an interval scale is a matter of convention or convenience, as is shown by the fact that the scale form remains invariant when a constant is added.

This point is illustrated by our two scales of temperature, Centigrade and Fahrenheit. Equal intervals of temperature are scaled off by noting equal volumes of expansion; an arbitrary zero is agreed upon for each scale; and a numerical value on one of the scales is transformed into a value on the other by means of an equation of the form $x' = ax + b$. Our scales of time offer a similar example. Dates on one calendar are transformed to those on another by way of this same equation. On these scales, of course, it is meaningless to say that one value is twice or some other proportion greater than another.

Periods of time, however, can be measured on ratio scales and one period may be correctly defined as double another. The same is probably true of temperature measured on the so-called Absolute Scale.

Most psychological measurement aspires to create interval scales, and it sometimes succeeds. The problem usually is to devise operations for equalizing the units of the scales—a problem not always easy of solution but one for which there are several possible modes of attack. Only occasionally is there concern for the location of a "true" zero point, because the human attributes measured by psychologists usually exist in a positive degree that is large compared with the range of its variation. In this respect these attributes are analogous to temperature as it is encountered in everyday life. Intelligence, for example, is usefully assessed on ordinal scales which try to approximate interval scales, and it is not necessary to define what zero intelligence would mean.

Ratio Scale

Ratio scales are those most commonly encountered in physics and are possible only when there exist operations for determining all four relations: equality, rank-order, equality of intervals, and equality of ratios. Once such a scale is erected, its numerical values can be transformed (as from inches to feet) only by multiplying each value by a constant. An absolute zero is always implied, even though the zero value on some scales (e.g. Absolute Temperature) may never be produced. All types of statistical measures are applicable to ratio scales, and only with these scales may we properly indulge in logarithmic transformations such as are involved in the use of decibels.

Foremost among the ratio scales is the scale of number itself—cardinal number—the scale we use when we count such things as eggs, pennies, and apples. This scale of the numerosity of aggregates is so basic and so common that it is ordinarily not even mentioned in discussions of measurement.

It is conventional in physics to distinguish between two types of ratio scales: *fundamental* and *derived*. Fundamental scales are represented by length, weight, and electrical resistance, whereas derived scales are represented by density, force, and elasticity.

These latter are *derived* magnitudes in the sense that they are mathematical functions of certain fundamental magnitudes. They are actually more numerous in physics than are the fundamental magnitudes, which are commonly held to be basic because they satisfy the criterion of *additivity*. Weights, lengths, and resistances can be added in the physical sense, but this important empirical fact is generally accorded more prominence in the theory of measurement than it deserves. The so-called fundamental scales are important instances of ratio scales, but they are only instances. As a matter of fact, it can be demonstrated that the fundamental scales could be set up even if the physical operation of addition were ruled out as impossible of performance. Given three balances, for example, each having the proper construction, a set of standard weights could be manufactured without it ever being necessary to place two weights in the same scale pan at the same time. The procedure is too long to describe in these pages, but its feasibility is mentioned here simply to suggest that physical addition, even though it is sometimes possible, is not necessarily the basis of all measurement. Too much measuring goes on where resort can never be had to the process of laying things end-to-end or of piling them up in a heap.

Ratio scales of psychological magnitudes are rare but not entirely unknown. The Sone scale discussed by the British committee is an example founded on a deliberate attempt to have human observers judge the loudness ratios of pairs of tones. The judgment of equal intervals had long been established as a legitimate method, and with the work on sensory ratios, started independently in several laboratories, the final step was taken to assign numerals to sensations of loudness in such a way that relations among the sensations are reflected by the ordinary arithmetical relations in the numeral series. As in all measurement, there are limits imposed by error and variability, but within these limits the Sone scale ought properly to be classed as a ratio scale.

To the British committee, then, we may venture to suggest by way of conclusion that the most liberal and useful definition of measurement is, as one of its members advised, "the assignment of numerals to things so as to represent facts and conventions about them." The problem as to what is and is not measurement then reduces to the simple question: What are the rules, if any, under which numerals are assigned? If we can point to a consistent set of rules, we are obviously concerned with measurement of some sort, and we can then proceed to the more interesting question as to the kind of measurement it is. In most cases a formulation of the rules of assignment discloses directly the kind of measurement and hence the kind of scale involved. If there remains any ambiguity, we may seek the final and definitive answer in the mathematical group-structure of the scale form: In what ways can we transform its values and still have it serve all the functions previously fulfilled? We know that the values of all scales can be multiplied by a constant, which changes the size of the unit. If, in addition, a constant can be added (or a new zero point chosen), it is proof positive that we are not concerned with a ratio scale. Then, if the purpose of the scale is still served when its values are squared or cubed, it is not even an interval scale. And finally, if any two values may be interchanged at will, the ordinal scale is ruled out and the nominal scale is the sole remaining possibility.

This proposed solution to the semantic problem is not meant to imply that all scales belonging to the same mathematical group are equally precise or accurate or useful or "fundamental." Measurement is never better than the empirical operations by which it is carried out, and operations range from bad to good. Any particular scale, sensory or physical, may be objected to on the grounds of bias, low precision, restricted generality, and other factors, but the objector should remember that these are relative and practical matters and that no scale used by mortals is perfectly free of their taint.

BURTON ANDREAS

2 Measurement and Statistics

Much of laboratory experimentation in psychology is aimed at finding functional relationships between independent and dependent variables. In many cases, the independent variables are physical stimulus dimensions that are quantified in accordance with conventional physical scales, like the Centigrade scale for temperature or a decibel scale for sound intensity. In other cases, stimulus materials may involve dimensions which have previously been subjected to psychological scaling procedures. Aspects of behavior which we select as dependent variables are also quantifiable by applying a variety of scales. These may be identical with scales used by the physicist, as when we measure the duration of a response in seconds or determine the force, in kilograms, with which a subject squeezes a dyna-

mometer. We may also use more complex measures of behavior like the number of trials required to memorize ten words or the per cent of subjects able to detect a tone of a given low intensity.

We obtain experimental data by using different measurement techniques. With measurement occupying so central a place in research, we need to become acquainted with various kinds of scales by which we may quantify behavior. These behavioral data are treated statistically in order to achieve an orderly quantitative description of the behavior. Here we explore the nature of measurement, the kinds of scales which we may use, the descriptive uses of statistics, and certain computational formulas. Elsewhere we will consider how statistical manipulations help us to assess the likelihood that the data support the hypothesis being tested.

Measurement Scales

DEFINITION OF MEASUREMENT

Our examination of how research workers in psychology quantify behavior will begin with a consideration of just what measurement is—in any part of science or in everyday life. "Measurement is the assignment of numerals to objects or events according to rules" says Stevens, paraphrasing Campbell. Let us see if this concise definition really applies to varied examples of measuring which come to mind. When we measure the width of a laboratory work table with a meter stick, are we assigning a numeral according to rules? There are, indeed, several rules which must be followed to make this physical measurement in valid fashion. The meter stick must cross the table squarely. The end of the stick, or some cardinal point on the stick, must be aligned with one edge of the table. We must observe from an appropriate angle to note the nearest graduation mark corresponding to the other edge of the table. We must subtract the meter stick readings aligned with the two edges to get the width of the table. Our rules may prescribe that we take the datum to the nearest centimeter, or may require a reading to the nearest millimeter. The really complete definition of this physical measurement is even more elaborate than this, involving reference to our conventionally graduated meter stick, and in turn to the standard meter of the metric system. It appears, then, that the measurement of the width of the table does indeed involve assigning a numeral according to the rules.

In measuring a person's reaction time, *RT*, are we also assigning a numeral according to rules? Our first step in using a chronometer is to check its calibration, if we are very rigorous in our approach to temporal quantification. With the soundness of the instrument assured, we next follow certain rules in placing it in the circuit of the *RT* apparatus. We make sure that the chronometer starts at the instant that the stimulus is presented and that it stops simultaneously with the making of the reaction. In reading the timer we take precautions not to distort the obtained value by viewing it from the wrong angle. All these steps are part of the series of operations we perform in quantifying the behavioral event represented in the *RT* experiment.

When we describe the sequential steps we take in obtaining *RT*, then, we are prescribing rules for its measurement. At the same time, we are operationally defining what we mean by *RT*. Thus, measurement of a behavioral event and its operational definition are practically identical. Consider additional facets of the experiment. When we instruct a subject to respond as quickly as possible, and when we take the average *RT* over many trials, we are further expanding our rules for *RT* measurement and our operational definition of this concept. No matter how we *verbally* define a dependent variable, be it *RT* or memory or esthetic judgment, our procedures for measuring it constitute the *operational* definition of it. This is the meaningful definition as we seek empirical functional relationships, or behavioral laws.

TYPES OF MEASUREMENT SCALES

Whenever we are confronted with behavioral data we need to ask exactly how the data were obtained. Although some aspects of behavior are measurable through the use of meter sticks and chronometers, many data in psychological research stem from elaborate techniques which constitute a complex scale. A scale may be defined as a prescribed series of steps employed in assigning a numeral to an object or event. Conventional measuring instruments like meter sticks and chronometers represent a consolidation of several steps in the complete series, thus offering a great economy of effort through reducing the number of remaining steps. We find that different classes or types of measurement scales are defined by different characteristics of the magnitudes being measured. In turn, these types of scales determine what statistical manipulations are appropriately applicable to the data they yield. We now turn to an examination of different types of scales and the numerical manipulations applicable to the data they give us.

Scale-Defining Operations. Different types of measurement scales are defined by the kind of operation which can validly be performed on the dimension under study. We shall use the physical dimension, length, to illustrate the various operations in question. It would

itself. They may be paralleled by mathematical operations performed on measurements which we might take of each line segment.

Operation I is the determination of greater, less, or equality. The way this operation is performed on physical length is illustrated in Figure 1B where we see the line segments arranged in parallel fashion with their left end points aligned. It is readily apparent that none of the segments is equal in length. S is greater in length than Q, T is of lesser length than R,

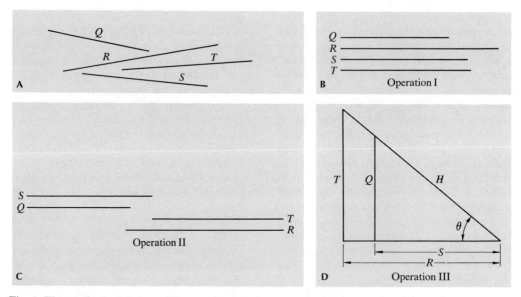

Fig. 1. The application of three different scale-defining operations to the physical dimension of length as represented by line segments Q, R, S, and T. (See text for explanation.)

be extremely difficult to portray the application of these operations to behavioral dimensions. However, if we can see them applied to length, we may be better able to appreciate the meaning of these operations and the scales to which they give rise.

In Figure 1A we see four different line segments to which we successively apply the scale-defining operations in other parts of the figure. These different operations are performed on the physical dimension, length,

etc. The operation of aligning the ends of the segments after making them parallel has revealed their different orders of magnitude.

Operation II is the determination of equality or inequality of differences. Is the difference between Q and S the same as the difference between R and T? To determine this by physical manipulation, we may align the segments as shown in Figure 1C. We have arranged them so as to bring into alignment the two differences in which we are interested.

By bringing Q and S into correspondence at the left and R and T into correspondence at the right, we can examine the differences, $S - Q$ and $R - T$, in direct physical comparison. When we examine the center part of this configuration we see that the difference between R and T is greater than that between S and Q. Our manipulation of the lengths has demonstrated the inequality of these differences. Our operation has revealed that the physical dimension of length is one for which it is possible to determine the equality or inequality of differences.

Operation III determines the equality of ratios of magnitudes. We ask the question, is the ratio of Q to S the same as the ratio of T to R? One way to manipulate the physical lengths to answer this question is to employ them as legs of a right triangle. In Figure 1D we see T and R utilized to form such a triangle with the angle θ having T/R as its tangent. By placing the lengths S and Q as shown, to form a similar right triangle, we see that Q/S is also the tangent value for the same angle, θ. The hypotenuse of the smaller triangle coincides completely with that of the larger one, indicated by H in the figure. As tangents of the same angle, θ, the ratios Q/S and T/R have been shown to be equal. Determining the equality or inequality of ratios has been shown to be possible by manipulating the magnitudes of length.

We have seen that length can be manipulated to test for three kinds of equality:

1. Equality of magnitudes, by Operation I.
2. Equality of differences, by Operation II.
3. Equality of ratios, by Operation III.

Of course, we might have measured the four line segments in Figure 1A and used the measurements obtained to check for these equalities. The mathematical process of subtraction could have been appropriately applied to these data to parallel Operations I and II, represented in Figures 1B and 1C, respectively. The processes of division and then subtraction could have been successively applied in a parallel to Operation III to determine the

equality of ratios, Q/S and T/R. Such mathematical processes are readily applicable to data of all sorts. Measurement theory, however, dictates that such computations are appropriate only when the dimension in question permits similar operations to be performed on the corresponding magnitudes themselves. Thus, a ratio of two measured lengths may be calculated because the ratio of the two physical lengths has meaning in certain geometrical configurations, as we saw in Figure 1D. Different types of measurement scales are determined by the kinds of operation that can be performed on the magnitudes in question.

Ratio Scales. A ratio scale is one applicable to magnitudes that permit us to perform Operations I, II, and III, previously described. We illustrated these with the example of physical length. This, then, is one dimension that we measure with a ratio scale. For other kinds of dimensions the three operations indicating the applicability of a ratio scale might be performed in other ways, suited to the dimension in question.

A ratio scale always has a zero point, either hypothetical or empirically determinable. When such a scale is used to obtain measurements, it is appropriate to speak of ratios which exist among the data. We may take an example from the temporal scale used to measure RT. Time is measured on a ratio scale. Although conventional techniques guard against obtaining RT measures of zero magnitude, we may consider that a response simultaneous with the stimulus presentation is hypothetically possible. A zero reading on a chronometer might even be obtained empirically, although not validly, if a subject took his cue for responding from the warning signal and timed his reaction to coincide with the stimulus. Having seen that the temporal scale of RT has a zero point, let us see the implications of a ratio scale for interpretation of the data obtained.

Suppose that a certain subject, No. 17, has demonstrated a simple RT, under "normal" conditions, of 180 msec. Suppose also that the corresponding datum for another subject, No. 22, is 190 msec. When we now test them after 48 continuous waking hours, we may find that No. 17 shows an *RT* of 198 msec and No. 22 gives us an *RT* of 209 msec. Under this amount of sleep deprivation, the *RT* values obtained exhibit a ratio of 11:10 when compared to "normal" *RT*. This equality of ratios, the 10 per cent increase of *RT* shown by both subjects, may be appropriately noted because we are dealing with a ratio scale. If Subject No. 17 had shown an *RT* of 189 msec under the experimental condition, we would be able to say that the sleep deprivation had led to a 5 per cent increase in *RT*. Our statements have meaning for the behavioral dimension, *RT*, as well as for the numerical data.

The fact that ratios and per cents are appropriately considered only with respect to ratio scales—those with a meaningful zero point—may become clearer if we consider data obtained with a scale that is not a ratio scale. Suppose that we had tested our subjects in the sleep deprivation experiment by a conventional hand steadiness test. The apparatus consists of a stylus which must be inserted, without touching, into holes drilled with a series of decreasing diameters in a brass plate. A series of numbers, assigned to these holes in order, provides a measurement scale. The smaller the hole into which the stylus is successfully inserted, the greater the score. Suppose that Subject No. 17 scored 5 under "normal" conditions and only 4 after sleep deprivation. The 5:4 ratio of these numbers does *not* mean a 20 per cent decrease in hand steadiness. The way in which the test apparatus was designed to assess steadiness does not permit such a reference to a ratio or per cent, since without a zero point and without meaningful expressions of ratio the series of possible scores does not constitute a ratio scale.

Returning to positive examples of ratio scales, we may note that in the study of motor performance we may borrow other scales, besides the temporal scale, from the physicist. In studying positioning movements, we borrow the dimension of length or angular displacement. Measuring responses in terms of centimeters for linear positioning or degrees for angular positioning, we may properly refer to an error being found to be 13 per cent greater, for example, under one condition than another. A positioning reaction, or an error in positioning, of zero magnitude is perfectly possible. The physical scales of length or angular displacement are true ratio scales.

Psychology, like other disciplines within empirical science, borrows the ratio scale of *numerosity* from mathematics. Whenever we assign numerals to objects or events by counting, we are employing this scale. For example, we might determine the number of subjects who are able to maintain a standing posture within prescribed limits on a body sway test. We might find that only half as many succeed in passing the test when blindfolded as when vision is permitted. It is appropriate to take note of this ratio of frequencies since we are dealing with a scale which has a possible zero point. Under certain conditions no one might be able to pass the test. Frequency measurements refer to a dimension of numerosity which permits the defining operations for a ratio scale.

Besides counting subjects who exhibit some behaviour, we may use the ratio scale of numerosity by counting the responses which a subject makes during a given period. This turns simple frequency into a measure of rate, but the potential zero point—no responses occurring—is maintained. When we have measured rates of response under different conditions, it is appropriate to compare them as ratios or to state that a particular per cent of difference was observed. When making such statements about the data taken by means of any scale of measurement, the complete operational definition of the scale must be kept in mind. Let us assume that a fifty per cent increase is found in the number of words understood in a speech intelligibility test when a particular change in condition is made. This ratio of improvement must be regarded as specific to the type of words chosen as test material, as well as to numerous other factors in the study. The ratio scale of numerosity is as subject to the limitations of a particular operational definition as are other scales of measurement in psychological research.

An area of psychological research where the construction of ratio scales has been attempted with some success is the measurement of sensory magnitudes. The operations for determining the equality of ratios are often centered in the responses of the subject when he attempts to adjust a comparison stimulus to make its sensory magnitude half as great as that aroused by a standard stimulus. For example, a subject might have to adjust a comparison tone until it seemed just half as loud as a standard tone. Ratios of 2:1 may thus be established using many standard tone magnitudes, and we may assume that all loudness ratios judged to be 2:1 are equal in experience to each other. In making a judgment like half as loud, the subject may be assumed to be utilizing a judged zero point as one end of the interval he is bisecting. This zero point and the equality of ratios as operationally defined satisfy the requirements for a ratio scale.

Interval Scales. An interval scale is one that may be applied to dimensions within which we can perform Operations I and II. We can determine the equality or inequality of magnitudes and of differences, but we cannot determine the equality of ratios. Thus Operation III is ruled out due to the lack of a true zero point.

One approach to interval scaling in psychology resembles the ratio scaling of sensory magnitudes. Just as dimensions like loudness may be scaled by direct manipulations of ratios, other dimensions may lend themselves to the direct determination of intervals in the responses given by experimental subjects. For example, we might ask a subject to indicate, by marks placed along a line, the distances he judges to separate samples of handwriting on a dimension of legibility. A subject might presumably manage this direct indicating of scale differences even though ratio scaling, requiring a notion of zero legibility, might not be easily accomplished.

Ordinal Scales. We are said to be working with an ordinal scale when the dimension in question permits us to apply only Operation I, determining equality or inequality of magnitudes, whether one is equal to, greater than, or less than, another. An example of this is the conventional hand steadiness measurement. We saw that the scores, determined by the size of hole into which the stylus could be inserted without touching, would not justify reference to ratios of hand steadiness. Even the comparison of intervals, Operation II, is not valid. We cannot say that the difference between scores of 4 and 5 represent the same increment in steadiness as the difference between scores of 7 and 8. The operational definition of hand steadiness does permit us to state, however, that greater steadiness is shown by successful insertion of the stylus into the smaller holes. A score of 5 represents steadier performance than a score of 4, since the hole numbered 5 is the smaller of the two and therefore represents a more exacting task.

A different instance of ordinal scaling in psychology is found in our requiring subjects to rank or rate various stimulus items on some continuum for which there is no simple physical correlate. For example, we might ask a group of people to rank several samples of floor tile on the esthetic appeal of their color combinations. Which set of colors is most pleasing to the eye? Which is next most attractive, and so on? We find that, as a psychological dimension, esthetic appeal—call it beauty or pleasantness, if you will—can be readily handled by Operation I. Subjects find it easy to judge different sample items with reference to one another. For many complex attributes like beauty, however, they would find it difficult or impossible to express ratio judgments—this one is twice as beautiful as that. Our measurement of numerous aspects of perceptual and evaluative experience, then, is limited to ordinal scaling.

Permissible Treatments of Data. The nature of the different kinds of scales we have discussed—ratio, interval, and ordinal —imposes certain limitation on the ways in which the data they yield may be treated. If the operations which yield the conventional ordinal scale of hand steadiness, for example, do not permit any manipulations to demonstrate the magnitude of a difference between two scale points, then it is meaningless to treat the two scores which correspond to these points as if they could yield a meaningful difference value. The subtraction of the numbers reveals that one magnitude of steadiness exceeds the other but does not validly indicate the size of the behavioral difference when an ordinal scale is involved. Such restrictions on treatment of data are reflected in the statistics which may legitimately be computed for numbers derived from the various types of scales. We shall indicate the applicability of different statistical analyses, referring to statistics which are possibly familiar to you or are presented for your study later in this chapter.

From data obtained from ordinal scales we may calculate the median and percentiles, as well as order correlation with similar sets of data. As the midmost item in a series of values, the median is identifiable even though we do not know the magnitudes of the differences separating the various values. By definition, we know the order of items that have been ordinally scaled, and it is its place in an ordered series that defines the median as well. Percentiles are calculated on the basis of cumulative frequencies of cases which fall in successive ordered intervals. As long as they are ordinally arranged, the magnitude of these intervals does not affect our computing of the number of cases included up to the end point of any interval. Order correlation, a measure of the relationship between two sets of paired ordinally scaled values, is similarly free from any restraint based on size of intervals between magnitudes. The computation is based only on rank order of the items, which is provided by ordinal scaling.

Interval scale values may be used in computing the three statistics just mentioned, and they permit us to use several additional statistics as well. For data obtained through interval scale measurement we may compute the mean and the standard deviation. If we have two sets of interval data on the same persons or items, we may compute a correlation of the product-moment type. These three statistics have meaning when the separations of the different values along the scale have meaning. Ordinal scale values, on the other hand, indicate no meaningful intervals of separation and therefore should not be treated with these statistics.

Ratio scales permit the application of all the statistics we have mentioned, from the median to the product-moment correlation. In addition, our knowledge of ratio scaled magnitudes with respect to an absolute zero point allows us to compute statistics like the geometric mean, not very often used in psychology.

ANDRÉ M. WEITZENHOFFER

3 Mathematical Structures and Psychological Measurements

The nature of psychological measurements in relation to mathematical structures and representations is examined. Some very general notions concerning algebras and systems are introduced and applied to physical and number systems, and to measurement theory. It is shown that the classical intensive and extensive dimensions of measurements with their respective ordinal and additive scales are not adequate to describe physical events without the introduction of the notions of dimensional units and of dimensional homogeneity. It is also shown that in the absence of these notions, the resulting systems of magnitudes have only a very restricted kind of isomorphism with the real number system, and hence have little or no mathematical representations. An alternative in the form of an extended theory of measurements is developed. A third dimension of measurement, the supra-extensive dimension, is introduced; and a new scale, the multiplicative scale, is associated with it. It is shown that supra-extensive magnitudes do constitute systems isomorphic with the system of real numbers and that they alone can be given mathematical representations. Physical quantities are supra-extensive magnitudes. In contrast, to date, psychological quantities are either intensive or extensive, but never of the third kind. This, it is felt, is the reason why mathematical representations have been few and without success in psychology as contrasted to the physical sciences. In particular, the Weber-Fechner relation is examined and shown to be invalid in two respects. It is concluded that the construction of multiplicative scales in psychology, or the equivalent use of dimensional analysis, alone will enable the development of fruitful mathematical theories in this area of investigation.

For some years now, I have asked myself a basic question. Why has mathematics been applied so successfully to the physical sciences, but not to psychology? For some peculiar reason, the data of psychology do not appear to be readily amenable to mathematical representation. To date no major mathematical structure has been devised in the domain of psychology. The few attempts in this line have proven themselves rather barren.[1] Is it in the

nature of psychological data that one must seek for the answer to this? Or is it in the way these data have been approached and handled?

It is the purpose of this paper to present what is, I believe, a partial answer, if not the whole answer to these questions. It may be stated from the outset that much of the material which follows will appear strange and perhaps forbidding to many readers. The very nature of the problem makes it so. I do not know of any way around this. Other readers may object to the lack of rigor in the treatment which follows, as well as to the brevity in the exposition of many ideas. This too has been largely

1. Mathematical statistics has of course been very fruitful in dealing with psychological data. This, however, is a matter which is quite different from the main topic of this paper, namely, the mathematical representation of psychological structures.

From *Psychometrika*, December 1951. By permission of the Psychometric Society.

forced by the necessity of keeping the scope of this paper within limits. An earlier attempt on my part to present a more complete discussion of the same material has shown me that anything really satisfactory would require the writing of a small monograph. Having neither the time nor the inclination to do this at this time, the present material is offered in its stead.

Some Basic Notions

We shall begin by defining an *aggregate*, *A*, as any collection of specified or unspecified objects one may wish to consider. These objects need not be related to each other in any other way than that of being included in the aggregate. They will be called the elements *a*, of *A*.[2]

It is, however, more usual to deal with aggregates the elements of which have a number of properties in common. We shall call an aggregate a *system*[3] when all of its elements possess at least one common property besides that of being part of the collection. A system, *S*, will be considered as given or defined when such a property has been stated, that is, when a necessary and sufficient condition for an object to be an element of *S* has been given. This will be referred to as the *property of membership*, ε. Any element of a system is called a *member* of it, and this is denoted by

$$a \, \varepsilon \, S.$$

An *n-ary relation*, *R*, in a system *S* is a property affecting the ordered collection $(a, b, c, \ldots)$ of *n* elements of *S*.

A relation of particular importance is that of *equality*, $x = y$, which denotes that the two

elements *x* and *y* of *S* are not distinct. The negation of this relation is called *diversity* and is denoted by $x \neq y$.

Another useful relation is that of *partial ordering*. It is a binary relation, $\geqslant$,[4] such that the following three laws hold for it and any two members of a system,

a. Reflexive Law: $x \geqslant x$ for all $x \, \varepsilon \, S$.
b. Anti-symmetric Law: If $x \geqslant y$ and $y \geqslant x$, then $x = y$.
c. Transitive Law: If $x \geqslant y$ and $y \geqslant z$, then $x \geqslant z$.

On the other hand, a relation, $>$, is said to be a *simple ordering* provided:

a. If $x > y$ and $y > z$, then $x > z$.
b. For each pair of elements $(x,y) \, \varepsilon \, S$, one of the three properties $x > y$, $x = y$, $y > x$ holds to the exclusion of the other two.

One defines a subsystem, *Sub S*, of *S* as any system every element of which is an element of *S*. A subsystem is said to be a *part* of *S*, or again to be *contained* (or included) in *S*. This last may be denoted by

$$S' \leqslant S \text{ (where } S' \text{ denotes } Sub \, S).$$

An *operation*, *o*, in a system *S* is a rule which associates with every specified group of elements of *S* another element of *S*. It is said to be *n-ary* whenever the specified group consists of *n* elements.

Clearly, any operation in *S* is also a relation and hence will partake of all the properties of relations.

Making use of this concept we can now define an *abstract algebra* as any system in which at least one operation is defined. Since algebras are obviously systems too, all of the properties and notions associated with the latter are applicable to algebras within the limits imposed by the operations.

One can go on with this sort of classification. By defining the elements, relations, and opera-

2. The term aggregate has been used by mathematicians to denote also such entities as classes and sets. This is rather unfortunate as it tends to lead to confusion. As will be seen shortly, the notion as presented here is much more general than that of classes or sets.
3. Whether this is to be identified with "set" depends upon the interpretation one places upon the term "rule". As defined by Cantor, a set or Menge is a collection of objects defined by some rule which determines unambiguously which objects belong to the collection and which do not.

4. Not to be confused with the notion of "greater than or equal to" of ordinary algebra.

tions of abstract algebras one may arrive at the notions of rings, fields, lattices, and so on, which play important roles in mathematics but which are not of interest to us at present.

It may however be remarked that whether one speaks of systems, algebras, or other mathematical entities, is entirely a question of convenience and of the properties upon which one wishes to focus attention. In other words, it is largely an arbitrary matter, although there are circumstances in which it is more profitable to speak in terms of one rather than another. For sure, classes are both aggregates and systems. They are also abstract algebras and are important enough as such that it is more usual to retain the expression "class" to designate this last aspect. Again, sets are classes, but of a very special kind, being collections of mathematical points.[5] Thus the use of a special name.

A very important characteristic of systems is their *structure*. This term, which has found its way in nearly every field of human knowledge, remains to date a most elusive notion. Everybody talks about it, but no one defines it. An entire volume has been devoted to the "structure of algebras," yet nowhere in it is it possible to find a definition of structure. Unsatisfactory as it may be, I wish to offer an attempt at some sort of definition of this notion which I believe expresses the consensus of meaning assigned to it. By a *structure* is meant *a totality of relations* conceived as a whole, and independently of the elements between which the relations hold. Thus, the structure of a system such as algebra is the totality of relations holding between its elements, as contrasted to its *content*, which is the totality of its elements, considered independently of any relations between them.

Systems themselves may be related in various ways. Among relations which may hold between systems in general, and algebras in particular, one has that of *correspondence*.

Two systems S_1 and S_2 are said to be in

correspondence when there exists a rule which associates to one or more elements of S_1 one or more elements of S_2. The correspondence may be many-one, one-many, many-many, or one-one. This last is said to exist if for every element of S_1 there is associated one and only one element of S_2, and conversely.

Two systems for which a one-one correspondence exists which *preserves all relations* are said to be *isomorphic*. Since the totality of relations in a system is defined to be its structure, one has the very important fact that *isomorphism preserves structure*, or again, that two systems which are isomorphic have the "same" structure. This last may be taken to define the *equivalence* of two systems.

In many situations, there exists a one-one correspondence which preserves only certain relations and operations, but not all of them. It is convenient to speak then of a *partial isomorphism*, or again of an "isomorphism *in respect*" to these relations and operations. That portion of the structure which is thus preserved can be referred to as a *substructure*.

With the introduction of these notions we shall now turn our attention to several important systems.

The Algebra of Number Systems

Let $(a, b, c, \ldots)$ denote any *integer*. Then we may define for these, two operations, called *addition*, $+$, and *multiplication*, $\times$, such that the following rules are obeyed:

(1) $a+b = b+a.$
(2) $ab = ba.$ $\Big\}$ (Commutative Law)

(3) $a+(b+c) = (a+b)+c.$
(4) $a(bc) = (ab)c.$ $\Big\}$ (Associative Law)

(5) $a(b+c) = ab+ac.$ (Distributive Law)

Here we have an example of an abstract algebra. It is applicable to the specific integers 1, 2, 3, etc., $\ldots$, being isomorphic with this system. But clearly, the elements $(a, b, c, \ldots)$ can be made to denote any other system of entities so long as there is isomorphism. That

5. There is a tendency to speak of point-sets nowadays to eliminate confusion with other classes.

not all systems can be represented by the above can be made clear by an example which Werkmeister (12) gives. For instance, considering addition and the commutative law alone, it is a fact of chemistry that one can add concentrated sulphuric acid to water to get a dilute acid solution, but adding water to concentrated sulphuric acid more likely than not will result in an explosion. Thus the commutative law does not hold in this case. The reader can easily think of other examples of this sort.

The above formulation is just the beginning of the algebra of numbers and really holds only for the integers. It is, however, a relatively easy matter to introduce additional notions into the algebra in order to arrive at one which is isomorphic with the algebra of the real numbers. Such concepts are those of inequality, subtraction, zero, negative and positive integers, fractions, division, powers, and roots. Provided division by zero is forbidden in the resulting algebra, the result is a *closed* system, that is, *one such that all operations performed within it always produce one of its elements.* Rather than expand upon this material, we refer the reader to the very readable account which has been given by Werkmeister (12).

Mathematical Representations

Consider any two isomorphic systems, A and B. These are equivalent in the sense that they have identical structures. By virtue of this, anything which holds true in one holds true in the other, provided the necessary correspondence is established between elements, relations, and operations. In particular, suppose one system, say A, is a physical system,[6] and the other, B, is some arbitrary algebra derived by a mathematician for his amuse-ment. Should these be isomorphic, that is, should a one-one correspondence exist between the elements of the algebra B and those of the physical system such that all relations are preserved, then the algebra would be a symbolic replica of the physical system. Any relation existing in the physical system will have an image in the algebra. And conversely, for every relation which exists in the latter, one should find a corresponding physical relation. The outcome of such a state of affairs is that we are enabled to speak about the physical system at a purely symbolic level, and even carry out at this level investigations of the properties of the system. We may say, generally speaking, that the algebra constitutes a *symbolic representation* of the physical system, or again that the latter has a representation in the algebra.

Again, speaking in general terms, three situations may arise. The physical system A is isomorphic with either the total algebra B, or only with a subalgebra of this latter. In both instances we shall say that A has a *complete* representation in B, but in addition in the first instance we shall speak of an *equivalent* representation. If on the other hand there is only partial isomorphism with respect to relations in the physical system A, the representation will be said to be *partial*.[7] Clearly, if A has a complete but not equivalent representation in B, then B can have only a partial representation in A, although it is not usual to speak of algebras as having representations in physical systems.

Of special interest is the situation in which the algebra of numbers constitutes a representation for a physical system. Inasmuch as the remainder of this paper will be largely devoted to just this matter, no more will be said about it here. Instead, a few remarks will be made concerning a particular difficulty which may arise in connection with partial

---

6. The notion of systems as introduced here has been quite general. The elements can be physical entities, events, other systems, and so on. If the elements are physical in nature, then the relations and operations must also be physical. It is here that the great value of being able to establish an isomorphism between physical systems and abstract systems makes itself evident.

7. A partial isomorphism in respect to B will still be considered under the heading of complete representation. Partial representation as defined above comes under the heading of *incomplete* representations which also includes cases in which only a subsystem of A is isomorphic with B or part of B.

and even complete, but non-equivalent, representations.

Namely, if a physical system does not have an equivalent representation in an algebra, then it is possible to derive relationships in the latter which have no correspondence in the physical system. Even new elements may be defined by the algebra which have no meaning in terms of the second system. In other words, everything which is true in the algebra needs not necessarily hold or have meaning in the physical system. This is just the type of situation which occurs in the domain of applied mathematics when extraneous solutions to equations are obtained. Very often these turn out to be negative or imaginary and quite clearly correspond to nothing in the physical world. While such instances have often led to the discovery of new elements and principles, as in the case of the Dirac electron, it is clear that they may signify nothing more than the fact that an incomplete representation exists.

The Classical Theory of Measurements

The present section will be devoted to a brief review of the logic of measurements as expounded by such investigators as Campbell (3), Bergmann and Spence (2), and Reese (8). This material will be familiar to most readers.

In general, it may be said that the basic behavioral process by which scientific data are collected is that of *observation*. Generally speaking, observations can be classified as being *qualitative* or *quantitative*.

A *measurement* is an *operation* as well as an observation performed upon the physical world by an observer and by means of which a certain class of signs are assigned to represent *properties* of physical objects[8] and events according to certain rules. Such signs are called *numerals*. Any measurable property is called a *magnitude* and the ordered set of all possible

numerals which can be assigned to such a property is called a *scale*.[9]

It is possible to distinguish between two classes of properties, those which are dichotomous or two-valued, and those which are non-dichotomous. To the first category belong such properties as male-female, to-the-right-of, to-the-left-of, and so on. To the second, belong such properties as length, weight, and so on. Non-dichotomous properties of and relations between physical objects and events are said to constitute, or rather to belong to, *physical dimensions*.

There are a number of equivalent ways in which the theory or logic of measurements can be formulated. The following appears to be best suited for the present discussion.

Let X and Y be any two physical events or objects having a property which defines a dimension D. Let $>$ denote the statement "X bears a certain relation $>$ to Y," and let $|>$ denote "X does not bear the relation $>$ to Y." Finally, let $>$ satisfy the following three criteria:

(6) If $X > Y$, then $Y |> X$. (Anti-symmetric law)

(7) If $X > Y$ and $Y > Z$, then $X > Z$. (Transitive law)

(8) $X |> X$. (Irreflexive law)[10]

Further, let us define a relation $=$ in terms of $>$ such that:

(9) $X = Y$ if and only if $X |> Y$ and $Y |> X$.[11]

(10) If $X = Y$, then $X > Z$ implies $Y > Z$, and $X |> Z$ implies $Y |> Z$.

(11) From (8), it follows that $X = X$.

Reference to our earlier discussion of ordered systems in Section 1 will show that the relation $>$ as defined above is one of

9. More extensive discussions of these notions will be found in the works of Werkmeister (12) and particularly of Russell (9).

10. I have never found this third axiom stated in the literature. Yet it seems to be necessary if measurements are to be unambiguous.

11. This is to say that one and only one of the three relations $X > Y$, $Y > X$, or $X = Y$ holds at any given instant of time.

8. Although we will refer here specifically to physical systems, the theory is quite general and applies equally well to biological, psychological, and other kinds of material.

simple ordering. Thus, in respect to the operation >, physical systems constitute simply ordered systems. It is for this reason that > is known in the theory of measurements as the relation of physical ordering.

Any physical dimension for which axioms 6 through 11 are satisfied is said to be *intensive*. It is possible to assign numerals[12] $N(X)$, $N(Y)$, and so on, in a non-unique manner to each object of an intensive dimension, such that two relations > and = exist satisfying,

I. $N(X) > N(Y)$ if and only if $X > Y$.
II. $N(X) = N(Y)$ if and only if $X = Y$.
III. $N(X) = N(X)$.[13]

The resulting ordered set of numerals is called an *ordinal scale*. From the above definition, it is seen that *an ordinal scale is isomorphic with simply ordered physical systems*, when these are described by measurements.

Given a dimension D which satisfies axioms 9 and 10, it will be said to be *extensive* if it is possible to perform a physical operation + on any two members of the dimension such that the result is always another member of the dimension, and such that the following axioms are satisfied:

12. If $X = Y$ and $V = W$, then $X+V = Y+W$.
13. $X+Y = Y+X$.
14. $X+(Y+Z) = (X+Y)+Z$.
15. $X+Y > X$ and $X+Y > Y$.

This new operation, +, will be called *addition*.

As previously, numerals can be assigned with an operation + to the properties of an extensive dimension in such a way that,

IV. $N(X+Y) = N(X)+N(Y)$

The resulting scale is called an *additive scale*.

This much constitutes the essence of what I have called the classical theory of measurements.

12. Not to be confused with "numbers," although the latter can be used as numerals. In this case their properties as numerals are quite independent of those they possess by virtue of being numbers.
13. See footnote 10.

The Extended Theory of Measurements

Now arises an interesting situation. Ordinal and additive scales have only partial isomorphism with the algebra of numbers. In fact it is a very restricted isomorphism. This will be seen by comparing the two algebras which have just been presented with that which has been given for the integers. We can, if we desire, use the number system as representation for measurements on ordinal and additive scales, provided one restricts one's self to using only the relations of "greater than," "lesser than," "equal to," and the operation of "addition."[14] To subtract measurements from one another at this stage is not allowable, and even less to multiply measurements together—simply because these concepts have not been defined for measurements, although they are well defined for numbers.

At the same time, it becomes clear why numbers may be chosen for numerals, and why, in respect to addition, equality, and inequality, they have the same properties as numerals that they have as numbers. They are isomorphic in respect to these relations and operations.

Now, aside from the fact that such a restricted isomorphism cannot lead to great consequences, there is also the fact that in practice one finds everyone happily multiplying together, dividing, and otherwise treating measurements as if they were equivalently isomorphic with the most general number systems. Yet, as just shown, this is certainly not true of either intensive or extensive magnitudes.

Campbell and those who have followed in his footsteps have attempted to resolve this problem partly by introducing the notion of derived measures. At this point, unfortunately, these investigators abandon the axiomatic approach with which they started out, and proceed to ignore the very restrictions they had imposed upon measures by setting up their various scales. The net result is some-

14. Of course, in the case of ordinal scales, one must also exclude addition.

thing which experientially speaking makes some sense, but which logically and mathematically does not.

Now as it happens, physical scientists resolved the problem in a very ingenious way many years before any one ever tried to write about the logic of physical measurements. They introduced the notion of *dimensional units* and the principle of *dimensional homogeneity.* Accordingly, a number by itself is not sufficient to specify a physical quantity. Its value must be determined by comparing the sample under consideration with a known amount of the same quantity. This constitutes the process of *measuring.*[15] The quantity used as reference is called the *unit,* and the result of any measurement is a statement of how many times the sample has been found to contain the reference quantity. Thus, if N be a numerical quantity, and U be a unit, a physical quantity, Q, will be represented as,

$$Q = N \cdot U$$

that is, a product of a numerical value and a unit. In consequence, Q is more than a number.

Now, given any physical quantity, there is an infinity of possible units one might use. For instance, take "weight." One can use "*pound,*" "*gram,*" "*drachm,*" and so on. In fact, any arbitrary standard will do provided it possesses in common with all these standards the unique property of being a distinct weight. It is convenient to make use of a general unit symbol, $[U]$, to denote *any* unit of weight. More generally then, we shall write

$$Q = N \cdot [Q]$$

and $[Q]$ will be called the *dimension* of the physical quantity Q, being the expression of a general unit associated with Q.[16]

The principle of *dimensional homogeneity*

15. It must be understood that we are now speaking in terms belonging to the language of the physical scientist, or more specifically in the language of dimensional analysis.
16. Those readers who are familiar with Cantor's definition of transfinite numbers will see here a notion defined in a manner very much like the definition of cardinal numbers.

simply states that given any equation involving physical quantities, *all terms of the equation,* which are of course physical quantities, *must have the same dimension* if the equation is to have physical sense.

This is a very important point, for without this principle, physical equations could not be treated as mathematical or numerical equations. For as will be seen from the above, dimensions or units have the properties of factors in the writing of physical quantities. Since the principle of dimensional homogeneity requires a common dimension throughout any equation, the latter may be cancelled out in each term, leaving only a numerical quantity to be dealt with.

To go further into the topic of dimensional analysis is beyond the scope of this paper, but the reader will be well-rewarded in looking up a more detailed treatment of this topic, such as has been presented by Bridgman (1), and by Eshbach (4). Now we must return to the axiomatic treatment of the problem.

If the reader will refer to axioms 6 through 11, he will note that by their very nature they require the elements for which the relations $>$, and $=$, and the operation $+$ hold to be of the same dimension. The principle of dimensional homogeneity is therefore inherent in the definition of ordinal and additive scales. But this is just about as far as the resemblance between the two approaches goes. For while in the system developed by dimensional analysis any physical equation is reducible to a numerical equation, and hence physical systems have general mathematical representation, that is not possible with the two scales developed by axiomatic methods.

I wish to propose at this point that physical measurements or magnitudes lie on a scale which is neither the ordinal nor the additive type of scale, nor a "derived" scale.

For lack of a better descriptive term, let us say that a dimension D satisfying all of the criteria of an extensive dimension is *supra-extensive* if it is possible to perform a physical operation on any two members of the dimension such that the result is always a member of *another* supra-extensive dimension, and such that the following axioms are satisfied:

16. If $X = Y$ and $V = W$, then $X \cdot V = Y \cdot W$.
17. $X \cdot Y = Y \cdot X$.
18. $X \cdot (Y \cdot Z) = (X \cdot Y) \cdot Z$.
19. $X \cdot (Y+Z) = X \cdot Y + X \cdot Z$, if and only if Y and Z are of the *same* dimension.

The new operation $\cdot$ will be called *multiplication*. As previously, one can assign numerals with the operation $\cdot$ to the properties of a supra-extensive dimension in such a way that,

V. $N(X \cdot Y) = N(X) \cdot N(Y)$.

The resulting scale will be called a *multiplicative* scale. It has of course all the properties of additive and ordinal scales too.

It is important here not to confuse "multiplication by an integer" with "multiplication" as defined for supra-extensive magnitudes. The former is, strictly speaking, a property of additive scales. More specifically, if a quantity A be added n times to itself (iterative addition), we may denote this by the "product" nA, where n is an integer, and where nA stands for the sum $(A + A + A + \ldots + A)$ of n terms. This is not the same thing as the "product" $A \cdot A$ defined earlier. The difference between the two kinds of products is the same here as it is, for instance, in the case of vectors,[17] where the product $n\bar{A}$ of a vector $\bar{A}$ by a scalar quantity n is to be distinguished from the vector product $\bar{A} \times \bar{B}$, or even the scalar product $\bar{A} \cdot \bar{B}$, of two vectors $\bar{A}$ and $\bar{B}$. The former is a vector of magnitude n times that of A and of similar orientation, while in general, the vector product of $\bar{A}$ and $\bar{B}$ is another vector at right angle to both of these and with magnitude equal to the product of their magnitudes times the sine of the angle they make with each other. In particular, $\bar{A} \times \bar{A} = 0$, and generally, $\bar{A} \times \bar{B}$ does not equal $\bar{B} \times \bar{A}$. The properties of scalar

products are still different. All of this is entirely consistent with the fact that vectors are not single numbers, but are really pairs of the same, that is, dyads, and as such have properties not common to cardinal numbers. In particular, vectors exist on a multiplicative scale not by virtue of the existence of products of the form $n\bar{A}$, but because of such products as $\bar{A} \times \bar{B}$.

Along the same line of thought as the above, one should not confuse the notion of multiplication by a *constant* with multiplication by a *numerical coefficient*. In closed systems, members of the system alone can be employed, and multiplication is as defined for the system. On the other hand, introduction of a numerical coefficient is equivalent to "multiplication by an integer" and is not allowable in a closed system unless some new operation such as the scalar product for vectors is defined.

It may be well to add one last remark concerning the establishment of multiplicative scales. Namely, inasmuch as multiplication as here defined always produces a supra-extensive dimension different from the dimensions of the factors in the product, it necessarily follows that this operation creates a relation between two or more different supra-extensive dimensions. It bridges the gap, so to speak, between different supra-extensive dimensions. This is a property which is unique and not found in the cases of intensive and extensive magnitudes. In turn, this means that corresponding relations must exist between the phenomena being measured. In practice, it is the very demonstration in most instances of such relations between phenomena which establish magnitudes on a multiplicative scale. That is, it is only by working with and causing entities belong to different supra-extensive dimensions to interact that one can formulate the multiplicative character of the corresponding magnitudes. For instance, voltage considered alone has only additive properties. Similarly for current. It is only when we consider the two together in term of power that their multiplicative properties become apparent.

There remains now very little more to be

17. It may be of interest to note here that fairly recently a new approach to dimensional analysis has been developed in terms of vectors in an affine space.

done in extending the theory of measurements. "Subtraction," "zero," and "multiplication by an integer" could have been introduced earlier by standard axiomatic methods in terms of the properties of additive scales before the notion of multiplicative scales was formulated. On the other hand, the notions of "division," "powers," "roots," "logarithms," and many others had to wait until the new scales had been defined. It would be instructive to develop the entire system thus outlined. As it is, space for this is lacking, and it may be said only that this development follows exactly the same steps as does that of the algebra of number systems. It is, however, not hard to see, even without doing this, that *multiplicative scales lead to an algebra which is isomorphic with the arithmetic (or algebra) of the real numbers.* Of the three scales which have been discussed, *it is the only one* which can do this. It is therefore the only one which can lead to a mathematical representation of physical phenomena.

Some Consequences for Psychology

I began this inquiry by asking why it is that mathematical representations have been so successful in the physical sciences and yet have so completely failed us in psychology, even in those areas where measurements are possible. I believe part of the answer lies in the previous pages.

It is my hope that it has been shown in a sufficiently clear manner that *the possibility of adequate mathematical representation for any system, physical or non-physical, depends upon the possibility of establishing a system of measurements which is isomorphic with the number system and other mathematical systems.* That is, it must be possible to replace the physical system by the mathematical system. In turn, this means that the two systems have the same structure or are equivalent. Even with partial isomorphism the representation may still be quite satisfactory provided a sufficiently large portion of the structures involved are preserved. On the other hand, nothing can ever be as satisfactory as equi-valent representation. The physical sciences have come close to achieving this ideal through their use of dimensional units and analysis. In the case of psychology, the situation is pretty much the opposite. Psychological measurements are largely made in terms of additive scales, and often using only ordinal scales. Consequently, the correspondence which may be established between psychological magnitudes and numbers is very limited. As can then be expected, mathematical representation of psychological phenomena is quasi-impossible, being far too restricted. This is not to say that improvements in the right direction have not been made in recent years. For instance, the use of dimensional units has been introduced for some subjective magnitudes. Thus we have a *sone* scale, a *mel* scale, and a *veg* scale, to mention only a few. And again, in learning theory, we have seen the introduction of various units, such as the *hab.* Thus far, however, most of the data of psychology, if not all, remain within the bounds of additive and ordinal scales. Even Stevens' (10) [Ch. 1 in this book] promising "ratio scale" turns out to be, as Reese (8) has previously observed, nothing more than an additive scale. This follows simply from the observation made earlier concerning the difference between "multiplication by an integer," and "multiplication" as understood for supra-extensive magnitudes. Or to say this another way, to state that a subjective magnitude is, for instance, half of another, is to say nothing more than the second is twice the first, this being expressible entirely in terms of addition. In addition to limitations imposed by the scales used, many psychological variables are "quantized," that is, they can take on only certain values. Thus, for instance, the number of trials made in a learning experiment cannot be fractional, or irrational, or negative, but must be a positive integral value. This fact imposes some rather serious restrictions upon the means available for representation.

Failure to recognize the fact that psychological magnitudes rarely have all of the properties of numbers has led to the formulation of mathematical equations which have a superficial appearance of validity, if not of mathematical sanction, but which are inherently unsound and certainly misleading.

A few examples of what is meant might be given. For instance, consider the well-known Fechner relation,

$$S = k \log R,$$

S being the subjective magnitude of the stimulus (sensation), and R the physical magnitude of the stimulus (stimulus intensity). One may, first of all, note a certain inherent ambiguity in the relation. For, $\log R$ is a pure number, as can be shown by dimensional analysis, regardless of the dimensions of R. If k also be assumed dimensionless, then the Principle of Dimensional Homogeneity requires the same be true of S. On the other hand, if we assume S to have some arbitrary dimension, then by the same principle, k must have the inverse dimension of S. Unfortunately, we have no way of deciding which of the alternatives is the correct one. Hence the essential ambiguity in this law. However, a much more serious defect in the relation lies in the fact that in general, S is *at best* only an additive quantity, while $k \log R$ has *all* of the properties of real numbers, being one itself. The equality relation which holds between the two members of the relation is therefore a contradiction of these facts. Actually, as written, the Fechner Law states that a quantity with only *some* of the properties of real numbers is the same as a real number. To make this example even more specific, we might consider Sanford's lifted weight experiment as presented by Guildford (5). Briefly, a subject was requested to lift various weights and to make five groups of these in such a way that the differences in the weights between neighboring groups would appear to be equal to him. In other words, the method of equal-appearing intervals was employed. This done, "subjective" values 1, 2, 3, 4, and 5 were assigned to the groups in order of increasing weights. The actual mean weights for each group were taken as the corresponding "physical" weights. These turned out to be: 6.52, 10.88, 11.87, 43.96, and

79.52 gm. Plotted one against the other, these two sets of magnitudes yield a logarithmic type of curve. Or again, plotting subjective values against the logarithm of the physical weights produces a straight line. Thus, the Fechner law appears to be substantiated in this instance.

But, inasmuch as the method of equal-appearing intervals does not produce anything better than additive quantities, and since $k \log R$ in this case is a real number, the equality between S and $k \log R$ is only partly true. Furthermore, the values taken by S are quantized. But without additional qualifying restrictions upon the relation which appears implied, one is led to the prediction of the existence of an innumerable quantity of *meaningless* values of S, namely, irrational values.

Such a situation is not unique to psychology. As a matter of fact, something of this sort has occurred in mathematics itself. For centuries, mathematicians tried to trisect exactly, by means of compass and ruler only, any angle whatsoever. While it is perfectly feasible and meaningful to calculate one third of an arbitrary angle, it is quite another matter to go through the physical operation of doing this in an exact manner with the above mentioned tools. As it eventually turned out, the problem is insoluble, because as was finally shown, dividing an angle by three does not admit of any representation in terms of compass and ruler. Said another way, the operations and relations one may obtain with a compass and ruler give rise to a structure which is not the same as that existing for numbers.

Fechner's Law is only one of the forms the general function $S = f(R)$ may take. For instance, Stevens and Harper (11), using a "ratio scale," find that "subjective weight" and "physical weight" are related according to

$$\log S = 14.58 \log (1 + \log R) - 6.94.$$

This is a far cry from Fechner's Law. Yet much of what has already been said concerning it applies here. Furthermore, the entire derivation of the above relation appears questionable. For, to do so, the investigators began by plotting log S against log R. But, as already indicated, S measured on a ratio scale *only has additive properties*, while taking the logarithm of S *presupposes or implies that S has multiplicative properties*.[18] Stated somewhat differently one cannot take the logarithm of S because in this instance it does not exist. In any case, it is not permissible to make the above plot.

Psychophysical laws are not the only ones to come under the above criticism. For instance, Hull (6) describes an experiment in learning in which the variables are "number of reactions to produce extinction" (n), and "number of reinforcement repetitions" (N). After plotting values of these two variables, he deduces that they are related according to the law

$$n = M(1 - 10^{kN}) + C.$$

Inasmuch as actually n and N can both only have integral values, while, on the contrary, the above places no such restrictions upon the values n and N may take, it hardly can be said that this relation is a mathematical representation of the true state of affairs.

Similarly, elsewhere, Hull (6) plots the "number of j.n.d.'s distant from the point of reinforcement" (d), against the "amplitude of galvanic skin response" (A). This plot, he claims, can be represented by the relation

$$A = 18.3 - 6(1 - 10^{-.0135d}).$$

Again, as stated here, the relation does not impose any restrictions upon the values d may take. As a matter of fact, it is mathematically allowable and entirely feasible to solve the equation for d. Mathematically speaking, d can be a fractional and even an irrational quantity and satisfy the above. Yet, to speak of fractional j.n.d.'s and even more so of irrational amounts of j.n.d.'s is rather meaningless. In fact, it is a self-contradiction![19]

18. This follows from the fact that
$$\log x = \frac{x-1}{x} + \frac{1}{2}\left(\frac{x-1}{x}\right)^2 + \frac{1}{3}\left(\frac{x-1}{x}\right)^3 + \cdots$$
19. Since the j.n.d. is by definition a "just noticeable difference," a fraction of j.n.d. would certainly not be noticeable and therefore could not be determined, or rather defined, empirically.

Actually, however, even if the necessary restrictions could be incorporated in the above, there remains the fact that the values of A lie on a multiplicative scale, while those of d, being j.n.d.'s are not of this type. Consequently the above relation once more equates quantities which are fundamentally different in respect to mathematical structure.

One last example of the kind of difficulties which may arise from faulty representations may be given. Some years back, considerable effort was directed at establishing a relationship between brain mass, or cortical area, and intelligence. Possibly less energy would have been expended along this line if the inherent fallacy of equating intelligence to a function of brain mass or of cortical area had been recognized. For suppose, to make the example simple, that one postulated and even found a trend that I.Q. $= kM$ (M being brain mass). Suppose, too, that two individuals were found with brain masses M_1 and M_2 such that $M_1 = 2M_2$. Then it would follow that I.Q.$_1 = kM_1 = 2kM_2 = 2 \cdot$ I.Q.$_2$. Since, however, I.Q.'s are not additive quantities, such a result is obviously a contradiction of the true state of affairs, as actual measurements would indeed show. This, one could have predicted from the outset, since mass and area are multiplicative quantities, while I.Q.'s are not.

One could go on in this manner *ad infinitum*. In brief, the chief difficulty appears to boil down to the fact that few, if any, experimental and theoretical data in psychology are ever given an appropriate mathematical representation. In nearly every instance, the relations which are developed assign to the psychological quantities properties which they do not and cannot have.

But, many psychologists will remark, we can plot our data, and certainly we do obtain geometrical figures to which mathematical formulas correspond. How can all this be? The answer to this is that plotting is no more permissible than writing down mathematical equations in the instances already cited. The reason for this is a perfect example of what may be done when structures are equivalent. Namely, there is an isomorphism between the points in a plane and pairs of numbers. What is incorrect to do in respect to one is also incorrect in respect to the other. If this were not so, the isomorphism could not be true. There is ample evidence, of course, that such is not the case. It is entirely permissible to use mathematical equations to denote symbolically a particular *trend*. One can go a step further and manipulate the equations, *provided this is done within the limitations* imposed by the properties of the magnitudes which are involved. It is very tempting when one has numbers for data to generalize, replace these by variables, and write equations. It is maybe even more tempting to go on and solve for various variables in terms of the others, to take derivatives, integrate, and do numerous other things. The trouble unfortunately is that, as I have pointed out, *"numbers" when used as "numerals" do not always have all the properties of "numbers."* This is a fact which the majority of psychologists appear either to forget or to be completely unaware of it. A simple solution to this state of affairs would be to employ numerals which can be distinguished from numbers as such and to set down in every case the rules, operations, and so on which are applicable. If this were done, for instance, for a non-multiplicative quantity A, one would never be led to plot log $N(A)$[20] against some other variable since this particular function is not definable and hence is meaningless in the case of the magnitude A. But if one uses a number like "5" as a numeral in the same instance, it is much too easy to overlook the fact that "log 5" is still not definable.

Yet, it should be clear that while paying strict attention to the above considerations would be a considerable improvement in psychology, it is doubtful that it would allow this discipline to attain equal footing with the physical sciences in respect to the use of mathematical representation, For, as I have tried to emphasize, the structure of psychological measurements as they exist today admits of *too limited* a mathematical representation. Seeking and developing special branches of mathematics which would have suitable structures would lead to representation which would be too limited in number and which would tend to be much too broad generalities. A typical instance of this sort of situation I have in mind is Lewin's (7) attempt to apply topology to psychology.

By far a more rational and promising approach would appear to lie in the direction of (a) developing multiplicative scales in psychological measurements, and (b) in redefining basic notions in terms of magnitudes which are susceptible to being measured on such types of scales. In other words, our best hope appears to lie in ending our efforts to force obviously unsuitable data into existing mathematical structures and trying instead to develop methods for obtaining more suitable material, if it exists. In particular, in accordance with a remark made earlier in connection with multiplicative scales, special effort should be made toward formulating relationships which have empirical correlates between psychological magnitudes. The more, the better. Quantities like "subjective weight (or force)," and "subjective length" have little value by themselves. In the final analysis, relating these to physical quantities, as is done in Fechner's Law, does not appear to me to be particularly significant in respect to understanding how the mind works. In any event, as shown previously, its use has numerous pitfalls. On the other hand, I believe that defining a concept such as "subjective work" and identifying it with the "product" of "subjective force" and "subjective length" is far more likely to lead to significant results. For if at a future date it becomes possible to associate with it actual measurements, then an important step will have been taken toward creating multiplicative psychological magnitudes, and the first step toward *adequate mathematical representation* in psychology will have been made.

20. In accord with the notation of page 18, $N(A)$ denotes any numerical associated with magnitude A.

Addendum

Since the writing of this article some twenty years ago, further research I have undertaken on problems of measurement in relation to applied mathematics has led me to revise my earlier views somewhat, particularly in relation to multiplication. I am indebted to Professor Lieberman for granting me the opportunity to present a summary of my more recent conclusions to supplement the article.

1. *Euclidian Measurement.* The further analysis of "physical measurement" as exemplified by the measurement of, say, weight, shows the following: (a) It is an assignment of numbers to physical attribute-instances, i.e., occurrences of attributes as exhibited by physical objects, systems, events, etc. (b) Of all measuring processes it establishes the most complete isomorphisms between the real number system and attribute-instance systems. (c) This last is accomplished through a functional mapping of the attribute-instances of a given attribute into the real numbers by means of an *external* binary operation between numbers, functioning as scalar *operators* (or multipliers) and the measured attribute-instances. (d) This mapping is made possible by the availability of an internal binary associative, commutative operation ("addition") defined over each set of instances constituting an attribute. The operation is closed for each attribute possessing it.

This mapping is not limited to the physical situation and may, therefore, be viewed as defining a general type of measuring process which, for historical reasons, is referred to as *Euclidian measurement* (or E-measurement). *Concrete (physical) additivity is the requisite for it.* E-measurement includes Stevens' ratio scaling, but the converse does not hold.

2. *Multiplication and Fourier's Principle.* Multiplication of numbers assigned by E-measurement and as used by physical scientists is found to follow rules resulting from the application of a principle first enunciated by Fourier in 1822, namely, the universality of fundamental laws of nature should be reflected in the invariance of the form of their mathematical expression. As specifically applied by him to expressions utilizing E-measurements, it reads: the form of mathematical descriptions of natural laws should not be affected by changes in the units of measurement used.

One consequence of this principle for E-measurements is that *only* certain mathematical expressions are admissible for describing relations between fundamentally measured instances of attributes, more specifically, products of powers of the associated variables and sums of certain of these products.

The multiplication rules which ensue are found, furthermore, to express the existence of an internal binary associative, commutative and close *relational* operation *among attributes* (not instances) as members of a set. Thus in the physical sciences the basic arithmetic operations are found to be simultaneously represented at two different levels, of attributes (multiplication) *and* of their instances (addition). In this regard, earlier conclusions drawn by this writer with respect to "multiplicative scales" need to be altered accordingly.

3. *Defined Quantities and Dimensional Formulas.* Another direct consequence of Fourier's Principle in the case of E-measurement is that the only attributes which can be *defined* in terms of other, fundamentally measured attributes are those which are associated with admissible expressions. This fact, in turn, allows one to view instances of both fundamental and defined attributes in this case as elements of a single set and, in fact, of a system which constitutes a linear (or vector) space. Additionally, this set possesses the following important feature: It can be partitioned into subsets of attributes so related that, for each subset, it is possible to E-measure a second-order property of the attributes it contains, said property being known as their *dimensionality.* This feature leads to the development of an adjunctive calculus of "dimensions" and, more specifically, of "dimensional formulas." This calculus, which can be and was historically arrived at by other

routes, constitutes the foundation of Dimensional Analysis.

Of particular interest and importance are those attributes which can be said of *dimensions zero* (but more often erroneously said "dimensionless") on the basis of the dimensional formulas associated with them. For these and only these, the restrictions imposed by Fourier's Principle on the class of admissible expressions are lifted. That is, one has free choice of any expression, but only at the cost of a compensatory limitation on the variables which can be thus related.

4. *General Applicability of Fourier's Principle.* The generalization of Fourier's Principle to any measuring process reads: If a mathematical expression describes a basic law of nature its form should be invariant with respect to the defining transformations (in the Stevens sense) of the scales which are utilized. In general, the classes of expressions which are admissible in the case of other scales *are much more limited* than in the case of E-scales. In fact, with certain combinations of scales there are no admissible expressions. Hence, the importance of E-measurement.

5. *Pragmatic Considerations.* The history of the physical sciences shows their outstanding growth can be largely ascribed to the implicit and explicit use over the centuries of Fourier's Principle in one form or another. An important implication of the Principle for the applications of mathematics in *any* discipline is that they entail much more than measuring, curve fitting, and making statistical tests. For the behavioral and social sciences, in particular, it suggests part of the low replicability of results and the dearth of meaningful mathematically expressible laws which characterize them have their source in the fact Fourier's Principle has been largely ignored by these disciplines, as much as in the lack of additive scales for them.

References

1. Bridgman, P. W. Dimensional analysis. New Haven: Yale Univ. Press, 1922.
2. Bergmann, G., and Spence, K. W. The logic of psychophysical measurement. *Psychol. Rev.*, 1944, 51, 1–24.
3. Campbell, N. R. An account of the principles of measurements and calculations. London: Longmans, Green, 1928.
4. Eshbach, O. W. Handbook of engineering fundamentals, Vol. I. New York: John Wiley and Sons, Inc., 1936.
5. Guilford, J. P. Psychometric methods. New York: McGraw-Hill Book Co., 1936.
6. Hull, C. L. Principles of behavior. New York: Appleton-Century Co., 1943.
7. Lewin, K. Principles of topological psychology. New York: McGraw-Hill Book Co., 1936.
8. Reese, T. W. Application of the theory of physical measurement to the measurement of psychological magnitudes with three experimental examples. *Psychol. Monogr.*, 1943, 55, No. 3.
9. Russell, B. Principles of mathematics. New York: W. W. Norton and Co., 1943.
10. Stevens, S. S. On the theory of scales of measurement. *Science*, 1946, 103, 677–680.
11. Stevens, S. S., and Harper, R. S. A psychological scale of weight and a formula for its derivation. *Amer. J. Psychol.*, 1948, 61, 343–351.
12. Werkmeister, W. H. The basis and structure of knowledge. New York: Harper and Brothers, 1948.

NORMAN H. ANDERSON

4 Scales and Statistics: Parametric and Nonparametric[1]

The recent rise of interest in the use of non-parametric tests stems from two main sources. One is the concern about the use of parametric tests when the underlying assumptions are not met. The other is the problem of whether or not the measurement scale is suitable for application of parametric procedures. On both counts parametric tests are generally more in danger than nonparametric tests. Because of this, and because of a natural enthusiasm for a new technique, there has been a sometimes uncritical acceptance of nonparametric procedures. By now a certain degree of agreement concerning the more practical aspects involved in the choice of tests appears to have been reached. However, the measurement theoretical issue has been less clearly resolved. The principal purpose of this article is to discuss this latter issue further. For the sake of completeness, a brief overview of practical statistical considerations will also be included.

A few preliminary comments are needed in order to circumscribe the subsequent discussion. In the first place, it is assumed throughout that the data at hand arise from some sort of measuring scale which gives numerical results. This restriction is implicit in the proposal to compare parametric and nonparametric tests since the former do not apply to strictly categorical data (but see 4). Second, parametric tests will mean tests of significance which assume equinormality, i.e., normality and some form of homogeneity of variance. For convenience, parametric test, F test, and

analysis of variance will be used synonymously. Although this usage is not strictly correct, it should be noted that the t test and regression analysis may be considered as special applications of F. Nonparametric tests will refer to significance tests which make considerably weaker distributional assumptions as exemplified by rank order tests such as the Wilcoxon T, the Kruskal-Wallis H, and by the various median-type tests. Third, the main focus of the article is on tests of significance with a lesser emphasis on descriptive statistics. Problems of estimation are touched on only slightly although such problems are becoming increasingly important.

Finally, a word of caution is in order. It will be concluded that parametric procedures constitute the everyday tools of psychological statistics, but it should be realized that any area of investigation has its own statistical peculiarities and that general statements must always be adapted to the prevailing practical situation. In many cases, as in pilot work, for instance, or in situations in which data are cheap and plentiful, nonparametric tests, shortcut parametric tests (27), or tests by visual inspection may well be the most efficient.

Practical Statistical Considerations

The three main points of comparison between parametric and non-parametric tests are significance level, power, and versatility. Most of the relevant considerations have been treated adequately by others and only a brief summary will be given here. For more detailed discussion, the articles of Cochran (3), Savage (21),

1. An earlier version of this paper was presented at the April 1959 meetings of the Western Psychological Association. The author's thanks are due F. N. Jones and J. B. Sidowski for their helpful comments.

Sawrey (22), Gaito (12), and Boneau (2) are especially recommended.

Significance level. The effects of lack of equinormality on the significance level of parametric tests have received considerable study. The two handiest sources for the psychologist are Lindquist's (16) citation of Norton's work and the recent article of Boneau (2) which summarizes much of the earlier work. The main conclusion of the various investigators is that lack of equinormality has remarkably little effect although two exceptions are noted: one-tailed tests and tests with considerably disparate cell n's may be rather severely affected by unequal variances.[2]

A somewhat different source of perturbation of significance level should also be mentioned. An over-all test of several conditions may show that something is significant but will not localize the effects. As is well known, the common practice of t testing pairs of means tends to inflate the significance level even when the over-all F is significant. An analogous inflation occurs with non-parametric tests. There are parametric multiple comparison procedures which are rigorously applicable in many such situations (9; 10) but analogous nonparametric techniques have as yet been developed in only a few cases.

Power. As Dixon and Massey (8) note, rank order tests are nearly as powerful as parametric tests under equinormality. Consequently, there would seem to be no pressing reason in most investigations to use parametric techniques for reasons of power *if* an appropriate rank order test is available (but see 25, p. 120). Of course, the loss of power involved in dichotomizing the data for a median-type test is considerable.

Although it might thus be argued that rank order tests should be generally used where applicable, it is to be suspected that such a

2. The split-plot designs (e.g. 16) commonly used for the analysis of repeated or correlated observations have been subject to some criticism (6; 14) because of the additional assumption of equal correlation which is made. However, tests are available which do not require this assumption (6; 14; 20).

practice would produce negative transfer to the use of the more incisive experimental designs which need parametric analyses. The logic and computing rules for the analysis of variance, however, follow a uniform pattern in all situations and thus provide maximal positive transfer from the simple to the more complex experiments.

There is also another aspect of power which needs mention. Not infrequently, it is possible to use existing data to get a rough idea of the chances of success in a further related experiment, or to estimate the N required for a given desired probability of success (8, Ch. 14). Routine methods are available for these purposes when parametric statistics are employed but similar procedures are available only for certain nonparametric tests such as chi square.

Versatility. One of the most remarkable features of the analysis of variance is the breadth of its applicability, a point which has been emphasized by Gaito (12). For present purposes, the ordinary factorial design will serve to exemplify the issue. Although factorial designs are widely employed, their uses in the investigation and control of minor variables have not been fully exploited. Thus, Feldt (11) has noted the general superiority of the factorial design in matching or equating groups, an important problem which is but poorly handled in current research (1). Similarly, the use of replications as a factor in the design makes it possible to test and partially control for drift or shift in apparatus, procedure, or subject population during the course of an experiment. In the same way, taking experimenters or stimulus materials as a factor allows tests which bear on the adequacy of standardization of the experimental procedures and on the generalizability of the results.

An analogous argument could be given for latin squares, largely rehabilitated by the work of Wilk and Kempthorne (28), which are useful when subjects are given successive treatments; for orthogonal polynomials and trend tests for correlated scores (13) which give the most sensitive tests when the independent variable is scaled; as well as for the multivariate analysis of variance (20) which is applicable to correlated dependent variables measured on incommensurable scales.

The point to these examples and to the more extensive treatment by Gaito is straightforward. Their analysis is more or less routine when parametric procedures are used. However, they are handled inadequately or not at all by current nonparametric methods.

It thus seems fair to conclude that parametric tests constitute the standard tools of psychological statistics. In respect of significance level and power, one might claim a fairly even match. However, the versatility of parametric procedures is quite unmatched and this is decisive. Unless and until nonparametric tests are developed to the point where they meet the routine needs of the researcher as exemplified by the above designs, they cannot realistically be considered as competitors to parametric tests. Until that day, nonparametric tests may best be considered as useful minor techniques in the analysis of numerical data.

Too promiscuous a use of F is, of course, not to be condoned since there will be many situations in which the data are distributed quite wildly. Although there is no easy rule with which to draw the line, a frame of reference can be developed by studying the results of Norton (16) and of Boneau (2). It is also quite instructive to compare p values for parametric and nonparametric tests of the same data.

It may be worth noting that one of the reasons for the popularity of nonparametric tests is probably the current obsession with questions of statistical significance to the neglect of the often more important questions of design and power. Certainly some minimal degree of reliability is generally a necessary justification for asking others to spend time in assessing the importance of one's data. However, the question of statistical significance is only a first step, and a relatively minor one at that, in the over-all process of evaluating a set of results. To say that a result is statistically significant simply gives reasonable ground for believing that some nonchance effect was obtained. The meaning of a nonchance effect rests on an assessment of the design of the investigation. Even with judicious design, however, phenomena are seldom pinned down in a single study so that the question of replicability in further work often arises also. The statistical aspects of these two questions are not without importance but tend to be neglected when too heavy an emphasis is placed on p values. As has been noted, it is the parametric procedures which are the more useful in both respects.

Measurement Scale Considerations

The second and principal part of the article is concerned with the relations between types of measurement scales and statistical tests. For convenience, therefore, it will be assumed that lack of equinormality presents no serious problem. Since the F ratio remains constant with changes in unit or zero point of the measuring scale, we may ignore ratio scales and consider only ordinal and interval scales. These scales are defined following Stevens (26). Briefly, an ordinal scale is one in which the events measured are, in some empirical sense, ordered in the same way as the arithmetic order of the numbers assigned to them. An interval scale has, in addition, an equality of unit over different parts of the scale. Stevens goes on to characterize scale types in terms of permissible transformations. For an ordinal scale, the permissible transformations are monotone since they leave rank order unchanged. For an interval scale, only the linear transformations are permissible since only these leave relative distance unchanged. Some workers (5) have considered various scales which lie between the ordinal and interval scales. However, it will not be necessary to take this further refinement of the scale typology into account here.

As before, we suppose that we have a measuring scale which assigns numbers to events of a certain class. It is assumed that this measuring scale is an ordinal scale but not necessarily an interval scale. In order to fix ideas, consider the following example. Suppose that we are interested in studying attitude toward the church. Subjects are randomly assigned to two groups, one of which reads Communication A, while the other reads Communication B. The subjects' attitudes towards the church are then measured by asking them to check a seven category pro-con rating scale. Our problem is whether the data give adequate reason to conclude that the two communications had different effects.

To ascertain whether the communications had different effects, some statistical test must be applied. In some cases, to be sure, the effects may be so strong that the test can be made by inspection. In most cases, however, some more objective method is necessary. An obvious procedure would be to assign the numbers 1 to 7, say, to the rating scale categories and apply the F test, at least if the data presented some semblance of equinormality. However, some writers on statistics (e.g., 24; 23) would object to this on the ground that the rating scale is only an ordinal scale, the data are therefore not "truly numerical," and hence that the operations of addition and multiplication which are used in computing F cannot meaningfully be applied to the scores. There are three different questions involved in this objection, and much of the controversy over scales and statistics has arisen from a failure to keep them separate. Accordingly, these three questions will be taken up in turn.

Question 1. Can the F test be applied to data from an ordinal scale? It is convenient to consider two cases of this question according as the assumption of equinormality is satisfied or not. Suppose first that equinormality obtains. The caveat against parametric statistics has been stated most explicitly by Siegel (24) who says:

The conditions which must be satisfied ... before any confidence can be placed in any probability statement obtained by the use of the t test are at least these: ... 4. The variables involved must have been measured in *at least* an interval scale ... (p. 19).

This statement of Siegel's is completely incorrect. This particular question admits of no doubt whatsoever. The F (or t) test may be applied without qualm. It will then answer the question which it was designed to answer: can we reasonably conclude that the difference between the means of the two groups is real rather than due to chance? The justification for using F is purely statistical and quite straightforward; there is no need to waste space on it here. The reader who has doubts on the matter should postpone them to the discussion of the two subsequent questions, or read the elegant and entertaining article by Lord (17). As Lord points out, the statistical test can hardly be cognizant of the empirical meaning of the numbers with which it deals. Consequently, the validity of a statistical inference cannot depend on the type of measuring scale used.

The case in which equinormality does not hold remains to be considered. We may still use F, of course, and as has been seen in the first part, we would still have about the same significance level in most cases. The F test might have less power than a rank order test so that the latter might be preferable in this simple two group experiment. However, insofar as we wish to inquire into the reliability of the difference between the measured behavior of the two groups in our particular experiment, the choice of statistical test would be governed by purely statistical considerations and have nothing to do with scale type.

Question 2. Will statistical results be invariant under change of scale? The problem of invariance of result stems from the work of Stevens (26) who observes that a statistic computed on data from a given scale will be invariant when the scale is changed according to any given permissible transformation. It is important to be precise about this usage of invariance. It means that if a statistic is computed from a set of scale values and this statistic is then transformed, the identical result will be obtained as when the separate scale values are transformed and the statistic is computed from these transformed scale values.

Now our scale of attitude toward the church is admittedly only an ordinal scale. Consequently, we would expect it to change in the direction of an interval scale in future work. Any such scale change would correspond to a monotone transformation of our original scale since only such transformations are permissible with an ordinal scale. Suppose then that a monotone transformation of the scale has been made subsequent to the experiment on attitude change. We would then have two sets of data: the responses as measured on the original scale used in the experiment, and the transformed values of these responses as measured on the new, transformed scale. (Presumably, these transformed scale values would be the same as the subjects would have made had the new scale been used in the original experiment, although this will no doubt depend on the experimental basis of the new scale.) The question at issue then becomes whether the same significance results will be obtained from the two sets of data. If rank order tests are used, the same significance results will be found in either case because any permissible transformation leaves rank order unchanged. However, if parametric tests are employed, then different significance statements may be obtained from the two sets of data. It is possible to get a significant F from the original data and not from the transformed data, and vice versa. Worse yet, it is even logically possible that the means of the two groups will lie in reverse order on the two scales.

The state of affairs just described is clearly undesirable. If taken uncritically, it would constitute a strong argument for using only rank order tests on ordinal scale data and restricting the use of F to data obtained from interval scales. It is the purpose of this section to show that this conclusion is unwarranted. The basis of the argument is that the naming of the scales has begged the psychological question.

Consider interval scales first, and imagine that two students, P and Q, in an elementary lab course are assigned to investigate some process. This process might be a ball rolling on

a plane, a rat running an alley, or a child doing sums. The students cooperate in the experimental work, making the same observations, except that they use different measuring scales. P decides to measure time intervals. He reasons that it makes sense to speak of one time interval as being twice another, that time intervals therefore form a ratio scale, and hence a

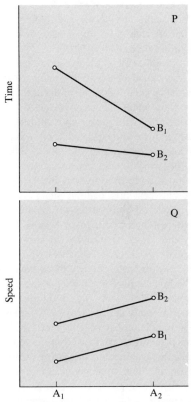

Fig. 1. Temporal aspects of some process obtained from a 2×2 design. (The data are plotted as a function of Variable A with Variable B as a parameter. Subscripts denote the two level of each variable. Note that Panel P shows an interaction, but that Panel Q does not.)

fortiori an interval scale. Q decides to measure the speed of the process (feet per second, problems per minute). By the same reasoning as used by P, Q concludes that he has an interval scale also. Both P and Q are aware of current strictures about scales and statistics.

However, since each believes (and rightly so) that he has an interval scale, each uses means and applies parametric tests in writing his lab report. Nevertheless, when they compare their reports they find considerable difference in their descriptive statistics and graphs (Figure 1), and in their F ratios as well. Consultation with a statistician shows that these differences are direct consequences of the difference in the measuring scales. Evidently then, possession of an interval scale does not guarantee invariance of interval scale statistics.

For ordinal scales, we would expect to obtain invariance of result by using ordinal scale statistics such as the median (26). Let us suppose that some future investigator finds that attitude toward the church is multidimensional in nature and has, in fact, obtained interval scales for each of the dimensions. In some of his work he chanced to use our original ordinal scale so that he was able to find the relation between this ordinal scale and the multidimensional representation of the attitude. His results are shown in Figure 2. Our ordinal scale is represented by the curved line in the plane of the two dimensions. Thus, a greater distance from the origin as measured along the line stands for a higher value on our ordinal scale. Points A and B on the curve represent the medians of Groups A and B in our experiment, and it is seen that Group A is more pro-church than Group B on our ordinal scale. The median scores for these two groups on the two dimensions are obtained simply by projecting Points A and B onto the two dimensions. All is well on Dimension 2 since there Group A is greater than Group B. On Dimension 1, however, a reversal is found: Group A is less than Group B, contrary to our ordinal scale results. Evidently then, possession of an ordinal scale does not guarantee invariance of ordinal scale statistics.

A rather more drastic loss of invariance would occur if the ordinal scale were measuring the resultant effect of two or more underlying processes. This could happen, for instance, in the study of approach-avoidance conflict, or ambivalent behavior, as might be the case with attitude toward the church. In such situations, two people could give identical responses on the one-dimensional scale and yet be quite different as regards the two underlying processes. For instance, the same resultant could occur with two equal opposing tendencies of any given strength. Representing such data in the space formed by the underlying dimensions would yield a smear of points over an entire region rather than a simple curve as in Figure 2.

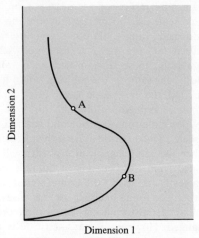

Fig. 2. The curved line represents the ordinal scale of attitude toward the church plotted in the two-dimensional space underlying the attitude. (Points A and B denote the medians of two experimental groups. The graph is hypothetical, of course.)

Although it may be reasonable to think that simple sensory phenomena are one-dimensional, it would seem that a considerable number of psychological variables must be conceived of as multidimensional in nature as, for instance, with "IQ" and other personality variables. Accordingly, as the two cited examples show, there is no logical guarantee that the use of ordinal scale statistics will yield invariant results under scale changes.

It is simple to construct analogous examples for nominal scales. However, their only relevance would be to show that a reduction of all results to categorical data does not avoid the difficulty with invariance.

It will be objected, of course, that the argument of the examples has violated the initial assumption that only "permissible" transformations would be used in changing the measuring scales. Thus, speed and time are not linearly related, but rather the one is a reciprocal transformation of the other. Similarly, Dimension 1 of Figure 2 is no monotone transformation of the original ordinal scale. This objection is correct, to be sure, but it simply shows that the problem of invariance of result with which one is actually faced in science has no particular connection with the invariance of "permissible" statistics. The examples which have been cited show that knowing the scale type, as determined by the commonly accepted criteria, does not imply that future scales measuring the same phenomena will be "permissible" transformations of the original scale. Hence the use of "permissible" statistics, although guaranteeing invariance of result over the class of "permissible" transformations, says little about invariance of result over the class of scale changes which must actually be considered by the investigator in his work.

This point is no doubt pretty obvious, and it should not be thought that those who have taken up the scale-type ideas are unaware of the problem. Stevens, at least, seems to appreciate the difficulty when, in the concluding section of his 1951 article, he distinguishes between psychological dimensions and indicants [See Ch. 1]. The former may be considered as intervening variables whereas the latter are effects or correlates of these variables. However, it is evident that an indicant may be an interval scale in the customary sense and yet bear a complicated relation to the underlying psychological dimensions. In such cases, no procedure of descriptive or inferential statistics can guarantee invariance over the class of scale changes which may become necessary.

It should also be realized that only a partial list of practical problems of invariance has been considered. Effects on invariance of improvements in experimental technique would also have to be taken into account since such improvements would be expected to purify or change the dependent variable as well as decrease variability. There is, in addition, a problem of invariance over subject population. Most researches are based on some handy sample of subjects and leave more or less doubt about the generality of the results. Although this becomes in large part an extrastatistical problem (28), it is one which assumes added importance in view of Crombach's (7) emphasis on the interaction of experimental and subject variables. In the face of these assorted difficulties, it is not easy to see what utility the scale typology has for the practical problems of the investigator.

The preceding remarks have been intended to put into broader perspective that sort of invariance which is involved in the use of permissible statistics. They do not, however, solve the immediate problem of whether to use rank order tests or F in case only permissible transformations need be considered. Although invariance under permissible scale transformations may be of relatively minor importance, there is no point in taking unnecessary risks without the possibility of compensation.

On this basis, one would perhaps expect to find the greatest use of rank order tests in the initial stages of inquiry since it is then that measuring scales will be poorest. However, it is in these initial stages that the possibly relevant variables are not well-known so that the stronger experimental designs, and hence parametric procedures, are most needed. Thus, it may well be most efficient to use parametric tests, balancing any risk due to possible permissible scale changes against the greater power and versatility of such tests. In the later stages of investigation, we would be generally more sure of the scales and the use of rank order procedures would waste information which the scales by then embody.

At the same time, it should be realized that even with a relatively crude scale such as the rating scale of attitude toward the church, the possible permissible transformations which are relevant to the present discussion are somewhat restricted. Since the F ratio is invariant under change of zero and unit, it is no restriction to assume that any transformed scale also runs from 1 to 7. This imposes a considerable limitation on the permissible scale transformations which must be considered. In addition, whatever psychological worth the original rating scale possesses will limit still further the transformations which will occur in practice.

Although rank order tests do possess some logical advantage over parametric tests when only permissible transformations are considered, this advantage is, in the writer's opinion, very slight in practice and does not begin to balance the greater versatility of parametric procedures. The problem is, however, an empirical one and it would seem that some historical analysis is needed to provide an objective frame of reference. To quote an after-lunch remark of K. MacCorquodale, "Measurement theory should be descriptive, not proscriptive, nor prescriptive." Such an inquiry could not fail to be fascinating because of the light it would throw on the actual progress of measurement in psychology. One investigation of this sort would probably be more useful than all the speculation which has been written on the topic of measurement.

Question 3. Will the use of parametric as opposed to nonparametric statistics affect inferences about underlying psychological processes? In a narrow sense, Question 3 is irrelevant to this article since the inferences in question are substantive, relating to psychological meaning, rather than formal, relating to data reliability. Nevertheless, it is appropriate to discuss the matter briefly in order to make explicit some of the considerations involved because they are often confused with problems arising under the two previous questions. With no pretense of covering all aspects of this question, the following two examples will at least touch some of the problems.

The first example concerns the two students, P and Q, mentioned above, who had used time and speed as dependent variables. We suppose that their experiment was based on a 2×2 design and yielded means as plotted in Figure 1. This graph portrays main effects of both variables which are seen to be similar in nature in both panels. However, our principal concern is with the interaction which may be visualized as measuring the degree of nonparallelism of the two lines in either panel. Panel P shows an interaction. The reciprocals of these same data, plotted in Panel Q, show no interaction. It is thus evident in the example, and true in general, that interaction effects will depend strongly on the measuring scales used.

Assessing an interaction does not always cause trouble, of course. Had the lines in Panel P, say, crossed each other, it would not be likely that any change of scale would yield uncrossed lines. In many cases also, the scale used is sufficient for the purposes at hand and future scale changes need not be considered. Nevertheless, it is clear that a measure of caution will often be needed in making inferences from interaction to psychological process. If the investigator envisages the possibility of future changes in the scale, he should also realize that a present inference based on significant interaction may lose credibility in the light of the rescaled data.

It is certainly true that the interpretation of interactions has sometimes led to error. It may also be noted that the usual factorial design analysis is sometimes incongruent with the phenomena. In a 2×2 design it might happen, for example, that three of the four cell means are equal. The usual analysis is not optimally sensitive to this one real difference since it is distributed over three degrees of freedom. In such cases, there will often be other parametric tests involving specific comparisons (25) or multiple comparisons (9) which are more appropriate. Occasionally also, an analysis of variance based on a multiplicative model (29) will be useful (15). A judicious choice of test may be of great help in dissecting the results. However, the test only answers set questions concerning the reliability of the results; only the research worker can say which questions are appropriate and meaningful.

Inferences based on nonparametric tests of interaction would presumably be less sensitive to certain types of scale changes. However, caution would still be needed in the interpretation as has been seen in Question 2. The problem is largely academic, however, since few nonparametric tests of interaction exist.[3] It might be suggested that the question of interaction cannot arise when only the ordinal properties of the data are considered since the interaction involves a comparison of differences and such a comparison is illegitimate with ordinal data. To the extent that this suggestion is correct, a parametric test can be used to the same purposes equally well if not better; to the extent that it is not correct, nonparametric tests will waste information.

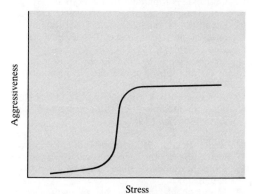

Fig. 3. Aggressiveness plotted as a function of stress. (The curve is hypothetical. Note the hypothetical threshold effect.)

One final comment on the first example deserves emphasis. Since both time and speed are interval scales, it cannot be argued that the difficulty in interpretation arises because we had only ordinal scales.

The second example, suggested by J. Kaswan, is shown in Figure 3. The graph,

3. There is a nomenclatural difficulty here. Strictly speaking, nonparametric tests should be called more-or-less distribution free tests. For example, the Mood-Brown generalized median test (Mood, 1950) is distribution free, but is based on a parametric model of the same sort as in the analysis of variance. As noted in the introduction, the usual terminology is used in this article.

which is hypothetical, plots amount of aggressiveness as a function of amount of stress. A glance at the graph leads immediately to the inference that some sort of threshold effect is present. Under increasing stress, the organism remains quiescent until the stress passes a certain threshold value, whereupon the organism leaps into full scale aggressive behavior.

Confidence in this interpretation is shaken when we stop to consider that the scales for stress and aggression may not be very good. Perhaps, when future work has given us improved scales, these same data would yield a quite different function such as a straight line.

One extreme position regarding the threshold effect would be to say that the scales give rank order information and no more. The threshold inference, or any inference based on characteristics of the curve shape other than the uniform upward trend, would then be completely disallowed. At the other extreme, there would be complete faith in the scales and all inferences based on curve shape, including the threshold effect, would be made without fear that they would be undermined by future changes in the scales. In practice, one would probably adopt a position between these two extremes, believing, with Mosteller (19), that our scales generally have some degree of numerical information worked into them, and realizing that to consider only the rank order character of the data would be to ignore the information that gives the strongest hold on the behavior.

From this ill-defined middleground, inferences such as the threshold effect would be entertained as guides to future work. Such inferences, however, are made at the judgment of the investigator. Statistical techniques may be helpful in evaluating the reliability of various features of the data, but only the investigator can endow them with psychological meaning.

Summary

This article has compared parametric and

nonparametric statistics under two general headings: practical statistical problems, and measurement theoretical considerations. The scope of the article is restricted to situations in which the dependent variable is numerical, thus excluding strictly categorical data.

Regarding practical problems, it was noted that the difference between parametric and rank order tests was not great insofar as significance level and power were concerned. However, only the versatility of parametric statistics meets the everyday needs of psychological research. It was concluded that parametric procedures are the standard tools of psychological statistics although nonparametric procedures are useful minor techniques.

Under the heading of measurement theoretical considerations, three questions were distinguished. The well-known fact that an interval scale is not prerequisite to making a statistical inference based on a parametric test was first pointed out. The second question took up the important problem of invariance. It was noted that the practical problems of invariance or generality of result far transcend measurement scale typology. In addition, the cited example of time and speed showed that interval scales of a given phenomenon are not unique. The discussion of the third question noted that the problem of psychological meaning is not basically a statistical matter. It was thus concluded that the type of measuring scale used had little relevance to the question of whether to use parametric or nonparametric tests.

References

1. Anderson, N. H. Education for research in psychology. *Amer. Psychologist*, 1959, 14, 695–696.
2. Boneau, C. A. The effects of violations of assumptions underlying the *t* test. *Psychol. Bull.*, 1960, 57, 49–64.
3. Cochran, W. G. Some consequences when the assumptions for the analysis of variance are not satisfied. *Biometrics*, 1947, 3, 22–38.
4. Cochran, W. G. Some methods for strengthening the common χ^2 tests. *Biometrics*, 1954, 10, 417–451.
5. Coombs, C. H. A theory of psychological scaling. *Bull. Engrg. Res. Inst. U. Mich.*, 1952, No. 34.
6. Cotton, J. W. A re-examination of the repeated measurements problem. Paper read at American Statistical Association, Chicago, December 1959.
7. Cronbach, L. J. The two disciplines of scientific psychology. *Amer. Psychologist*, 1957, 11, 671–684.
8. Dixon, W. J., & Massey, F. J., Jr. *Introduction to statistical analysis.* (2nd ed.) New York: McGraw-Hill, 1957.
9. Duncan, D. B. Multiple range and multiple *F* tests. *Biometrics*, 1955, 11, 1–41.
10. Federer, W. T. *Experimental design.* New York: Macmillan, 1955.
11. Feldt, L. S. A comparison of the precision of three experimental designs employing a concomitant variable. *Psychometrika*, 1958, 23, 335–354.
12. Gaito, J. Nonparametric methods in psychological research. *Psychol. Rep.*, 1959, 5, 115–125.
13. Grant, D. A. Analysis-of-variance tests in the analysis and comparison of curves. *Psychol. Bull.*, 1956, 53, 141–154.
14. Greenhouse, S. W., & Geisser, S. On methods in the analysis of profile data. *Psychometrika*, 1959, 24, 95–112.
15. Jones, F. N., & Marcus, M. J. The subject effect in judgments of subjective magnitude. *J. exp. Psychol.*, 1961, 61, 40–44.
16. Lindquist, E. F. *Design and analysis of experiments.* Boston: Houghton Mifflin, 1953.
17. Lord, F. M. On the statistical treatment of football numbers. *Amer. Psychologist*, 1953, 8, 750–751.
18. Mood, A. M. *Introduction to the theory of statistics.* New York: McGraw-Hill, 1950.
19. Mosteller, F. The mystery of the missing corpus. *Psychometrika*, 1958, 23, 279–290.
20. Rao, C. R. *Advanced statistical methods in biometric research.* New York: Wiley, 1952.
21. Savage, I. R. Nonparametric statistics. *J. Amer. Statist. Ass.*, 1957, 52, 331–344.
22. Sawrey, W. L. A distinction between exact and approximate nonparametric methods. *Psychometrika*, 1958, 23, 171–178.
23. Senders, V. L. *Measurement and statistics.* New York: Oxford, 1958.
29. Siegel, S. *Nonparametric statistics.* New York: McGraw-Hill, 1956.
25. Snedecor, G. W. *Statistical methods.* (5th ed.) Ames: Iowa State Coll. Press, 1956.
26. Stevens, S. S. Mathematics, measurement, and psychophysics. In S. S. Stevens (Ed.), *Handbook of experimental pyschology.* New York: Wiley, 1951.

29. Tate, M. W., & Clelland, R. C. *Nonparametric and shortcut statistics.* Danville, Ill.: Interstate, 1957.

28. Wilk, M. B. & Kempthorne, O. Fixed, mixed, and random models. *J. Amer. Statist. Ass.,*

1955, 50, 1144–1167.

29. Williams, E. J. The interpretation of interactions in factorial experiments. *Biometrika,* 1952, 39, 65–81.

PATRICK SUPPES   JOSEPH L. ZINNES

5 Basic Measurement Theory[1]

Although measurement is one of the gods modern psychologists pay homage to with great regularity, the subject of measurement remains as elusive as ever. A systematic treatment of the theory is not readily found in the psychological literature. For the most part, a student of the subject is confronted with an array of bewildering and conflicting catechisms, catechisms that tell him whether such and such a ritual is permissible or, at least, whether it can be condoned. To cite just one peculiar, yet uniformly accepted, example, as elementary science students we are constantly warned that it "does not make sense" (a phrase often used when no other argument is apparent) to add numbers representing distinct properties, say, height and weight. Yet as more advanced physics students we are taught, with some effort no doubt, to multiply numbers representing such things as velocity and time or to divide distance numbers by time numbers. Why does multiplication make "more sense" than addition?

Rather than chart the etiology and course of these rituals our purpose in this chapter is to build a consistent conceptual framework within which it is possible to discuss many (hopefully most) of the theoretical questions of measurement. At the same time, we hope to suppress as much as possible the temptation to enunciate additional dogmas or to put our stamp of approval on existing ones. Our overriding faith, if we may call it that, is that once the various theoretical issues have been formulated in the terms set forth here simple and specific answers with a clear logical basis can be given. To be sure, in some cases the answers to questions phrased within this framework are not so simple and may require extensive mathematical work. It may, for example, be a difficult mathematical problem to show that a given scale is (or is not) an interval scale, but this is not to suggest that the existence of an interval scale is a matter for philosophical speculation or that it depends on the whims and fancies or even the position of the experimenter. On the contrary, the answers to questions of measurement have the same unambiguous status as the answers to mathematical questions posed in other fields of science.

General Theory of Fundamental Measurement

One systematic approach to the subject of measurement begins by the formulation of two fundamental problems. Briefly stated, the first problem is *justification of the assignment of numbers to objects or phenomena.* The second

[1]. We are indebted to John Tukey for a number of helpful comments on an earlier draft.

second problem concerns *the specification of the degree to which this assignment is unique.* Each problem is taken up separately. (The general viewpoint to be developed in this section was first articulated in Scott & Suppes (32).)

FIRST FUNDAMENTAL PROBLEM: THE REPRESENTATION THEOREM

The early history of mathematics shows how difficult it was to divorce arithmetic from particular empirical structures. The ancient Egyptians could not think of $2 + 3$, but only of 2 bushels of wheat plus 3 bushels of wheat. Intellectually, it is a great step forward to realize the assertion that 2 bushels of wheat plus 3 bushels of wheat equal 5 bushels of wheat involves the same mathematical considerations as the statement that 2 quarts of milk plus 3 quarts of milk equal 5 quarts of milk.

From a logical standpoint there is just one arithmetic of numbers, not an arithmetic for bushels of wheat and a separate arithmetic for quarts of milk. The first problem for a theory of measurement is to show how various features of this arithmetic of numbers may be applied in a variety of empirical situations. This is done by showing that certain aspects of the arithmetic of numbers have the same structure as the empirical situation investigated. The purpose of the definition of *isomorphism* to be given later is to make the rough-and-ready intuitive idea of "same structure" precise. The great significance of finding such an isomorphism of structures is that we may then use many of our familiar computational methods of arithmetic to infer facts about the isomorphic empirical structure.

More completely, we may state the first fundamental problem of an exact analysis of any procedure of measurement as follows:

Characterize the formal properties of the empirical operations and relations used in the procedure and show that they are isomorphic to appropriately chosen numerical operations and relations.

Since this problem is equivalent to proving what is called a numerical representation theorem, the first fundamental problem is hereafter referred to as the *representation problem* for a theory or procedure of measurement.

We may use Tarski's notion (39) of a *relational system* to make the representational problem still more precise. A relational system is a finite sequence of the form $\mathfrak{A} = \langle A, R_1,\ldots,R_n \rangle$, where A is a nonempty set of elements called the *domain* of the relational system $\mathfrak{A}$ and $R_1,\ldots,R_n$ are relations on A.[2]

Two simple examples of relational systems are the following. Let A_1 be the set of human beings now living and let R_1 be the binary relation on A_1 such that, for all a and b in A_1, aR_1b if and only if a was born before b. $\mathfrak{A}_1 = \langle A_1, R_1 \rangle$ is then a relational system in the sense just defined. Let A_2 be a set of sounds and let D_2 be the quaternary relation representing judgment by a subject of relative magnitude of differences of pitch among the elements of A_2, i.e., for any a, b, c and d in A_2, $abDcd$ if and only if the subject judges the difference in pitch between a and b to be equal to or less than the difference between c and d. The ordered couple $\mathfrak{A}_2 = \langle A_2, D_2 \rangle$ is then also a relational system.

The most important formal difference between $\mathfrak{A}_1$ and $\mathfrak{A}_2$ is that R_1 is a binary relation of ordering and D_2 is a quaternary relation for ordering of differences. It is useful to formalize this difference by defining the *type* of relational system. If $s = \langle m_1,\ldots,m_n \rangle$ is an n-termed sequence of positive integers, then a relational system $\mathfrak{A} = \langle A, R_1,\ldots,R_n \rangle$ is of type s if for each $i = 1,\ldots,n$ the relation R_i is an m_i-ary relation. Thus $\mathfrak{A}_1$ is of type $\langle 2 \rangle$ and $\mathfrak{A}_2$ is

---

2. It is no restriction on generality to consider only relations, for from a formal standpoint operations are simply certain special relations. For example, a ternary relation T is a binary operation if whenever $T(x, y, z)$ and $T(x, y, z')$ then $z = z'$, and we may define the binary operation symbol "$\circ$" by the equation

$$x \circ y = z \quad \text{if and only if} \quad T(x, y, z).$$

Moreover, there are reasons special to theories of measurement to be mentioned [on pp. 64–66] for minimizing the role of operations.

of type $\langle 4 \rangle$. Note that the sequence s reduces to a single term for these two examples because each has exactly one relation. A relational system $\mathfrak{A}_3 = \langle A_3, P_3, I_3 \rangle$ where P_3 and I_3 are binary relations on A_3 is of type $\langle 2, 2 \rangle$. The point of stating the type of relational system is to make clear the most general set-theoretical features of the system. We say that two relational systems are *similar* if they are of the same type.

We now consider the important concept of isomorphism of two similar relational systems. Before stating a general definition it will be helpful to examine the definition for systems of type $\langle 2 \rangle$, that is, systems like $\mathfrak{B}_1$. Let $\mathfrak{A} = \langle A, R \rangle$ and $\mathfrak{B} = \langle B, S \rangle$ be two systems of type $\langle 2 \rangle$. Then $\mathfrak{A}$ and $\mathfrak{B}$ are *isomorphic* if there is a one-one function f from A onto B such that for every a and b in A

$$aRb \text{ if and only if } f(a) \, Sf(b).$$

As already stated, the intuitive idea is that $\mathfrak{A}$ and $\mathfrak{B}$ are isomorphic just when they have the same structure.

For instance, let

$$A = \{1, 3, 5, 7\},$$
$$A' = \{1, 4, 20, -5\},$$
$$R = \leqslant,$$
$$R' = \geqslant.$$

Then $\mathfrak{A} = \langle A, R \rangle$ and $\mathfrak{A}' = \langle A', R' \rangle$ are isomorphic. To see this, let

$$f(1) = 20,$$
$$f(3) = 4,$$
$$f(5) = 1,$$
$$f(7) = -5.$$

On the other hand, let

$$R'' = <.$$

Then $\mathfrak{A} = \langle A, R \rangle$ and $\mathfrak{A}'' = \langle A', R'' \rangle$ are not isomorphic, for suppose they were. Then there would exist a function f such that $f(1)$ $R'' f(1)$, that is,

$$f(1) < f(1), \qquad\qquad \text{Eq. 1}$$

because 1 R 1, that is $1 \leqslant 1$, but Eq. 1 is absurd.

To illustrate another point, let

$$A = \{1, 2\},$$
$$A' = \{8, 9, 10\},$$
$$R = <,$$
$$R' = >.$$

Then $\mathfrak{A} = \langle A, R \rangle$ and $\mathfrak{A}' = \langle A', R' \rangle$ are not isomorphic just because A and A' do not have the same number of elements and thus there can be no one-one function from A to A'.

From this discussion it should be clear how the general definition of isomorphism runs. Let $\mathfrak{A} = \langle A, R_1, \ldots, R_n \rangle$ and $\mathfrak{B} = \langle B, S_1, \ldots, S_n \rangle$ be similar relation systems. Then $\mathfrak{B}$ is an *isomorphic* image of $\mathfrak{A}$ if there is a one-one function f from A onto B such that, for each $i = 1, \ldots, n$ and for each sequence $\langle a_1, \ldots, A_{m_i} \rangle$ of elements of A, $R_i(a_1, \ldots, a_{m_i})$ if and only if $S_i(f(a_1), \ldots, f(a_{m_i}))$. Instead of saying that $\mathfrak{B}$ is an isomorphic image of $\mathfrak{A}$, we also often simply say that $\mathfrak{A}$ and $\mathfrak{B}$ are *isomorphic*.

On occasion it is too strict to require that the function f be one-one, for it may be natural in some cases to assign the same number to two distinct objects; for instance, two objects may have the same weight or length. In such cases we weaken the definition by dropping the requirement that f be one-one and then speak of $\mathfrak{B}$ as the *homomorphic* image of $\mathfrak{A}$.

The formal definitions given thus far are not special to the theory of measurement. A more direct connection is made by first distinguishing between a *numerical relational system* and an *empirical relational system*. A numerical relational system is a relational system $\langle A, R_1, \ldots, R_n \rangle$ whose domain A is a set of real numbers. Although this definition places no restrictions on the relations R_i in the numerical system, these relations in practice are limited to certain common relations obtaining between numbers. It is possible, for example, to define a numerical relational system $\langle A, R_1 \rangle$ in which

$$A = \{1, 3, 5, 7\}$$
$$R_1 = \{\langle 1, 3 \rangle, \langle 5, 7 \rangle, \langle 7, 7 \rangle\},$$

but such a numerical system will not prove useful. The relational systems described in the preceding discussion of isomorphism are examples of more common (and useful) numerical systems. It should be obvious, but nevertheless it bears emphasizing, that a numerical relational system is not necessarily isomorphic to what is ordinarily called the real number system. For example, let Re be the set of all real numbers and let $<$ be the ordinary numerical relation of *less than*; then the numerical relational system $\langle \text{Re}, < \rangle$ is certainly not isomorphic to the usual system of real numbers employing the operations of addition and multiplication.

An empirical relational system is a relational system whose domain is a set of identifiable entities, such as weights, persons, attitude statements, or sounds. If, for example, the domain A of the relational system $\langle A, R_2 \rangle$ consisted of weights, then the relation R_2 would likely be the relation *is less heavy than*, that is, for a and b in A, aR_2b indicates that weight a is less heavy than b.

The first fundamental problem of measurement may be cast as the problem of showing that *any empirical relational system that purports to measure (by a simple number) a given property of the elements in the domain of the system is isomorphic (or possibly homomorphic) to an appropriately chosen numerical relational system.*

There are two aspects to this statement of the representation problem that perhaps need further amplification. Since, as we have emphasized, the numerical relational system does not completely characterize the real number system, the homomorphism that is required by the representation problem is *not* a homomorphism between the empirical relational system and the real number system. This does *not* mean, as is often suggested, that manipulations of the numbers in the domain of a given numerical system—to infer facts about the elements in the domain of the corresponding empirical system—must involve only those relations in the given numerical system. Relations neither contained in a given numeri-

cal system nor having a direct correspondence in the related empirical system may nevertheless be used. There are, of course, certain limitations imposed upon the manipulations of the numbers of a numerical system, but these limitations relate to certain criteria of meaningfulness of individual sentences rather than to those relations contained in a numerical system. These matters are discussed in detail on pp. 51–56.

The second aspect of the representation problem needing amplification concerns the phrase "appropriately chosen numerical relational system" which appears in the last statement of the representation problem. The representation problem is not adequately solved if the isomorphism is established between a given empirical system and a numerical system employing unnatural or "pathological" relations. In fact, if the empirical system is finite or denumerable (i.e., has a finite or denumerable domain), some numerical system can always be found that is isomorphic to it. It is of no great consequence therefore merely to exhibit some numerical system that is isomorphic to an empirical system. It is of value, however, to exhibit a numerical system that is not only isomorphic to an empirical system but employs certain simple and familiar relations as well. A complete or precise categorization of the intuitively desirable relations is unfortunately somewhat elusive, so for this reason the statement of the representation problem refers merely to an "appropriately chosen" numerical system.

SECOND FUNDAMENTAL PROBLEM:
THE UNIQUENESS THEOREM

Solution of the representation problem for a theory of measurement does not completely lay bare the structure of the theory, for it is a banal fact of methodology that there is often a formal difference between the kind of assignment of numbers arising from different procedures of measurement. As an illustration, consider the following five statements:

1. The number of people now in this room is 7.
2. Stendhal weighed 150 on September 2, 1839.
3. The ratio of Stendhal's weight to Jane Austen's on July 3, 1814, was 1.42.
4. The ratio of the maximum temperature today to the maximum temperature yesterday is 1.10.
5. The ratio of the difference between today's and yesterday's maximum temperature to the difference between today's and tomorrow's maximum temperature will be 0.95.

The empirical meaning of statements 1, 3, and 5 is clear, provided we make the natural assumptions, namely, for 3 that the same scale of weight, whether avoirdupois or metric, was being used, and for 5 that the same temperature scale is being used, whether Fahrenheit or centigrade. In contrast, 2 and 4 have no clear empirical meaning unless the *particular* scale used for the measurement is specified. On the basis of these five statements we may formally distinguish three kinds of measurement. Counting is an example of an *absolute* scale. The number of members of a given collection of objects is determined uniquely. There is no arbitrary choice of unit or zero available. In contrast, the usual measurement of mass or weight is an example of a *ratio* scale. A chemist, measuring a sample of a certain ferric salt on an equal arm balance with a standard series of metric weights, might make the statement:

6. This sample of ferric salt weighs 1.679 grams. But this statement may be replaced by the statement:
7. The ratio of the mass of this sample of ferric salt to the gram weight of my standard series is 1.679, and the manufacturer of my series has certified that the ratio of my gram weight to the standard kilogram mass of platinum iridium alloy at the International Bureau of Weights and Measures, near Paris, is 0.0010000.

In general, any empirical procedure for measuring mass does not determine the unit of mass. The choice of a unit is an empirically arbitrary decision made by an individual or group of individuals. Of course, once a unit of measurement has been chosen, such as the gram or pound, the numerical mass of every other object in the universe is uniquely determined. Another way of stating this is to say that the measurement of mass is unique up to multiplication by a positive constant. (The technical use of "up to" will become clear later.) The measurement of distance is a second example of measurement of this sort. The ratio of the distance between Palo Alto and San Francisco to the distance between Washington and New York is the same whether the measurement is made in miles or yards.

The usual measurement of temperature is an example of the third formally distinct kind of measurement mentioned earlier. An empirical procedure for measuring temperature by use of a thermometer determines neither a unit nor an origin. (We are excluding from consideration here the measurement of absolute temperature whose zero point is not arbitrary.) In this sort of measurement the ratio of any two intervals is independent of the unit and zero point of measurement. For obvious reasons measurements of this kind are called *interval* scales. Examples other than measurement of temperature are provided by the usual measurements of temporal dates, linear position, or cardinal utility.

In terms of the motion of absolute, ratio, and interval scales, we may formulate the second fundamental problem for any exact analysis of a procedure of measurement: *determine the scale type of the measurements resulting from the procedure.* We have termed this problem the *uniqueness* problem for a theory of measurement. The reason for this terminology is that from a mathematical standpoint the determination of the scale type of measurements arising from a given system of empirical relations is the determination of the way in which any two numerical systems are related then they use the same numerical relations and are homomorphic to the given empirical system. In the case of mass, for example, the four following statements are equivalent.

8. The measurement of mass is on a ratio scale.
9. The measurement of mass is unique up to multiplication by a positive number (the number corresponding to an arbitrary choice of unit).
10. The measurement of mass is unique up to a similarity transformation (such a transformation is just multiplication by a positive number).
11. Given any empirical system for measuring mass, then any two numerical systems that use the same numerical relations and are homomorphic to the given empirical system are related by a similarity transformation.

The validity of statement 11 is demonstrated on pp. 64–66, where an axiom system for measuring mass is presented.

FORMAL DEFINITION AND CLASSIFICATION
OF SCALES OF MEASUREMENT

It is unusual to find in the literature of measurement an exact definition of scales. Within the formal framework developed in this chapter it is possible to give an exact characterization that seems to correspond rather closely to many of the intuitive ideas of a scale.

Two preliminary definitions are needed. First, we say that a numerical relational system is *full* if its domain is the set of all real numbers. Second, a *subsystem* of a relational system $\mathfrak{A}$ is a relational system obtained from $\mathfrak{A}$ by taking a domain that is a subset of the domain of $\mathfrak{A}$ and restricting all relations of $\mathfrak{A}$ to this subset. For example, let

Re = the set of all real numbers,
$<$ = less than,
N = the set of nonnegative integers,
$<_N$ = less than restricted to N.

Then $\langle N, <_N \rangle$ is a subsystem of $\langle \text{Re}, < \rangle$, which is itself a full numerical relational system. As a second example, let

$$A = \{1, 2, 3\},$$
$$R = \{\langle 1,1 \rangle, \langle 2,2 \rangle, \langle 1,2 \rangle, \langle 3,3 \rangle\},$$
$$B = \{1, 2\},$$
$$S_1 = \{\langle 1,1 \rangle, \langle 2,2 \rangle, \langle 1,2 \rangle\},$$
$$S_2 = \{\langle 1,1 \rangle, \langle 2,2 \rangle\}.$$

Then $\mathfrak{B}_1 = \langle B, S_1 \rangle$ is a subsystem of $\mathfrak{A} = \langle A, R \rangle$, but $\mathfrak{B}_2 = \langle B, S_2 \rangle$ is not such a subsystem, for S_2 is not the relation R restricted to the set B.

We may now define scales. Let $\mathfrak{A}$ be an empirical relational system, let $\mathfrak{N}$ be a full numerical relational system, and let f be a function that maps $\mathfrak{A}$ homomorphically onto a subsystem of $\mathfrak{N}$. (If no two distinct objects in the domain of $\mathfrak{A}$ are assigned the same number, f is an isomorphic mapping.) We say then that the ordered triple $\langle \mathfrak{A}, \mathfrak{N}, f \rangle$ is a *scale*.

As should be apparent from the discussion on pp. 42–44, the type of scale is determined by the relative uniqueness of the numerical assignment f. We say, for instance, that a ratio scale is unique up to a similarity transformation. (A function ϕ from the set of real numbers to the set of real numbers is a similarity transformation if there exists a positive real number α such that, for every real number x, $\phi(x) = \alpha x$.) How may we make this uniqueness statement precise in terms of our definition of scales? The answer is reasonably simple. Let $\langle \mathfrak{A}, \mathfrak{N}, f \rangle$ be a scale and g be any function having the property that $\langle \mathfrak{A}, \mathfrak{N}, g \rangle$ is also a scale. Then $\langle \mathfrak{A}, \mathfrak{N}, f \rangle$ is a *ratio* scale if there exists a similarity transformation ϕ such that

$$g = \phi \circ f,$$

where $\circ$ denotes the composition of functions [i.e., $(\phi \circ f)(a) = \phi(f(a))$]. Note that in general f and g map $\mathfrak{A}$ into different subsystems, although both are subsystems of the same full numerical relational system. This is necessary in order not to have different numerical interpretations of the basic empirical relations. That such different interpretations are possible even for the measurement of mass is illustrated on pp. 64–66.

The definition of other types of scales is analogous to the one just given for ratio scales, and we may briefly state them by giving the restriction on the transformation ϕ. For a given scale, the transformation ϕ is frequently called an *admissible transformation*.

For *absolute* scales, ϕ must be the identity transformation, that is, $\phi(x) = x$, and we say that an absolute scale is unique up to the identity transformation.

For *interval* scales, ϕ must be a (positive) linear transformation, that is, there is a positive real number α and a number β (positive, zero, or negative) such that, for every real number x, $\phi(x) = \alpha x + \beta$. If in the measurement of temperature we wish to convert x in degrees Fahrenheit to centigrade we use the linear transformation defined by $\alpha = \frac{5}{9}$ and $\beta = -\frac{160}{9}$; that is,

$$y = \frac{5}{9}(x - 32) = \frac{5}{9}x - \frac{160}{9}.$$

Obviously every similarity transformation is a linear transformation with $\beta = 0$.

Another scale which is less well known but nevertheless useful is a *difference scale*.[3] For this scale the function ϕ is a translation transformation, that is, there is a real number β such that, for every real number x, $\phi(x) = x + \beta$. The assignment of numbers on a difference scale is unique up to an additive constant.

Still another type of scale is one which is *arbitrary except for order*. Moh's hardness scale, according to which minerals are ranked in regard to hardness as determined by a scratch test, and the Beaufort wind scale, whereby the strength of a wind is classified as calm, light air, light breeze, etc., are examples. We define them as follows. For *ordinal* scales ϕ must be a monotone transformation. Rather

than define monotone transformations directly, it is convenient first to define monotone increasing and monotone decreasing transformations. A function ϕ is a *monotone increasing transformation* if and only if for all numbers x and y in the domain of ϕ, if $x < y$, then $\phi(x) < \phi(y)$. Obviously every linear transformation is a monotone increasing transformation on the set of all real numbers. The squaring function, that is, the function ϕ such that

$$\phi(x) = x^2, \qquad \text{Eq. 2}$$

is not a linear transformation but is monotone increasing on the set of nonnegative real numbers. Notice that it does not have this property on the set of all real numbers for $-5 < 4$ but

$$\phi(-5) = 25 > 16 = \phi(4).$$

It is important to realize that a monotone increasing transformation need not be definable by some simple equation like Eq. 2. For example, consider the set

$$A = \{1, 3, 5, 7\}$$

and let ϕ be the function defined on A such that

$$\phi(1) = -5,$$
$$\phi(3) = 5,$$
$$\phi(5) = 289,$$
$$\phi(7) = 993.$$

Clearly ϕ is monotone increasing on A but does not satisfy any simple equation.

A function ϕ is a *monotone decreasing transformation* if and only if for all numbers x and y in the domain of ϕ, if $x < y$, then $\phi(x) > \phi(y)$. Two examples of monotone decreasing transformations on the set of all real numbers are

$$\phi(x) = -x$$

and

$$\phi(x) = -x^3 + 2.$$

As another instance, consider the set A again, and let ϕ be defined on A such that

3. As far as we know this terminology was first suggested by Donald Davidson.

$$\phi(1) = 6,$$
$$\phi(3) = 4,$$
$$\phi(5) = 2,$$
$$\phi(7) = -10.$$

Obviously ϕ is monotone decreasing on A.

It will be noted that monotone transformations are simply transformations that are either monotone increasing or monotone decreasing. Although we have characterized ordinal scales in terms of monotone transformations, in practice it is often convenient to consider only monotone increasing or monotone decreasing transformations, but this restriction is mainly motivated by hallowed customs and practices rather than by considerations of empirical fact.

Numbers are also sometimes used for *classification*. For example, in some states the first number on an automobile license indicates the county in which the owner lives. The assignment of numbers in accordance with such a scale may be arbitrary except for the assignment of the same number to people in the same county and distinct numbers to people in distinct counties.

The weakest scale is one for which numbers are used simply to name an object or person. The assignment is completely arbitrary. Draft numbers and the numbers of football players are examples of this sort of measurement. Such scales are usually called *nominal* scales.

For classificatory and nominal scales, ϕ is required to be only a one-one transformation.

In addition to these classical scale types, four of which were originally proposed by Stevens (33) [Ch. 1 in this book], another type may be mentioned: *hyperordinal scales*. These scales are similar to the ordered metric scales proposed by Coombs (17) and are characterized by transformations (called *hypermonotone*) which preserve first differences. More formally, a function ϕ is a *hypermonotone (increasing) transformation* if and only if ϕ is a monotone transformation, and for every x, y, u, and v in the domain of ϕ, if

$$x - y < u - v,$$

then

$$\phi(x) - \phi(y) < \phi(u) - \phi(v).$$

Naturally every linear transformation is a hypermonotone increasing transformation, but the converse is not true. Consider for example,

$$A = \{1, 2, 4, 8\}$$

and the function ϕ such that

$$\phi(1) = 1,$$
$$\phi(2) = 2,$$
$$\phi(4) = 5,$$
$$\phi(8) = 15.$$

Clearly ϕ is hypermonotone increasing but not linear on A. Various methods of measuring sensation intensities or utility yield hyperordinal scales.

There is, strictly speaking, a nondenumerable infinity of types of scales which are characterized by various groups of numerical transformations, but most of them are not of any real empirical significance. Also, it is possible to extend the notion of measurement to relational systems like lattices and partial orderings which cannot be represented numerically in any natural way. (Such an extension is urged in Coombs, Raiffa, & Thrall (19).)

By way of summary and to point out the major differences with current usage, the following aspects of the uniqueness question should be noted. Numerical assignments and scales are two different entities: the first is a function that maps an empirical system homomorphically onto a numerical system; the second is a triple, one of whose terms is a numerical assignment. If only the numerical assignment is known, its scale type or degree of uniqueness cannot be determined. To determine its uniqueness, we need to know the scale, which means that we need to know both an empirical relational system and a full numerical relational system. From a knowledge of the scale, we can, at least theoretically, infer precisely what the uniqueness properties of the numerical assignment are. In general, it should be noted that if the full numerical system is changed, then the numerical assignment will have quite different uniqueness properties, despite the fact that the empirical relational system may be unchanged. Therefore, when we speak of the uniqueness properties of a numerical assignment or equivalently of the admissible numerical assignments, it must always be relative to an explicit or implicit scale.

Some writers of measurement theory appear to define scales in terms of the existence of certain empirical operations. Thus interval scales are described in terms of the existence of an empirical operation which permits the subject (observer or experimenter) to compare intervals and to indicate in some way whether or not they are equal. In the present formulation of scale type, no mention is made of the kinds of "direct" observations or empirical relations that exist (in the empirical relational system). Scale type is defined entirely in terms of the class of numerical assignments which map a given empirical system homomorphically onto a subsystem of the same full numerical system. If in a given instance these numerical assignments are related by a linear transformation, then we have an interval scale. Precisely what empirical operations are involved in the empirical system is of no consequence. It may contain operations that permit the subject to compare intervals "directly," or the operations may be considerably more subtle.

One merit in this approach is that it takes away some of the implications generally associated with the question of scale type. For example, instead of asking how we know certain intervals are "really" equal, we ask if all the admissible numerical assignments are related by a linear transformation.

EXTENSIVE AND INTENSIVE PROPERTIES

Following Campbell (12), most measurement theorists distinguish between quantities (or extensive properties) and qualities (or intensive properties) and between fundamental and derived measurement. Campbell defines these terms essentially as follows. Quantities are properties for each of which there exists an empirical operation similar to the arithmetical operation of addition. Qualities are characterized by an absence of this additive operation. Measurement is fundamental if it involves no previous measurement (13, p. 14). If it does, it is derived. It should be added that measurement, for Campbell, implies obtaining at least an interval (or possibly a ratio) scale.

The relationship that Campbell attributes to these two pairs of terms leads to another (implicit) definition of fundamental measurement. Only quantities, he maintains, are amenable to fundamental measurement. Frequently, therefore, Campbell implicitly defines fundamental measurement in terms of the existence of an additive operation. Thus, in his discussion of temperature measurements, he concludes that such measurements cannot be fundamental since "there is no physical process of addition for temperature" (12, p. 396). Eight years later Campbell says, in regard to temperature, "...the temperature which is actually employed in physics is, in principle, as arbitrary and empirical as the hardness employed in mineralogy" (13, p. 119).

More recent writers (e.g. 14; 25) have tended to follow the essential position developed by Campbell (either that fundamental measurement *is* the measurement of extensive properties or, more precisely, that it can be performed only on extensive properties).

It is of historical interest to note that a complete and rigorous set of axioms for extensive properties was given as early as 1901 by Hölder. His axioms specify, among other things, precisely the properties the addition operation is to have [pp. 64–66]. The search for fundamental scales in psychology has frequently been identified with the search for an additive operation. (Some notable exceptions are 27; 34; 41.) Since it is generally recognized that additive operations are so far almost nonexistent in psychology, it has been suggested that fundamental scales of mental tests will occur only when we have direct observation of underlying physiological phenomena (15).

Since we attach no special virtue to the existence or nonexistence of an additive operation, we shall not attempt to give a more formal definition of the extensive-intensive distinction. In the next section, however, we give a definition of derived measurement. Our definition of fundamental measurement should be evident from the preceding sections. We may state it explicitly as follows. A function that maps an empirical relational system $\mathfrak{A}$ homomorphically onto a numerical relational system is said to be a *fundamental numerical assignment* for the empirical system $\mathfrak{A}$. In other words, if $\langle \mathfrak{A}, \mathfrak{R}, f \rangle$ is a scale, then the function f is a fundamental numerical assignment for the empirical system $\mathfrak{A}$. And, finally, *fundamental measurement* of set A with respect to the empirical system $\mathfrak{A}$ involves the establishment of a fundamental numerical assignment for $\mathfrak{A}$; in other words, it involves the establishment of a representation theorem for $\mathfrak{A}$. Note that to establish a fundamental numerical assignment for $\mathfrak{A}$ it is obviously necessary and sufficient to find just one numerical system homomorphic to $\mathfrak{A}$.

The fact that fundamental measurement procedures exist that are not based on an addition operation but that lead to ratio (interval or ordinal) scales is amply demonstrated [on pp. 51–56]. Furthermore, [on pp. 66–73] it will be evident (we hope) that the specification of the meaningful functional relationships between scales requires only a knowledge of the relevant scale types (the admissible transformations) but does not require a knowledge of the relations that are involved in the corresponding empirical or numerical relational systems.

General Theory of Derived Measurement

The preceding section has been concerned with the general theory of fundamental measurement. Fundamental measurement of a set A is always with respect to an empirical system $\mathfrak{A}$. (A scale $\langle \mathfrak{A}, \mathfrak{R}, f \rangle$ we shall henceforth call a *fundamental* scale.)

In contrast, derived measurement does not depend on an empirical relational system directly but on other numerical assignments. The classic example of a derived measurement is that of density defined as the ratio of mass to volume.

The central issue for a theory of derived measurement is the status of the two basic problems of fundamental measurement, the representation and uniqueness problems.

THE REPRESENTATION PROBLEM

We began the discussion of the representation problem for fundamental measurement by introducing the notion of an empirical relational system. In derived measurement the role of that concept is played by the concept of what we shall call a *derived measurement system* $\mathfrak{B} = \langle B, f_1, \ldots, f_n \rangle$ where B is a nonempty set of objects and $f_1, \ldots, f_n$ are numerical-valued functions defined on B or on Cartesian products of B with itself. Thus in the case of density, $\mathfrak{B}$ would be the triple $\langle B, m, V \rangle$, where m is the mass function and V is the volume function. In the case of pair comparison methods of scaling, the derived measurement system is a couple $\mathfrak{B} = \langle B, p \rangle$ such that p is defined on $B \times B$ and for all a, b in B, $0 < p_{ab} < 1$, $p_{ab} + p_{ba} = 1$, and $p_{aa} = \frac{1}{2}$. The usual interpretation of p_{ab} is that it is the relative frequency with which a is preferred to or is, in some sense, greater than b. A number of derived measures defined in terms of $\langle B, p \rangle$ have been considered in the literature; these measures are variously interpreted, sometimes as measures of utility, often as measures of response strength.

Our approach to the representation problem is to define, in terms of derived measurement systems, *derived scales*. Let $\mathfrak{B} = \langle B, f_1, \ldots, f_n \rangle$ be a derived measurement system, let g be a numerical-valued function on B (or Cartesian products of B with itself), and let R be a relation between $f_1, \ldots, f_n$ and g. We say that the triple $\langle \mathfrak{B}, R, g \rangle$ is a *derived scale*, R is the *representing relation* for the scale, and g is the *derived numerical assignment*. In most cases R is defined by an equation.

To make the ideas clearer, let us consider two examples, beginning with density. As we have already said, $\mathfrak{B} = \langle B, m, V \rangle$ is the derived measurement of density and the representing relation R is defined by

$$R(m, V, d) \qquad \text{Eq. 3}$$

if and only if for every a in B

$$d(a) = \frac{m(a)}{V(a)}.$$

The triple $\langle \mathfrak{B}, R, d \rangle$ is then the derived scale of density. The particularly simple form of the representing relation R for density is deceptive. The definition of Eq. 3 is an equation explicitly defining d in terms of m and V. Matters are not always this simple, as our second example will show.

Let $\mathfrak{B} = \langle B, p \rangle$ be a derived system for pair comparisons. We may define Bradley-Terry-Luce derived scales in the following manner. Let v be the derived numerical assignment of response strength and let R_1 be the representing relation such that $R_1(p, v)$ if and only if for every a and b in B

$$\frac{v(a)}{v(a) + v(b)} = p_{ab}.$$

Then $\langle \mathfrak{B}, R_1, v \rangle$ is a Bradley-Terry-Luce derived scale of response strength. First, the important point for the moment is that Eq. 4 does not explicitly define the function v in terms of p. As is evident from Eq. 4, we could determine v only up to a similarity transformation. Second it is equally clear that unless some restrictions are placed on the relative frequencies p_{ab}, the function p may not stand in the relation R_1 to any v, that is, the set of equations defined by Eq. 4 may not have a solution in terms of the unknown quantities $v(a)$, $v(b)$, etc.

From this last example it should be clear how we may formulate the representation problem for derived measurements. Given a derived system $\mathfrak{B}$ and the definition of a representing relation R, the representation problem is solved by showing that there exists a derived numerical assignment g such that $\langle \mathfrak{B}, R, g \rangle$ is a derived scale. In the case of density, the proof of the existence of g is trivial. For Bradley-Terry-Luce scales such a function does not in general exist.

We have already pointed out that more than one representation theorem may be proved for empirical relational systems of a given kind. Similarly, different representations leading to different derived scales for a given derived system may be obtained by selecting a different representing relation R.

THE UNIQUENESS PROBLEM

In the earlier discussion of fundamental scales we defined scale type in a relatively simple way. For instance, if $\langle \mathfrak{A}, \mathfrak{N}, f \rangle$ is a fundamental scale such that, for any other scale $\langle \mathfrak{A}, \mathfrak{N}, f' \rangle$, f and f' are related by a similarity transformation, then $\langle \mathfrak{A}, \mathfrak{N}, f \rangle$ is a ratio scale.

A natural analogue of this definition may be formulated for derived scales. Ratio scales are defined as follows. Let $\langle \mathfrak{B}, R, g \rangle$ be a derived scale. Then it is a *ratio scale in the narrow sense* if for any other scale $\langle \mathfrak{B}, R, g' \rangle$, g and g' are related by similarity transformation. We have specified "in the narrow sense" for the following reason. According to this definition, density is an absolute scale because for a fixed $\mathfrak{B} = \langle B, m, V \rangle$ the function d is uniquely determined. This is not true for the response strength function v for pair comparison data, as we shall see later.

The definition of the other standard scale types is an immediate generalization of that given for ratio scales. A more important problem is to distinguish other senses of uniqueness. Density may again furnish a paradigm. It is commonly said that density is a derived ratio scale, and it is not difficult to define a second sense of ratio scale that catches this idea. The basis for the idea is, of course, that if we change measurements of mass from $m(a)$

to $\alpha m(a)$ and measurements of volume from $V(a)$ to $\beta V(a)$ then we change measurements of density from $d(a)$ to $\alpha m(a)/\beta V(a)$, and the ratio α/β defines a derived similarity transformation on the density function d.

The formal definition that corresponds to this example runs as follows: let $\langle \mathfrak{B}, R, g \rangle$ be a derived scale, let $\mathfrak{B}'$ result from $\mathfrak{B}$ by applying admissible transformations to the numerical assignments of $\mathfrak{B}$. Then $\langle \mathfrak{B}, R, g \rangle$ is a *ratio scale in the wide sense* if for any scale $\langle \mathfrak{B}', R, g' \rangle$, g and g' are related by a similarity transformation. Obviously density is a ratio scale in the wide sense.

The reason for the separation between narrow and wide scale types is to distinguish between independent and dependent admissible transformations of derived numerical assignments. The narrow admissible transformations, those defined by the narrow scale types, can be performed without at the same time transforming one of the fundamental assignments in the derived system. For the wide admissible transformations this is not necessarily the case. These transformations of the derived numerical assignments may need to be accompanied by related transformations to certain fundamental numerical assignments. This property of wide scale types will be seen to be important [pp. 66–73].

POINTER MEASUREMENT

In addition to fundamental and derived measurements, a third type, called *pointer measurement*, may be noted. By pointer measurement we mean a numerical assignment (either fundamental or derived) based on the direct readings of some validated instrument. An instrument is validated if it has been shown to yield numerical values that correspond to those of some fundamental or derived numerical assignment. Consider the measurement of mass. The fundamental measurement of mass is a long and tedious operation [see pp. 64–66]. However, once this has been accomplished, there is no need to go through this procedure to determine the mass (or weight proportional

to it) of some particular object such as a steak. As every housewife knows, the weight of a steak is determined by placing it on a measuring instrument (a "scale") and then noting the deflection of the pointer. The housewife assumes, however, that the stamp of approval on the scale (by, say, the department of weights and measures) means that someone has taken the trouble to verify that the deflections of the pointer under certain "standard" conditions do indeed correspond to the values of a given fundamental or derived numerical assignment. In other words, the housewife assumes that the instrument has been validated.

To construct an instrument that will provide direct or at least quick measurement of some fundamental or derived scale, it is generally necessary to utilize some established empirical law or theory involving the fundamental or derived scale in question. In the case of mass an instrument is frequently constructed that is based on Hooke's law (the extension of a spring is proportional to the force acting on the spring) and on the law of gravity (the force exerted by an object is proportional to its mass). Once a spring has been selected that satisfies Hooke's law within the accuracy desired (under "standard" conditions of temperature, humidity, etc.), the next step is to calibrate the spring, that is, to determine what amount of mass would be required to produce each possible extension of the spring, or, equivalently, each possible deflection of the pointer attached to the spring. Generally, the calibration is performed by selecting two known weights, say 32 and 212 kg, and then spacing off 180 equal divisions between the two deflections corresponding to the two weights. If higher accuracy is required and if it is possible, further division of the "scale" is carried out.

Although the construction and use of a pointer instrument is obviously an important practical problem, it is not our purpose to treat it in detail here. There are two aspects of pointer measurements of theoretical interest, and these pertain to the two fundamental problems of measurement theory: the problem of justifying the numerical assignment, in this case the readings of the instrument, and that of specifying the uniqueness of the numerical assignment. The answer to the first problem for pointer measurement has already been given; the readings are justified by comparing them to the appropriate fundamental or derived numerical assignment. All too often in the behavioral sciences a direct reading instrument is available (and used) despite the fact that its readings are not justified; the readings do not correspond to any *known* fundamental or derived numerical assignment. On the surface it would appear that such pseudopointer instruments would be useless and their readings meaningless. Their prevalence in psychology (e.g., mental tests, questionnaires, indices), however, suggests that this conclusion may be too strong. The difficulty with rejecting out of hand pseudo-pointer instruments is that they may be converted (all too easily) into a fundamental measurement procedure yielding an absolute scale. This can be done by merely asserting first that the instrument is not intended to be a pointer instrument; it is not intended to give readings corresponding to some *known* numerical assignment. Second, the readings are based entirely on the counting operation, the readings merely referring to the number of divisions that are to the left (or right) of the pointer after each deflection. Since the counting operation can always yield a fundamental absolute scale, there can be no logical quarrel with anyone who uses this procedure to convert what would appear to be a pseudo-pointer instrument into a fundamental measuring instrument. One can, however, ask the question: what is accomplished by the use of such an instrument? Generally speaking, the answer seems to be that the instrument may be able to predict some future event of practical importance. A mental test score, for example, based on the number of correct answers may be able to predict success in college or in a job. The justification in the use of such instruments would then lie solely in the degree to which they are able to predict significant

events, not as with most "normal" fundamental measures, in the homomorphism between an empirical system and a numerical system.

The answer to the second problem, the uniqueness problem, for pointer measurement has been the source of some confusion. The uniqueness of the readings is determined by the uniqueness of the corresponding fundamental or derived numerical assignment, not, as might appear, by the method of calibrating the pointer instrument. The fact that the pointer instrument for measuring mass gives a ratio scale is not because of the equal spacing of the divisions on the dial; it would be quite possible to use a nonlinear spring and have the divisions of the dial unequally spaced without altering the scale type. On the other hand, neither is it because of the fact that two points (e.g., 32 kg and 212 kg) are generally fixed or determined by the calibration procedure. Suppose, for example, the fundamental measurement of mass yielded only an ordinal scale and the extension of the spring were monotonically related to mass. Then, although precisely the same calibration procedure could be carried out, that is, two points could be fixed and the dial divided into equally spaced divisions, the resulting readings of the instrument would nevertheless be only on an ordinal scale. Thus the scale type of a pointer instrument derives directly from the scale type of the corresponding fundamental or derived numerical assignment. As a corollary to this, it follows that merely inspecting the divisions of the dial of a pointer instrument, or even observing the calibration procedures of the instrument, does not enable one to infer the scale type of the measurements obtained from the instrument.

Examples of Fundamental Measurement

In this section some concrete examples of different empirical systems are given, and in each case solutions to the representation and uniqueness problems are exhibited. The empirical systems themselves are not necessarily of interest. Many are too restrictive in one way or another to have direct application to significant psychological situations. These systems, however, permit bringing into focus some of the essential aspects of measurement.

The proofs establishing representation and uniqueness theorems are generally long and involved. For most empirical systems, therefore, we shall have to content ourselves with simply stating the results. This means that for each empirical system described a full numerical system is stated, and then, more particularly, at least one subsystem which is a homomorphic image of the empirical system is given. The uniqueness problem is answered by giving the relationship between any two subsystems (of the full system) that are homomorphic images of the empirical system. Two proofs are given. The first proof [pp. 52–56] is relatively simple and it will serve to introduce some of the necessary terms and ideas that are generally encountered. The second proof [pp. 56–59] is considerably more difficult so that it will give some notion of the complexity of the representation problem.

There is, as was indicated previously [pp. 40–42], some degree of arbitrariness in the selection of a full numerical system for a given empirical system. In each case other full numerical systems could have been chosen and a different representation theorem established. Thus it should be emphasized that, although the representation problem is solved for each empirical system by exhibiting *one* homomorphic numerical system having certain reasonably natural and simple properties, the existence of other, perhaps equally desirable, numerical systems is not ruled out.

QUASI-SERIES

Nominal and classificatory scales are somewhat trivial examples of measurements so that we shall consider first an empirical system leading to an ordinal scale. The empirical system to be described is one that might, for example, be applicable to a lifted weight experiment in which subjects are given the weights in pairs and are instructed to indicate whether one weight of each pair seems heavier or whether they seem equally heavy.

Some useful definitions are as follows. A relational system $\mathfrak{A} = \langle A, R \rangle$ consisting of a set A and a single binary relation R is called a *binary system*. A binary system $\langle A, I \rangle$ is called a *classificatory* system if and only if I is an *equivalence relation* on A, that is, if and only if I has the following properties:

1. Reflexive: if $a \in A$, then aIa;
2. Symmetric: if $a, b \in A$ and aIb, then bIa;
3. Transitive: if $a, b, c \in A$ and if aIb, bIc, then aIc,

where $a \in A$ means that a is a member of the set A. A common example of an equivalence relation is the identity relation $=$. In psychological contexts it is convenient to think of the indifference relation or the "seems alike" relation as an equivalence relation, although there are many cases in which the transitivity property fails to hold.

We can now define a quasi-series (27).

Definition 1. The relational system $\mathfrak{A} = \langle A, I, P \rangle$ *is a* quasi-series *if and only if*

1. $\langle A, I \rangle$ *is a classificatory system*;
2. P *is a binary, transitive relation.*
3. *If* $a, b \in A$, *then exactly one of the following holds*: aPb, bPa, aIb.

If, for example, A were a set of persons, I the relation *the same height as*, and P the relation *shorter in height than*, then the relational system $\langle A, I, P \rangle$ would be a quasi-series. An important feature of a quasi-series is that the subject may be permitted to express his indifference when two simuli seem alike.

Let us assume that the quasi-series $\langle A, I, P \rangle$ is an empirical relational system, A being a certain set of stimuli and I and P being observable or empirical binary relations. Solving the representation problem for this empirical system will mean finding a (simple) homomorphic, rather than isomorphic, numerical system. If two elements a and b in A are related by I, that is, if aIb, we can reasonably expect that it will be necessary to assign the same number to both a and b. Hence the numerical assignment cannot be one-one.

One way of establishing a representation theorem for a quasi-series and at the same time dealing with the easier notion of isomorphism is to group or partition the elements of A in certain subsets. If the subsets have been selected judiciously enough, then it may be possible to establish an isomorphism between these subsets and a numerical system. All the elements within a given subset could then be assigned the same number; the numerical assignment defined on the subsets would be one-one, that is, each subset would correspond to a distinct number. To accomplish this end, we introduce the notion of I-equivalence classes.

If a is in A, then the *I-equivalence class of which a is a member* is the set of all elements b in A such that aIb. This equivalence class is denoted by $[a]$. In symbols

$$[a] = \{b \mid b \in A \ \& \ aIb\}.$$

The set of all I-equivalence classes obtainable from A is denoted by A/I. As an example, let A be the set of persons born in the United States. If I is the relation of equivalence such that aIb if and only if a and b are born in the same state, then [Abraham Lincoln] is the set of all persons born in Kentucky and [Robert Taft] the set of all persons born in Ohio. In this example there are approximately 400 million elements in A and 50 elements (corresponding to the 50 states) in the set A/I.

One of the properties of equivalence classes that is important is their property of partitioning the set A into disjoint subsets or classes. Each element of A then belongs to one and only one equivalence class. We state this property as a theorem.

Theorem 1. If $[a]$, $[b] \in A/I$ *then either* $[a] = [b]$ *or* $[a] \cap [b] = \phi$.

Proof. Assume that $[a] \cap [b] \neq \phi$. Let c be an element in both $[a]$ and $[b]$ and let a' be an arbitrary element of $[a]$. We have then aIc, bIc, and aIa' from the definition of equivalence classes. From the symmetry and transitivity of I, we infer bIa', whence

$[a] \subseteq [b]$. By an exactly similar argument $[b] \subseteq [a]$, whence $[a] = [b]$, and the theorem is proved.

Thus if each element in A/I is assigned a unique number—and this is our aim—every element of A will be associated with exactly one number. The net effect then of obtaining a numerical system isomorphic to an empirical system having A/I as its domain is to obtain the desired homomorphic numerical system for the system $\langle A, I, P \rangle$.

There is another useful property of equivalence classes which should also be apparent. If a, $b \in A$ and if aIb, then the equivalence class of a equals the equivalence class of b, and conversely. This property is also stated as a theorem.

Theorem 2. If $[a]$, $[b] \in A/I$, *then* $[a] = [b]$ *and only if* aIb.

Proof. First, assume aIb. Let a' be an arbitrary element in $[a]$. Then aIa' by the definition of $[a]$, and bIa from the symmetry of I, hence bIa'. Consequently, by definition of $[b]$, $a' \in [b]$. Since a' is an arbitrary element of $[a]$, we have then established that $[a] \subseteq [b]$. By a similar argument, it is easy to show that $[b]$ is a subset of $[a]$. Since $[a] \subseteq [b]$ and $[b] \subseteq [a]$, we conclude that $[a] = [b]$.

Next, assume $[a] = [b]$. Since $b \in [b]$, using our assumption we infer at once that $b \in [a]$, hence aIb. Q.E.D.

We next want to define a relation on the elements of A/I. So far only the relations I and P have been defined on the elements of A and obviously to establish the desired isomorphism we shall have to have a relation defined on A/I. This relationship should of course correspond in some way to the relation P. Accordingly, we define the binary relation P^* as follows.

Definition 2. $[a]P^*[b]$ *if and only if* aPb.

This definition needs some preliminary justification because it could lead to contradictions. We must rule out the possibility that for some element $a' \in [a]$, and for some element $b' \in [b]$, both $b'Pa'$ and aPb hold. The following two theorems are therefore required before we can safely proceed to use Def. 2. The first theorem asserts that if aPb, then every element in $[a]$ may be substituted for a.

Theorem 3. If aPb and $a'Ia$, then $a'Pb$.

Proof. Assume $a'Ia$ and aPb. From Assumption 3 of a quasi-series exactly one of the following must hold: $a'Ib$, bPa', and $a'Pb$. However, we cannot have $a'Ib$, since by the transitivity and symmetry property of I, $a'Ib$ and $a'Ia$ imply aIb, which contradicts our initial assumption. Furthermore, we cannot have bPa', since, by the transitivity property of P, aPb, and bPa' imply aPa', which also contradicts our initial assumption. Hence we must have $a'Pb$. Q.E.D.

Theorem 4. If aPb and $b'Ib$, then aPb'.

The proof is similar to the proof of Theorem 3.

Both theorems taken together imply that if aPb, then, for any element $a' \in [a]$ and for any element $b' \in [b]$, $a'Pb'$.

From Theorems 3 and 4 it follows that the relation P^* will not lead to inconsistencies; hence we define the relational system $\mathfrak{A}/I = \langle A/I, P^* \rangle$, which is obtained from the quasi-series $\mathfrak{A} = \langle A, I, P \rangle$. The representation problem can then be solved by establishing an isomorphism between $\langle A/I, P^* \rangle$ and an appropriate numerical relational system. The numerical relational system to be used for this purpose is called a *numerical series*. (It is not a series of numerical terms.) Consider first the definition of a *series*. A binary system $\langle A, R \rangle$ is a *series* if R has the following properties:

1. R is asymmetric in A, that is, if aRb then not bRa;
2. R is transitive in A;
3. R is connected in A, that is, if $a \neq b$, then either aRb or bRa.

By a *numerical series* we mean a binary numerical relational system $\langle N, R \rangle$ in which N is a set of real numbers and R is either the arithmetical relation *less than* or the arithmetical relation *greater than* restricted to the set N. Clearly R satisfies the properties of asymmetry, transitivity, and connectedness so that a numerical series is a series. As would be expected, we also have the following theorem.

Theorem 5. If $\langle A, I, P \rangle$ is a quasi-series then $\langle A/I, P^* \rangle$ is a series, that is, P^* is asymmetric, transitive and connected in A/I.

Theorem 5 follows directly from the definition of P^* in Def. 2 and from the properties of P and I given in the definition of the quasi-series $\langle A, I, P \rangle$.

The representation theorem for a finite or denumerable quasi-series can now be stated. Some additional restrictions are needed for the non-denumerable case.

Theorem 6 (Representation Theorem). Let the relational system $\mathfrak{A} = \langle A, I, P \rangle$ be a quasi-series where A/I is a finite or denumerable set. Then there exists a numerical series isomorphic to $\langle A/I, P^* \rangle$.

Proof. We give the proof for the denumerable case. The proof for A/I finite is much simpler and is essentially a special case.

Because A/I is a denumerable set, its elements may be enumerated as $a_1, a_2, \ldots, a_n, \ldots$ (It is important to note that this is in general *not* the ordering of A/I under P^* but is rather an ordering we know exists under the hypothesis that A/I is denumerable.) We now define by induction the appropriate isomorphism function f—the induction being on the enumeration $a_1, a_2, \ldots, a_n, \ldots$. We first set

$$f(a_1) = 0,$$

and then consider a_n. There are three cases, the first two of which are very simple.

Case 1. $a_i P^* a_n$, for $i = 1, 2, \ldots, n-1$. Then set

$$f(a_n) = n.$$

Case 2. $a_n P^* a_i$, for $i = 1, 2, \ldots, n-1$. Here set

$$f(a_n) = -n.$$

Case 3. There are integers i and j less than n such that $a_i P^* a_n P^* a_j$. Define

$$a_n^* = \max \{a_i \mid a_i P^* a_n \text{ \& } i < n\}$$
$$b_n^* = \min \{a_j \mid a_n P^* a_j \text{ \& } j < n\}.$$

The maximum and minimum are with respect to the ordering P^*, for example, a_n^* is such that $a_n^* P^* a_n$ and for every $i < n$ if $a_i \neq a_n^*$

then $a_i P^* a_n^*$. The existence of a unique greatest lower bound a_n^* just before a_n under P^* and somewhere before a_n in the enumeration $a_1, a_2, \ldots, a_n, \ldots$, and the similar existence of the unique least upper bound b_n^* depends on all the axioms for a series as well as the fact that the number of elements of A/I before a_n in the enumeration $a_1, a_2, \ldots a_n, \ldots$ is finite. If P^* is not connected, there could be two elements a_n^* and a_n^{**} satisfying the condition that they both preceded a_n in the ordering P^* and nothing else was between each of them and a_n under the ordering P^*. Similar difficulties could ensue if either transitivity or asymmetry were dropped as conditions on P^*. On the other hand, the finiteness of the number of elements a_i, for $i < n$, is necessary to establish that at least one maximal a_n^* and one minimal b_n^* exist.

At this point we need to use the fact that the rational numbers are also denumerable and thus may be enumerated as $r_1, r_2, \ldots, r_n, \ldots$. We define $f(a_n)$ as a rational number for each a_n, and more particularly, for Case 3, we define $f(a_n)$ as the first r_i between $f(a_n^*)$ and $f(b_n^*)$ in our enumeration of the rational numbers; if $f(a_n^*) < f(b_n^*)$ and $f(a_n^*) \geqslant f(b_n^*)$, we set $f(a_n) = 0$. (The existence of r_i for $f(a_n^*) < f(b_n^*)$ follows immediately from the fact that between any two rational numbers there exists another rational number.)

We want to show that this second possibility —$f(a_n^*) \geqslant f(b_n^*)$—leads to absurdity and thereby establish at the same time that

$$a_i P^* a_j \text{ if and only if } f(a_i) < f(a_j). \quad \text{Eq. 5}$$

Let a_n be the first element in our enumeration for which, for $i, j < n$, Eq. 5 does not hold. Thus Eq. 5 holds for $i, j < n-1$, and the failure must be due to $i = n-1$ or $j = n-1$. Now a_{n-1} must follow under one of the three cases. Clearly, if it falls under Case 1 or 2, Eq. 5 is satisfied. Consider now Case 3. Because a_{n-1}^* and b_{n-1}^* precede a_{n-1} in the enumeration and because by definition of a_{n-1}^* and b_{n-1}^*, together with the transitivity of P^*, we must have $a_{n-1}^* P^* b_{n-1}^*$, it follows from Eq.

5 that $f(a_{n-1}^*) < f(b_{n-1}^*)$. But then by definition of $f(a_{n-1})$, we have

$$f(a_{n-1}^*) < f(a_{n-1}) < f(b_{n-1}^*),$$

and also $a_{n-1}^* P^* a_{n-1} P^* b_{n-1}^*$ and, contrary to our supposition, Eq. 5 holds for a_{n-1}. Thus Eq. 5 holds for every n, and our theorem is established. (Note that the one-one character of f follows at once from Eq. 5.) Q.E.D.

To complete the solution of the representation problem for quasi-series, two definitions are needed to characterize necessary and sufficient conditions for an infinite quasi-series which is not finite or denumerable to be numerically representable. The classical example to show that additional restrictions are needed is the lexicographic ordering of the set of all ordered pairs of real numbers. The ordering P is defined as follows for any real numbers x, y, u, and v.

$$\langle x, y \rangle P \langle u, v \rangle$$

if and only if

$$x < u \text{ or } (x = u \text{ and } y < v).$$

The proof that the set of pairs of real numbers under the ordering P cannot be represented as a numerical series we leave as an exercise.

One definition is needed. Let the binary system $\mathfrak{A} = \langle A, R \rangle$ be a series and let B be a subset of A. Then B is *order-dense in* $\mathfrak{A}$ if and only if for every a and b in A and not in B there is a c in B such that aRc and cRb. Speaking loosely in terms of sets rather than relational systems, the set of rational numbers is a subset that is order-dense in the real numbers with respect to the natural ordering less than. Observe that the notions just defined could have been defined for arbitrary relational systems $\mathfrak{A} = \langle A, R \rangle$, which are not necessarily series, but then certain relational systems which are not dense in any intuitive sense would turn out to be dense under the definition. A simple example is the system $\langle N, \leqslant \rangle$ where N is the set of positive integers.

Theorem 7 (*Representation Theorem*). *Let the structure* $\mathfrak{A} = \langle A, I, P \rangle$ *be a quasi-series* *in which A/I is an infinite set. Then a necessary and sufficient condition for the existence of a numerical series isomorphic to $\langle A/I, P^* \rangle$ is the existence of a denumerable subset B of A/I which is order dense in $\langle A/I, P^* \rangle$.*

The proof of this theorem is omitted. A proof may be found in Birkhoff (7, p. 32). It may be remarked that the proof of necessity requires the axiom of choice. Economists and others interested in applications of theorems like Theorem 7 to utility theory or demand analysis often deal with questions of continuity concerning the isomorphism function. Various sufficient topological conditions are given in Debreu (23). He does not treat necessary conditions, which would require an extremely difficult topological classification of quasi-series.

Theorems 6 and 7 together give necessary and sufficient conditions for any quasi-series to be representable by a numerical series. We now turn to the simple solution of the uniqueness problem for quasi-series.

Theorem 8 (Uniqueness Theorem). Let $\mathfrak{A} = \langle A, I, P \rangle$ be a quasi-series. Then any two numerical series isomorphic to $\mathfrak{A}/I$ are related by a monotone transformation.

Proof. Let $\langle N_1, R_1 \rangle$ and $\langle N_2, R_2 \rangle$ be two numerical series isomorphic to $\mathfrak{A}/I$. (R_1 and R_2 may each be either the relation $<$ or the relation $>$.) We want to find a function ϕ such that the domain of ϕ is N_1 and the range is N_2, that is

$$D(\phi) = N_1$$
$$R(\phi) = N_2$$

and for every x, y in N_1, if xR_1y then $\phi(x)R_2\phi(y)$, that is, we want a monotonic function which maps N_1 onto N_2.

Let f_1 and f_2 be two functions satisfying the hypothesis, that is, f_1 maps $\langle A/I, P^* \rangle$ isomorphically onto the numerical series $\langle N_1, R_1 \rangle$ and f_2 maps $\langle A/I, P^* \rangle$ isomorphically onto the numerical series $\langle N_2, R_2 \rangle$. Consider the domains and ranges of f_1 and f_2 and their inverses:

$$D(f_1) = D(f_2) = R(f_1{}^{-1}) = R(f_2{}^{-1}) = A/I$$
$$R(f_1) = D(f_1{}^{-1}) = N_1$$
$$R(f_2) = D(f_2{}^{-1}) = N_2.$$

Consider then the function $f_2 \circ f_1{}^{-1}$. Has it the desired properties?

$$D(f_2 \circ f_1{}^{-1}) = N_1$$
$$R(f_2 \circ f_1{}^{-1}) = N_2.$$

Suppose x, $y \in N_1$ and xR_1y. Then $f_1{}^{-1}(x)P^* f_1{}^-(y)$; hence from the definition of $f_2, f_2(f_1{}^{-1}(x))R_2 f_2(f_1{}^{-1}(y))$, that is, $(f_2 \circ f_1{}^{-1})(x) R_2(f_2 \circ f_1{}^{-1})(y)$, which completes the proof.

We have shown that given any two isomorphic numerical series they are related by a monotone transformation. That in general the numerical series are not related by any stronger transformation can be easily proved by a counterexample.

SEMIORDERS

In Luce (29) the concept of a semiorder is introduced as a natural and realistic generalization of quasi-series. The intuitive idea is that in many situations judgments of indifference concerning some attribute of stimuli, like the pitch or loudness of tones or the utility of economic goods, is not transitive. Thus a subject may judge tone a to be just as loud as tone b and tone b to be just as loud as tone c but find to his surprise that he judges tone a definitely louder than tone c.

In his original paper Luce uses a system consisting of two binary relations, that is, the kind of system used above for quasi-series. In Scott & Suppes (32) Luce's axioms are simplified and only a binary system is used. The latter analysis is considered here.

Definition 3. A semiorder is a binary system $\mathfrak{A} = \langle A, P \rangle$ in which the following three axioms are satisfied for all a, b, c, d in A:

1. *Not aPa;*
2. *If aPb and cPd then either aPd or cPb;*
3. *If aPb and bPc then either aPd or dPc.*

In the case of loudness, P is interpreted as *definitely louder than*. To make the last two axioms more intuitive, we may illustrate the third axiom by a simple geometrical picture. We place a, b, and c on the line such that they are separated by at least one *jnd*. The axiom asserts that for any element d it is then the case that either aPd or dPc. The four different kinds of positions d can have are shown as d_1, d_2, d_3, and d_4 in the drawing below. It is evident that for d_1 and d_2 we have d_1Pc and d_2Pc; and for d_3 and d_4 the other alternative holds, namely, aPd_3 and aPd_4.

The indifference relation I can be defined in terms of P as follows.

Definition 4. aIb if and only if not aPb and not bPa.

In contrast to a quasi-series, the indifference relation I in a semiorder is not an equivalence relation. It lacks the transitivity property. However, we may define a relation E in terms of I which is an equivalence relation.

Definition 5. aEb if and only if for every c in A, aIc if and only if bIc.

The fact that E is an equivalence relation, that it is reflexive, symmetric, and transitive can easily be verified. As in the case of a quasi-series we introduce a relation P^{**} corresponding to P defined on the E-equivalence classes of A, that is, on the elements of A/E.

Definition 6. $[a]P^{**}[b]$ if and only if aPb.

To justify Def. 6, theorems corresponding to Theorems 3 and 4 are needed. They are easily proved.

Theorem 9. If aPc and aEb, then bPc.

Theorem 10. If cPa and aEb then cPb.

Unlike the relation P^* in Def. 2, the relation P^{**} does not have the connectedness property. In fact, we may define the relation I^* as follows.

Definition 7. $[a]I^*[b]$ if and only if aIb.

It may be seen that $[a]I^*[b]$ does *not* imply that $[a] = [b]$ so that P^{**} is, in fact, not connected. This means that the relational system $\langle A/E, P^{**} \rangle$ is not a series and, moreover, P^{**} does not order the elements of A/E as was the case for the relation P^* and the set A/I of a quasi-series. A relation R which does order the elements of A/E can be defined in terms of P^{**} as follows.

Definition 8. $[a]R[b]$ if and only if for all $[c]$ in A/E, if $[c]P^{**}[a]$ then $[c]P^{**}[b]$, and if $[b]P^{**}[c]$ then $[a]P^{**}[c]$.

The relation R, it can be verified, is a *simple order*, that is, it is reflexive, antisymmetric ($[a]R[b]$ and $[b]R[a]$ implies $[a] = [b]$), transitive, and connected in A/E. The connection between P^{**} and R is clearer if one notices that $[a]P^{**}[b]$ implies $[a]R[b]$ but not conversely. The simple ordering property of R will be useful in the proof establishing the representation theorem. The representation problem consists of establishing an isomorphism between the relational system $\mathfrak{A}/E = \langle A/E, P^{**} \rangle$ and an appropriate numerical relational system.

In Luce (29) no representation theorem in our sense is proved for semiorders because a just noticeable difference function is introduced, which varies with the individual elements of A, that is, the jnd function is defined on A, and no fixed numerical interpretation of P and I is given which holds for all elements of A. Actually, it would be intuitively more desirable if Luce's results were the strongest possible for semiorders. Unfortunately, a stronger result than his can be proved, namely a numerical interpretation of P can be found, which has as a consequence that the jnd function is constant for all elements of A.

We turn now to the formal solution of the representation problem for semiorders. The proof is that given in Scott & Suppes (32).

The numerical relational system to be selected for the representation theorem is called a *numerical semiorder*. A binary system $\langle N, \gg_\delta \rangle$ is a *numerical semiorder* if and only if N is a set of real numbers, and the relation $\gg_\delta$ is the binary relation having the property that for all x and y in N, $x \gg_\delta y$ if and only if $x > y + \delta$. The number δ is the numerical measure of the jnd. It is easily checked that the relation $\gg_\delta$ satisfies the axioms for a semiorder and thus any numerical semiorder is a semiorder. Furthermore, it is an immediate consequence of $\gg_\delta$ that δ is positive.[4]

---

4. It is a technical point worth noting that it would not be correct to define a numerical semiorder as a triple $\langle N, \gg, \delta \rangle$ for there is nothing in $\langle A/E, P^{**} \rangle$ of which δ is the isomorphic image. Taking the course we do makes δ part of the definition of $\gg$.

The representation theorem for finite sets is as follows.

Theorem 11 (*Representation Theorem*). *Let the binary system* $\mathfrak{A} = \langle A, P \rangle$ *be a semiorder and let* A/E *be a finite set. Then* $\langle A/E, P^{**} \rangle$ *is isomorphic to some numerical semiorder.*

Proof. Under the relation R, A/E is simply ordered. Let $A/E = \{a_0, a_1, \ldots, a_n\}$ where $a_i R\, a_{i-1}$ and $a_i \neq a_{i-1}$. To simplify the notation of the proof, we set $\delta = 1$ and write $\gg$ instead of $\gg_1$. (The proof shows in fact that we may always take $\delta = 1$ if we so desire.) Define the function f as follows:

$$f(a_i) = x_i, \quad i = 0, 1, \ldots n,$$

where x_i is determined uniquely by the following two conditions:

1. If $a_i I^* a_0$, then

$$x_i = \frac{i}{i+1}.$$

2. If $a_i I^* a_j$ and $a_i P^{**} a_{j-1}$ where $j > 0$, then

$$x_i = \frac{i}{i+1} x_j + \frac{1}{i+1} x_{j-1} + 1.$$

Condition 1 holds when a_i and a_0 are separated by less than a jnd, but x_i is defined so that $x_{i-1} < x_i$. Similar remarks apply to condition 2. Note that in condition 2 the hypothesis implies that $j \leq i$. Note further that every element a_i comes under either condition 1 or 2. If for no j, $a_i P^{**} a_{j-1}$, then $a_i I^* a_0$ and condition 1 applies. Also if $a_i I^{**} a_j$ and $a_i I^{**} a_{j-1}$, we find an earlier a_j in the ordering such that $a_i P^{**} a_{j-1}$.

To show that the numerical semiorder $\langle \{x_i\}, \gg \rangle$ is an isomorphic image of $\langle A/E, P^{**} \rangle$, we must show that f is one-one and $a_i P^{**} a_j$ if and only if $x_i \gg x_j$.

The one-one property of f can be shown by proving that $x_i > x_{i-1}$. This we do by induction on i. To simplify the presentation, we give an explicit breakdown of cases.

Case 1. $a_i I^* a_0$. Then also $a_{i-1} I^* a_0$, and

$$x_i = \frac{i}{i+1} > x_{i-1} = \frac{i-1}{i}.$$

Case 2. $a_i I^* a_j$ and $a_i P^{**} a_{j-1}$ for some j.

2a. $a_{i-1} I^* a_0$. Then $x_{i-1} < 1$ and, since $x_{j-1} > x_0 = 0$, from condition 2, $x_i > 1$.

2b. $a_{i-1} P^{**} a_0$. Let a_k be the first element such that $a_{i-1} I^* a_k$ and $a_{i-1} P^{**} a_{k-1}$. By definition

$$x_{i-1} = \frac{i-1}{i} x_k + \frac{1}{i} x_{k-1} + 1.$$

We then have two subcases of subcase 2b to consider.

2b1. $j = i$. Then by virtue of condition 2

$$x_i = \frac{i}{i+1} x_i + \frac{1}{i+1} x_{i-1} + 1,$$

whence simplifying

$$x_i = x_{i-1} + i + 1,$$

and thus

$$x_i > x_{i-1}.$$

2b2. $j < i$. It is easily shown that by selection of k, $k \leq j$. We know that for this case $a_i R a_{i-1}$, $a_{i-1} R a_j$, and $a_i I^* a_j$, whence $a_{i-1} I^* a_j$ because a_{i-1} is "between" a_i and a_j (with possibly $a_j = a_{i-1}$). If $k > j$, then, from definition of R, $a_{i-1} P^{**} a_{j-1}$, which contradicts the assumption that k is the first element (in the ordering generated by R) such that $a_{i-1} I^* a_k$ and $a_{i-1} P^{**} a_{k-1}$, and so we conclude $k \leq j$.

If $k = j$, we have at once from condition 2

$$x_{i-1} = x_k - \frac{1}{i}(x_k - x_{k-1}) + 1,$$

$$x_i = x_k - \frac{1}{i+1}(x_k - x_{k-1}) + 1,$$

and, since $1/(i+1) < 1/i$, we infer that $x_i > x_{i-1}$.

If $k < j$, the argument is slightly more complex. By our inductive hypothesis $x_k < x_j$ and $x_{k-1} < x_{j-1}$, whence $x_k \leq x_{j-1}$. Now from condition 2

$$x_{i-1} < x_k + 1$$
$$x_i > x_{j-1} + 1,$$

whence $x_i > x_{j-1}+1 \geqslant x_k+1 > x_{i-1}$, and the proof that $x_{i-1} < x_i$ is complete for all cases.

The next step is to prove that, if $a_iP^{**}a_k$, then $x_i > x_k+1$. Let a_j be the first element such that $a_iI^*a_j$ and $a_iP^{**}a_{j-1}$. We have $j-1 \geqslant k$, and, in view of the preceding argument, $x_{j-1} \geqslant x_k$. But $x_{j-1}+1 < x_i$, whence $x_i > x_k+1$.

Conversely, we must show that if $x_i > x_k+1$ then $a_iP^{**}a_k$. The hypothesis, of course, implies $i > k$. Assume by way of contradiction that not $a_iP^{**}a_k$. It follows that $a_iI^*a_k$. Let a_j be the first element such that $a_iI^*a_j$; then $k \geqslant j$ and $x_k \geqslant x_j$. If $j = 0$, then $a_iI^*a_0$ and $a_kI^*a_0$ because a_iRa_k. But then $0 \leqslant x_i < 1$ and $0 \leqslant x_k < 1$, which contradicts the inequality $x_i > x_k+1$. We conclude that $j > 0$. Now $x_i < x_j+1$, but $x_k \geqslant x_j$, and thus $x_i < x_k+1$, which again is a contradiction. Q.E.D.

The proof just given is not necessarily valid for the denumerable case, and which is the strongest representation theorem that may be proved when A/E is an infinite set is an open problem.

The uniqueness problem for semiorders is complicated and appears to have no simple solution.

INFINITE DIFFERENCE SYSTEMS

A relational system $\langle A, D \rangle$ is called a *quaternary system* if D is a quaternary relation. In this section and the one following quaternary systems leading to interval scales are considered.

The notion behind the quaternary relation D is that $abDcd$ holds when the subjective (algebraic) difference between a and b is equal to or less than that between c and d. In the case of utility or value, the set A would be a set of alternatives consisting of events, objects, experiences, etc. The interpretation $abDcd$ is that the difference in preference between a and b is not greater than the difference in preference between c and d. Such an interpretation could be made, for example, if a subject having in his possession objects a and c decides that he will

not pay more money to replace a by b than he will to replace c by d, or if he does not prefer the pair a and d to the pair b and c. Similar interpretations of utility differences can be made using gambles or probability mixtures as alternatives. (A detailed analysis of a probabilistic interpretation of quaternary systems is to be found in Davidson, Suppes, & Siegel (22).) If the set A consisted of color chips, the interpretation of $abDcd$ could be that stimuli a and b are at least as similar to each other as are stimuli c and d.

The empirical relational system to be considered here is a quaternary system that is an *infinite difference system* (abbreviated as i.d. system). To define an i.d. system it is convenient to introduce certain relations defined in terms of the quaternary relation D.

Definition 9. aPb if and only if not abDaa.

For the case of utility measurement, the relation P is interpreted as a strict preference relation, a relation that is transitive and asymmetric in A.

Definition 10. AIb if and only if abDba and baDab.

The relation I is the familiar relation of indifference. Note, of course, that the expected properties (like transitivity) of the binary relations P and I cannot be proved merely on the basis of these definitions. For that purpose the axioms to be given in the definition of the i.d. system are needed.

Definition 11. abMcd if and only if abDcd, cdDab and b I c.

If we think of a, b, c, and d as points on a line, then $abMcd$ implies that the interval (a, b) equals the interval (c, d) and the points b and c coincide. Higher powers of the relation M are defined recursively.

Definition 12. abM¹cd if and only if abMcd; abM^{n+1}cd if and only if there exists e and f in A such that abM^nef and efMcd.

Again letting a, b, c, and d be points on a line, the relation abM^ncd implies that the intervals (a, b) and (c, d) are of the same length and that there are $(n-1)$ intervals of this length between b and c. More particularly consider the following diagrams:

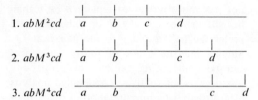

1. abM^2cd

2. abM^3cd

3. abM^4cd

The interval (a, d) under condition 1 is three times the length of the interval (a, b); under condition 2 it is four times, etc. Thus from M and its powers we may infer specific length relations. Later, when we discuss the Archimedean axiom, we shall see that the relation M enables us to establish commensurability of all differences with each other.

We are now in position to define an infinite difference system.

Definition 13. A quaternary system $\mathfrak{A} = \langle A, D \rangle$ is an infinite difference system *if and only if the following seven axioms are satisfied for every a, b, c, d, e, and f in A:*

1. *If $abDcd$ and $cdDef$, then $abDef$;*
2. *$abDcd$ or $cdDab$,*
3. *If $abDcd$, then $acDbd$,*
4. *If $abDcd$, then $dcDba$,*
5. *There is a c in A such that $acDcb$ and $cbDac$,*
6. *If aPb and not $abDcd$, then there is an e in A such that aPe, ePb, and $cdDae$,*
7. *If aPb and $abDcd$, then there are e, f in A and an n such that ceM^nfd and $ceDab$.*[5]

These axioms are essentially those given in Suppes & Winet (38). The first four axioms establish some of the elementary properties of the relation D. Axiom 1 indicates that D is transitive and Axiom 2 that it is strongly connected in A.

The last three are existence axioms and are basic to the proof of the representation and uniqueness theorems. Axiom 5 may be interpreted to mean that between any two elements in A there exists a third element in A which is a midpoint. A direct consequence of

this axiom is that the set A is infinite (in all nontrivial cases). Axiom 6 postulates a kind of continuity condition; and 7 is the Archimedean axiom. The general Archimedean principle may be formulated as follows. Let L_1 be a distance no matter how large, and let L_2 be a distance no matter how small. Then there is a positive integer n such that an nth part of L_1 is smaller than L_2. On the other hand, there is a positive integer m such that if we lay off L_2 m times on a line the resulting distance or length will be greater than L_1. In other words, any two quantities in an Archimedean system are comparable in measurement. Every system of measurement that leads to an interval or ratio scale must satisfy the Archimedean principle in some form in order for a numerical representation theorem to be proved. Axiom 7 is one appropriate formulation for the system at hand.

The numerical relational system that we shall use to establish the representation theorem for an i.d. system is called a *numerical infinite difference system*, or more simply, a *numerical i.d. system*. This numerical relational system is defined as follows. Let N be a nonempty set of real numbers closed under the formation of midpoints, that is, if x and y are in N, then $(x + y)/2$ is in N. Let Δ be the quaternary relation restricted to N such that for any real numbers x, y, z, w in N

$$xy \Delta zw$$

if and only if

$$x - y \leqslant z - w.$$

Then the quaternary system $\mathfrak{N} = \langle N, \Delta \rangle$ is a *numerical i.d. system*.

As usual we may state the representation theorem either in terms of a homomorphism or in terms of an isomorphism between empirical and numerical relational systems. To utilize this alternative, we need merely introduce the relational system $\mathfrak{A}/I = \langle A/I, D^* \rangle$ where the set A/I consists of the I-equivalence classes of A and the relation D^* is defined as follows.

Definition 14. $[a][b]D^*[c][d]$ if and only if $abDcd$.

5. We are indebted to Michael Levine for showing that the following axiom is a consequence of Axioms 1 to 3 and thus may be eliminated: if bIa or bPa and $bcDef$, then $acDef$.

Thus, using the isomorphism concept, the representation theorem for an i.d. system may now be stated.

Theorem 12 (Representation Theorem). If a quaternary system $\mathfrak{A} = \langle A, D \rangle$ is an i.d. system, then $\mathfrak{A}/I = \langle A/I, D^* \rangle$ is isomorphic to a numerical i.d. system.

The proof is omitted. (See Suppes & Winet (38), which also includes a proof of the next theorem.) For the uniqueness problem we have the following theorem.

Theorem 13 (Uniqueness Theorem). If a quaternary system $\mathfrak{A} = \langle A, D \rangle$ is an i.d. system, then any two numerical i.d. systems isomorphic to $\mathfrak{A}/I = \langle A/I, D^* \rangle$ are related by a linear transformation.

The proof of Theorem 13 is also omitted. However, we shall give the much simpler proof of a related theorem. The point of this related theorem is that as long as we restrict ourselves to the primitive and defined notions of quaternary systems it is not possible to do better than obtain measurement unique up to a linear transformation. Thus Theorem 13 cannot be improved by adding additional axioms to those given in the definition of the i.d. system. Since the proof does not depend on any of the axioms of an i.d. system, we may state it for arbitrary quaternary systems. Generalizing the numerical i.d. system slightly, a quaternary system $\mathfrak{N} = \langle N, \Delta \rangle$ is a *numerical difference system* if N is a set of real numbers and Δ is the numerical quaternary relation defined previously. We may then formulate our result.

Theorem 14. Let a quaternary system $\mathfrak{A} = \langle A, D \rangle$ be isomorphic to a numerical difference system $\mathfrak{N} = \langle N, \Delta \rangle$, and let $\mathfrak{N}' = \langle N', \Delta' \rangle$ be a numerical difference system related to $\mathfrak{N}$ by a linear transformation. Then $\mathfrak{A}$ is isomorphic to $\mathfrak{N}'$.

Proof. The proof of the theorem is very simple; it hinges upon the purely set-theoretical, axiom-free character of the definition of isomorphism. Since the relation of being isomorphic is transitive, to show that $\mathfrak{A}$ and $\mathfrak{N}'$ are isomorphic it suffices to show that $\mathfrak{N}$ and $\mathfrak{N}'$ are isomorphic.

Let f be the linear transformation from N

to N'. It is clear that f is the appropriate isomorphism function, for it is one-one, and, if for every x in N,

$$f(x) = \alpha x + \beta, \quad \alpha > 0,$$

we have the following equivalences for any x, y, u, and v in N:

$$xy \, \Delta \, uv$$

if and only if

$$x - y \leqslant u - v$$

if and only if

$$(\alpha x + \beta) - (\alpha y + \beta) \leqslant (\alpha u + \beta) - (\alpha v + \beta)$$

if and only if

$$f(x) - f(y) \leqslant f(u) - f(v)$$

if and only if

$$f(x) f(y) \, \Delta' \, f(u) f(v). \qquad \text{Q.E.D.}$$

One interpretation of infinite difference systems is of sufficiently general importance to be emphasized. This interpretation is closely related to classical scaling methods for pair comparisons. . . . Subjects are asked to choose between alternatives or stimuli, and they are asked to make this choice a number of times. There are many situations—from judging the hue of colors to preference among economic bundles—in which subjects vacillate in their choices. The probability p_{ab} that a will be chosen over b may be estimated from the relative frequency with which a is so chosen. From inequalities of the form $p_{ab} \leqslant p_{cd}$ we then obtain an interpretation of the quaternary relation $abDcd$. Thus the representation and uniqueness theorems proved here have direct application to pair comparison methods.

An important problem for infinite difference systems is the idealization involved in the transitivity of the indifference relation I, which is a consequence of the first four axioms. The question naturally arises: can infinite difference systems be generalized in the way that semiorders generalize series or simple ordering? Surprisingly enough, mathematical work on this problem goes back to an early paper of Norbert Wiener (43). Unfortunately, Wiener's paper is extremely difficult to read: it is written in the notation of the latter two volumes of Whitehead and Russell's *Principia Mathematica*,[6] no clear axioms are formulated, and no proofs are given. On the other hand, the focus of the paper is the important problem of explicitly considering nontransitivities that arise from subliminal phenomena. A discussion of similar problems in economic contexts is to be found in the interesting series of papers of W. E. Armstrong (3, 4, 5). An exact axiomatic reconstruction of Wiener's ideas is to be found in the dissertation of Muriel Wood Gerlach (24); her axioms are too complicated to state here. Moreover, they suffer from not making distinguishability of stimuli a probabilistic concept, although a probabilistic interpretation similar to that just given for the quaternary relation D is also possible for her primitive concepts.

FINITE EQUAL DIFFERENCE SYSTEMS

Since the infinite difference systems of the preceding section are not easily realized in many empirical situations, it is desirable to have at hand a finite empirical relational system that yields the same measurement results. To this end we now develop briefly the theory of finite equal difference systems, abbreviated as f.d. systems (21; 36, Chapter 12). The intuitive idea is that we select a finite set of stimuli so that when we order the stimuli according to some characteristic, such as hue, pitch, or utility, two stimuli adjacent in the ordering will have the same difference in intensity as any two other such adjacent stimuli. It is to be emphasized that no sort of

6. It is of some historical interest to note that a rather elaborate theory of measurement is given in Vol. 3 of *Principia Mathematica*, but as far as we know it has had little impact on the theory of measurement— actually with good reason, for the developments there are more closely connected with classical mathematical topics like Eudoxus' theory of proportion and the construction of the real numbers than with any formal questions which arise in an empirical context.

underlying physical scale need be assumed to apply this theory. It is not a psychophysical theory of measurement.

One new elementary definition is needed.

Definition 15. aJb if and only if aPb and for all c in A if aPc, then either bIc or bPc.

The indifference relation I and the strict preference relation P in Def. 15 are defined in Defs. 9 and 10. The interpretation of J is that aJb holds when a is an immediate predecessor of b with respect to the relation P. In the following definition of an f.d. system the final axiom referring to the relation J replaces the three existence axioms that were used to characterize an infinite difference system. Note that the first four axioms below are just the same as those for i.d. systems.

Definition 16. A finite equal difference system *is a quaternary system* $\mathfrak{A} = \langle A, D \rangle$ *in which A is a finite set, and for every a, b, c, d, e, and f in A the following five axioms are satisfied.*

1. *If $abDcd$ and $cdDef$, then $abDef$;*
2. *$abDcd$ or $cdDab$;*
3. *If $abDcd$, then $acDbd$;*
4. *If $abDcd$, then $dcDba$;*
5. *If aJb and cJd, then $abDcd$ and $cdDab$.*

In Axiom 5 the equal spacing assumption is imposed.

For the corresponding numerical relational system we have a *numerical f.d. system* which we define as follows. Let N be a finite, nonempty set of numbers such that differences between numbers adjacent under the natural ordering $<$ are equal, and let Δ be the numerical quaternary relation already defined restricted to N. Then the quaternary system $\mathfrak{N} = \langle N, \Delta \rangle$ is a *numerical f.d. system.*

We may now state representation and uniqueness theorems for finite equal difference systems.

Theorem 15 (Representation Theorem). If a quaternary system $\mathfrak{A} = \langle A, D \rangle$ *is an f.d. system, then $\mathfrak{A}/I = \langle A/I, D^* \rangle$ is isomorphic to a numerical f.d. system.*

Theorem 16 (Uniqueness Theorem). If a quaternary system $\mathfrak{A} = \langle A, D \rangle$ *is an f.d.*

system, then any two numerical f.d. systems isomorphic to $\mathfrak{A}/I$ are related by a linear transformation.

One might be tempted to conjecture that the first four axioms of Def. 16 would characterize all finite difference systems for which a numerical representation could be found (the representations of a given system would not necessarily be related by a linear transformation). The resulting theory would then represent one formalization of Coombs' ordered metric scale. However, Scott and Suppes (32) have proved that the theory of all representable finite difference systems is not characterized by these four axioms and, worse still, cannot be characterized by any simple finite list of axioms.

The f.d. systems are not as artificial or as impractical as they may seem. One theory for approximating these systems is to be found in Davidson, Suppes, & Siegel (22, Chapter 2). However, these systems can have more general usefulness if they are used to establish a "standard set" of stimuli. In the case of tones, for example, a set of tones may be selected in a successive manner so that the set satisfies Axiom 5. If this standard set of tones also satisfies the remaining four axioms, then we know from Theorem 15 that the tones may be assigned numbers that are on an interval scale. Arbitrary tones that are not in the standard set but that satisfy the first four axioms may then be located within intervals bounded by adjacent tones in the standard set. This means that by decreasing the spacing between the standard tones any arbitrary tone may be measured within any desired degree of accuracy. This is in fact what a chemist does in using a standard set of weights and an equal arm balance to determine the weight of an unknown object. His accuracy of measurement is limited by the size of the smallest interval between the standard weights or, if he also uses a rider, by the gradations on the rider.

Other relational systems closely related to f.d. systems may appropriately be mentioned at this point. Among the simplest and most appealing are the *bisection* systems $\mathfrak{A} = \langle A, B \rangle$, where B is a ternary relation on the set A with the interpretation that $B(a, b, c)$ if and only if b is the midpoint of the interval between a and c. The method of bisection, which consists in finding the midpoint b, has a long history in psychophysics. The formal criticism of many experiments in which it has been used is that the variety of checks necessary to guarantee isomorphism with an appropriate numerical system is not usually performed. For example, if $B(a, b, c)$ implies that aPb and bPc, where P is the usual ordering relation, then from the fact that $B(a, b, c)$, $B(b, c, d)$, and $B(c, d, e)$ we should be able to infer $B(a, c, e)$. But the explicit test of this inference is too seldom made. Without it there is no real guarantee that a subjective scale for a stimulus dimension has been constructed by the method of bisection.

Because of the large number of axiomatic analyses already given in this section, we shall not give axioms for bisection systems. The axioms in any case are rather similar to those of Def. 16, and the formal connection between the difference relation D and the ternary bisection relation B should be obvious:

$$B(a, b, c)$$

if and only if

$$ab\,Dbc \text{ and } bc\,Dab.$$

As an alternative to giving general axioms for bisection systems, it may be of some interest to look at the problem of characterizing these systems in a somewhat different manner, namely, by simply listing for a given number n of stimuli the relations that must hold. In perusing this list it should be kept in mind that we assume that bisection systems have the same property of equal spacing possessed by f.d. systems. As examples, let us consider the cases of $n = 5$ and $n = 6$.

For $n = 5$; let $A = \{a, b, c, d, e\}$ with the ordering $aPbPcPdPe$. We then have exactly four instances of the bisection relation, namely, $B(a, b, c)$, $B(b, c, d)$, $B(c, d, e)$, and $B(a, c, e)$.

For $n = 6$, we may add the element f to A with the ordering $aPbPcPdPePf$. To the four instances of the bisection relation for $n = 5$, we now add two more, namely, $B(d, e, f)$ and $B(b, d, f)$. We may proceed in this manner for any n to characterize completely the bisection system with n stimuli, none of which is equivalent with respect to the property being studied. Establishing the representation and uniqueness theorems is then a trivial task. The disadvantages of this approach to characterizing those relational systems for which numerical representation theorems exist are twofold. In the first place, in contrast to the statement of general axioms, the listing of instances does not give us general insight into the structure of the systems. Second, for systems of measurement that have a more complicated or less sharply defined structure than bisection systems, the listing of instances can become tedious and awkward—semiorders provide a good example.

EXTENSIVE SYSTEMS

We consider next a relational system leading to a ratio scale. Since this relational system contains an operation ∘ that corresponds to an addition operation, we may justifiably call this system an *extensive system* [see pp. 47–48]. The axioms that we shall use to define an extensive system (Suppes, 35) are similar to those first developed by Hölder (28). Hölder's axioms, however, are more restrictive than necessary in that they require the homomorphic numerical relational systems to be nondenumerable (and nonfinite). The present set of axioms applies both to denumerable and nondenumerable but infinite relational systems.

Definition 17. An extensive system $\langle A, R, \circ \rangle$ *is a relational system consisting of the binary relation R, the binary operation ∘ from $A \times A$ to A, and satisfying the following six axioms for a, b, c in A.*

    1. *If aRb and bRc, then aRc;*
    2. $(a \circ b) \circ cRa \circ (b \circ c)$;
    3. *If aRb, then $a \circ cRc \circ b$;*

    4. *If not aRb, then there is a c in A such that $aRb \circ c$ and $b \circ cRa$;*
    5. *Not $a \circ bRa$;*
    6. *If aRb, then there is a number n such that $bRna$ where the notation na is defined recursively as follows: $1a = a$ and $na = (n-1) a \circ a$.*

It can be shown that the relation R is a weak ordering (it is transitive and strongly connected) of the elements of A. If A is a set of weights, then the interpretation of aRb is that a is either less heavy than b or equal in heaviness to b. The interpretation of $a \circ b$ for weights is simply the weight obtained by combining the two weights a and b, for example, by placing both on the same side of an equal arm balance. Axiom 2 establishes the associativity property of the operation ∘. Axiom 5 implies that mass, for example, is always positive. This axiom together with the order properties of R and the definition of ∘ as an operation from $A \times A$ to A imply that the set A is infinite. Axiom 6 is another form of the Archimedean principle mentioned earlier.

Again we introduce the indifference relation I so that A may be partitioned into equivalence classes.

Definition 18. aIb if and only if aRb and bRa. Corresponding to R and ∘, we define R^* and ∘* which are defined for the elements of A/I.

Definition 19. $[a]R^*[b]$ if and only if aRb.

Definition 20. $[a]\circ^*[b] = [a \circ b]$.

For the representation theorem we seek now a numerical relational system isomorphic to $\langle A/I, R^*, \circ^* \rangle$. The numerical system we shall use for this purpose is defined as follows. Let $\langle N, \leqslant, + \rangle$ be a numerical relational system in which N is a nonempty set of positive real numbers closed under addition and subtraction of smaller numbers from larger numbers, that is, if $x, y \in N$ and $x > y$, then $(x+y) \in N$ and $(x-y) \in N$. Let $\leqslant$ be the usual numerical binary relation and $+$ the usual numerical binary operation of addition, both relations restricted to the set N. Then $\langle N, \leqslant, + \rangle$ is a *numerical extensive system.* An example of a numerical extensive system is the system consisting of the set of positive integers (together with $\leqslant$ and $+$).

The representation and uniqueness theorems can now be expressed as follows.

Theorem 17 (Representation Theorem). If a relational system $\mathfrak{A} = \langle A, R, \circ \rangle$ *is an extensive system, then* $\mathfrak{A}/I = \langle A/I, R^*, \circ^* \rangle$ *is isomorphic to a numerical extensive system.*

The proof of this theorem, which we omit (see 35), consists in defining the numerical assignment f as follows:

$$f([a]) = \text{the greatest lower}$$
$$\text{bound of } S([a], [e]),$$

where $S([a], [e])$, a set of rational numbers, is given by

$$S([a], [e]) = \left\{ \frac{m}{n} \mid n[a]R^*m[e], \right.$$

$$\left. n, m \text{ positive integers} \right\},$$

and e is an arbitrarily chosen element from A and where $n[a]$ is defined recursively: $1[a] = [a]$ and $n[a] = (n-1)[a] \circ {}^* [a]$. Since $f([e]) = 1$, the choice of $[e]$ corresponds to the choice of a unit. The remainder of the proof consists in showing that f has the required properties, namely, that

1. $[a]R^*[b]$ if and only if $f([a]) \leqslant f([b])$;
2. $f([a] \circ {}^* [b]) = f([a]) + f([b])$;
3. If $[a] \neq [b]$, then $f([a]) \neq f([b])$, that is, f is one-one.

Theorem 18 (Uniqueness Theorem). If a relational system $\mathfrak{A} = \langle A, R, \circ \rangle$ *is an extensive system, then any two numerical extensive systems isomorphic to* $\mathfrak{A}/I = \langle A/I, R^*, \circ^* \rangle$ *are related by a similarity transformation.*

Proof. Let g be any numerical assignment establishing an isomorphism between the system $\langle A/I, R^*, \circ^* \rangle$ and some numerical extensive system. It will suffice to show that g is related by a similarity transformation to the function f defined above. Let $g([e]) = \alpha$. We show by a *reductio ad absurdum* that for every a in A

$$g([a]) = \alpha f([a]). \qquad \text{Eq. 6}$$

Suppose now that for some a in A

$$g([a]) < \alpha f([a]). \qquad \text{Eq. 7}$$

From Eq. 7 it follows that a rational number m/n exists such that

$$\frac{g([a])}{\alpha} < \frac{m}{n} < f([a]), \qquad \text{Eq. 8}$$

which from the definition of f implies that

$$m[e]R^*n[a]. \qquad \text{Eq. 6}$$

However, by our initial assumption g is also a numerical assignment which establishes the desired isomorphism. Hence from Eq. 9 we have

$$mg([e]) \leqslant ng([a]), \qquad \text{Eq. 10}$$

which, because $g([e]) = \alpha$, can be written as

$$\frac{m}{n} \leqslant \frac{g([a])}{\alpha}. \qquad \text{Eq. 11}$$

But Eq. 11 contradicts Eq. 8. Similarly, by assuming an a exists in A such that $\alpha f([a]) < g([a])$, we may also arrive at a contradiction. Hence Eq. 6 is established. Q.E.D.

Although Theorem 18 asserts that extensive systems lead to ratio scales, this should not be construed as implying, as some have suggested [see pp. 47–48], that *only* extensive systems will yield these scales. As a brief example of a nonextensive system (a system not containing the operation $\circ$) leading to a ratio scale, let us construct a system along the lines of an i.d. or f.d. system $\langle A, D \rangle$, but with the following modifications. Let B be a set of elements drawn from $A \times A$, that is, if $e = (a, b)$ is in B, then a and b are in A. Let S be the binary relation on B corresponding to the relation D, that is, if $e = (a, b)$ and $f = (c, d)$ are in B, then eSf if and only if $ab\,Dcd$. By using a set of axioms corresponding to those of an i.d. or f.d. system we may conclude that the relational system $\langle B, S \rangle$ will yield a ratio scale. This follows from the fact that infinite difference and finite difference systems lead to interval scales and that the intervals of such a scale lie on a ratio scale.

There are two remarks we want to make about extensive systems to conclude this brief analysis of them. The first concerns the necessity of interpreting the operation ∘ as numerical addition. That this is not necessary is shown by the fact that it is a simple matter to construct another representation theorem in which the operation ∘ corresponds to the multiplication operation ·. One simple way of establishing the existence of a numerical system $\mathfrak{N}^* = \langle N^*, \leqslant, \cdot \rangle$ homomorphic to the extensive system $\mathfrak{A} = \langle A, R, \leqslant \rangle$ is to apply an exponential transformation to $\mathfrak{N} = \langle N, \leqslant, + \rangle$; that is, let

$$N^* = \{y \mid y = e^x \text{ for some } x \text{ in } N\}.$$

Obviously $\mathfrak{N}$ is isomorphic to $\mathfrak{N}^*$, and since $\mathfrak{A}$ is homomorphic to $\mathfrak{N}$ it is therefore homomorphic to $\mathfrak{N}^*$ as well. From a mathematical standpoint the representation theorem based on $\mathfrak{N}^*$ is as valid and useful as the one based on $\mathfrak{N}$, so there is no basis for interpreting the operation ∘ as intrinsically an addition operation rather than, say, a multiplication operation.

The representation theorem you choose does, of course, affect the uniqueness properties of the numerical assignment. The numerical assignment $f(a)$, which maps $\mathfrak{A}$ onto $\mathfrak{N}$, we know from Theorem 18 is determined up to a similarity transformation. But since $y = \exp(x)$, if x is transformed to kx, then y will transform to y^k. Thus the numerical assignment $f'(a)$, which maps $\mathfrak{A}$ onto $\mathfrak{N}^*$, is determined up to a power transformation, not a similarity transformation.

The second remark concerns the fact that for any extensive system $\mathfrak{A} = \langle A, R, \circ \rangle$ the set A must be infinite. It is the most patent fact of empirical measurement that to determine the weight or length of a physical object it is sufficient to consider only a finite number of objects. The difficulty with Def. 17 is a too slavish imitation of the number system. The essential point is that the empirical ternary relation of combination that is meant to correspond to the arithmetical operation of addition should not actually have all the formal properties of numerical addition. In particular, in order to avoid the infinity of A, it is simplest to drop the closure requirement on the operation ∘ in Def. 18 and replace it by a ternary relation that is technically not a binary operation on A. With this change we can then construct a theory of finite extensive systems which is similar to the theory of finite difference systems. Finite extensive systems thus constructed correspond closely in structure to standard series of weights and measures commonly used in physical and chemical laboratories. We do not pursue in this chapter the axiomatic analysis of finite extensive systems because they are more pertinent to physics than to psychology. The important methodological point is that from the standpoint of fundamental measurement there is no difference between difference systems and extensive systems, finite or infinite. One system is just as good a methodological example of fundamental measurement as the other.

The Problem of Meaningfulness

Closely related to the two fundamental issues of measurement—the representation and uniqueness problems—is a third problem which we shall term the meaningfulness problem. Although this problem is not central to a theory of measurement, it is often involved with various aspects of how measurements may be used, and as such it has engendered considerable controversy. It therefore merits some discussion here, although necessarily our treatment will be curtailed.

DEFINITION

To begin with, it will be well to illustrate the basic source of the meaningfulness problem with two of the statements given previously. For convenience they are repeated here.

4. The ratio of the maximum temperature

today (t_n) to the maximum temperature yesterday (t_{n-1}) is 1.10.

5. The ratio of the difference between today's and yesterday's maximum temperature $(t_n$ and $t_{n-1})$ to the difference between today's and tomorrow's maximum temperature $(t_n$ and $t_{n+1})$ will be 0.95.

Statement 4 was dismissed for having no clear empirical meaning and 5, on the other hand, was said to be acceptable. Here we wish to be completely explicit regarding the basis of this difference. Note first that both statements are similar in at least one important respect: neither statement specifies which numerical assignment from the set of admissible numerical assignments is to be used to determine the validity or truth of the statement. Are the temperature measurements to be made on the centigrade, Fahrenheit, or possibly the Kelvin scale? This question is not answered by either statement.

The distinguishing feature of statement 4 is that this ambiguity in the statement is critical. As an example, suppose by using the Fahrenheit scale we found that $t_n = 110$ and $t_{n-1} = 100$. We would then conclude that 4 was a true statement, the ratio of t_n to t_{n-1} being 1.10. Note, however, that if the temperature measurements had been made on the centigrade scale we would have come to the opposite conclusion, since then we would have found that $t_n = 43.3$ and $t_{n-1} = 37.8$ and a ratio equal to 1.15 rather than 1.10. In the case of 4 the selection of a particular numerical assignment influences the conclusions we come to concerning the truth of the statement.

In contrast, consider statement 5. The choice of a specific numerical assignment is not critical. To illustrate this point assume that when we measure temperature on a Fahrenheit scale we find the following readings: $t_{n-1} = 60$, $t_n = 79.0$, and $t_{n+1} = 99.0$. Then the ratio described in 5 is equal to

$$\frac{60-79}{79-99} = \frac{-19}{-20} = 0.95$$

which would indicate that the statement was valid. Now, if, instead, the temperature measurements had been made on the centigrade scale, we would have found that $t_{n-1} = 15.56$, $t_n = 26.11$, and $t_{n+1} = 37.20$. But, since the ratio of these numbers is

$$\frac{15.56-26.11}{26.11-37.20} = \frac{-10.55}{-11.09} = 0.95,$$

we would also have come to the conclusion that 5 was true. In fact, it is easy to verify that if we restrict ourselves to numerical assignments which are linearly related to each other then we will always arrive at the same conclusion concerning the validity of 5. If the statement is true for one numerical assignment, then it will be true for all. And, furthermore, if it is untrue for one numerical assignment, then it will be untrue for all. For this reason we can say that the selection of a specific numerical assignment to test the statement is not critical.

The absence of units in statements 4 and 5 is deliberate because the determination of units and an appreciation of their empirical significance comes *after*, not before, the investigation of questions of meaningfulness. The character of 4 well illustrates this point. If the Fahrenheit scale is specified in 4, the result is an empirical statement that is unambiguously true or false, but it is an empirical statement of a very special kind. It tells us something about the weather relative to a completely arbitrary choice of units. If the choice of the Fahrenheit scale were not arbitrary, there would be a meteorological experiment that would distinguish between Fahrenheit and centigrade scales and thereby narrow the class of admissible transformations. The recognized absurdity of such an experiment is direct evidence for the arbitrariness of the scale choice.

Fom the discussion of 4 and 5 it should be evident what sort of definition of meaningfulness we adopt.

Definition 33. A numerical statement is meaningful if and only if its truth (or falsity) is constant under admissible scale transformations of any of its numerical assignments, that is, any of its numerical functions expressing the results of measurement.

Admittedly this definition should be buttressed by an exact definition of "numerical statement," but this would take us further into technical matters of logic than is desirable in the present context. A detailed discussion of these matters, including construction of a formalized language, is to be found in Suppes (37).[7] The kind of numerical statements we have in mind will be made clear by the examples to follow. The import of the definition of meaningfulness will be clarified by the discussion of these examples.

It will also be convenient in what follows to introduce the notion of *equivalent statements.* Two statements are equivalent if and only if they have the same truth value. In these terms we can say that a numerical statement is meaningful in the sense of Def. 33 if admissible transformations of any of its numerical assignments always lead to equivalent numerical statements.

EXAMPLES

To point out some of the properties and implications of Def. 33, we discuss a number of specific examples. In each case a particular numerical statement is given as well as the transformation properties of all the numerical assignments referred to in the statement. For each example we ask the question: is it meaningful? To show that it is meaningful, admissible transformations are performed on all the numerical assignments and the transformed numerical statement is shown to be equivalent to the initial one. In most cases, when the two statements are in fact equivalent,

7. It can also be well argued that Def. 33 gives a necessary but not sufficient condition of meaningfulness. For example, a possible added condition on the meaningfulness of statements in classical mechanics is that they be invariant under a transformation to a new coordinate system moving with uniform velocity with respect to the old coordinate system (cf. McKinsey & Suppes (31). However, this is not a critical matter for what follows in this section.

the transformed statement can generally be reduced to the original statement by using various elementary rules of mathematics or logic. To show that a statement is meaningless, we must show that the transformed statement is not equivalent or cannot be reduced to the original. When this is not obvious, the simplest way of proceeding is to construct a counterexample, an example in which the truth value of the statement is not preserved after a particular admissible transformation is performed.

In the following examples we conform, for simplicity, to common usage and denote numerical assignments by x, y, and z instead of by $f(a)$ or $g(a)$. Thus instead of writing

$$\text{for all } a \in A, f(a) = \phi(g(a)),$$

we simply write

$$y = \phi(x).$$

When it is necessary to distinguish between the values of a given numerical assignment for two distinct objects a and b, subscript notation is used. Thus, for example, x_a and x_b might be the masses of two weights a and b. The parameters of the admissible transformations are j, k, l, m, ... and the numerical assignments that result from these transformations of x, y, and z are x', y', and z', respectively.

Example 1.

$$x_a + x_b > x_c. \qquad \text{Eq. 12}$$

First assume that the numerical assignment x is unique up to a similarity transformation. Then if x is transformed to kx, Eq. 12 becomes

$$kx_a + kx_b > kx_c, \qquad \text{Eq. 13}$$

and Eq. 13 is obviously equivalent to Eq. 12. Hence Eq. 12, under the assumption that x lies on a ratio scale, is meaningful.

Assume instead that x is specified up to a linear transformation. Then when x transforms to $kx + l$, Eq. 12 transforms to

$$(kx_a + l) + (kx_b + l) > (kx_c + l), \qquad \text{Eq. 14}$$

which does not reduce to Eq. 12. For a specific

counterexample, let $x_a = 1$, $x_b = 2$, $x_c = 2$, $k = 1$, and $l = -1$. Equation 12 then becomes

$$1 + 2 > 2. \qquad \text{Eq. 15}$$

But substituting the transformed values of x_a and x_b into Eq. 12 gives

$$(1-1) + (2-1) > (2-1)$$

or

$$0 + 1 > 1, \qquad \text{Eq. 16}$$

which obviously does not have the same truth value as Eq. 15. Hence Eq. 12 is meaningless when x lies on an interval scale. Thus we can say, for example, that if mass is on a ratio scale it is meaningful to say that the sum of the masses of two objects exceeds the mass of a third object. On the other hand, if temperature is on an interval scale, then it is not meaningful to say that the sum of the maximum temperatures on two days exceeds the maximum temperature on a third day.

These last remarks should not be interpreted to mean that addition can always be performed with ratio scales and never with interval scales. Consider the statement

$$x_a + x_b > (x_c)^2. \qquad \text{Eq. 17}$$

This statement is meaningless for a ratio scale, since

$$(kx_a) + (kx_b) > (kx_c)^2 \qquad \text{Eq. 18}$$

is clearly not equivalent to Eq. 17.

An example of a meaningful numerical statement which involves both addition and multiplication of a numerical assignment having only interval scale properties is the following.

Example 2. Let S_1 and S_2 be two sets having n_1 and n_2 members, respectively. Then

$$\frac{1}{n_1} \sum_{a \in S_1} x_a > \frac{1}{n_2} \sum_{b \in S_2} x_b. \qquad \text{Eq. 19}$$

One interpretation of Eq. 19 is that the mean maximum temperature of the days in January exceeds the mean maximum temperature of the days in February. We wish to show that

when x is unique up to a linear transformation

$$\frac{1}{n_1} \sum_{a \in S_1} x_a' > \frac{1}{n_2} \sum_{b \in S_2} x_b' \qquad \text{Eq. 20}$$

is equivalent to Eq. 19 where x' is another admissible numerical assignment. Substituting $x' = kx + l$ into Eq. 19 gives

$$\frac{1}{n_1} \sum_{a \in S_1} (kx_a + l) > \frac{1}{n_2} \sum_{b \in S_2} (kx_b + l)$$

or

$$\frac{1}{n_1} [k(\sum_{a \in S_1} x_a) + n_1 l] > \frac{1}{n_2} [k(\sum_{b \in S_2} x_b) + n_2 l]$$

$$\text{Eq. 21}$$

and Eq. 21 can be reduced to Eq. 19. Hence Eq. 19 is meaningful under these conditions. In general, it may be observed that the question whether a particular mathematical operation can be used with a particular scale cannot be answered with a simple yes or no. The admissibility of any mathematical operation depends not only on the scale type of the relevant numerical assignments but on the entire numerical statement of which the operation is a part.

Example 3.

$$x_a x_b > x_c. \qquad \text{Eq. 22}$$

If x is unique up to a similarity transformation, then Eq. 22 is meaningless, since

$$(kx_a)(kx_b) > (kx_c) \qquad \text{Eq. 23}$$

does not reduce to Eq. 22 for all values of k. Since Eq. 22 is meaningless for a ratio scale, it follows a fortiori that it is meaningless for an interval scale as well. It does not follow that Eq. 22 is meaningless for all scales. As an example, let x be unique up to a power transformation [see pp. 64–65 for an illustration]. Then as x is transformed to x^k, Eq. 23 becomes

$$x_a^k x_b^k > x_c^k,$$

and since this is equivalent to Eq. 23 statement 23 is meaningful.

In the following examples we consider

numerical statements involving at least two independent numerical assignments, x and y.

Example 4.

$$y = \alpha x. \qquad \text{Eq. 24}$$

If the numerical assignments x and y are not completely unique, then it is clear that Eq. 24 will in general be meaningless, since most non-identity transformations applied to x and y will transform Eq. 24 to a nonequivalent statement. One approach frequently used to make Eq. 24 meaningful under more general conditions permits the constant α to depend upon the parameters k, l, m, n, ... of the admissible transformations (but not on x or y). This approach is used here, so that in the remaining discussion statement 24 will be understood to mean the following: there exists a real number α such that for all $a \in A$, $y_a = \alpha x_a$. If x is transformed to x' and y to y', then Eq. 24 interpreted in this way will be meaningful if there exists an α', not necessarily equal to α, such that $y_a' = \alpha' x_a'$ for all $a \in A$.

Assume that x and y are specified up to a similarity transformation. Letting x go to kx, y to my, and α to α' (at present unspecified), Eq. 24 transforms to

$$my = \alpha' kx. \qquad \text{Eq. 25}$$

If we let $\alpha' = (m/k)\alpha$, then Eq. 25 will be equivalent to Eq. 24 for all (nonzero) values of m and k and therefore Eq. 24 will be meaningful.

Assume instead that x and y are both specified up to linear transformations. Let x transform to $(kx+l)$, y to $(my+n)$, and α to α'. We then have

$$(my+n) = \alpha'(kx+l). \qquad \text{Eq. 26}$$

Inspection of Eq. 26 suggests that no transformation of α to α' that depends solely on the parameters k, l, m, or n will reduce Eq. 26 to Eq. 24. This conclusion can be established more firmly by constructing a counterexample. Consider the following in which $A = \{a, b\}$. Let $x_a = 1$, $y_a = 2$, $y_b = 2$, and $y_b = 4$. Then, if $\alpha = 2$, Eq. 24 will be true for all a in A. Now let x go to $(kx+l)$, y to $(my+n)$, where

$k = l = m = n = 1$, and α to α'. Equation 24 then becomes for a in A

$$3 = \alpha'2, \qquad \text{Eq. 27}$$

indicating that if the truth value of Eq. 24 is to be preserved we must have $\alpha' = \frac{3}{2}$. However, for $b \in A$ we have

$$5 = \alpha'3, \qquad \text{Eq. 28}$$

which can be true only if $\alpha' = \frac{5}{3}$ and, in particular, is false if $\alpha' = \frac{3}{2}$. Both Eqs. 27 and 28 cannot be true and the truth value of Eq. 24 is not preserved in this example. Hence, under these conditions, Eq. 24 is meaningless.

Example 5.

$$x + y = \alpha. \qquad \text{Eq. 29}$$

In this example we assume first that x and y are unique up to a similarity transformation. One interpretation of Eq. 29 would be that the sum of the weight and height of each person in A is equal to a constant. As usual we let x transform to kx, y to my, and α to α'. Then Eq. 29 becomes

$$kx + my = \alpha', \qquad \text{Eq. 30}$$

but, since it is evident that no value of α' will reduce this equation to one equivalent to Eq. 29, we may conclude that Eq. 29 is meaningless under these assumptions.

Although this result confirms the common-sense notion that it does not make sense to add weight and length, there are conditions under which Eq. 29 is certainly meaningful. One example is the assumption that x and y lie on difference scales; that is, they are unique up to an additive constant. This can be verified by letting x transform to $x+l$, y to $y+n$, and α to $(\alpha+l+n)$, for then Eq. 29 transforms to

$$(x+l)+(y+n) = \alpha+l+n, \qquad \text{Eq. 31}$$

which is certainly equivalent to Eq. 29.

To illustrate the effects of a derived numerical assignment, as well as another set of assumptions for which Eq. 29 is meaningful, consider the following. Assume that y is a derived numerical assignment and that it depends in part on x. Assume that when x is transformed to kx, y is transferred to $(ky+2k)$. Therefore, if α transforms to α' Eq. 29 becomes

$$kx+(ky+2k) = \alpha', \qquad \text{Eq. 32}$$

and, clearly, if $\alpha' = k(\alpha+2)$, this equation will be equivalent to Eq. 29. Equation 29 is therefore meaningful under these conditions. Thus, whether it is meaningful to add weight and length depends not so much on the physical properties of bodies but on the uniqueness properties of the numerical assignments associated with weight and length.

Another common dictum frequently encountered is that one can take the logarithm only of a numerical assignment that lies on an absolute scale or, as it is customarily said, of a dimensionless number. With this in mind, we consider the following example.

Example 6.

$$y = \alpha \log x. \qquad \text{Eq. 33}$$

Assume first that x and y have ratio scale properties. Then as x transforms to kx, y to my, and α to α', Eq. 33 transforms to

$$my = \alpha' \log kx$$

or to

$$my = \alpha' \log x + \alpha' \log k, \qquad \text{Eq. 34}$$

and Eq. 34 cannot be made equivalent to Eq. 33 by any value of α'. Therefore, under these assumptions, we again have the common-sense result, viz., that Eq. 33 is meaningless.

However, assume next that x is unique up to a power transformation and that y is unique up to a similarity transformation. Then when x transforms to x^k, y to my, and α to $(m/k)\alpha$ Eq. 33 transforms to

$$my = \left(\frac{m}{k}\right)\alpha \log(x^k). \qquad \text{Eq. 35}$$

Since Eq. 35 is clearly equivalent to Eq. 33, the latter is meaningful under these conditions, common sense notwithstanding.

Another example involving the logarithm of a nonunique numerical assignment is the following.

Example 7.

$$y = \log x + \alpha. \qquad \text{Eq. 36}$$

From the previous example it should be evident that Eq. 36 will not be meaningful when x and y have ratio scale properties. But if y is on a difference scale and x is on a ratio scale, then Eq. 36 will be meaningful. This can be verified by letting x transform to kx, y to $y+n$, and α to $\alpha+n-\log k$, since then Eq. 36 transforms to

$$(y+n) = \log kx = (\alpha+n-\log k) \qquad \text{Eq. 37}$$

and Eq. 37 is equivalent to Eq. 36. The interesting feature of Eq. 36 is that the required transformation of α is not a simple or elementary function of the parameters k and n. Although most, if not all, of the "dimensional constants" encountered in practice have simple transformation properties (usually a power function of the parameters), there is no a priori reason why these constants cannot be allowed to have quite arbitrary transformations. Of course, if the transformation properties of the constants are limited, the conditions under which numerical statements will be meaningful will ordinarily be changed.

EXTENSIONS AND COMMENTS

It will be noted that the definition of meaningfulness in Def. 33 contains no reference to the physical operations that may or may not have been employed in the measurement procedure. There are at least two other points of view on this issue that the reader should be aware of.

One point of view (e.g., 42) asserts that meaningful statements may employ only mathematical operations that correspond to known physical operations. In terms of empirical and relational systems, this point of view may be described as requiring that for each empirical system the admissible mathematical operations be limited to those contained in the selected homomorphic numerical system (or alternatively in *some* homomorphic numerical system).

The second point of view (e.g., 25) appears to be less severe. It asserts that all rules of arithmetic are admissible when physical addition exists (and, presumably, satisfies some set of axioms such as those [on pp. 64–66]). Without physical addition the application of arithmetic is limited (to some undefined set of rules or operations). In terms of relational systems, this point of view appears to imply that all statements "satisfying" the rules of arithmetic are meaningful when the selected homomorphic numerical system contains the arithmetical operation of addition (or, perhaps, when at least one homomorphic numerical system exists which contains the addition operation). When this is not the case, fewer statements are meaningful.

In contrast to these two positions, Def. 33 implies that the meaningfulness of numerical statements is determined solely by the uniqueness properties of their numerical assignments, not by the nature of the operations in the empirical or numerical systems.

One of our basic assumptions throughout this section has been that a knowledge of the representation and uniqueness theorems is a prerequisite to answering the meaningfulness question. It can be argued, though, that these assumptions are too strong, since in some cases the uniqueness properties of the numerical assignments are not precisely known. For example, although we have a representation theorem for semiorders [pp. 56–59], we have no uniqueness theorem. In these cases we often have an approximation of a standard ordinal, interval, or ratio scale. Without stating general definitions, the intuitive idea may be illustrated by consideration of an example.

Suppose we have an empirical quaternary system $\mathfrak{A} = \langle A, D \rangle$ for which there exists a numerical assignment f such that $abDcd$ if and only if

$$f(a) - f(b) \leqslant f(c) - f(d). \qquad \text{Eq. 38}$$

We also suppose that the set A is finite. In

addition, let $\mathfrak{N}$ be the full numerical relational system defined by Eq. 38. Let $\langle \mathfrak{A}, \mathfrak{N}, f \rangle$ be a scale and $\langle \mathfrak{A}, \mathfrak{N}, g \rangle$ be any scale such that, for two elements a and b in A, $f(a) \neq f(b)$, $f(a) = g(a)$, and $f(b) = g(b)$; that is, f and g assign the same number to at least two elements of A that are not equivalent. We then say that $\langle \mathfrak{A}, \mathfrak{N}, f \rangle$ is an ϵ-approximation of an interval scale if

$$\max_{a,\, g} \left| f(a) - g(a) \right| \leqslant \epsilon,$$

where the maximum is taken over all elements of A and numerical assignments g satisfying the condition just stated. It is clearly not necessary that there be an ϵ such that the scale $\langle \mathfrak{A}, \mathfrak{N}, f \rangle$ be an ϵ-approximation of an interval scale. Consider, for instance, the three element set $A = \{a, b, c\}$, with $f(a) = 1$, $f(b) = 1.5$, and $f(c) = 3$. Then, if $g(a) = 1$ and $g(b) = 1.5$, we may assign any number for the value $g(c)$ provided $g(c) > 2$, and thus there is no finite $\max|f(a) - g(a)|$. On the other hand, if A has 20 or more elements, say, and no intervals are too large or too small in relation to the rest, $\langle \mathfrak{A}, \mathfrak{N}, f \rangle$ will be an ϵ-approximation of an interval scale for ϵ reasonably small in relation to the scale of f.

The relation between ϵ-approximations of standard scales and issues of meaningfulness is apparent. A statement or hypothesis that is meaningful for interval or ratio scales has a simple and direct analogue that is meaningful for ϵ-approximations of these scales. For example, consider the standard proportionality hypothesis for two ratio scales, that is, there exists a positive α such that for every a in A

$$f(a) = \alpha\, h(a). \qquad \text{Eq. 39}$$

This equation is meaningful, as we have seen ([p. 68–71], Example 4), when f and h are determined up to a similarity transformation. If f and h, or more exactly $\langle \mathfrak{A}, \mathfrak{N}, f \rangle$ and $\langle \mathfrak{A}', \mathfrak{N}', h \rangle$, are ϵ- and δ-approximations of ratio scales, respectively, then Eq. 39 is no longer meaningful but the appropriate analogue of Eq. 39, namely

$$\left| f(a) - \alpha\, h(a) \right| \leqslant \epsilon + \alpha\delta$$

is meaningful.

Problems of meaningfulness and the issue of the applicability of certain statistics to data that are not known to constitute an interval or ratio scale have been closely tied in the psychological literature. Unfortunately, we have insufficient space to analyze this literature. We believe that the solution lies not in developing alternative definitions of meaningfulness but rather in clarifying the exact status of the measurements made. One way is to make explicit the empirical relational system underlying the empirical procedures of measurement. A second is along the lines we have just suggested in sketching the theory of ϵ-approximations. A third possibility for clarification is to give a more explicit statement of the theory or hypotheses to which the measurements are relevant.

References

1. Adams, E. W., & Messick, S. *An axiomatization of Thurstone's successive intervals and paired comparison scaling models.* Tech. Rept. No. 12, Contr. Nonr 225(17), Applied Math. and Stat. Lab., Stanford Univer., 1957.
2. Adams, E. W., & Messick, S. An axiomatic formulation and generalization of successive intervals scaling. *Psychometrika,* 1958, 23, 355–368.
3. Armstrong, W. E. The determinateness of the utility function. *Econ. J.,* 1939, 49, 453–467.
4. Armstrong, W. E. Uncertainty and the utility function. *Econ. J.,* 1948, 58, 1–10.
5. Armstrong, W. E. Utility and the theory of welfare. *Oxford Economic Papers,* 1951, 3, 259–271.
6. Bennett, J. F., & Hays, W. L. Multidimensional unfolding: determining the dimensionality of ranked preference data. *Psychometrika,* 1960, 25, 27–43.
7. Birkhoff, G. *Lattice theory.* (Rev. ed.) American Math. Society, colloq. series, 1948, 25.
8. Bradley, R. A. Incomplete block rank analysis: on the appropriateness of the model for a method of paired comparisons. *Biometrics,* 1954, 10, 375–390. (a)
9. Bradley, R. A. Rank analysis of incomplete block designs. II. Additional tables for the method of paired comparisons. *Biometrika,* 1954, 41, 502–537. (b)
10. Bradley, R. A. Rank analysis of incomplete block designs. III. Some large-sample results on estimation and power for a method of paired comparisons. *Biometrika,* 1955, 42, 450–470.
11. Bradley, R. A., & Terry, M. E. Rank analysis of incomplete block designs. I. The method of paired comparisons. *Biometrika,* 1952, 29, 324–345.
12. Campbell, N. R. *Physics: the elements.* London: Cambridge Univer. Press, 1920. (Reprinted as *Foundations of Science.* New York: Dover, 1957. Pagination references pertain to this edition.)
13. Campbell, N. R. *An account of the principles of measurements and calculations.* London: Longmans, Green, 1928.
14. Cohen, M. R., & Nagel, E. *An introduction to logic and scientific method.* New York: Harcourt, Brace, 1934.
15. Comrey, A. L. Mental testing and the logic of measurement. *Educational and Psychological Measurement,* 1951, 11, 323–34.
16. Coombs, C. H. Psychological scaling without a unit of measurement. *Psychol. Rev.,* 1950, 57, 145–158.
17. Coombs, C. H. A theory of psychological scaling. *Engr. Res. Instit. Bull.* No. 34. Ann Arbor: Univer. of Mich. Press, 1952.
18. Coombs, C. H. A theory of data. *Psychol. Rev.,* 1960, 67, 143–159.
19. Coombs, C. H., Raiffa, H., & Thrall, R. M. Some views on mathematical models and measurement theory. *Psychol. Rev.,* 1954, 61, 132–144.
20. Davidson, D., & Marschak, J. Experimental tests of a stochastic decision theory. In C. W. Churchman and P. Ratoosh (Eds.), *Measurement: definition and theories.* New York: Wiley, 1959. Pp. 233–269.
21. Davidson, D., & Suppes, P. A finitistic axiomatization of subjective probability and utility. *Econometrica,* 1956, 24, 264–275.
22. Davidson, D., Suppes, P., & Siegel, S. *Decision-making: an experimental approach.* Stanford: Stanford Univer. Press, 1957.
23. Debreu, G. Representation of a preference ordering by a numerical function. In R. M. Thrall, C. H. Coombs, and R. L. Davis (Eds.), *Decision processes.* New York: Wiley, 1954. Pp. 159–165.
24. Gerlach, Muriel W. *Interval measurement of subjective magnitudes with subliminal differences.* Tech. Rept. No. 7. Contr. Nonr 225(17), Applied Math. and Stat. Lab., Stanford Univer., 1957.
25. Guilford, J. P. *Psychometric methods.* (2nd ed.) New York: McGraw-Hill, 1954.
26. Hefner, R. *Extensions of the law of comparative judgment to discriminable and multi-dimensional stimuli.* Unpublished doctoral dissertation, Univer. of Mich, 1958.

27. Hempel, C. G. Fundamentals of Concept formation in empirical science. *International Encyclopaedia of Unified Science, II*, No. 7. Chicago: Univer. of Chicago Press, 1952.
28. Hölder, O. Die Axiome der Quantität und die Lehre von mass. *Ber. Säch., Gesellsch. Wiss., Math-Phy. Klasse*, 1901, 53, 1–64.
29. Luce, R. D. Semi-orders and a theory of utility discrimination. *Econometrica*, 1956, 24, 178–191.
30. Luce, R. D. *Individual choice behavior*. New York: Wiley, 1959.
31. McKinsey, J. C. C., & Suppes, P. On the notion of invariance in classical mechanics. *British Journal for Philosophy of Science*, 1955, 5, 290–302.
32. Scott, D., & Suppes, P. Foundational aspects of theories of measurement. *J. Symbolic Logic*, 1958, 23, 113–128.
33. Stevens, S. S. On the theory of scales of measurement. *Science*, 1946, 103, 677–680.
34. Stevens, S. S. Mathematics, measurement and psychophysics. In S.S. Stevens (Ed.), *Handbook of experimental psychology*. New York: Wiley, 1951, Pp. 1–49.
35. Suppes, P. A set of independent axioms for extensive quantities. *Portugaliae Mathematica*,

1951, 10, 163–172.
36. Suppes, P. *Introduction to logic*. Princeton, N.J.: Van Nostrand, 1957.
37. Suppes, P. Measurement, empirical meaningfulness and three-valued logic. In C. W. Churchman and P. Ratoosh (Eds.), *Measurement: definition and theories*. New York: Wiley 1959. Pp. 129–143.
38. Suppes, P., & Winet, Muriel. An axiomatization of utility based on the notion of utility differences. *Mgmt. Sci.*, 1955, 1, 259–270.
39. Tarski, A. Contributions to the theory of models, I, II. *Indagationes Mathematicae*, 1954, 16, 572–588.
40. Thurstone, L. L. A law of comparative judgment. *Psychol. Rev.*, 1927, 34, 273–286.
41. Torgerson, W. S. *Theory and methods of scaling*. New York: Wiley, 1958.
42. Weitzenhoffer, A. M. Mathematical structures and psychological measurement. *Psychometrika*, 1951, 16, 387–406.
43. Wiener, N. A new theory of measurement: a study in the logic of mathematics. *Proc. London Math. Soc.*, 1921, 19, 181–205.
44. Young, G., & Householder, A. S. Discussion of a set of points in terms of their mutual distances. *Psychometrika*, 1938, 3, 19–22.

ERNEST W. ADAMS

6 On the Nature and Purpose of Measurement

Introduction

This paper consists of two main parts, the first being a critique of a currently widely held view as to the nature of measurement, and the second being a sketch of an alternative view which I hope to show is more adequate to the actual practice of measurement in science. The theory of measurement which I will criticize is what might be called the "representational" theory: namely that measurement consists in assigning numbers to things in such a way that certain operations on and relations among the assigned numbers come to "correspond to" or

"represent" observable relations and operations on the things to which they are assigned. This view is associated with such writers as N. R. Campbell (3), and more recently B. Ellis (7) and P. Suppes (21), (22), though its main ideas were fairly clearly stated earlier by H. Helmholtz (9) (and one can make a case that Euclid's axioms about addition of equals, etc., constitute a non-numerical statement of many of the fundamental assumptions of this doctrine). Much recent work on measurement theory in the field of mathematical psychology has taken the representational view as its

From *Synthese*, **16**, 1966. Copyright © 1966 by D. Reidel Publishing Co., and reprinted by permission.

point of departure (see, for example, Luce and Tukey (13), Krantz (10), Davidson and Suppes (5), Pfanzagl (16), Eisler (6), and Tversky (24)). I will try to show that, though the work of Campbell and others in the representational tradition has contributed to our understanding of measurement, the proponents of this approach have neglected to consider what it is that measurements are made *for*, and in so doing have been led to conclusions as to what measurement *ought* to be which are in serious disagreement with what scientists do. The alternative view which I sketch in the second part of the paper is based on the assumption that at least one of the principal reasons for making measurements is to provide objective *indices* of phenomena. This leads to a kind of *informational* account of measurement, and to the view that measures of a quantity are not so much "true" or "false" as they are more or less informative about the phenomena which they are supposed to be indices of. Without going farther into the consequences of this change in viewpoint, let us proceed directly to the discussion of the representational theory.

Critique of Representational Measurement Theory

There are five basic assumptions which seem to me to be associated with the representational theory. These are:

1. Measurement is the assignment of numbers (perhaps numerals) to objects or phenomena according to rule.
2. At least in the case of fundamental measurement, the numbers assigned to objects according to a given procedure are assigned in such a way that certain operations and relations among the objects measured come to correspond to or be represented by operations and relations among the numbers.
3. The problem of the foundations of measurement, as it is concerned with a particular kind of measurement, is to determine "the conditions under which measurement is possible," which requires determining the

empirical laws which the objects must satisfy in order that it should be possible to assign numbers to them such that the empirical operations and relations can be made to correspond to numerical operations and relations.
4. Any given kind of measurement system determines the numerical measures to be assigned in it only with a specified degree of uniqueness, and the remaining arbitrariness of the measurement determines the *scale type* of the system, and its class of permissible transformations (Stevens, 19, 20).
5. The permissible transformations of a system of measurement determine what can legitimately be done with measurements of the system: what statistical treatments are "appropriate" to them, and what can "meaningfully" be said about them.

Of the above 5 assumptions, the first three might be regarded as basic to pure representational measurement theory, while the last two are characteristic of the theory of scale types and permissible transformations. The two groups of assumptions are brought together here in order to emphasize their logical interconnections. In point of fact, however, though many writers seem to accept all of the assumptions (e.g., Suppes (22) and Luce and Tukey (13)), there are some (e.g. Pfanzagl (16)) who accept only the first three, and at least one (S. S. Stevens) who explicitly adopts only 1, 4, and 5.

Readers acquainted with modern writings in the logic of measurement will I hope recognize the above assumptions, but for the sake of clarity it may help to illustrate them in their application to a particular example— say the time honored one of weight measurement by the use of an equal arm balance, which is often cited as an example of *extensive* measurement. In its main outlines, the representational theory goes as follows. The objects measured comprise a class, K, and determining the weight of an object x in K means assigning to x a real number, $w(x)$, which is the value of the weight of x in some units, say pounds. The basic principles to be adhered to in assigning numerical weights to objects, so goes the theory, are that the relations of greater and lesser in weight, as determined by observation of balance comparisons, must correspond to the relations of greater and lesser numerical values of the assigned weights, and that the physical operation of putting two objects together ("physical addition") must correspond to the numerical operation of adding their weights. Stated more precisely, the assumptions are: if xHy means that x is heavier than y (x descends when placed opposite y in the pans of a balance), and $x \circ y$ represents the operation of putting x and y together in one pan of a balance, then, for all x and y in K

(R1) xHy if and only if $w(x) > w(y)$

and

(R2) $w(x \circ y) = w(x) + w(y)$.

Given that numerical weights are supposed to satisfy the above "correspondence rules," the problem of the foundations of measurement (the "representation problem," Suppes and Zinnes (23, p. 4)) is to determine the laws which must be satisfied by objects in order that such a correspondence be possible. Thus in particular, the relation H should be transitive, for if there were three objects, x, y and z such that xHy, yHz and zHx, it would not be possible to assign weights $w(x)$, $w(y)$ and $w(z)$ to them in such a way that correspondence (R1) was satisfied. The representation problem is usually regarded as solved by deriving a "representation theorem" showing that if the objects in K satisfy specified observational laws, then it is possible to assign numerical measures to them in such a way that correspondence conditions R1 and R2 are satisfied. Pfanzagl (16), Suppes (21), and Suppes and Zinnes (23) all prove representation theorems for what are essentially extensive measurement systems.

The beam balance procedure for measuring weight can also be used to illustrate assumptions 4 and 5. Purely formal analysis shows that correspondence rules R1 and R2 do not by themselves uniquely determine the numerical weights to be assigned to objects, and that

one must also arbitrarily fix on a *unit* of weight measurement, say the standard pound, whose weight is set at 1. One may obtain another class of numerical weight assignments which also satisfy rules R1 and R2 by simply multiplying all weights in pounds by some fixed constant, say 16 (to give weights in ounces), and thus it is said that weights are determined uniquely only up to multiplication by a positive constant, and so, by definition, weight is a *ratio scale* (Stevens (19)), and multiplication by a positive constant is a *permissible transformation* of weight. Finally, the fact that weights can always be multiplied by positive constants is said to entail that only certain statistical operations can be applied to weights and certain statements be meaningfully made about them. Roughly, the principle is that if the result of the statistical operation or the truth of the statement depends on arbitrary features in the measurement (e.g., the choice of the unit), then the operation is not appropriate, or the statement is not empirically meaningful. Though S. S. Stevens is somewhat vague as to exactly what statistical operations might be excluded by this principle (see Adams, Fagot, and Robinson (1) for discussion of this point), the following one presumably would be: given a series of weights $w(x_1), \ldots w(x_n)$ to form the "statistic"

$$w(x_1) + w(x_2)^2 + \ldots + w(x_n)^n.$$

The reason for excluding this statistic would be that it violates a "comparison invariance" condition (Adams, Fagot, and Robinson (1), p. 106): namely that two different series might be found to be equal in this statistic when weights are measured in pounds, but unequal in the same statistic with weights measured in ounces.

Below I will criticize each of the five basic theses listed above, taken as principles which systems of measurement *ought* to satisfy. Before entering into details, though, we may observe that nowhere in the foregoing statement of basic assumptions has there been given any *argument* that measurement systems should satisfy them, and the fact is that such arguments are conspicuously lacking in the writings of the proponents of this view of measurement. What plausibility these assumptions have stems, I would suggest, from the fact that they do describe the practice of measurement fairly well in certain cases (e.g., that of weight, though even here the description is inaccurate in important respects). But even a cursory survey of scientific measuring procedures also shows that these assumptions fit not at all or very badly in many other cases, which should at least raise the suspicion that it is the assumptions which are ill founded, and not the practice. Later I will argue that, given certain objectives to be gained by measurement, there is no reason why the five assumptions should be satisfied: these objectives *may* be gained using procedures of measurement conforming to the representational conception of measurement, but they may be gained as well in other ways too. Now I list briefly criticisms of each of the specific assumptions of the representational theory.

It seems to me that in characterizing measurement as the assignment of numbers to objects according to rule, the proponents of the representational theory have fastened on something which is undoubtedly of great importance in modern science, but which is not by any means an *essential* feature of measurement. What is important is that the real numbers provide a very sophisticated and convenient conceptual framework which can be employed in *describing* the results of making measurements: but, what can be conveniently described with numbers can be less conveniently described in other ways, and these alternative descriptions no less "give the measure" of a thing than do the numerical descriptions. Thus, the hardness of a mineral specimen may alternatively be described as 7 on the Mohs scale, or as of the same hardness as quartz. The weight of an object may be equivalently stated in any of the four forms: 1) 1.5 lbs., 2) 24 ozs., 3) 1 lb., 8 ozs., 4) equal to that of the standard pound, together with another object which added to an object of the same weight, is equal to the standard

pound. Note, too, that the ancient Greeks did not have our concepts of rational, much less real numbers, yet it seems absurd to say that they could not measure because they did not assign numbers to objects. In sum, I would say that the employment of numbers in describing the results of measurement is not essentially different from their employment in other numerical descriptions, and that this employment is neither a necessary nor a sufficient condition for making or describing measurements.

Even granting the assumption that measurement necessarily involves assigning numbers, it seems to me to be far from true that in making these assignments it is always the case that mathematical operations and relations are made to correspond to or represent empirical relations and operations. Actually, this assumption is supposed to hold only for "fundamental measurement," but unless this is an implicit definition of "fundamental measurement," even the restricted assumption seems to me invalid. Of three of the kinds of measurement often called "fundamental" in physics, mass, length, and time, the claim is only plausible for the first two (and even these turn out not to satisfy the assumption upon closer examination). To my knowledge, no one has yet succeeded in saying what operations and relations among *times* are made to correspond to operations and relations among numbers in the measurement of time. The situation is worse with most of the widely used measures in the behavioral sciences, like I.Q.s. and aptitude test scores. It may be claimed, of course, that these are not really measurements at all, but to justify this, some argument would have to be given, unless the theory of representational measurement is not to degenerate into a mere definition (I.Q.s are not measurements *because* they do not establish numerical representations of empirical operations and relations). Later I will argue that I.Q.s. and other such scales do in fact satisfy what seem to me to be the essential requirements for measurement systems.

The third basic thesis of the representational

theory of measurement is closely linked to the first and second. The most general way to formulate this thesis is: certain empirical laws must be satisfied by the objects measured in order that measurement be possible, in the sense that if these laws are not satisfied then it is logically impossible to represent the empirical operations and relations by mathematical operations and relations in the required way. Thus, the empirical relation "heavier than" must be transitive if this relation is to be made to correspond to the numerical relation "greater than." This, of course, takes for granted what I have already questioned, that measurement necessarily involves establishing numerical representations. A more direct objection to this thesis, though, is that at least some of the "laws" which have usually been held to be necessary conditions for the possibility of measurements are false. For example, Campbell (3), Suppes (21), and Ellis (7) all assume that the supposedly empirical relation of equality (in measure) must be transitive (since it is represented by the relation of numerical equality, which is transitive), and yet it is notorious that observational judgements of equality are non-transitive. At best the assumption that empirical equality is transitive must be regarded as an idealization, and if axioms of measurement were ordinary empirical theories, such idealizations might be tolerated as they are in other scientific theories. However, it is absurd to hold that these axioms state conditions which must be satisfied in order that measurement be possible, or that it be justified, since measurement clearly is possible and justified even though some of the measurement axioms are false. Later I will try to show that though the axioms of measurement which have been derived by Campbell and others are not necessary conditions for the possibility of measurement, they do have some significance in that they reveal some of the empirical information which the determination of a measure gives (which is itself somewhat inexact).

Coming to the fourth tenet often associated with representational measurement theory,

that every scale of measurement has associated with it a class of "permissible" transformations, it seems to me that this doctrine is even less well founded than the first three, and that it must ultimately come to be regarded as "unscientific metaphysics." It is true that this assumption is supported by the earlier ones, since, granted that fundamental measurement consists in establishing numerical representations for empirical operations and relations, one can define a permissible transformation as one which alters the numbers assigned without altering the representation. On the other hand, the theory of scale types has often been extended to include kinds of measurements (e.g., time and I.Q.) which have so far resisted "representational" analysis (see, e.g., the discussion between Lord (12), Anderson (2), Stevens (20), Senders (18) and Comrey (4) concerning the assignment of football numbers), without any justification. These objections to the theory of scale types would not matter were it not that the word "permissible" carries a normative connotation, and that strictures about legitimate uses of measurements have been formulated in terms of permissible transformations. This leads to consideration of the fifth and last assumption of the representational theory.

Even taking for granted the usual classification of the scale types of measurements, and the associated sets of permissible transformations, I would argue that invariance under permissible transformations is neither a necessary nor a sufficient condition for appropriateness of a statistical operation (Stevens (19) and (20), or the meaningfulness of a statement made about the measurements (Suppes (22)). Adams, Fagot, and Robinson (1) have criticized Stevens' own formulations of the invariance conditions (because Stevens states two non-equivalent criteria, without saying which should be imposed where, and without saying what is objectionable about employing statistics violating the criteria), but have argued that, with qualifications, both of Stevens' criteria can be interpreted as necessary conditions which statistical operations have to satisfy in order for certain kinds of statements about them to be "empirically significant." The sense in which statements are said to be empirically significant is that in which their truth depends just on the "quantities measured," and not on arbitrary features of the measurement, such as the unit. Thus interpreted, the basic requirement is that statements be empirically significant, and the appropriateness criterion for statistics is viewed as being imposed only to insure that the more basic requirement is met by statements about the statistics. But, one example should show that even the invariance criterion for statements cannot in general be maintained as a condition for scientific significance in an intuitive sense. Among statements which are not invariant are, in fact, all statements reporting the results of particular measurements—e.g., "Ernest Adams weighs 190 lbs." If such statements were excluded on the grounds that they are not "meaningful," all *data* would be banished from science.

One final criticism which can be brought against most of the representational theories of measurement is that in their associated axiomatic analyses, they assume that the objects measured do not *change* in relevant observable relations to one another over time. Thus, Campbell's and Suppes' theories of extensive measurement both take as a primitive notion the relation of empirical equality (say equality in weight) between two objects. Yet, unless it is assumed that two objects which are equal at one time always remain equal, the non-temporally qualified relation of empirical equality is ambiguous. Now, there are various reasons for leaving change out of account in attempting to formulate scientific theories which are explicitly taken to be idealizations. But, as already argued, it makes no sense to regard a theory purporting to describe the conditions under which measurement is *possible* as a good idealization. Moreover, in abstracting from change, representational measurement theory prevents itself from considering one very important aspect of measurement: namely, the very special role

played by *standards*.

The foregoing objections to the representational conception of measurement are not decisive, and some of them may be easily answerable. In what follows, however, I hope to show that an alternative account of the nature of measurement is able to accommodate much of what is useful in the representational theories, while avoiding the objections. The conclusions I draw about measurement grow directly out of an examination of a variety of measurement procedures currently used in science (but not solely in *research*), and they are most easily explained in the light of the discussion of a couple of specific examples. The two examples I will choose are both frequently cited in writings on the logic of measurement: the Mohs scale of hardness, and the measurement of weight.

First Example: the Mohs Scale of Hardness

I will not describe in detail the physical procedures to be followed in determining the Mohs scale hardness of an object, but confine myself to those general features which appear to me to be significant. The two basic things to know about this measure are: 1) what it is used for, and 2) how it is made. The most important practical use of this measure is as an adjunct to mineral identification (there seem to be some uses also in ceramic technology). In this it seems to serve primarily as a quick and rough "screening" procedure for making tentative identifications in the field or laboratory prior to making more definitive determinations such as can be done with optical and chemical analyses. To determine the hardness of a mineral specimen it is necessary to find out how easily the specimen is scratched by objects of known hardness or it scratches such objects. For instance "if the mineral under examination is scratched by a knife blade as easily as calcite its hardness is said to be 3; if less easily than calcite and more so than fluorite its hardness is 3.5" (Ford (8), p. 214). That minerals comparable to calcite are described as having hardness 3, and those lying between calcite and fluorite are said to have hardness 3.5 is because calcite and fluorite are the third and fourth minerals, respectively, in Mohs' original scale of hardness (which ranges from talc at the lowest, with hardness 1, to diamond at the highest, with hardness 10). As an aid in determining the mineral composition of a sample, the hardness measure is used in an obvious way. Quick inspection (color, shape, appearance of fractures, feel, even taste) plus background knowledge concerning the locale in which the sample was found usually narrows the reasonable possibilities to just a few (usually under 10). Frequently all but one possibility is then eliminated by a rough determination of the hardness, which may be done by scratching the sample with a fingernail, knifeblade, broken edge of a file, and so on, by which persons familiar with minerals can quickly learn to gauge their hardness. A most important aid in this identification are mineral handbooks, which list thousands of minerals and specify their characteristic hardnesses on the Mohs scale in some such form as "H. = 4–4.5" (for zincite, Ford (8), p. 480). As noted, though, definitive identification requires more positive tests.

It seems to me that many things about the Mohs hardness scale are easily explained just in terms of the purposes which such measures are designed to serve: namely as aids in mineral identification. First, it explains why only objects or substances of the hardness of minerals have a position on this scale. In common speech we speak of all sorts of things as being harder or softer than other things (pillows, gelatin that is setting, and rubber balls, for example), but usually do not make fine discriminations among the hardnesses of various rocks. "Rock hard" is just one degree of hardness in ordinary speech. It would not do to say that the scientific measure of hardness applies only to rocks because rocks are the objects studied by science, since science studies other things.

Second, the fact that specimens of the same

mineral in general behave in the same way, but not in exactly the same way, on scratching comparisons explains both the usefulness and limitations of scratch tests in determining mineral composition. Clearly scratch tests would be useless in identification if mineral content were not highly correlated with behavior on scratch tests. On the other hand whether one rock will scratch another, and to what extent, obviously depends not just on the mineral compositions of the rocks (it depends besides on the pressure applied, condition of the surfaces, even the direction of scratch in some cases). Some of these factors may be controlled, e.g., by the use of a sclerometer, but to require the use of the latter would be to rob the scratch test of its usefulness as a quick screening device. That small differences in scratching behavior are not reliable indices of mineral content explains, I surmise, why fine subdivisions of the Mohs scale are not made.

Third, I conjecture that at least some factors leading to the choice of the ten *standard* minerals in the Mohs scale may be explained by reference to the use of the scale in mineral identification. That most minerals lie between diamond and talc in hardness is important, for if a substantial portion of all minerals lay outside of the extremes on the Mohs scale in hardness, then comparing specimens of them to the ten standards would be of little use in determining their compsotion. I conjecture also that the variability of specimens of any one of the standard minerals in their hardness is probably small or at least not large by comparison with the variabilities of other minerals (I have been told that some minerals have a variability of as much as 2 degrees on the Mohs scale). This would be essential if comparison with specimens of the standard minerals were to give a reliable indication of mineral content. It is to be observed, too, that no two standard minerals are very similar to one another in their scratching characteristics. It is clear that very similar standards would not be useful in mineral identification, since comparing an unknown specimen with both would not yield substantially more information than would comparison of the specimen with just one of them. It is also important, probably, that samples of the standards be readily obtainable, if comparison with them is to be easy. Generalizing from the foregoing, I suggest that the standards are probably well chosen in the sense that using the kind of rough scratching procedures described above, comparison of rock specimens with the ten standards (or determining their position relative to the standards, e.g., by knife scratching) yields close to a maximum of reliable information as to their mineral compositions. These rather vague surmises suggest the desirability of a more precise and quantitative formulation. A sketch of such a quantitative analysis is given in the Appendix, but for the present I shall confine myself to informal observations.

One final observation on the Mohs hardness scale seems to me important. That scratch comparisons for the determination of hardness are reliable indices of mineral content explains why the Mohs scale is used in geology, but also suggests that alternative measures of hardness based on other kinds of observations may be more suitable where the hardness measure is to be used as an index of other things. This is borne out in mechanical engineering, especially in machine design, where hardness measures are used to help predict the wearing qualities of surfaces. Here the mineral composition is not the primary consideration, and as is well known, other measures of hardness are used: e.g., the Brinell Hardness Number. The Brinell measure is essentially an indentation test, and not a scratch test, and is therefore only contingently correlated with Mohs scale hardness. The fact that we have different and possibly not perfectly correlated measures of hardness is itself significant. "Hardness" as a term of everyday discourse is probably rather vague: given two objects such as a rubber band and piece of paper we have no generally accepted "criteria" for settling the question which is the harder. The same is less true of measure of hardness. That we should call the Mohs scale a measure of

hardness at all is probably due to the fact that it employs in a systematic way *some* of the same kinds of observations we ordinarily base our hardness judgements on, and hence does not disagree with everyday usage, where that is unambiguous. But, the very vagueness of the everyday concept and the variety of procedures we ordinarily use in judging it (probably no one of which is "criterial") allows the possibility of introducing for particular purposes alternative *measures* or *criteria* of hardness, each of which is equally entitled to be called a "measure of hardness."

Second Example: Weight Measurement

The intimate involvement of weight with physical theory makes the analysis of this concept far more difficult than that of hardness. The modern physical definition of weight applies to bodies at or near the earth's surface, and is, roughly, the force of the earth's gravitational attraction on a body. The measurement of weight would therefore appear to be a special case of the measurement of force, and the attempt to specify the procedures for the measurement of force leads to all of the well known problems involved with this concept in the foundations of physics. I will simply sidestep these problems here, and discuss instead certain features of frequently used approximate measures of weight. Note incidentally that the equal arm balance procedure of weight measurement, which is often given as an example of fundamental measurement, itself only yields approximate measures of weight, which must be corrected to take into account the effects of atmospheric pressure in determining physical weight. In this respect the modern theory of fundamental measurement as applied to weights actually represents a retrogression from medieval conceptions. Fourteenth-century writings on the theory of weights (18), for instance, deal explicitly with weights in various fluids, and in particular with weight in air.

The following are several conjectures about the everyday (non-physical) concept of weight, and the relations of weight measures to it. The non-comparative concept to which the notion of weight is related is "heavy," and to say that an object is heavy is to say that, though un-attached to other objects, it is relatively immovable—it is hard to lift and hard to push around. Like other adjectives of its type, "heavy" is strongly category dependent: for example, a heavy mouse is lighter than a light dog. The comparative relation "heavier than" is less category dependent, but everyday discourse has no single criterial procedure for determining whether one physical object is heavier than another. No doubt the most primitive observations upon which judgements of relative heaviness are based involve simple manual manipulations of the objects (e.g., "hefting" them).

The most familiar weight measuring devices —spring scales of various kinds and beam balances—are essentially procedures for comparing the objects being weighed with objects of known weight. In the case of the beam balance the comparison is direct, since the unknown object and the known standards are both present during the weighing. In the case of the spring scale, what is in effect determined is that the object being weighted causes the same extension or compression of the spring as does some known standard. Note that neither weighing procedure involves observations of the most primitive kind. All that one can say is that the result of carrying out the weighing procedure is *indicative* of the relative difficulty in manipulating the objects involved. Much (but far from all) of the practical usefulness of weight measurements is due to the fact that they provide useful information about manipulability, and it is doubtful that we would call them "weight" measures had they not this use. On the other hand, these weight measurement procedures are both more objective and more precise than direct manual comparison. They are more objective because it is possible to obtain better agreement among people as to the outcome of, say, comparing two objects on a beam balance, than it is if they are compared just "by heft." The measur-

ing procedures are more precise in that they lead to finer discriminations than do direct comparisons (this point is closely connected with that about objectivity).

There are two important facts to be noted about the *standards* against which unknown weights are measured: 1) they are used *combinatively*, and 2) they are much more *uniform* than most objects. Consider first the combinative use: that is to say, not only are unknown objects compared with known standards individually, but they are compared with numbers of them put together (e.g., we may determine the weight of an object to be 1 lb., 2 oz. if it balances a standard weight of 1 lb. combined with two standard weights of one ounce). This feature is not present with the Mohs scale of hardness, since it makes no obvious sense to scratch the "combination" of two standard minerals. The feature is present in many other measures of varying degrees of crudeness, however. For example, one might legitimately use as a rough measure of loudness the number of objects producing a known standard noise which would have to be combined to give a noise as loud as the noise to be measured (thus, one might roughly describe a noise as being as loud as 76 trombones). In the case of weight measurement, though, there are laws relating weights of objects which are physical combinations of other objects to the weights of the "components" of the combination which give weight measures a significance which combinative measures do not have in other cases in which, though combination is possible (as it is with sounds), these laws are not satisfied. The key law which is satisfied by weights but not by many other modes of combination (at least, the law is not nearly as exactly satisfied) is that of *substitutivity*: if two objects are equal in weight, then each can be substituted for the other in a combination without affecting the weight of the whole. This fact gives weight measures a multiple significance: not only does the measure indicate how heavy individual objects are, but it also indicates how heavy complex combinations will be.

The foregoing observations on the combinative laws of weights have an important bearing on the significance of the "representational" theory of extensive measurement. What the investigations of Helmholtz, Hölder, Campbell, Suppes and others have shown is what some of the laws of weight combination (and some other kinds of physical combination) are, which give weight measures the kind of combinative significance they have. Representational theorists are mistaken, I believe, in concluding that weights *must* obey these laws for weight measurement to be possible or legitimate. In fact, it is probable that weights do not exactly satisfy these laws, and it is certain that there can be legitimate measurement, even using combinations of standards, which do not conform to these laws at all. All that one could say if it should prove that the combinative laws of extensive measurement are not satisfied by weights, is that weight measures of individual objects would not be completely reliable indices of the weights of the complex objects containing them. But even somewhat unreliable indices may be better than nothing, and clearly we would be very well justified in continuing to use balance comparisons as measures of weights even if the principle of substitutivity should be found to be not exactly satisfied.

Turning now to the uniformity property of the standards, the sense in which I am calling standards *uniform* is that in which these objects do not change in their weight relations relative to one another. Ordinary objects—people, pencils, etc.—change relatively rapidly in their weight relations through time. I am heavier than my son now, but he will probably be heavier than me in a few years. Standards are much less changeable in this respect: that is not to say that they do not change relative to objects which are not standards, but that they change much less relative to other standards. The very delicate procedures of constructing, storing and using fundamental standards are all designed to assure that the conditions which we now know can best preserve relative unchangeability are satisfied.

I suggest that the reason why we select relatively unchanging objects as standards is that comparison of other objects with them is more informative about the things which weight measures are supposed to indicate than are comparisons with more variable objects.

Two final comments are to be made concerning the uniformity requirement for standards. The first bears on the criticism made [on pp. 75–79] to the effect that representational measurement theories do not take into account the possibility of change in the measures of objects through time, or, what is the same thing, that the objects measured do not change in relevant observable relations to each other. If the suggestion above is correct, that ideal *standards* should not change in relevant respects relative to one another, then the representational theory of extensive measurement might be more correctly viewed as a theory of ideal standards of measurement, and not as a theory of all of the objects measured.

The second comment has to do with the definitional status of standards. Superficially, it would seem that standards of weight define weight measures, so that, for instance, the statement "object *A* weighs *x* pounds" appears to *mean* that object *A* balances *x* replications of the standard pound combined together. From this it would also seem to follow that *if* the standard pound were to shrink or be destroyed, then all statements about weights in pounds would become meaningless, or else all weights in pounds would have to be changed by some constant multiplier (thus disproving all of the laws of physics at one fell swoop). Nothing could be more absurd, of course, since it is clear that we would not say that the weights of objects, even in pounds, had changed any more than they normally do, but rather that the standard had suffered an accident—the standard pound no longer weighed one pound.

I would argue the following concerning this. Though weight measurement procedures are more systematic and objective than direct, non-instrumental ways of comparing weights, and weight standards play a systematic role in them, even these procedures cannot be described as "criterial" in the ultimate sense that we would always accept the result of applying them as the final court of appeal in determining the truth or falsity of statements about weight. And, the discussion of the *use* of weight measures should make it clear why we would abandon the procedure under certain circumstances: namely under those in which the outcome of the measuring procedure failed for some reason or other to be a reliable index of the things which we employ the procedure to tell us about. Thus, I would say that in the last analysis it is just as wrong to look for criterial *definitions* of weight measurement as it is to suppose that we have such criteria for applying our everyday, pre-scientific concepts of weight. (These remarks suggest conventionalism; compare especially Reichenbach's discussion of the similar problem for length measurement in (17, p. 20).)

The discussion of weight will be concluded with some rather speculative observations on two further topics. As already noted, the beam balance and the spring scale as ordinarily employed yield only approximate measures of weight defined as the force of the earth's gravitational attraction for an object. I will suppose what is no doubt a considerable over-simplification: namely that physical weight can be measured by employing the beam balance in a vacuum (thus making it unnecessary to correct for the buoyant effect of atmospheric pressure). It is clear that in the case of relatively dense objects the results will be little different from those which are obtained by weighing in air, and this small difference will determine how good an approximation weight in air is to physical weight. Physical weight, just as much as weight in air, is *a* weight measure in that it is a reliable indicator of manipulability. (At some extremes physical weight is not so good an indicator as weight in air, as when it is used to indicate how hard it is to lift very buoyant objects. But, of course, we can make the corrections necessary to determine weight in air from physical weight.)

Physical weight, however, yields information about a great many other things besides manipulability, and it is this which gives it its great importance. Thus, physical weight is proportional to inertia, it is what is conserved through chemical reactions, and so on, none of which is true (or quite so exactly true) of weight in air. To sum up: I would say that both weight in air and physical weight are legitimately characterizable as weight measures and to say that the former is approximate is an elliptical way of saying that it is a fairly good approximation to physical weight, which is the more informative measure for scientific purposes.

The approximation or inexactness involved in taking weight in air as a good approximation to physical weight is closely related to a kind of "intrinsic" inexactness which occurs even in using beam balances or spring scales to measure weight in air. These are the sorts of inaccuracy which are ordinarily ascribed to imperfections in the measuring apparatus (or its user). Thus, insensitivity in the balance leads us to say that we cannot determine that a given object A weights *exactly* 2 lbs., or even that A has exactly the same weight as B ("weight" here meaning weight in air). Why should we say this? I think that the *informational* import of saying that the measurement is inexact is that some of the consequences which follow from the statement reporting the observation are not reliable. Thus, we may report that an object weighs 2 lbs., after weighing it on a crude balance, but we would be unsafe in infering from this that if the object were augmented very slightly in size, then the augmented object would weigh more than 2 lbs. To ascribe limits of accuracy is, I suggest, to set bounds on the reliability of inferences which can be drawn from the reports of measurements. That we should speak of more or less accuracy in the case of weight measurement is due to the fact that more refined observations and instruments can give more reliable information about weights (for instance, about total weights of complex objects which are deduced from the weights of their components). I also conjecture that we do not speak of more or less accurate Mohs scale hardness measures because more exact or uniform hardness measuring procedures (e.g., using a sclerometer) do not give much additional useful information (about mineral content) beyond that obtainable by crude methods.

Some General Conclusions About Measurement

Generalizing from the foregoing examples and some others, the following conclusions can be at least tentatively asserted:

1. At least one very important reason for introducing measurement procedures is to provide systematic, objective indices of phenomena. Numbers may enter into the reports of applying measurement procedures, but this is not essential to their function as indices.

2. The proper question to ask of a procedure of measurement for measuring some quantity (say weight) is not "is it a true measure of the quantity or not?", but "how good an indicator is it of the phenomena it is supposed to give information about?" Intrinsically, there is no such thing as a "more fundamental" procedure for measuring a quantity than another—spring scales and beam balances are to be compared only as to their relative reliability and informativeness about weight phenomena (e.g. manipulability).

3. There are laws of measurement: namely those which connect the result of making the measurement with the phenomena which it is used to give information about. These laws need not be exactly satisfied for the measurement to be useful, and may not be exactly formulable (as in the case of, say, I.Q., in which the measure is useful primarily because it is somewhat informative about that vague but important thing, intelligence). The laws of measurement here spoken of are not the same as those which representational measurement theorists claim must be satisfied for measurement to be possible; however, some of the laws occurring in some of the representa-

tional measurement theories (e.g., that of substitutivity for equal weights) are ones which, to the extent that they are satisfied, give certain kinds of measurements greater informational content than they would otherwise have.

4. Measurement procedures do not *define* the concept or quantity they measure in the sense that they provide logically necessary and sufficient conditions for it. The use of a specific procedure is strictly predicated on the assumption that the basic laws of measurement mentioned in 3) hold. For example, if a fundamental standard of weight is injured, we do not continue to use it in weight measurements, but modify the procedure by substituting a new standard.

5. Measurement procedures are generally more *objective* than are the everyday procedures used to determine the things which the measurement is supposed to provide information about. For instance, it is possible to obtain more general agreement about the results of comparing weights on a beam balance, or an individual's score on an aptitude test, than about the things which these measures are supposed to indicate: ease of manipulability, or aptitude. The greater objectivity is relative, however, and there are almost always areas of application of measurement procedures upon which there is not general agreement.

6. Many measurement procedures employ *standards*, which are known objects such that the comparison of unknown objects with them yields the information upon which the measurement is based. Many of the facts having to do with the selection of standards are to be explained in terms of the informativeness of comparisons with them. One thing in particular seems significant: namely that standards are usually much less variable in relevant respects than are the objects to which they are compared. This invariability is relative, that is to say, that standards are invariable relative to other standards, or other things of the same kind kept under the same conditions.

I hope the foregoing theses about measurement are sufficiently well illustrated in the discussions of hardness and weight measurement not to need further elaboration. It should be conceded at once that not all of these ideas are original, and quite possibly none are. The view of measurement as an index is quite explicit in the writings of some economists, and also in the work of psychologists in the field of test construction. McGill and Garner (14) have even taken the further step of applying mathematical information theory to the analysis of information contributed by numerical measurements. Concerning the special role played by standards, much of the discussion by E. Bright Wilson (25) seems to me to agree fairly closely with what was said above about standards.

In the next sections I will comment briefly and speculatively on some things which appear to be entailed by the basic theses just stated.

The Distinction Between Fundamental and Derived Measurement

The distinction between fundamental and derived measurement, which is generally accepted by representational measurement theorists, can, I believe, still be made within the framework of the revised conception of measurement which I am advocating. Before drawing the distinction, though, we should take note of what appears to be an essential disagreement as to how derived measurements are to be characterized. Campbell (3, p. 346) and B. Ellis (7) following him characterize derived measurement as "measurement by means of constants in numerical laws." Suppes and Zinnes (23, p. 17) give a rather technical definition of derived measurement such that it "does not depend on an empirical relational system directly but on other numerical assignments," which can be roughly paraphrased as saying that derived measurements are measurements which are defined in terms of other numerical measurements. All three authors take density, defined as the ratio of weight to volume, as an example of derived measurement. A somewhat more instructive

example, discussed by Nagel in (15), is the "gas constant" R occurring in the Boyle-Charles Law:

$$pV = mRT,$$

where p, V, m and T are, respectively, the pressure, volume, mass, and absolute temperature of a given quantity of gas, and R is a constant depending on the kind of gas in question. In this example, the Boyle-Charles Law is regarded as an equation defining the derived measure R in terms of pressure, volume, mass, and temperature.

From the point of view of the theory here advanced, the Campbell-Ellis characterization of derived measurement, vague as it is, is superior to the Suppes-Zinnes, at least in that it guarantees that derived measurements satisfy the requirement of being informative indices. According to the Suppes-Zinnes definition, any quantity whatever which is determined by calculation from numerical measures is a derived measurement. By that definition, for instance, wV and $w + V$ (weight times volume and weight plus volume) are just as much derived measurements as density $= w/V$. That a numerical constant enters into a numerical law in which all the other variables occurring are measured by already established measurement procedures (which is the status of the gas constant "R" in the Boyle-Charles Law) in itself guarantees that it is an indicator of something significant. In the Boyle-Charles case, knowing the value of R for a particular kind of gas permits the prediction of any one of p, V, m or T, given a knowledge of the other three: thus, a knowledge of R is highly informative about the relation subsisting between p, V, m and T. Generalizing, one might say that constants occurring in numerical laws are measures which provide information about relationships between the remaining numerical measures appearing in the statement of the law. At least as a first approximation, therefore, the fundamental-derived distinction may still be made in our formulation, in that fundamental measures may be characterized as measures primarily indicative of phenomena (not the results of other measurements), whereas derived measurements are primarily indicative of relations among the values of other measurements. This picture is complicated, of course, by the fact that a given kind of measurement may be used on different occasions for many different things, particularly where, as in physics, it is involved in an extremely complicated set of interrelations with other measurements.

Before leaving this topic, it is well to contrast the fundamental-derived measurement distinction with another distinction between measurements which may be made in terms of their primary use, which I will call the "intrinsic-extrinsic" distinction. By an "intrinsic" measurement procedure (or better, a procedure of primarily intrinsic significance), I mean, roughly, one which involves only observations of the same kind of phenomenon which the measurement is used primarily to give information about. For example, if the Mohs hardness measure were used primarily to yield predictions as to which of two mineral specimens would scratch the other, then it would be of mainly intrinsic significance, since determining Mohs scale hardness involves making scratch comparisons, and it would be used to predict scratch comparisons. The same would be true of beam balance weight measurement, if such measurements were used primarily to predict the outcomes of other beam balance weight comparisons. Since neither Mohs scale measures nor beam balance comparisons are used primarily to yield this kind of intrinsic information, I characterize them as extrinsic measures, or as measures of primarily extrinsic significance.

The importance of making this new distinction is that the axioms exhibited in the representational analyses of such measurement procedures as the Mohs scale hardness determination, and beam balance weight determination are ones that guarantee that these measures are intrinsically significant (i.e. informative about the kinds of phenomena observed in making the measurement). One might say that representational measurement

theory looks upon measurement procedures as yielding only intrinsic information, and it analyzes the laws which would have to be satisfied in order that the measures be maximally informative. The distinction between intrinsic and extrinsic information also suggests a formal problem which is touched on, though not resolved, in the Appendix: namely, to what extent can one neglect consideration of the extrinsic information in developing a procedure of measurement which will be maximally informative? This question arises in particular in the consideration of Mohs scale hardness, where one may ask whether, in selecting standards for comparison (the ten standard minerals), one can safely assume that if they are chosen so that comparison of other objects with the standards yields maximal information about scratch comparisons, then these comparisons will also be maximally informative concerning mineral composition.

Measurement Systems and Frames of Reference

If we focus only on the intrinsic informational content of measurement procedures, many procedures can be regarded essentially as ones which locate objects (the objects measured) in frames of reference (the known standards). To locate an object A in a spatial reference frame S is to determine the spatial relation of A to S (e.g., to determine how far A is and in what direction from a given "origin"). Similarly, to determine the Mohs scale hardness of a rock is to determine its scratching relations to known mineral standards, and to weigh an object on a beam balance is to determine what combination of standard weights it balances. The intrinsic information obtained through measuring Mohs scale hardness or beam balance weight is also similar to that obtained by locating an object in a spatial reference frame. What we can determine from a knowledge of the positions of objects $A_1, \ldots, A_n$ relative to some spatial reference frame S is the spatial relations of $A_1, \ldots, A_n$ to one another. Similarly, knowing the positions of two or more objects on the Mohs scale of hardness gives us a knowledge of their scratching relations to one another (though this information is not as reliable as the spatial information), and giving the beam balance weights of several objects relative to standard weights determines how they will behave with respect to one another in the pans of the balance.

The analogy of measurement to determining location in a reference frame somewhat reinforces, I think, the thesis that there is nothing essentially numerical about measurement. In giving locations on the Earth's surface, the latitude and longitude system provides a useful reference frame, but positions need not be described numerically at all (thus, it is equally correct to say that something is at 90° N. latitude, or that it is at the North Pole). The analogy should also help to emphasize the fact that reference frames are chosen for convenience and informativeness and so are standards and numerical descriptions. As in the case of position, in which some common coordinate systems are non-linear transformations of others, there is no reason to maintain that all systems for numerically describing weights *must* be linear transformations of one another. This, then, is another criticism of the "permissible transformation" or "scale type" conception of measurement.

Meaningfulness

According to the present theory, it is correct to assess measurement procedures in terms of their informativeness, and I will now suggest that what writers like Stevens (19) and Suppes (22) have tried to formulate in their theories of appropriate statistics and of meaningfulness of statements about measurements (also the theory of Adams, Fagot, and Robinson (1)) are more or less objective means for assuring that statistical "measures" and statements be informative. The question of meaningfulness or appropriateness usually is raised about numbers calculated from numerical measurements and statements made about them. Thus, it is sometimes said that *differences*

in Mohs scale hardness measures are not meaningful, and that taking the mean of Mohs scale hardness measures of all of the rocks in a class is not appropriate. I conjecture that, to the extent that we have intuitive feelings about meaningfulness and appropriateness, we tend to judge these operations and the statements made about them to be meaningful, significant, appropriate, etc., according as they are informative about things of concern to us. I think that we intuitively regard differences and means of Mohs scale hardness measures as insignificant simply because (so far as we know) they are not reliable indicators of anything besides themselves: i.e., these quantities are not derived measures. If we were to discover, say, that differences in Mohs scale hardness were highly correlated with some other relation between rock specimens besides scratching, then this would immediately confer on differences a significance or "meaningfulness" which they are not now known to have.

The situation is somewhat more complicated in the case of statistical operations, such as taking means. The added complication is due to the fact that the significance of a statistic is difficult to assess under the best of circumstances. That is to say, such statistics as means are population measures (which are derived from the measures of individuals) which are designed to give significant information about the population, and yet the fact that it is so easy to "lie with statistics" shows that this information is hard to understand and easy to misinterpret. I regard much of statistical theory as having as its objective the clarification of the significance of various population and sample statistics. And, it seems to me that Stevens' theory of appropriate statistics can be viewed as setting up criteria which will assure that certain statistical measures will be used only under circumstances in which their significance is understood.

Alternative Descriptions; Invariance as a Criterion of Meaningfulness

It is clear that we can describe the outcome of

a single weighing or hardness determination in several logically equivalent ways already discussed, some of which may not be numerical at all. Not all of these ways of describing measurements need be equivalent as concerns their simplicity and "usability," however, and clearly numerical descriptions have the advantage where the measures satisfy laws which have a convenient numerical formulation (though the numerical formulation itself may not be essential, since the law may be equivalently statable without using functions taking real numbers as values). At a given stage in the development of science, there are clearly "preferred standard descriptive systems" (one is tempted to say "preferred frames of reference"). At present, physical weights are most conveniently given in grams, but only slightly less conveniently in pounds and ounces, and less conveniently (for scientific purposes) in pounds plus remainders in ounces.

Why should two alternative ways of describing measurements appear to be "equivalent" in more than a logical sense? Why, for example, should descriptions of weights in pounds and in ounces seem about on a par, whereas we would regard a description giving the reciprocal of weight in pounds as essentially different? The reason, I conjecture, is that we calculate all of the significant derived measures based on weights in the same way, given weights in pounds or in ounces, whereas we would first have to take reciprocals in order to calculate these derived measures from reciprocals of weights in pounds. Thus, we could give weight in reciprocals of pounds, but we could not calculate the weight of a complex object from the weights of its parts on this basis in the same way we do it given weights in pounds or ounces (by simple addition). It seems likely that at a given juncture in the development of science, the preferred "standard descriptions" of the results of measuring are all ones in which the significant derived measures based on the kind of measurement in question are calculated from these descriptions in the same way.

The history of the development of temperature measures may be a case in point. Without going in detail into the rather complicated history of temperature, it is sufficient to note that there were at least three distinct phases in the development: one in which temperature measurements were "anchored" at two arbitrarily chosen points, and the subdivision of the interval between these extremes was also rather arbitrary, another in which the unit and origin remained arbitrary, but subdivisions of the scale were made in accordance with the rule that an increase of one degree on the temperature scale represented an addition of one unit of heat (for a standard quantity of water), and a third in which absolute temperature measures were introduced. Going from the first to the second stage coincided with the discovery of the laws of calorimetry, and the introduction of absolute temperature measures was connected with the discovery of the general gas laws and the development of the statistical conception of heat. The discovery of new laws into which temperature enters was associated with the fact that new derived measures based on temperature measures were found to have significance. That temperatures can be measured in such a way that equal differences of temperature correspond to equal increments of heat suggests (but does not dictate) that we describe temperature measurements in this way, and the discovery that temperature can be measured in such a way that pV/m is proportional to it suggests the utility of measuring it so that that condition is also satisfied.

The foregoing remarks bear on the notion that invariance is a criterion of meaningfulness. What seems to me to be the case is that, at any stage in the development of science, the preferred standard measurement descriptions are ones such that all of the then known significant derived measures can be calculated from them in the same way. Permissible transformations can be viewed simply as ones which carry one preferred measurement description system (e.g., weights in pounds) into another (e.g., weights in ounces). It would follow then that standard descriptions are chosen in such a way that the significant derived measures will turn out to be invariant under the permissible transformations. Thus, invariance does not determine meaningfulness, but rather discovery of meaningfulness or significance may be expected to change standard descriptions and permissible transformations in such a way that significant derived measurements are invariant.

Measurement and Theory

That the acceptance of scientific theories may have an influence on measurement procedures and practices is obvious. The influence may take at least three forms. First, any newly discovered law which establishes a correlation between two phenomena automatically provides the basis of new procedures of measuring either one: namely by observation of the other. In the sense that measurement procedures are fundamentally ones whose purpose is to provide indications of phenomena clearly any correlation between phenomena suggests at least a potential measurement procedure. Second, as Kuhn (11) has argued, even provisionally accepted theories are often used as criteria of reliability or exactness in measurement. An example cited by Kuhn, that of the measurement of short time intervals in early studies of falling and sliding bodies, is a good case in point. In Galileo's day there were no reliable instruments (i.e., "uniform" instruments in the sense of this paper) for the measurement of such short time intervals as were involved in these studies. According to Kuhn, acceptance of Galileo's theories led to judging time measurements as exact to the extent that they agreed with these theories. From the point of view of the present theory, the reliance on a theory to provide criteria of exactness may be quite well justified, given the basic purposes of measurement: what it suggests is that, to the extent that the theory is well grounded, there is good reason to believe that measurements in agreement with its laws are better indices of the phenomena they are supposed to indicate than are measurements

in less good agreement. At the moment, of course, this is only a conjecture, and further study of this topic is needed.

The third major influence of theory on measurement arises from the fact that theories may suggest ways for making more uniform standards of measurement. Huyghens' "corrected" pendulum clock (whose period is at least theoretically independent of its amplitude) might be taken as an example of a practical improvement in chronometry which is based on scientific principles. According to Newtonian theory at least, such clocks should serve as better (i.e., more uniform) time measuring standards than uncorrected ones, because any two such standards ought to "stay in step" or "keep time" better than uncorrected pendula. (I am taking for granted here that clocks—i.e., standards of time comparison—are sequentially repeating processes, and that the uniformity requirement for this kind of standard is that any two such standard processes, if started at the same time, continue to stay in time with each other.) Note that in this case, though theory leads to the conclusion that two such corrected pendula ought to stay very nearly in step, this conclusion is at least in principle checkable by observation (though problems arise in reducing friction to the point where enough swings of the pendula can be observed to obtain a reliable comparison).

In the foregoing observations I have deliberately avoided discussion of the well known philosophical problems concerning the meaning, testing and confirmation of theories themselves. The view I have been advocating on measurement certainly does not provide any obvious help in the solution of these problems. To a considerable extent, the problems arise because theories are stated in terms of the results of measurements, but very seldom do they explicitly specify the procedures to be used to make the measurements they refer to. If, as I have argued, alternative procedures, even ones yielding inconsistent results, may with equal right be called measures of the same thing, this suggests that theories stated in terms of the results of such measures (e.g., in terms of time measures) are ambiguous. The problem, to explain in what sense or senses these theories are interpreted, is one I cannot resolve, and all that I will do here is to note two factors controlling the interpretation of measurements entering into the formulation of theories. First, though there is no such thing as "the" criterial procedure for measuring, say, weight, any weight measurement procedure used in the application or testing of a theory involving weight ought to be *a* weight measure in the sense that its results should be highly correlated with the results of other weight measurement procedures. This requirement does not remove all vagueness from the interpretation of theory, but it does at least guarantee that the theory has empirical content: it must be informative about weight as measured in familiar ways. Second, to the extent that measures are defined with reference to standards, and standards are required to be uniform, the discovery or construction of more uniform standards will narrow the class of possible alternative measures and so restrict the range of possible interpretations of the theory. Thus, the theory might be regarded as "predicting" the laws which would be satisfied by perfectly uniform standards, based on the assumption that such standards can be arbitrarily closely approximated. As before, all this is highly speculative, and stands in need of much more study.

A final comment on the relation of measurement to theory has to do with a view of Nagel's (15, p. 123) on the purpose of measurement:

Consequently, if we inquire why we measure in physics, the answer will be that if we do measure, and measure in certain ways, then it will be possible to establish the equations and theories which are the goal of inquiry.

Whether or not this quotation accurately states Nagel's views, it seems to me to illustrate a very basic difference in point of view between my position and that of Nagel and a good many other writers on scientific method.

Nagel seems to consider measurements primarily as they are made in the course of *research*, the ultimate objective of which is the establishment of new or more refined theories. My position emphasizes the role of measurement in *application*, where a theory may be involved, but the objective is to do something or anticipate something, and not to create or test a theory. A comprehensive theory of science should give both aspects of it their due, of course, yet it seems to me that much recent writing greatly overemphasizes the "inquiry" or research aspect—perhaps derogating the applied aspect as "mere engineering." If there is any validity to the theory of measurement I am advocating, this should suggest the desirability of more detailed examination of engineering aspects of science than has hitherto been made by philosophers of science.

Note: The article from which this selection is taken concludes with an Appendix, showing how the statistical theory of information may be applied to one of the systems of measurement discussed in the article, in such a way as to give a mathematical formulation to informal claims made there concerning the *informativeness* of measurement procedures.

References

1. Adams, E. W., Fagot, R. F., and Robinson, R. E., A Theory of Appropriate Statistics, *Psychometrika* 30 (1965) 99–127.
2. Anderson, N. H. Scales and Statistics: Parametric and Nonparametric, *Psychological Bulletin* 58 (1961) 305–16.
3. Campbell, N. R., *Physics: The Elements*, Cambridge 1920. Reprinted as *The Foundations of Science*, New York 1957.
4. Comrey, A. L., Mental Testing and the Logic of Measurement, *Educational and Psychological Measurement* 11 (1951) 323–34.
5. Davidson, D., and Suppes, P., A Finitistic Axiomatization of Subjective Probability and Utility, *Econometrica*, 24 (1956) 264–75.
6. Eisler, H., On psychophysics in General and the General Psycho-Physical Equation in Particular, *Scandinavian Journal of Psychology* 6 (1965) 85–102.

7. Ellis, B., Some Fundamental Problems of Direct Measurement, *Australasian Journal of Philosophy* 38 (1960) 37–47.

8. Ford, W. E. *Dana's Textbook of Mineralogy*, 4th edition, New York, 1947.

9. von Helmholtz, H., Zählen und Messen erkenntnis-theoretisch betrachtet in *Philosophische Aufsätze Eduard Zeller gewidmet*, Leipzig 1887.

10. Krantz, D., Conjoint Measurement: the Luce-Tukey Axiomatization and Some Extensions, *Journal of Mathematical Psychology* 1 (1964) 249–78.

11. Kuhn, T., The Function of Measurement in Modern Physical Science, *Isis* 52 (1961) 161–93.

12. Lord, F., On the Statistical Treatment of Football Numbers, *American Psychologist* 8 (1953) 750–51.

13. Luce, R. D., and Tukey, J. W., Simultaneous Conjoint Measurement: a New Type of Fundamental Measurement, *Journal of Mathematical Psychology* 1 (1964) 1–27.

14. McGill, W. J. and Garner, W. R. The Relation Between Information and Variance Analysis, *Psychometrika* 21 (1956) 219–28.

15. Nagel, E., Measurement, *Erkenntnis* 2 (1931) 313–33; reprinted in Danto, A. and Morgenbesser, S. (eds.), *Philosophy of Science*, New York 1960.

16. Pfanzagl, J., *Die axiomatischen Grundlagen einer allgemeinen Theorie des Messens* (Schriftenreihe des Statistischen Instituts der Universität Wien, Neue Folge 1), Würzburg 1959.

17. Reichenbach, H., *Space and Time*, New York 1958.

18. Senders, V. L. A Comment on Burke's Additive Scales and Statistics, *Psychological Review* 60 (1953) 423–24.

19. Stevens, S. S., On the Theory of Scales of Measurement, *Science* 103 (1946) 667–80.

20. Stevens, S. S., Measurement, Psychophysics, and Utility, in C. W. Churchman and P. Ratoosh (eds.), *Measurement: Definitions and Theories*, New York 1959.

21. Suppes, P., A Set of Independent Axioms for Extensive Quantities, *Portugaliae Mathematica* 10 (1951) 163–72.

22. Suppes, P., Measurement, Meaningfulness, and Three-Valued Logic, in C. W. Churchman and P. Ratoosh (eds.), *Measurement: Definitions and Theories*, New York 1959.

23. Suppes, P. and Zinnes, J. L., Basic Measurement Theory, in R. D. Luce, R. R. Bush, and E. Galanter (eds.), *Handbook of Mathematical Psychology*, Vol. I, New York 1963.

24. Tversky, A., *Finite Additive Structures*, Report MMPP 64–6, Department of Psychology, University of Michigan, Ann Arbor, Mich., 1964.

25. Wilson, E. B., *An Introduction to Scientific Research*, New York 1952.

CLETUS J. BURKE

7 Measurement Scales and Statistical Models

During the past fifteen or twenty years, there have been several flurries of papers about issues related to statistics and measurement. A controversy has arisen over the interrelation of statistics and measurement; the two opposed viewpoints can be named the measurement-directed position and the measurement-independent position. Proponents of the measurement-directed position, who will be referred to in the sequel as "measurement-directeds," hold that statistical techniques are directed by measurement considerations. Proponents of the measurement-independent position, referred to in the sequel as "measurement-independents," hold that measurement and statistics are separate, independent domains and that therefore measurement considerations do not influence statistical techniques. We shall define the issue between these two positions and summarize their views on important questions, with special reference to practical applications of statistics. Finally, we shall try to re-examine the whole issue and propose a resolution.

The Measurement-Directed Position

Briefly, adherents of this position hold that measurement scales are frequently subject to certain laws of regularity which we shall call measurement models. Thus the measurement model for physical length or for physical weight is a system of ten or so axioms and the theorems which can be derived from them. The power and utility of a measurement scale derives, at least for certain problems, from the properties of the measurement model and its applicability to data. Statistical usage involves operations with numbers, such as the addition of numbers, which may be valid with some kinds of measurement scales and invalid with others. The validity of any statistical operation is to be decided on the basis of an underlying measurement model; for example, with any given measurement scale, the statistical operation of taking the mean may or may not be valid. Since the operation of taking the mean involves the addition of numbers, it will be valid only when the measurement scale has an additive property.

The measurement-directed view has its roots in writings in physics and in the philosophy of physics but takes form in psychology essentially in the writings of Stevens. Stevens (16) classifies scales of measurement into four classes, namely, nominal, ordinal, interval, and ratio scales. The nominal scale is simply a classification based on what Stevens calls a determination of equality (in other words, of common class membership), and the only permissible statistical measure of central tendency is the mode. The ordinal scale has order based on the empirical operation of the determination of greater or less, and the median is a permissible measure. The interval scale is based on the determination of the equality of

intervals or of differences, and the arithmetic mean is a permissible measure. The ratio scale is based on the empirical operation of the determination of the equality of ratios, and the geometric mean or the harmonic mean are permissible measures of central tendency. We can readily see that this classification of scales is based on properties of a measurement model but that recommendations based on the classification are carried over into the domain of statistics.

The philosophical origins of the measurement-directed view seem to be Platonic. Until a few short years ago, much of psychology rested in Plato's special world. Psychological concepts and dimensions were conceived as existing independently of the body of psychological knowledge. Among the denizens of the Platonic world were entities such as intelligence, will, and feeling. The psychologist's task was to discover in the complex world of reality the laws governing the operation and interaction of such entities. We might remark parenthetically that physics, too, has spent much of its career in this world. In the past half century, a number of psychological workers from Watson through Kantor, Stevens, and Tolman to Skinner, Graham, and Spence have accomplished a revolution in psychological thought. As a result, the concepts of the psychologist are frankly recognized as scientific constructions made to organize the data of the behavioral domain. In contemporary literature such words as *construct*, *operation*, and *criterion* replace words such as *true* or *real*. Consequently, the Platonic world is now primarily of archaeological interest, but I suspect that living fossils lurk and defend themselves in the area of psychological measurement.

Much of the writing of the measurement-directed school can be understood on the basis of the following hypothesis, namely, there exists a Platonic world of real lengths and real temperatures, and in that world our present measurements of length and absolute temperature correspond to the truth, but our measurements of centigrade temperature do not. This Platonic world is composed of real intelligences which, as scientific measures, are every bit as good as the real lengths. In scientific practice, however, the intelligences are inferior to lengths, because we have not yet found the way to measure them which corresponds to the underlying truth. However, a Platonic world of real loudnesses also exists, and here in recent years we have found the proper way to measure. That this sort of hypothesis is found in the writings of Stevens is curious, for he is one of the psychologists who has promoted the revolution of the past thirty years away from such concepts in psychology.

The Measurement-Independent Position

Proponents of this position hold that the results of measurement operations are sets of numbers and, further, that statistical techniques are methods for drawing inferences about sets of numbers of making comparisons between sets of numbers. Hence, once the numbers are available, the statistician is free to proceed with his methods without bothering about any outside considerations. In particular, no properties of a measurement model can have any relevance for statistical operations.

On the philosophical side, the measurement-independent position rejects Platonism. So far as measurements are concerned, the scales may be more or less adequate for the scientific jobs they are expected to do. A completely adequate scale is a scale which exists within a comprehensive and successful scientific theory and which permits accurate and useful computations and predictions. According to this hypothesis, length has been a successful scale in physics because Euclidian geometry has been successfully applied, and temperature has been a successful scale because thermodynamics is a valid and enduring science.

Every empirical domain now covered by polished and viable theory whose history I have studied exhibits in its early development very crude measuring techniques. The workers in every field have reserved complete freedom in performing numerical and algebraic operations on the numbers resulting from the crude measurements. Such freedom of operation has often led to the discovery of important empirical laws which point the way to the final polished theory. Incidentally, empirical laws also point the way to the final adequate measurement scale, but one cannot reach even the first signpost on this way unless he has taken some crude measurement as a starting point and unless he has reserved for himself freedom for operating with the numbers resulting from that crude measurement. Such freedom, however, is categorically denied the scientific worker by the measurement-directed position.

The origins of the measurement-independent position are also partly in statistics. The view of statistics embodied in that position is, as has been previously asserted, that statistics is a set of methods which begins and ends with numbers, a set of methods which is concerned with inferences about sets of numbers, comparisons between sets of numbers, and ultimately statements about sets of numbers.

The Issues

There are a number of issues on which the two positions should be compared. They are in agreement with respect to 1) the definition of measurement and 2) the philosophical status of measurement properties. They are in disagreement with respect to 1) their view of statistics, 2) their view of the role of numbers in scientific work, 3) the resolution of certain difficulties in the application of statistical methods to monotonic transformations of simple measures, and 4) the criteria according to which selection is to be made from alternative non-parametric or distribution-free tests. These differences in the positions are, of course, all related to the fundamental difference on the question of the relevance or irrelevance for statistical procedures of measurement considerations. We shall proceed to compare the two positions with respect to the points of similarity and difference.

The points of agreement are easily disposed of.

1. Definitions of measurement: proponents of the two positions have agreed, so far as one can tell, on a definition of measurement as the assignment, according to fixed rules, of numbers to objects.

2. Philosophical status of measurement properties: proponents of the two positions agree that the measurement properties of a scale refer to semantic relations between the numbers of the scale and certain phenomena outside the scale.

The points of difference require somewhat more discussion.

1. The view of statistics: the picture of statistics which characterizes the measurement-directed position makes statistics directly dependent upon measurement. Statistics is conceived as a group of techniques not for comparing sets of numbers but for comparing sets of objects. The comparison of the sets of objects must somehow involve more than the comparison of the sets of numbers which represent the objects. The "more" which is involved is a measurement model which sets out certain correspondences between properties of the objects and properties of the numbers. The position may be summarized in the following quotation from Stevens (18):

The kind of scale we work with depends, of course, upon the concrete empirical operations we are able to perform, and, as we might expect, the character of the operations determines the kind of statistics that are permissible.

This comes about because a scale erected by a given set of operations can be transformed in certain permissible ways without doing violence to the essential nature of the scale. As a matter of fact, the best way to specify the nature of the scale is in terms of its "group structure"—the group of mathematical transformations that leave the scale form invariant. And it follows quite naturally that the statistics applicable to a given scale are those that remain appropriately invariant under the nsformation permitted by the scale.

The measurement-independents maintain that statistical techniques are techniques for the comparison of sets of numbers as numbers and, therefore, that measurement properties of a scale are irrelevant for statistical tests.

2. The role of numbers in science; adherents of both positions recognize the power of numbers in scientific work. The measurement-directeds ascribe this power entirely to the properties of numbers as they occur in measurement models. Whenever gains result from the use of numbers, attempts are made to derive the gains from properties of a measurement model. The measurement-independents hold that numbers have had great use and success in science simply because, after measurements have been made, difficult, clumsy, and sometimes impossible comparisons between objects can be replaced by easy, and often elegant, comparisons between numbers. Such comparisons will be statistical when statistical questions are involved. They may be comparisons of order or other properties when measurement models are involved. They may be, in addition, almost any sort of comparison which the ingenuity of a scientific theorist operating with a theory finds relevant.

3. Statistical methods and monotonic transformations: proponents of the measurement-independent position hold that, for statistical purposes, the important property of the measurement scale is order and, further, that in making statistical comparisons one deals with the numbers as numbers alone. The consequences of these two assumptions when applied to monotonic transformations undoubtedly influence the measurement-directed position.

One can obtain a set of measurements and run a test without finding statistical significance. One may then make a monotonic transformation of the numbers by looking up their logarithms, say, or taking their reciprocals. The monotonic transformation changes nothing about the order of the numbers, yet the same test on the transformed set may yield statistical significance. Steven's writings (13–19), as well as those of Senders (11) and Siegel (12), make clear that their common viewpoint toward measurement and statistics is brought about at least in part by a desire for strictures to prohibit statistical turpitude. Without some sort of stricture, whether a person uses a set of numbers, or their logarithms, or some other monotonic transformation, is arbitrary. Thus the measurement-directeds seek to legislate statistical honesty by imposing measurement restrictions.

The measurement-independent position admits these difficulties. Of course, the investigator can reach one conclusion by applying a statistical test to a set of measures but another by applying the same test to a set of monotonic transforms. He can also reach different conclusions by applying different tests of the same hypothesis to the same set of measures. Either of these dilemmas is a statistical dilemma. For statistical purposes selection of the proper measurement with a given test or the proper test with a given measurement must be based on statistical grounds. A vast literature defines optimal statistical procedures and gives the conditions under which given procedures are optimal. The conditions are usually concerned with the form of the underlying population. Empirical information about the populations dealt with is necessary for making good choices of either a test or a transformation. Introducing irrelevancy to ignorance does not help solve the problems.

4. Selection of non-parametric or distribution-free tests: in distribution-free statistics a number of alternative tests for the same hypothesis frequently exist. To choose among them is difficult. The measurement-directed position invokes measurement properties for making the selection. The entire theoretical burden of Siegel's book on non-parametric statistics is concerned with the use of measurement properties for making such a choice.

The measurement-independents hold that the choice among alternative distribution-free tests involves difficult statistical problems. The tests are distribution-free only when the hypotheses being tested are true. Thus the probability of a type I error can be calculated without recourse to the distribution. But the power of a distribution-free test is scarcely nonparametric. In other words, when the hypothesis being tested is false, selection of a distribution-free test should be motivated by a consideration of the most likely alternative hypotheses. This observation points up a number of unsolved statistical problems. Since the problems are unsolved, the suggestion given here is of little practical value for a person wishing to make a selection at the present time. However, the proper problem is the determination of statistical criteria for the selection and is only hidden by the introduction of irrelevant measurement considerations. What must be carried forward is work on the type II error in testing various sorts of hypotheses by distribution-free methods.

There are several papers which deal with various aspects of the issues in general or philosophical terms. Bergmann and Spence (1) have dealt excellently with the concomitants of the two viewpoints, giving special reference to the history of physics. The emphasis of the remainder of the present paper is on the statistical aspects of the issues.

Statistical Practice

As the positions of the measurement-directeds and the measurement-independents have been described, some differences certainly appear to exist. Whether the differences are of more than philosophical import depends upon whether they have any effects on statistical practice. We shall show concretely that the proponents of both positions approach their statistical problems in the same way but that the adherents of the measurement-independent position will work with greater statistical efficiency.

The operations of the measurement-independents in statistical inference are easily described. 1) They assess the sample data. Obviously, no statements of scientific interest can be made about populations without looking at the data at least in samples. 2) The relation of the sample to the population from which it arises is considered. Specifically, the sampling method is taken into account; usually a random sampling will have been made. 3) Statistical theorems are employed to make statements about the population on the basis of the sample data and the relation of the sample to the population. 4) A scientific interpretation of the results is made. For the interpretation the only important requirement is that the order of the numbers preserve some order in the underlying objects. A fundamental question is whether the measurement-directeds proceed in any different way. To see that they do not, the simplest procedure is to consider a few examples.

Example 1. The Use of the Responses of Children as Measuring Instruments. In Table 1

Table 1. Number of paces needed by each child to measure each course

	CHILD			
Course	*M*	*T*	*S*	*K*
A	22	24	30	30
B	66	75	86	111
(B–A)	44	51	56	81

is given the simplest batch of data which could be collected to illustrate the point. There are two courses, A and B, and we are concerned with the lengths of the courses. We ask four children to walk the courses naturally, counting their steps. No child is told how many steps any other child takes. This is a physical measurement, to be sure, but a bad one. I suspect that the scale is not an interval scale, for parenthood has taught me that even a fairly large child will take anywhere from four to ten times as many steps in walking two miles as in walking one. Our problem is to find out whether one course is longer than the other. We proceed by testing the hypothesis that they are of the same length. For purposes of argument we shall agree that the scale is not interval; however, as we proceed, we shall see that this is of no great importance.

The measurement-independent proceeds according to the following steps: 1) He sets up the physical or geometrical hypothesis that the courses are of the same length. 2) He assumes that the number of steps taken by any child preserves the order of length but does not

necessarily have any stronger measurement properties. 3) From 1 and 2 he deduces that any number assigned by any child is as likely to be assigned to course A as to course B. 4) From 3 he deduces his statistical hypothesis, namely, that the population mean of the difference between the numbers assigned by the children to the two courses, A and B, is zero.

Note that the statistical hypothesis of step 4 has reference only to the population mean of a set of numbers. Furthermore, this so-called null hypothesis has been derived from considerations of order alone.

The measurement-independent will probably make an assumption of normality and test the hypothesis by using the t-test, since the absence of an interval scale does not, for him, prohibit the calculation of means and variances. He will obtain a value of 3.6 for t on the given data, which is significant with 3 df at beyond the five-per-cent level.

A measurement-directed will insist on a non-parametric test of the hypothesis if he agrees that the scale is not interval. He goes through the following steps: 1) He hypothesizes that the two courses have the same length. 2) He assumes that order in the numbers reflects order in the lengths. 3) From 1 and 2 he deduces that any number assigned by any child is as likely to be assigned to course A as to course B. 4) From 3 he concludes that for any child the number assigned to course A is as likely to be larger as to be smaller than the number assigned to course B.

As with the proponents of the other position, the statistical hypothesis of step 4 is a statement about, and only about, a population of numbers. Again it has been derived solely from a physical hypothesis and considerations of order.

Proponents of the measurement-directed position would work up the data by means of the sign test, obtaining a level of significance of 1/8, which is as strong a level as is possible for a double-ended sign test on these data.

What should be clear is that: 1) The statement of the physical or geometrical hypothesis is the same in the two cases. 2) The assumption of the preservation of order is common to the two cases. 3) The deduction of the indifference of the assignment of numbers with respect to courses is the same in the two cases. 4) The relationship between the indifference of assignment of numbers and the statistical hypothesis is equivalent in the two cases, differing only as the hypotheses differ in detail of statement. Therefore, the only difference between the two positions in this example is the question of the statistical efficiency of the test selected.

The conclusion based on the statistical test can, of course, be wrong. The population may not be normal, in which case the method of the measurement-independent would be biased, but surely this merely statistical question is not among the points at issue. Or the sampling might not be random, in which case both methods would be biased, not necessarily equally. Finally, the experiment might be bad in that the order of step-numbers might not reflect order of length (for example, course A might be level but course B sharply inclined, or each child might be fatigued after walking course A, so that he would take more steps on course B), but such lack of preservation of order is equally damaging to both procedures.

Before passing to the next example, we remark that A and B can be any objects—physical, psychological, or whatnot. Our four children can provide the numbers of the slide as measures of any property of the objects A and B. The measures may be test scores, ratings of aggression, or anything. Whatever they represent, if we agree that their order is correct, aside from possible errors of measurement, then by the argument just concluded, the procedures characteristic of both positions are still defensible. The decision on procedure should be based on statistical criteria, entirely within the realm of numbers.

Example 2. The Mean and Median from a Normal Population. This example is more abstract than the first, but it makes the same point. Suppose we have two random samples from populations known to be normal and of unit variance. We wish to test the hypothesis

that the two populations have the same mean —or median, since the distribution is symmetrical—under the assumption that the scale is ordinal at best.

Measurement-independents will emphasize the normal form of the population and, seeking statistical stability, will use the t-test to compare the sample means. Measurement-directeds will emphasize the weakness of the measurement scale and will compare the sample medians.

The interpretive question on whether the measures reflect some desired extra-numerical property is not at issue, since adherents of the two positions test equivalent hypotheses by assessing information from identical samples of numbers. Hence, the measurement properties of the scale are simply irrelevant. But a great gain in statistical efficiency obtains for the measurement-independents. When the population is normal, the sample mean is more stable that the sample median. For every 100 subjects run by a measurement-independent, the measurement-directed must run 250 subjects to obtain the same experimental precision. His statistical luxury is again experimentally wanton.

Example 3. Latencies in Hullian Theory. When a variable exists within the framework of a systematic theory, the structure of the theory tells us how to manipulate numbers representing the variable. To show the importance of theory for the present discussion, let us make the friendly assumption that the learning theory of Hull and Spence is comprehensive and successful and that all parameters have been evaluated. Then let us suppose that we have the problem of comparing two sets of response latencies.

Among the basic relations of the theory is one between response latency and momentary effective reaction potential. Response latency as a time measure has several well-understood and presumably desirable measurement properties but has a badly skewed and poorly-understood distribution; in fact, if the theory of Hull is accurate, the distribution of latencies is very bad—none of the moments exist. Momentary effective reaction potential, on the other hand, may be an abominable variable from the point of view of measurement models, but it has a simple, well-understood normal distribution. If a proponent of the measurement-directed position were faced with this problem in an experimental interpretation of the learning theory, I am convinced that he would use the t-test on the momentary effective reaction potential rather than mess with the difficult and unstable distribution of response latencies.

That the random variables on which statistical tests and estimates are based are themselves mathematical entities is simply a matter of fact. It follows therefore that statistical decisions cannot depend on measurement properties.

Re-examination and Re-evaluation

If the statistical practices of proponents of the two viewpoints are as we have described, the question arises as to why any disagreement exists at all. Why has not the position of the measurement-independents carried the day? A possible answer is that the issues have not yet been explored at sufficient depth and that adequate exploration will reveal weaknesses in the position. A second possibility is that misunderstandings have arisen through unclarity of language.

In connection with the second possibility, we might note that in the literature on measurement and statistics the term "measurement" is used with several meanings. We shall here distinguish four concepts, each of which is often called *measurement*, namely, *measurement model*, *measurement operation*, *measurement result*, and *measurement*. A *measurement model* is a theory based on a measurement scale. A *measurement operation* is a collection of empirical and numerical manipulations which leads to the assignment of a single number to a unique object. A *measurement result* is the single number assigned through a measurement operation. The fourth term, *measurement*, will be discussed at length below.

We shall not review in detail the literature separating the four meanings of the term but will state a conviction that much misunderstanding can be avoided if the four meanings are kept clearly separated.

More serious misunderstandings may have arisen because of the first possibility, the possibility that the fundamental definition of measurement, although agreed upon by the two positions, has been given in insufficient depth. The definition given for measurement corresponds really to the definition we have just given for measurement operation. Yet, in interesting cases, whether in physics, psychology, or whatever science, a measurement operation clearly falls short of what we mean by measurement. If we examine practice instead of homily, we discover that scientific measurement is the attempt to assign a statistical population to a unique object.

Examples abound. The velocity of light is given as two numbers, an index of central tendency accompanied by an index of variability. Our first attempts to weigh a chemical object with great accuracy were guided by instructions to perform several weighings (*three* is the magic number of my own recollection) and to base the final weight on all. Nor is there any indication in finding or precept that repetition of precisely the same operations on presumably the same object will always lead to the same result. On the contrary, variability is expected as well as encountered whenever we try to make very accurate determinations of quantity.

This has been recognized before. But it has been described Platonically. The stick has been described as having a fixed but unknown number for its length and the scientist as making errors in trying to evaluate the number. Surely the length of the stick is more accurately described as a population of numbers whose properties depend upon the stick and the technique of measurement. In point of fact, one never assigns the population. At best, one performs finitely many measurement operations and thus draws a sample of finite size. Indeed, experience has shown that with certain scales and for certain purposes a sample of unit size suffices.

The stochastic view of measurement as the assignment of a population to an object is consistent with much of the language of measurement. When one speaks of making enough observations to get a stable result or describes the mean of several observations as better than any single observation, one is clearly in the realm of statistical estimation.

For many purposes—testing an additivity property of a measurement model, for example—it is necessary to represent each object by a single number. Such necessity does not contradict the stochastic view of measurement. The number to be used is simply an estimate of some parameter of the population, most often an index of central tendency. Historically the population mean has almost invariably been estimated in measurement problems. There is no a priori reason, however, why one should not find an additive property characterizing a measurement scale which is based on population modes or medians.

In recognition of the needs set out in the previous paragraph, we distinguish between two classes of stochastic measurement. *Extended measurement* is the attempt to assign a statistical population to an object. *Restricted measurement* is the assignment of a single number to the object via extended measurement and statistical estimation. Restricted measurement can occur with respect to any parameter which can be estimated. Historically the concepts named here as *measurement operation* and *restricted measurement* have been inextricably confused.

The important point to be made is that, when scientific measurement is considered in proper depth, statistical models intervene between the measurement operations and the measurement models. The statistical models deal with the measurement results, which are already samples of numbers. Hence, measurement scales and models are based on statistical models.

Returning to the two basic positions on measurement and statistics, we see that they are both inadequate when viewed from the standpoint of stochastic measurement. The statistical practices advocated by the measurement-independents are the correct ones, but the independence of measurement and statistics postulated by adherents of this position is incorrect. The measurement-directed position is correct in asserting an interdependence of measurement and statistics, but the dependence which they postulate is in the wrong direction. Measurement scales are dependent upon statistical models which are themselves dependent upon measurement results. Each position has a partial, but only a partial, truth. However, the arguments of earlier sections of this paper showing the correctness of the measurement-independent view of statistical practice remain valid. Statistical problems should be solved with statistical theorems. Measurement models are irrelevant.

References

1. Bergmann, G., and Spence, K. W. Logic of psychophysical measurement. *Psychol. Rev.*, 1944, 51, 1–24.
2. Boring, E. G. The logic of the normal law of error in mental measurement. *Amer. J. Psychol.*, 1920, 31, 1–33.
3. Burke, C. J. Additive scales and statistics. *Psychol. Rev.*, 1953, 60, 73–75.
4. Burke, C. J. The gazelle and the hippopotamus. *Worm Runner's Digest* (in press).
5. Campbell, N. R. *Physics, the elements.* London: Cambridge Univ. Press, 1920.
6. Comrey, A. L. An operational approach to some problems in psychological measurement. *Psychol. Rev.*, 1950, 57, 217–228.
7. Davidson, D., Siegel, S., and Suppes, P., *Some experiments and related theory on the measurement of utility and subjective probability*. Rep. 4, Stanford Value Theory Project. 1955.
8. Gulliksen, H. Paired comparisons and the logic of measurement. *Psychol. Rev.*, 1946, 53, 199–213.
9. Hull, Clark L., *Principles of behavior*. New York: D. Appleton-Century Co., 1943.
10. Senders, Virginia L. A comment on Burke's additive scales and statistics. *Psychol. Rev.*, 1953, 60, 423–424.
11. Senders, Virginia L. *Measurement and statistics.* New York: Oxford, 1958. Chapter 2 provides a discussion of "Numbers, things, and measurement."

12. Siegel, S. *Nonparametric statistics for the behavioral sciences.* New York: McGraw-Hill, 1956.
13. Stevens, S. S. A scale for the measurement of a psychological magnitude: loudness. *Psychol. Rev.*, 1936, 43, 405–416.
14. Stevens, S. S. On the problem of scales for the measurement of psychological magnitudes. *J. Unif. Sci.*, 1939, 9, 94–99.
15. Stevens, S. S. On the theory of scales of measurement. *Science*, 1946, 103, 677–680.
16. Stevens, S. S. Mathematics, measurement, and psychophysics. In S. S. Stevens (ed.), *Hand-*

book of experimental psychology. New York: Wiley, 1951, pp. 1–49.
17. Stevens, S. S. The measurement of loudness. *J. Acoust. Soc. Amer.*, 1955, 27, 815–829.
18. Stevens, S. S. On the averaging of data. *Science*, 1955, 121, 113–116.
19. Stevens, S. S. On the psychophysical law. *Psychol. Rev.*, 1957, 64, 153–181.
20. Stevens, S. S., and Galanter, E. H. Ratio scales and category scales for a dozen perceptual continua. *J. Exp. Psychol.*, 1957, 54, 377–411.

S. S. STEVENS

8 Measurement, Statistics and the Schemapiric View

A curious antagonism has sometimes infected the relations between measurement and statistics. What ought to proceed as a pact of mutual assistance has seemed to some authors to justify a feud that centers on the degree of independence of the two domains. Thus Humphreys (1) dispenses praise to a textbook because its authors "do not follow the Stevens dictum concerning the precise relationships between scales of measurement and permissible statistical operations." Since that dictum, so-called, lurks as the *bête noire* behind many recurrent complaints, there is need to reexamine its burden and to ask how measurement and statistics shape up in the scientific process—the schemapiric endeavor in which we invent schematic models to map empirical domains.

In those disciplines where measurement is noisy, uncertain, and difficult, it is only natural that statistics should flourish. Of course, if there were no measurement at all, there would be no statistics. At the other extreme, if

accurate measurement were achieved in every inquiry, many of the needs for statistics would vanish. Somewhere between the two extremes of no measurement and perfect measurement, perhaps near the psychosocial-behavioral center of gravity, the ratio of statisticizing to measuring reaches its maximum. And that is where we find an acute sensitivity to the suggestion that the type of measurement achieved in an experiment may set bounds on the kinds of statistics that will prove appropriate.

After reviewing the issues Anderson (2) concluded that "the statistical test can hardly be cognizant of the empirical meaning of the numbers with which it deals. Consequently," he continued, "the validity of the statistical inference cannot depend on the type of measuring scale used." This sequitur, if we may call it that, demands scrutiny, for it compresses large issues into a few phrases. Here let me observe merely that, however much we may agree that the statistical test

From *Science*, Vol. 161, 30 August 1968, pp. 849–56. Copyright © 1968 by the American Association for the Advancement of Science. Reprinted by permission.

cannot be cognizant of the empirical meaning of the numbers, the same privilege of ignorance can scarcely be extended to experimenters.

Speaking as a statistician, Savage (3) said, "I know of no reason to limit statistical procedures to those involving arithmetic operations consistent with the scale properties of the observed quantities." A statistician, like a computer, may perhaps feign indifference to the origin of the numbers that enter into a statistical computation, but that indifference is not likely to be shared by the scientist. The man in the laboratory may rather suspect that, if something empirically useful is to emerge in the printout, something empirically meaningful must be programed for the input.

Baker, Hardyck, and Petrinovich (4) summed up the distress: "If Stevens' position is correct, it should be emphasized more intensively; if it is incorrect, something should be done to alleviate the lingering feelings of guilt that plague research workers who deliberately use statistics such as *t* on weak measurements." If it is true that guilt must come before repentence, perhaps the age of statistical indifference to the demands of measurement may be drawing to a close. Whatever the outcome, the foregoing samples of opinion suggest that the relation between statistics and measurement is not a settled issue. Nor is it a simple issue, for it exhibits both theoretical and practical aspects. Moreover, peace is not likely to be restored until both the principles and the pragmatics have been resolved.

The Schemapiric Principle

Although measurement began in the empirical mode, with the accent on the counting of moons and paces and warriors, it was destined in modern times to find itself debated in the formal, schematic, syntactical mode, where models can be made to bristle with symbols. Mathematics, which like logic constitutes a formal endeavor, was not always regarded as an arbitrary construction devoid of substantive content, an adventure of postulate and theorem. In early ages mathematics and empirical measurement were as warp and woof, interpenetrating each other so closely that our ancestors thought it proper to prove arithmetic theorems by resort to counting or to some other act of measurement. The divorce took place only in recent times. And mathematics now enjoys full freedom to "play upon symbols," as Gauss phrased it, with no constraints imposed by the demands of empirical measurement.

So also with other formal or schematic systems. The propositions of a formal logic express tautologies that say nothing about the world of tangible stuff. They are analytic statements, so-called, and they stand apart from the synthetic statements that express facts and relations among empirical objects. There is a useful distinction to be made between the analytic, formal, syntactical propositions of logic and the synthetic, empirical statements of substantive discourse.

Sometimes the line may be hard to draw. Quine (5) the logician denies, in fact, that any sharp demarcation can be certified, and debate on the issue between him and Carnap has reached classic if unresolved proportions. For the scientist, meanwhile, the usefulness of the formal-empirical distinction need not be imperiled by the difficulty of making rigorous decisions in borderline cases. It is useful to distinguish between day and night despite the penumbral passage through twilight. So also is it useful to tune ourselves to distinguish between the formally schematic and the empirical substantive.

Probability exhibits the same double aspect, the same schemapiric nature. Mathematical theories of probability inhabit the formal realm as analytic, tautologous, schematic systems, and they say nothing at all about dice, roulette, or lotteries. On the empirical level, however, we count and tabulate events at the gaming table or in the laboratory and note their relative frequencies. Sometimes the relative frequencies stand in isomorphic relation to some property of a mathematical model of probability; at other times the observed frequencies exhibit scant accord with "expectations."

Those features of statistics that involve a probabilistic schema provide a further instance of a formal-empirical dichotomy: the distinction between the probability model and the statistical data. E. B. Wilson (6), mathematician and statistician, made the point "that one must distinguish critically between probability as a purely mathematical subject of one sort or another, and statistics which cannot be so regarded." Statistics, of course, is a young discipline—one whose voice changes depending on who speaks for it. Many spokesmen would want to broaden the meaning of statistics to include a formal, mathematical segment.

In another context N. R. Hanson (7) pressed a similar distinction when he said, "Mathematics and physics on this account seem *logically* different disciplines, such that the former can only occasionally solve the latter's problems." Indeed, as Hanson later exclaimed, "Physicists have in unison pronounced, 'Let no man join what nature hath sundered, namely, the *formal creation* of spaces and the physical *description* of bodies.' " Yet it is precisely by way of the proper and judicious joining of the schematic with the empirical that we achieve our beneficial and effective mappings of the universe—the schemapiric mappings known as science. The chronic danger lies in our failure to note the distinction between the map and the terrain, between the simulation and the simulated. The map is an analogue, a schema, a model, a theory. Each of those words has a separate flavor, but they all share a common core of meaning. "Contrary to general belief," wrote Simon and Newell (8), "there is no fundamental, 'in principle,' difference between theories and analogies. All theories are analogies, and all analogies are theories." Indeed, the same can be said for all the other terms that designate the associative binding of schematics to empirics—what I have called the schemapiric bond.

Scales and Invariance

Although it could be otherwise if our choice dictated, most measurement involves the assignment of numbers to aspects of objects or events according to one or another rule or convention. The variety of rules invented thus far for the assignment of numbers has already grown enormous, and novel means of measuring continue to emerge. It has proved possible, however, to formulate an invariance criterion for the classification of scales of measurement (9). The resulting systemization of scale types has found uses in contexts ranging from physics (10) to the social sciences (11), but the conception has not enjoyed immunity from criticism (12).

Let me sketch the theory. It can be done very briefly, because details are given in other places (13). The theory proposes that a scale type is defined by the group of transformations under which the scale form remains invariant, as follows.

A *nominal scale* admits any one-to-one substitution of the assigned numbers. Example of a nominal scale: the numbering of football players.

An *ordinal scale* can be transformed by any increasing monotonic function. Example of an ordinal scale: the hardness scale determined by the ability of one mineral to scratch another.

An *interval scale* can be subjected to a linear transformation. Examples of interval scales: temperature Fahrenheit and Celsius, calendar time, potential energy.

A *ratio scale* admits only multiplication by a constant. Examples of ratio scales: length, weight, density, temperature Kelvin, time intervals, loudness in sones.

The foregoing scales represent the four types in common use. Other types are possible. The permissible transformations defining a scale type are those that keep intact the empirical information depicted by the scale. If the empirical information has been preserved, the scale form is said to remain invariant. The critical isomorphism is main-

Table 1..Examples of statistical measures appropriate to measurements made on various types of scales. The scale type is defined by the manner in which scale numbers can be transformed without the loss of empirical information. The statistical measures listed are those that remain invariant, as regards either value or reference, under the transformations allowed by the scale type.

Scale type	Measures of location	Dispersion	Association or correlation	Significance tests
Nominal	Mode	Information H	Information transmitted T	Chi square Fisher's exact test
Ordinal	Median	Percentiles	Rank correlation	Sign test Run test
Interval	Arithmetic mean	Standard deviation Average deviation	Product-moment correlation Correlation ratio	t test F test
Ratio	Geometric mean Harmonic mean	Percent variation Decilog dispersion		

tained. That indeed is the principle of invariance that lies at the heart of the conception. More formal presentations of the foregoing theory have been undertaken by other authors, a recent one, for example, by Lea (14).

Unfortunately, those who demand an abstract tidiness that is completely aseptic may demur at the thought that the decision whether a particular scale enjoys the privilege of a particular transformation group depends on something so ill defined as the preservation of empirical information. For one thing, an empirical operation is always attended by error. Thus Lebesgue (15), who strove so well to perfect the concept of mathematical measure, took explicit note that, in the assignment of number to a physical magnitude, precision can be pushed, as he said, "in actuality only up to a certain error. It never enables us," he continued, "to discriminate between one number and all the numbers that are extremely close to it."

A second disconcerting feature of the invariance criterion lies in the difficulty of specifying the empirical information that is to be preserved. What can it be other than the information that we think we have captured by creating the scale in the first place? We may, for example, perform operations that allow us simply to identify or discriminate a particular property of an object. Sometimes we want to preserve nothing more than that simple outcome, the identification or nominal classification of the items of interest. Or we may go further, provided our empirical operations permit, and determine rank orders, equal intervals, or equal ratios. If we want our number assignments to reflect one or another accrual in information, we are free to transform the scale numbers only in a way that does not lose or distort the desired information. The choice remains ours.

Although some writers have found it possible to read an element of prescription—even proscription—into the invariance principle, as a systematizing device the principle contains no normative force. It can be read more as a description of the obvious than as a directive. It says that, once an isomorphism has been mapped out between aspects of objects or events, on the one hand, and some one or more features of the number system, on the other hand, the isomorphism can be upset by whatever transformations fail to preserve it. Precisely what is preserved or not preserved in a particular circumstance depends upon the empirical operations. Since actual day-to-day measurements range from muddled to meticulous, our ability to classify them in terms of scale type must range from hopelessly uncertain to relatively secure.

The group invariance that defines a scale type serves in turn to delimit the statistical procedures that can be said to be appropriate to a given measurement scale (16). Examples of appropriate statistics are tabulated in Table 1. Under the permissible transformations of a measurement scale, some appropriate statistics remain invariant in value (example: the correlation coefficient r keeps its value under linear transformations). Other statistics change value but refer to the same item or location (example: the median changes its value but continues to refer to mid-distribution under ordinal transformations).

Reconciliation and New Problems

Two developments may serve to ease the apprehension among those who may have felt threatened by a theory of measurement that seems to place bounds on our freedom to calculate. One is a clearer understanding of the bipartite, schemapiric nature of the scientific enterprise. When the issue concerns only the schema—when, for example, critical ratios are calculated for an assumed binomial distribution—then indeed it is purely a matter of relations within a mathematical model. Natural facts stand silent. Empirical considerations impose no constraints. When, however, the text asserts a relation among such things as measured differences or variabilities, we have a right and an obligation to inquire about the operations that underlie the measurements. Those operations determine, in turn, the type of scale achieved.

The two-part schemapiric view was expressed by Hays (17) in a much-praised book: "If the statistical method involves the procedures of arithmetic used on numerical scores, then the numerical answer is formally correct.... The difficulty comes with the interpretation of these numbers back into statements about the real world. If nonsense is put into the mathematical system, nonsense is sure to come out."

At the level of the formal model, then, statistical computations may proceed as freely as in any other syntactical exercise, unimpeded by any material outcome of empirical measurement. Nor does measurement have a presumptive voice in the creation of the statistical models themselves. As Hogben (18) said in his forthright dissection of statistical theory, "It is entirely defensible to formulate an axiomatic approach to the theory of probability as an internally consistent set of propositions, if one is content to leave to those in closer contact with reality the last word on the usefulness of the outcome." Both Hays and Hogben insist that the user of statistics, the man in the laboratory, the maker of measurements, must decide the meaning of the numbers and their capacity to advance empirical inquiry.

The second road to reconciliation winds through a region only partly explored, a region wherein lies the pragmatic problem of appraising the wages of transgression. What is the degree of risk entailed when use is made of statistics that may be inappropriate in the strict sense that they fail the test of invariance under permissible scale transformations? Specifically, let us assume that a set of items can be set in rank order, but, by the operations thus far invented, distances between the items cannot be determined. We have an ordinal but not an interval scale. What happens then if interval-scale statistics are applied to the ordinally scaled items? Therein lies a question of first-rate substance and one that should be amenable to unemotional investigation. It promises well that a few answers have already been forthcoming.

First there is the oft-heeded counsel of common sense. In the averaging of test scores, says Mosteller (19), "It seems sensible to use the statistics appropriate to the type of scale I think I am near. In taking such action we may find the justification vague and fuzzy. One reason for this vagueness is that we have not yet studied enough about classes of scales, classes appropriate to real life measurement, with perhaps real life bias and error variance."

How some of the vagueness of which Mosteller spoke can perhaps be removed is illustrated by the study of Abelson and Tukey (20) who showed how bounds may be determined for the risk involved when an interval-scale statistic is used with an ordinal scale. Specifically, they explored the effect on r^2 of a game against nature in which nature does its best (or worst!) to minimize the value of r^2. In this game of regression analysis, many interesting cases were explored, but, as the authors said, their methods need extension to other cases. They noted that we often know more about ordinal data than mere rank order. We may have reason to believe, they said, "that the scale is no worse than mildly curvilinear, that Nature behaves smoothly in some sense." Indeed the continued use of parametric statistics with ordinal data rests on that belief, a belief sustained in large measure by the pragmatic usefulness of the results achieved.

In a more synthetic study than the foregoing analysis, Baker *et al.* (4) imposed sets of monotonic transformations on an assumed set of data, and calculated the effect on the t distribution. The purpose was to compare distributions of t for data drawn from an equal-interval scale with distributions of t for several types of assumed distortions of the equal intervals. By and large, the effects on the computed t distributions were not large, and the authors concluded "that strong statistics such as the t test are more than adequate to cope with weak [ordinal] measurements...". It should be noted, however, that the values of t were affected by the nonlinear transformations. As the authors said, "The correspondence between values of t based on the criterion unit interval scores and values of t based on [nonlinear] transformations decreases regularly and dramatically...as the departure from linear transformations becomes more extreme."

Whatever the substantive outcome of such investigations may prove to be, they point

the way to reconciliation through orderly inquiry. Debate gives way to calculation. The question is thereby made to turn, not on whether the measurement scale determines the choice of a statistical procedure, but on how and to what degree an inappropriate statistic may lead to a deviant conclusion. The solution of such problems may help to refurbish the complexion of measurement theory, which has been accused of proscribing those statistics that do not remain invariant under the transformations appropriate to a given scale. By spelling out the costs, we may convert the issue from a seeming proscription to a calculated risk.

The type of measurement achieved is not, of course, the only consideration affecting the applicability of parametric statistics. Bradley is one of many scholars who have sifted the consequences of violating the assumptions that underlie some of the common parametric tests (21). As one outcome of his studies, Bradley concluded, "The contention that, when its assumptions are violated, a parametric test is still to be preferred to a distribution-free test because it is 'more efficient' is therefore a monumental *non sequitur*. The point is not at all academic...violations in a test's assumptions may be attended by profound changes in its power." That conclusion is not without relevance to scales of measurement, for when ordinal data are forced into the equal-interval mold, parametric assumptions are apt to be violated. It is then that a so-called distribution-free statistic may prove more efficient than its parametric counterpart.

Although better accommodation among certain of the contending statistical usages may be brought about by computer-aided studies, there remain many statistics that find their use only with specific kinds of scales. A single example may suffice. In a classic text-book, written with a captivating clarity, Peters and Van Voorhis (22) got hung up on a minor point concerning the procedure to be used in comparing variabilities. They noted that Karl Pearson had proposed a measure called the coefficient of variation, which expresses the standard deviation as a percentage of the mean. The authors expressed doubts about its value, however, because it tells "more about the extent to which the scores are padded by a dislocation of the zero point than it does about comparable variabilities." The examples and arguments given by the authors make it plain that the coefficient of variation has little business being used with what I have called interval scales. But since their book antedated my publication in 1946 of the defining invariances for interval and ratio scales, Peters and Van Voorhis did not have a convenient way to state the relationship made explicit in Table 1, namely, that the coefficient of variation, being itself a ratio, called for a ratio scale.

Complexities and Pitfalls

Concepts like relative variability have the virtue of being uncomplicated and easy for the scientist to grasp. They fit his idiom. But in the current statistics explosion, which showers the investigator with a dense fallout of new statistical models, the scientist is likely to lose the thread on many issues. It is then that the theory of measurement, with an anchor hooked fast in empirical reality, may serve as a sanctuary against the turbulence of specialized abstraction.

"As a mathematical discipline travels far from its empirical source," said von Neumann (23), "there is grave danger that the subject will develop along the line of least resistance, that the stream, so far from its source, will separate into a multitude of insignificant branches, and that the discipline will become a disorganized mass of details and complexities." He went on to say that, "After much 'abstract' inbreeding, a mathematical subject is in danger of degeneration. At the inception the style is usually classical; when it shows signs of becoming baroque, then the danger signal is up."

There is a sense, one suspects, in which statistics needs measurement more than measurement needs statistics. R. A. Fisher

alluded to that need in his discourse on the nature of probability (24). "I am quite sure," he said, "it is only personal contact with the business of the improvement of natural knowledge in the natural sciences that is capable to keep straight the thought of mathematically-minded people who have to grope their way through the complex entanglements of error. . . ."

And lest the physical sciences should seem immune to what Schwartz (25) called "the pernicious influence of mathematics," consider his diagnosis: "Thus, in its relations with science, mathematics depends on an intellectual effort outside of mathematics for the crucial specification of the approximation which mathematics is to take literally. Give a mathematician a situation which is the least bit ill-defined—he will first of all make it well defined. Perhaps appropriately, but perhaps also inappropriately. . . . That form of wisdom which is the opposite of single-mindedness, the ability to keep many threads in hand, to draw for an argument from many disparate sources, is quite foreign to mathematics. . . . Quite typically, science leaps ahead and mathematics plods behind."

Progress in statistics often follows a similar road from practice to prescription—from field trials to the formalization of principles. As Kruskal (26) said "Theoretical study of a statistical procedure often comes after its intuitive proposal and use." Unfortunately for the empirical concerns of the practitioners, however, there is, as Kruskal added, "almost no end to the possible theoretical study of even the simplest procedure." So the discipline wanders far from its empirical source, and form loses sight of substance.

Not only do the forward thrusts of science often precede the mopping-up campaigns of the mathematical schema builders, but measurement itself may often find implementation only after some basic conception has been voiced. Textbooks, those distilled artifices of science, like to picture scientific conceptions as built on measurement, but the working scientist is more apt to devise his measurements to suit his conceptions. As Kuhn (27) said, "The route from theory or law to measurement can almost never be travelled backwards. Numbers gathered without some knowledge of the regularity to be expected almost never to speak for themselves. Almost certainly they remain just numbers." Yet who would deny that some ears, more tuned to numbers, may hear them speak in fresh and revealing ways?

The intent here is not, of course, to affront the qualities of a discipline as useful as mathematics. Its virtues and power are too great to need extolling, but in power lies a certain danger. For mathematics, like a computer, obeys commands and asks no questions. It will process any input, however devoid of scientific sense, and it will bedeck in formulas both the meaningful and the absurd. In the behavioral sciences, where the discernment for nonsense is perhaps less sharply honed than in the physical sciences, the vigil must remain especially alert against the intrusion of a defective theory merely because it carries a mathematical visa. An absurdity in full formularized attire may be more seductive than an absurdity undressed.

Distributions and Decisions

The scientist often scales items, counts them, and plots their frequency distributions. He is sometimes interested in the form of such distributions. If his data have been obtained from measurements made on interval or ratio scales, the shape of the distribution stays put (up to a scale factor) under those transformations that are permissible, namely, those that preserve the empirical information contained in the measurements. The principle seems straightforward. But what happens when the state of the art can produce no more than a rank ordering, and hence nothing better than an ordinal scale? The abscissa of the frequency distribution then loses its metric meaning and becomes like a rubber band, capable of all sorts of monotonic stretchings. With each non-linear transformation of the

scale, the form of the distribution changes. Thereupon the distribution loses structure, and we find it futile to ask whether the shape approximates a particular form, whether normal, rectangular, or whatever.

Working on the formal level, the statistician may contrive a schematic model by first assuming a frequency function, or a distribution function, of one kind or another. At the abstract level of mathematical creation, there can, of course, be no quarrel with the statistician's approach to his task. The caution light turns on, however, as soon as the model is asked to mirror an empirical domain. We must then invoke a set of semantic rules—coordinating definitions—in order to identify correspondences between model and reality. What shall we say about the frequency function $f(x)$ when the problem before us allows only an ordinal scale? Shall x be subject to a nonlinear transformation after $f(x)$ has been specified? If so, what does the transformation do to the model and to the predictions it forecasts?

The scientist has reason to feel that a statistical model that specifies the form of a canonical distribution becomes uninterpretable when the empirical domain concerns only ordinal data. Yet many consumers of statistics seem to disregard what to others is a rather obvious and critical problem. Thus Burke (28) proposed to draw "two random samples from populations known to be normal" and then "to test the hypothesis that the two populations have the same mean...under the assumption that the scale is ordinal at best." How, we must ask, can normality be known when only order can be certified?

The assumption of normality is repeated so blithely and so often that it becomes a kind of incantation. If enough of us sin, perhaps transgression becomes a virtue. But in the instance before us, where the numbers to be fed into the statistical mill result from operations that allow only a rank ordering, maybe we have gone too far. Consider a permissible transformation. Let us cube all the numbers. The rank order would stand as before. But what do we then say about normality? If we can know nothing about the intervals on the scale of a variable, the postulation that a distribution has a particular form would appear to proclaim a hope, not a circumstance.

The assertion that a variable is normally distributed when the variable is amenable only to ordinal measurement may loom as an acute contradiction, but it qualifies as neither the worst nor the most frequent infraction by some of the practitioners of hypothesis testing. Scientific decision by statistical calculation has become the common mode in many behavioral disciplines. In six psychological journals (29), for example, the proportion of articles that employed one or another kind of inferential statistic rose steadily from 56 percent in 1948 to 91 percent in 1962. In the *Journal of Educational Psychology* the proportion rose from 36 to 100 percent.

What does it mean? Can no one recognize a decisive result without a significance test? How much can the burgeoning of computation be blamed on fad? How often does inferential computation serve as a premature excuse for going to press? Whether the scholar has discovered something or not, he can sometimes subject his data to an analysis of variance, a *t* test, or some other device that will produce a so-called objective measure of "significance." The illusion of objectivity seems to preserve itself despite the admitted necessity for the investigator to make improbable assumptions, and to pluck off the top of his head a figure for the level of probability that he will consider significant. His argument that convention has already chosen the level that he will use does not quite absolve him.

Lubin (30) has a name for those who censure the computational and applaud the experimental in the search for scientific certainty. He calls them stochastophobes. An apt title, if applied to those whose eagerness to lay hold on the natural fact may generate impatience at the gratuitous processing of data. The extreme stochastophobe is likely to ask: What scientific discoveries owe their existence to the techniques of statistical analysis or inference? If exercises in statistical inference have occasioned few instances of a scientific breakthrough, the stochastophobe may want to ask by what magical view the stochastophile perceives glamour in statistics. The charm may stem in part from the prestige that mathematics, however inapposite, confers on those who display the dexterity of calculation. For some stochastophiles the appeal may have no deeper roots than a preference for the prudent posture at a desk as opposed to the harsher, more venturesome stance in the field or the laboratory.

The aspersions voiced by stochastophobes fall mainly on those scientists who seem, by the surfeit of their statistical chants, to turn data treatment into hierurgy. These are not the statisticians themselves, for they see statistics for what it is, a straightforward discipline designed to amplify the power of common sense in the discernment of order amid complexity. By showing how to amend the mismatch in the impedance between question and evidence, the statistician improves the probability that our experiments will speak of greater clarity. And by weighing the entailments of relevant assumptions, he shows us how to milk the most from some of those fortuitous experiments that nature performs once and may never perform again. The stochastophobe should find no quarrel here. Rather he should turn his despair into a hope that the problem of the relevance of this or that statistical model may lead the research man toward thoughtful inquiry, not to a reflex decision based on a burst of computation.

Measurement

If the vehemence of the debate that centers on the nature and conditions of statistical inference has hinted at the vulnerability of the conception, what can be said about the other partner in the enterprise? Is the theory of measurement a settled matter? Apparently not, for it remains a topic of trenchant inquiry, not yet ready to rest its case. And debate continues.

The typical scientist pays little attention to the theory of measurement, and with good reason, for the laboratory procedures for most measurements have been well worked out, and the scientist knows how to read his dials. Most of the variables are measured on well-defined, well-instrumented ratio scales.

Among those whose interests center on variables that are not reducible to meter readings, however, the concern with measurement stays acute. How, for example, shall we measure subjective value (what the economists calls utility), or perceived brightness, or the seriousness of crimes? Those are some of the substantive problems that have forced a revision in our approach to measurement. They have entailed a loosening of the restricted view bequeathed us by the tradition of Helmholtz and Campbell—the view that the axioms of additivity must govern what we call measurement (31). As a related development, new axiomatic systems have appeared, including axioms by Luce and Tukey (32) for a novel "conjoint" approach to fundamental measurement. But the purpose here is not to survey the formal, schematic models that have flowered in the various sciences, for the practice and conception of measurement has as yet been little influenced by them.

As with many syntactical developments, measurement models sometimes drift off into the vacuum of abstraction and become decoupled from their concrete reference. Even those authors who freely admit the empirical features as partners in the formulation of measurement may find themselves seeming to downgrade the empirical in favor of the formal. Thus we find Suppes and Zinnes (33) saying, "Some writers ... appear to define scales in terms of the existence of certain empirical operations. ... In the present formulation of scale type, no mention is made of the kinds of 'direct' observations or empirical relations that exist. ... Precisely what empirical operations are involved in the empricial system is of no consequence."

How then do we distinguish different types of scales? How, in particular, do we know whether a given scale belongs among the interval scales? Suppes and Zinnes gave what I think is a proper answer: "We ask if all the admissible numerical assignments are related by a linear transformation." That, however, is not a complete answer. There remains a further question: What is it that makes a class of numerical assignments admissible? A full theory of measurement cannot detach itself from the empirical substrate that gives it meaning. But the theorist grows impatient with the empirical lumps that ruffle the fine laminar flow within his models just as the laboratory fellow may disdain the arid swirls of hieroglyphics that pose as paradigms of his measurements.

Although a congenial conciliation between those two polar temperaments, the modeler and the measurer, may lie beyond reasonable expectations, a tempering détente may prove viable. The two components of schemapirics must both be accredited, each in its own imperative role. To the understanding of the world about us, neither the formal model nor the concrete measure is dispensable.

Matching and Mapping

Instead of starting with origins, many accounts of measurement begin with one or another advanced state of the measuring process, a state in which units and metrics can be taken for granted. At that level, the topic already has the crust of convention upon it, obscuring the deeper problems related to its nature.

If we try to push the problem of measurement back closer to its primordial operations, we find, I think, that the basic operation is always a process of matching. That statement may sound innocent enough, but it contains a useful prescription. It suggests, for example, that if you would understand the essence of a given measuring procedure, you should ask what was matched to what. If the query leads to a pointer reading, do not stop there; ask the same question about the calibration procedure that was applied to the instruments anterior to the pointer: What was matched to what? Diligent pursuit of that question along the chain of measuring operations leads to some of the elemental operations of science.

Or we may start nearer the primordium. The sketchiness of the record forces us to conjecture the earliest history, but quite probably our forefather kept score on the numerosity of his possessions with the aid of piles of pebbles (Latin: *calculi*) or by means of some other tallying device. He paired off items against pebbles by means of a primitive matching operation, and he thereby measured his hoard.

Let us pause at this point to consider the preceding clause. Can the ancestor in question be said to have measured his possessions if he had no number system? Not if we insist on taking literally the definition often given, namely, that measurement is the assignment of numbers to objects or events according to rule. This definition serves a good purpose in many contexts, but it presumes a stage of development beyond the one that we are now seeking to probe. In an elemental sense, the matching or assigning of numbers is a sufficient but not a necessary condition for measurement, for other kinds of matching may give measures.

Numbers presumably arose after our ancestor invented names for the collection of pebbles, or perhaps for the more convenient collections, the fingers. He could then match name to collection, and collection to possessions. That gave him a method of counting, for, by pairing off each item against a finger name in an order decided upon, the name of the collection of items, and hence the numerosity of the items, was specified.

The matching principle leads to the concept of cardinality. Two sets have the same cardinal number if they can be paired off in one-to-one relation to each other. By itself, this cardinal pairing off says nothing about order. (Dictionaries often disagree with the mathematicians on the definition of cardinality, but the mathematical usage recommends itself here.) We find the cardinal principle embodied in the symbols used for the numerals in many forms of writing. Thus the Roman numeral VI pictures a hand V and a finger I.

Let us return again to our central question. In the early cardinal procedure of matching item to item, fingers to items, or names to items, at what point shall we say that measurement began? Perhaps we had best not seek a line of demarcation between measurement and matching. It may be better to go all the way and propose an unstinted definition as follows: Measurement is the matching of an aspect of one domain to an aspect of another.

The operation of matching eventuates, of course, in one domain's being mapped into another, as regards one or more attributes of the two domains. In the larger sense, then, whenever a feature of one domain is mapped isomorphically in some relation with a feature of another domain, measurement is achieved. The relation is potentially symmetrical. Our hypothetical forefather could measure his collection of fish by means of his pile of pebbles, or his pile of pebbles by means of his collection of fish.

Our contemporary concern lies not, of course, with pebbles and fish, but with a principle. We need to break the hull that confines the custom of our thought about these matters. The concern is more than merely academic, however, especially in the field of psychophysics. One justification for the enlarged view of measurement lies in a development in sensory measurement known as cross-modality matching (34). In a suitable laboratory setup, the subject is asked, for example, to adjust the loudness of a sound applied to his ears in order to make it seem equal to the perceived strength of a vibration applied to his finger. The amplitude of the vibration is then changed and the matching process is repeated. An equal sensation function is thereby mapped out, as illustrated in Fig. 1. Loudness has been matched in that manner to ranges of values on some ten other perceptual continua, always with the result that the matching function approximates a power function (35). In other words, in order to produce equal apparent intensity, the amplitude of the sound p must be a power function of the amplitude of the vibration a, or $p = a^b$, where b is the exponent. Or, more simply, the logarithms of the stimuli are linearly related, which means that ratios of stimuli are proportional.

Experiments suggest that the power function obtains between all pairs of intensive perceptual continua, and that the matchings exhibit a strong degree of transitivity in the sense that the exponents form an interconnected net. If two matching functions have one continuum in common, we can predict fairly well the exponent of the matching function between the other two continua.

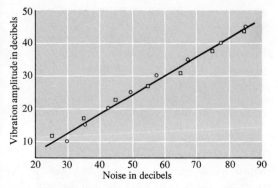

Fig. 1. Equal-sensation function for cross-modality matching between loudness and vibration. The squares indicate that the observers adjusted the intensity of vibration on the fingertip to match the loudness of a noise delivered by earphones. The circles indicate that the observers adjusted the loudness to match the vibration. Each point is the decibel average of 20 matches, two by each often observers. Since the coordinates are logarithmic, the straight line indicates a power function.

Now, once we have mapped out the matching function between loudness and vibration, we can, if we choose, measure the subjective strength of the vibration in terms of its equivalent loudness. Or, more generally, if all pairs of continua have been matched, we can select any one continuum to serve as the reference continuum in terms of which we then measure the subjective magnitude on each of the other continua.

In the description of a measurement system that rests on cross-modality matching, no mention has been made of numbers. If we are willing to start from scratch in a measurement of this kind, numbers can in principle be dispensed with. They would, to be sure, have practical uses in the conduct of the experiments, but by using other signs or tokens to identify the stimuli we could presumably eliminate numbers completely. It would be a tour de force, no doubt, but an instructive one.

Instead of dispensing with numbers, the practice in many psychophysical studies has been to treat numbers as one of the perceptual continua in the cross-modality matching experiment. Thus in what has come to be known as the method of magnitude estimation, numbers are matched to loudness, say. In the reverse procedure, called magnitude production, the subject adjusts the loudness to match a series of numbers given by the experimenter (36). And as might be expected, despite all the other kinds of cross-modality matches that have been made, it is the number continuum that most authors select as the reference continuum (exponent = 1.0) in terms of which the exponent values for the other perceptual continua are stated. But the point deserves to be stressed: the choice of number as the reference continuum is wholly arbitrary, albeit eminently convenient.

Summary

Back in the days when measurement meant mainly counting, and statistics meant mainly the inventory of the state, the simple descriptive procedures of enumeration and averaging occasioned minimum conflict between measurement and statistics. But as measurement pushed on into novel behavioral domains, and statistics turned to the formalizing of stochastic models, the one-time intimate relation between the two activities dissolved into occasional misunderstanding. Measurement and statistics must live in peace, however, for both must participate in the schemapiric enterprise by which the schematic model is made to map the empirical observation.

Science presents itself as a two-faced, bipartite endeavor looking at once toward the formal, analytic, schematic features of model-building, and toward the concrete, empirical, experiential observations by which we test the usefulness of a particular representation. Schematics and empirics are both essential to science, and full understanding demands that we know which is which.

Measurement provides the numbers that enter the statistical table. But the numbers that issue from measurements have strings attached, for they carry the imprint of the operations by which they were obtained. Some transformations on the numbers will leave intact the information gained by the measurements; other transformations will destroy the desired isomorphism between the measurement scale and the property assessed. Scales of measurement therefore find a useful classification on the basis of a principle of invariance: each of the common scale types (nominal, ordinal, interval, and ratio) is defined by a group of transformations that leaves a particular isomorphism unimpaired.

Since the transformations allowed by a given scale type will alter the numbers that enter into a statistical procedure, the procedure ought properly to be one that can withstand that particular kind of number alteration. Therein lies the primacy of measurement: it sets bounds on the appropriateness of statistical operations. The widespread use on ordinal scales of statistics appropriate only to interval or ratio scales can be said to violate a technical canon, but in many instances the outcome has demonstrable utility. A few workers have begun to assess the degree of risk entailed by the use of statistics that do not remain invariant under the permissible scale transformations.

The view is proposed that measurement can be most liberally construed as the process of matching elements of one domain to those of another domain. In most kinds of measurement we match numbers to objects or events,

but other matchings have been found to serve a useful purpose. The cross-modality matching of one sensory continuum to another has shown that sensory intensity increases as the stimulus intensity raised to a power. The generality of that finding supports a psychophysical law expressible as a simple invariance: equal stimulus ratios produce equal sensation ratios.

References

1. L. Humphreys, *Contemp. Psychol.* 9, 76 (1964).
2. N. H. Anderson, *Psychol. Bull.* 58, 305 (1961).
3. I. R. Savage, *J. Amer. Statist. Ass.* 52, 331 (1957).
4. B. O. Baker, C. D. Hardyck, L. F. Petrinovich, *Educ. Psychol. Meas.* 26, 291 (1966).
5. W. V. O. Quine, *The Ways of Paradox and Other Essays* (Random House, New York, 1966), pp. 126–134.
6. E. B. Wilson, *Proc. Natl. Acad. Sci. U.S.* 51, 539 (1964).
7. N. R. Hanson, *Philos. Sci.* 30, 107 (1963).
8. H. A. Simon and A. Newell, in *The State of the Social Sciences*, L. D. White, Ed. (Univ. of Chicago Press, Chicago, 1956), pp. 66–83.
9. S. S. Stevens, *Science* 103, 677 (1946).
10. F. B. Silsbee, *J. Wash. Acad. Sci.* 41, 213 (1951).
11. B. F. Green, in *Handbook of Social Psychology*, G. Lindzey, Ed. (Addison-Wesley, Reading, Mass., 1954), pp. 335–369.
12. Among those who have commented are B. Ellis, *Basic Concepts of Measurement* (University Press, Cambridge, England, 1966); B. Grunstra, "On Distinguishing Types of Measurement," *Boston Studies Phil. Sci.*, vol. 4 (Humanities Press, in press); S. Ross, *Logical Foundations of Psychological Measurement* (Scandinavian University Books, Munksgaard, Copenhagen, 1964); W. W. Rozeboom, *Synthese* 16, 170–233 (1966); W. S. Torgerson, *Theory and Methods of Scaling* (Wiley, New York, 1958).
13. S. S. Stevens, in *Handbook of Experimental Psychology*, S. S. Stevens, Ed. (Wiley, New York, 1951), pp. 1–49; in *Measurement: Definitions and Theories*, C. W. Churchman and P. Ratoosh, Eds. (Wiley, New York, 1959), pp. 18–64.
14. W. A. Lea, "A Formalization of Measurement Scale Forms" (Technical Memo. KC-T-024, Computer Research Lab., NASA Electronics Res. Ctr., Cambridge, Mass., June 1967).

15. H. Lebesgue, *Measure and the Integral*, K. O. May, Ed. (Holden-Day, San Francisco, 1966).
16. Other summarizing tables are presented by V. Senders, *Measurement and Statistics* (Oxford Univ. Press, New York, 1958). A further analysis of appropriate statistics has been presented by E. W. Adams, R. F. Fagot, R. E. Robinson, *Psychometrika* 30, 99 (1965).
17. W. L. Hays, *Statistics for Psychologists* (Holt, Rinehart & Winston, New York, 1963).
18. L. Hogben, *Statistical Theory* (Norton, New York, 1958.)
19. F. Mosteller, *Psychometrika* 23, 279 (1958).
20. R. P. Abelson and J. W. Tukey, *Efficient Conversion of Non-Metric Information into Metric Information* (Amer. Statist. Ass., Social Statist. Sec., December 1959), pp. 226–230; see also *Ann. Math. Stat.* 34, 1347 (1963).
21. J. V. Bradley, "Studies in Research Methodology: II. Consequences of Violating Parametric Assumptions—Facts and Fallacy" (WADC Tech. Rep. 58-574 [II]. Aerospace Med. Lab., Wright-Patterson AFB, Ohio, September 1959).
22. C. C. Peters and W. R. Van Voorhis, *Statistical Procedures and Their Mathematical Bases* (McGraw-Hill, New York, 1940).
23. J. von Neumann, in *The Works of the Mind*, R. B. Heywood, Ed. (Univ. of Chicago Press, Chicago, 1947), pp. 180–196.
24. R. A. Fisher, *Smoking, the Cancer Controversy* (Oliver and Boyd, Edinburgh, 1959).
25. J. Schwartz, in *Logic, Methodology and Philosophy of Science*, E. Nagal *et al.*, Eds., (Stanford Univ. Press, Stanford, Calif., 1962), pp. 356–360.
26. W. R. Kruskal, in *International Encyclopedia of the Social Sciences* (Macmillan and Free Press, New York, 1968), vol. 15, pp. 206–224.
27. T. S. Kuln, in *Quantification*, H. Woolf, Ed. (Bobbs-Merrill, Indianapolis, Ind., 1961), pp. 31–63.
28. C. J. Burke, in *Theories in Contemporary Psychology*, M. H. Marx, Ed. (Macmillan, New York, 1963), pp. 147–159.
29. The journals were tabulated by E. S. Edgington, *Amer. Psychologist* 19, 202 (1964); also personal communication.
30. A. Lubin, in *Annual Review of Psychology* (Annual Reviews, Palo Alto, Calif., 1962), vol. 13, pp. 345–370.
31. H. v. Helmholtz, "Zählen und Messen," in *Philosophische Aufsätze* (Fues's Verlag, Leipzig, 1887), pp. 17–52; N. R. Campbell, *Physics: the Elements* [1920] (reissued as *The Philosophy of Theory and Experiment* by Dover, New York, 1957; *Symposium: Measurement and its Importance for Philosophy*, Aristotelian Soc., suppl., vol. 17 (Harrison and Sons, London, 1938).
32. R. D. Luce and J. W. Tukey, *J. Math. Psychol.* 1, 1 (1964).
33. P. Suppes and J. L. Zinnes, in *Handbook of Mathematical Psychology*, R. D. Luce *et al.*, Eds. (Wiley, New York, 1963), pp. 1–76.
34. S. S. Stevens, *J. Exp. Psychol.* 57, 201 (1959); *Amer. Sci.* 54, 385 (1966).
35. S. S. Stevens, *Percept. Psychophys.* 1, 5 (1966).
36. S. S. Stevens and H. B. Greenbaum, *ibid.*, p. 439.
37. This article (Laboratory of Psychophysics Rept. PPR-336-118) was prepared with support from NIH grant NB-02974 and NSF grant GB-3211.

2

Inference and Null-Hypothesis Testing

Very early in his study of statistics the student learns the distinction between descriptive statistics and statistical inference. While descriptive statistics are not without their problems and subtleties, their use is relatively straightforward—statistical inference, however, is more difficult and perplexing, and students usually need some time to master these techniques.

In "The Fallacy of Null-Hypothesis Testing," W. Rozeboom offers a provocative critique of the entire null-hypothesis decision procedure, arguing that the procedure leads to a decision, which he believes is undesirable. He argues that rather than reach a decision, the investigator should use his evidence to alter his belief about the validity of a proposition. In Section 4 this argument will be more fully developed in the selections which discuss Bayesian Statistics.

In "Testing the Null-Hypothesis and the Strategy and Tactics of Investigating Theoretical Models," D. Grant argues that null-hypothesis decision procedures should be replaced by more precise theories that enable us to make detailed predictions so that our data will more obviously confirm or disconfirm our theories. We should not rely on the gross evidence of statistical differences between two groups.

The articles by A. Binder, W. Edwards, D. Bakan, W. Wilson *et al.*, and R. La Forge discuss these and related issues.

The article by C. Boneau compares the power of the U and t tests.

WILLIAM W. ROZEBOOM

9 The Fallacy of the Null-Hypothesis Significance Test

The theory of probability and statistical inference is various things to various people. To the mathematician, it is an intricate formal calculus, to be explored and developed with little professional concern for any empirical significance that might attach to the terms and propositions involved. To the philosopher, it is an embarrassing mystery whose justification and conceptual clarification have remained stubbornly refractory to philosophical insight. (A famous philosophical epigram has it that induction (a special case of statistical inference) is the glory of science and the scandal of philosophy.) To the experimental scientist, however, statistical inference is a research instrument, a processing device by which unwieldy masses of raw data may be refined into a product more suitable for assimilation into the corpus of science, and in this lies both strength and weakness. It is strength in that, as an ultimate *consumer* of statistical methods, the experimentalist is in position to demand that the techniques made available to him conform to his actual needs. But it is also weakness in that, in his need for the tools constructed by a highly technical formal discipline, the experimentalist, who has specialized along other lines, seldom feels competent to extend criticisms or even comments; he is much more likely to make unquestioning application of procedures learned more or less by rote from persons assumed to be more knowledgeable of statistics than he. There is, of course, nothing surprising or reprehensible about this—one need not understand the principles of a complicated tool in order to make

From *Psychological Bulletin*, Vol. 57, No. 5, pp. 416–28, 1960. Copyright © 1960 by the American Psychological Association and reprinted by permission.

effective use of it, and the research scientist can no more be expected to have sophistication in the theory of statistical inference than he can be held responsible for the principles of the computers, signal generators, timers, and other complex modern instruments to which he may have recourse during an experiment. Nonetheless, this leaves him particularly vulnerable to misinterpretation of his aims by those who build his instruments, not to mention the ever present dangers of selecting an inappropriate or outmoded tool for the job at hand, misusing the proper tool, or improvising a tool of unknown adequacy to meet a problem not conforming to the simple theoretical situations in terms of which existent instruments have been analyzed. Further, since behaviors once exercised tend to crystallize into habits and eventually traditions, it should come as no surprise to find that the tribal rituals for data-processing passed along in graduate courses in experimental method should contain elements justified more by custom than by reason.

In this paper, I wish to examine a dogma of inferential procedure which, for psychologists at least, has attained the status of a religious conviction. The dogma to be scrutinized is the "null-hypothesis significance test" orthodoxy that passing statistical judgment on a scientific hypothesis by means of experimental observation is a decision procedure wherein one rejects or accepts a null hypothesis according to whether or not the value of a sample statistic yielded by an experiment falls within a certain predetermined "rejection region" of its possible values. The thesis to be advanced is that despite the awesome pre-eminence this method has attained in our experimental journals and textbooks of applied statistics, it is based upon a fundamental misunderstanding of the nature of rational inference, and is seldom if ever appropriate to the aims of scientific research. This is not a particularly original view—traditional null-hypothesis procedure has already been superceded in modern statistical theory by a variety of more satisfactory inferential techniques. But the percep-

tual defenses of psychologists are particularly efficient when dealing with matters of methodology, and so the statistical folkways of a more primitive past continue to dominate the local scene.

To examine the method in question in greater detail, and expose some of the discomfitures to which it gives rise, let us begin with a hypothetical case study.

A Case Study in Null-Hypothesis Procedure; or, A Quorum of Embarrassments

Suppose that according to the theory of behavior, T_0, held by most right-minded, respectable behaviorists, the extent to which a certain behavioral manipulation M facilitates learning in a certain complex learning situation C should be null. That is, if "ϕ" designates the degree to which manipulation M facilitates the acquisition of habit H under circumstances C, it follows from the orthodox theory T_0 that $\phi = 0$. Also suppose, however, that a few radicals have persistently advocated an alternative theory T_1 which entails, among other things, that the facilitation of H by M in circumstances C should be appreciably greater than zero, the precise extent being dependent upon the values of certain parameters in C. Finally, suppose that Igor Hopewell, graduate student in psychology, has staked his dissertation hopes on an experimental test of T_0 against T_1 on the basis of their differential predictions about the value of ϕ.

Now, if Hopewell is to carry out his assessment of the comparative merits of T_0 and T_1 in this way, there is nothing for him to do but submit a number of Ss to manipulation M under circumstances C and compare their efficiency at acquiring habit H with that of comparable Ss who, under circumstances C, have *not* been exposed to manipulation M. The difference, d, between experimental and control Ss in average learning efficiency may then be taken as an operational measure of the degree, ϕ, to which M influences acquisition of

H in circumstances C. Unfortunately, however, as any experienced researcher knows to his sorrow, the interpretation of such an observed statistic is not quite so simple as that. For the observed dependent variable d, which is actually a performance measure, is a function not only of the extent to which M influences acquisition of H, but of many additional major and minor factors as well. Some of these, such as deprivations, species, age, laboratory conditions, etc., can be removed from consideration by holding them essentially constant. Others, however, are not so easily controlled, especially those customarily subsumed under the headings of "individual differences" and "errors of measurement." To curtail a long mathematical story, it turns out that with suitable (possibly justified) assumptions about the distributions of values for these uncontrolled variables, the manner in which they influence the dependent variable, and the way in which experimental and control Ss were selected and manipulated, the observed sample statistic d may be regarded as the value of a normally distributed random variate whose average value is ϕ and whose variance, which is independent of ϕ, is unbiasedly estimated by the square of another sample statistic, s, computed from the data of the experiment.

The import of these statistical considerations for Hopewell's dissertation, of course, is that he will not be permitted to reason in any simple way from the observed d to a conclusion about the comparative merits of T_0 and T_1. To conclude that T_0, rather than T_1, is correct, he must argue that $\phi = 0$, rather than $\phi > 0$. But the observed d, whatever its value, is logically compatible both with the hypothesis that $\phi = 0$ and the hypothesis that $\phi > 0$. How then, can Hopewell use his data to make a comparison of T_0 and T_1? As a well-trained student, what he *does*, of course, is to divide d by s to obtain what, under H_0, is a t statistic, consult a table of the t distributions under the appropriate degrees-of-freedom, and announce his experiment as disconfirming or supporting T_0, respectively, according to

whether or not the discrepancy between d and the zero value expected under T_0 is "statistically significant"—i.e., whether or not the observed value of d/s falls outside of the interval between two extreme percentiles (usually the 2.5th and 97.5th) of the t distribution with that df. If asked by his dissertation committee to justify this behavior, Hopewell would rationalize something like the following (the more honest reply, that this is what he has been taught to do, not being considered appropriate to such occasions):

In deciding whether or not T_0 is correct, I can make two types of mistakes: I can reject T_0 when it is in fact correct [Type I error], or I can accept T_0 when in fact it is false [Type II error]. As a scientist, I have a professional obligation to be cautious, but a 5% chance of error is not unduly risky. Now if all my statistical background assumptions are correct, then, if it is really true that $\phi = 0$ as T_0 says, there is only one chance in 20 that my observed statistic d/s will be smaller than $t_{.025}$ or larger than $t_{.975}$, where by the latter I mean, respectively, the 2.5th and 97.5th percentiles of the t distribution with the same degrees-of-freedom as in my experiment. Therefore, if I reject T_0 when d/s is smaller than $t_{.025}$ or larger than $t_{.975}$, and accept T_0 otherwise, there is only a 5% chance that I will reject T_0 incorrectly.

If asked about his Type II error, and why he did not choose some other rejection region, say between $t_{.475}$ and $t_{.525}$, which would yield the same probability of Type I error, Hopewell should reply that although he has no way to compute his probability of Type II error under the assumptions traditionally authorized by null-hypothesis procedure, it is presumably minimized by taking the rejection region at the extremes of the t distribution.

Let us suppose that for Hopewell's data, $d = 8.50$, $s = 5.00$, and $df = 20$. Then $t_{.975} = 2.09$ and the acceptance region for the null hypothesis $\phi = 0$ is $-2.09 < d/s < 2.09$, or $-10.45 < d < 10.45$. Since d does fall within this region, standard null-hypothesis decision procedure, which I shall henceforth abbreviate "NHD," dictates that the experiment is to be reported as supporting theory T_0. (Although many persons would like to conceive NHD testing to authorize only rejection of the hypothesis, not, in addition, its acceptance when the test statistic fails to fall in the rejection region, if failure to reject were not taken as grounds for acceptance, then NHD procedure would involve no Type II error, and no justification would be given for taking the rejection region at the extremes of the distribution, rather than in its middle.) But even as Hopewell reaffirms T_0 in his dissertation, he begins to feel uneasy. In fact, several disquieting thoughts occur to him:

1. Although his test statistic falls within the orthodox acceptance region, a value this divergent from the expected zero should nonetheless be encountered less than once in 10. To argue in favor of a hypothesis on the basis of data ascribed a p value no greater than .10 (i.e., 10%) by that hypothesis certainly does not seem to be one of the more impressive displays of scientific caution.

2. After some belated reflection on the details of theory T_1, Hopewell observes that T_1 not only predicts that $\phi > 0$, but with a few simplifying assumptions no more questionable than is par for this sort of course, the value that ϕ should have can actually be computed. Suppose the value derived from T_1 in this way is $\phi = 10.0$. Then, rather than taking $\phi = 0$ as the null hypothesis, one might just as well take $\phi = 10.0$; for under the latter, $(d - 10.0)/s$ is a 20 df t statistic, giving a two-tailed, 95% significance, acceptance region for $(d - 10.0)/s$ between $-.209$ and 2.09. That is, if one lets T_1 provide the null hypothesis, it is accepted or rejected according to whether or not $-.45 < d < 20.45$, and by this latter test, therefore, Hopewell's data must be taken to support T_1—in fact, the likelihood under T_1 of obtaining a test statistic this divergent from the expected 10.0 is a most satisfactory three chances in four. Thus it occurs to Hopewell that had he chosen to cast his professional lot with the T_1-ists by selecting $\phi = 10.0$ as his null hypothesis, he could have made a strong argument in favor of T_1 by precisely the same line of statistical reasoning he has used to support T_0 under $\phi = 0$ as the null hypothesis. That is, he could have made an argument

that persons partial to T_1 would regard as strong. For behaviorists who are already convinced that T_0 is correct would howl that since T_0 is the dominant theory, only $\phi = 0$ is a legitimate null hypothesis. (And is it not strange that what constitutes a valid statistical argument should be dependent upon the majority opinion about behavior theory?)

3. According to the NHD test of a hypothesis, only two possible final outcomes of the experiment are recognized—either the hypothesis is rejected or it is accepted. In Hopewell's experiment, all possible values of d/s between -2.09 and 2.09 have the same interpretive significance, namely, indicating that $\phi = 0$, while conversely, all possible values of d/s greater than 2.09 are equally taken to signify that $\phi \neq 0$. But Hopewell finds this disturbing, for of the various possible values that d/s might have had, the significance of $d/s = 1.70$ for the comparative merits of T_0 and T_1 should surely be more similar to that of, say, $d/s = 2.10$ than to that of, say, $d/s = -1.70$.

4. In somewhat similar vein, it also occurs to Hopewell that had he opted for a somewhat riskier confidence level, say a Type I error of 10% rather than 5%, d/s would have fallen outside the region of acceptance and T_0 would have been rejected. Now surely the degree to which a datum corroborates or impugns a proposition should be independent of the datum-assessor's personal temerity. Yet according to orthodox significance-test procedure, whether or not a given experimental outcome supports or disconfirms the hypothesis in question depends crucially upon the assessor's tolerance for Type I risk.

Despite his inexperience, Igor Hopewell is a sound experimentalist at heart, and the more he reflects on these statistics, the more dissatisfied with his conclusions he becomes. So while the exigencies of graduate circumstances and publication requirements urge that his dissertation be written as a confirmation of T_0, he nonetheless resolves to keep an open mind on the issue, even carrying out further research if opportunity permits. And reading his experimental report, so of course would we—has any responsible scientist ever made up his mind about such a matter on the basis of a single experiment? Yet in this obvious way we reveal how little our actual inferential behavior corresponds to the statistical procedure to which we pay lip-service. For if we did, in fact, accept or reject the null hypothesis according to whether the sample statistic falls in the acceptance or in the rejection region, then there would be no replications of experimental designs, no multiplicity of experimental approaches to an important hypothesis—a single experiment would, by definition of the method, make up our mind about the hypothesis in question. And the fact that in actual practice, a single finding seldom even tempts us to such closure of judgment reveals how little the conventional model of hypothesis testing fits our actual evaluative behavior.

Decisions vs. Degrees of Belief

By now, it should be obvious that something is radically amiss with the traditional NHD assessment of an experiment's theoretical import. Actually, one does not have to look far in order to find the trouble—it is simply a basic misconception about the purpose of a scientific experiment. The null-hypothesis significance test treats acceptance or rejection of a hypothesis as though these were *decisions* one makes on the basis of the experimental data—i.e., that we elect to adopt one belief, rather than another, as a result of an experimental outcome. *But the primary aim of a scientific experiment is not to precipitate decisions, but to make an appropriate adjustment in the degree to which one accepts, or believes, the hypothesis or hypotheses being tested.* And even if the purpose of the experiment *were* to reach a decision, it could not be a decision to accept or reject the hypothesis, for decisions are voluntary commitments to action—i.e., are *motor* sets—whereas acceptance or rejection of a hypothesis is a *cognitive* state which may provide the basis for rational decisions, but is not itself arrived at by such a decision (except perhaps indirectly in that a

decision may initiate further experiences which influence the belief).

The situation, in other words, is as follows: As scientists, it is our professional obligation to reason from available data to explanations and generalities—i.e., beliefs—which are supported by these data. But belief in (i.e., acceptance of) a proposition is not an all-or-none affair; rather, it is a matter of degree, and the extent to which a person believes or accepts a proposition translates pragmatically into the extent to which he is willing to commit himself to the behavioral adjustments prescribed for him by the meaning of that proposition. For example, if that inveterate gambler, Unfortunate Q. Smith, has complete confidence that War Biscuit will win the fifth race at Belmont, he will be willing to accept any odds to place a bet on War Biscuit to win; for if he is absolutely *certain* that War Biscuit will win, then odds are irrelevant—it is simply a matter of arranging to collect some winnings after the race. On the other hand, the more that Smith has doubts about War Biscuit's prospects, the higher the odds he will demand before betting. That is, the *extent* to which Smith accepts or rejects the hypothesis that War Biscuit will win the fifth at Belmont is an important determinant of his betting decisions for that race.

Now, although a scientist's data supply *evidence* for the conclusions he draws from them, only in the unlikely case where the conclusions are logically deducible from or logically incompatible with the data do the data warrant that the conclusions be entirely accepted or rejected. Thus, e.g., the fact that War Biscuit has won all 16 of his previous starts is strong evidence in favor of his winning the fifth at Belmont, but by no means warrants the unreserved acceptance of this hypothesis. More generally, the data available confer upon the conclusions a certain *appropriate degree of belief*, and it is the inferential task of the scientist to pass from the data of his experiment to whatever *extent* of belief these and other available information justify in the hypothesis under investigation. In particular, the proper inferential procedure is *not* (except in the deductive case) a matter of deciding to accept (without qualification) or reject (without qualification) the hypothesis: even if adoption of a belief were a matter of voluntary action—which it is not—neither such extremes of belief or disbelief are appropriate to the data at hand. As an example of the disastrous consequences of an inferential procedure which yields only two judgment values, acceptance and rejection, consider how sad the plight of Smith would be if, whenever weighing the prospects for a given race, he always worked himself into either supreme confidence or utter disbelief that a certain horse will win. Smith would rapidly impoverish himself by accepting excessively low odds on horses he is certain will win, and failing to accept highly favorable odds on horses he is sure will lose. In fact, Smith's two judgment values need not be *extreme* acceptance and rejection in order for his inferential procedure to be maladaptive. All that is required is that the degree of belief arrived at be in general inappropriate to the likelihood conferred on the hypothesis by the data.

Now, the notion of "degree of belief appropriate to the data at hand" has an unpleasantly vague, subjective feel about it which makes it unpalatable for inclusion in a formalized theory of inference. Fortunately, a little reflection about this phrase reveals it to be intimately connected with another concept relating conclusion to evidence which, though likewise in serious need of conceptual clarification, has the virtues both of intellectual respectability and statistical familiarity. I refer, of course, to the *likelihood*, or *probability*, conferred upon a hypothesis by available evidence. Why should not Smith *feel* certain, in view of the data available, that War Biscuit will win the fifth at Belmont? Because it *is* not certain that War Biscuit will win. More generally, what determines how strongly we should accept or reject a proposition is the probability given to this hypothesis by the information at hand. For while our voluntary actions (i.e., decisions) are determined by our intensities of belief in the relevant proposi-

tions, not by their actual probabilities, expected utility is maximized when the cognitive weights given to potential but not yet known-for-certain pay-off events are represented in the decision procedure by the probabilities of these events. We may thus relinquish the concept of "appropriate degree of belief" in favor of "probability of the hypothesis," and our earlier contention about the nature of data-processing may be rephrased to say that the proper inferential task of the experimental scientist is not a simple acceptance or rejection of the tested hypothesis, but determination of the probability conferred upon it by the experimental outcome. This likelihood of the hypothesis relative to whatever data are available at the moment will be an important determinant for decisions which must currently be made, but is not itself such a decision and is entirely subject to revision in the light of additional information.

In brief, what is being argued is that the scientist, whose task is not to prescribe actions but to establish rational beliefs upon which to base them, is fundamentally and inescapably committed to an explicit concern with the problem of inverse probability. What he wants to know is how plausible are his hypotheses, and he is interested in the probability ascribed by a hypothesis to an observed experimental outcome only to the extent he is able to reason backwards to the likelihood of the hypothesis, given this outcome. Put crudely, no matter how improbable an observation may be under the hypothesis (and when there are an infinite number of possible outcomes, the probability of any particular one of these is, usually, infinitely small—the familiar p value for an observed statistic under a hypothesis H is not actually the probability of that outcome under H, but a partial integral of the probability-density function of possible outcomes under H), it is still confirmatory (or at least nondisconfirmatory, if one argues from the data to rejection of the background assumptions) so long as the likelihood of the observation is even smaller under the alternative hypotheses. To be sure, the theory of hypothesis-likelihood and inverse probability is as yet far from the level of development at which it can furnish the research scientist with inferential tools he can apply mechanically to obtain a definite likelihood estimate. But to the extent a statistical method does not at least move in the *direction* of computing the probability of the hypothesis, given the observation, that method is not truly a method of *inference*, and is unsuited for the scientist's cognitive ends.

The Methodological Status of the Null-Hypothesis Significance Test

The preceding arguments have, in one form or another, raised several doubts about the appropriateness of conventional significance-test decision procedure for the aims it is supposed to achieve. It is now time to bring these charges together in an explicit bill of indictment.

1. The null-hypothesis significance test treats "acceptance" or "rejection" of a hypothesis as though these were decisions one makes. But a hypothesis is not something, like a piece of pie offered for dessert, which can be accepted or rejected by a voluntary physical action. Acceptance or rejection of a hypothesis is a cognitive process, a *degree* of believing or disbelieving which, if rational, is not a matter of choice but determined solely by how likely it is, given the evidence, that the hypothesis is true.

2. It might be argued that the NHD test may nonetheless be regarded as a legitimate decision procedure if we translate "acceptance (rejection) of the hypothesis" as meaning "acting as though the hypothesis were true (false)." And to be sure, there are many occasions on which one must base a course of action on the credibility of a scientific hypothesis. (Should these data be published? Should I devote my research resources to and become identified professionally with this theory? Can we test this new Z bomb without exterminating all life on earth?) But such a move to salvage the traditional pro-

cedure only raises two further objections. (*a*) While the scientist—i.e., the person—must indeed make decisions, his *science* is a systematized body of (probable) *knowledge*, not an accumulation of decisions. The end product of a scientific investigation is a degree of confidence in some set of propositions, which then constitutes a *basis* for decisions. (*b*) Decision theory shows the NHD test to be woefully inadequate as a decision procedure. In order to decide most effectively when or when not to act as though a hypothesis is correct, one must know both the probability of the hypothesis under the data available and the utilities of the various decision outcomes (i.e., the values of accepting the hypothesis when it is true, of accepting it when it is false, of rejecting it when it is true, and of rejecting it when it is false). But traditional NHD procedure pays no attention to utilities at all, and considers the probability of the hypothesis, given the data—i.e., the inverse probability—only in the most rudimentary way (by taking the rejection region at the extremes of the distribution rather than in its middle). Failure of the traditional significance test to deal with inverse probabilities invalidates it not only as a method of rational inference, but *also* as a useful decision procedure.

3. The traditional NHD test unrealistically limits the significance of an experimental outcome to a mere two alternatives, confirmation or disconfirmation of the null hypothesis. Moreover, the transition from confirmation to disconfirmation as a function of the data is discontinuous—an arbitrarily small difference in the value of the test statistic can change its significance from confirmatory to disconfirmatory. Finally, the point at which this transition occurs is entirely gratuitous. There is absolutely no reason (at least provided by the method) why the point of statistical "significance" should be set at the 95% level, rather than, say the 94% or 96% level. Nor does the fact that we sometimes select a 99% level of significance, rather than the usual 95% level, mitigate this objection—one is as arbitrary as the other.

4. The null-hypothesis significance test introduces a strong bias in favor of one out of what may be a large number of reasonable alternatives. When sampling a distribution of unknown mean μ, different assumptions about the value of μ furnish an infinite number of alternate null hypotheses by which we might assess the sample mean, and whichever hypothesis is selected is thereby given an enormous, in some cases almost insurmountable, advantage over its competitors. That is, NHD procedure involves an inferential double standard—the favored hypothesis is held innocent unless proved guilty, while any alternative is held guilty until no choice remains but to judge it innocent. What is objectionable here is not that some hypotheses are held more resistant to experimental extinction than others, but that the differential weighing is an all-or-none side effect of a personal choice, and especially, that the method *necessitates* one hypothesis being favored over all the others. In the classical theory of inverse probability, on the other hand, all hypotheses are treated on a par, each receiving a weight (i.e., its "a priori" probability) which reflects the credibility of that hypothesis on grounds other than the data being assessed.

5. Finally, if anything can reveal the practical irrelevance of the conventional significance test, it should be its failure to see genuine application to the inferential behavior of the research scientist. Who has ever given up a hypothesis just because one experiment yielded a test statistic in the rejection region? And what scientist in his right mind would ever feel there to be an appreciable difference between the interpretive significance of data, say, for which one-tailed $p = .04$ and that of data for which $p = .06$, even though the point of "significance" has been set at $p = .05$? In fact, the reader may well feel undisturbed by the charges raised here against traditional NHD procedure precisely because, without perhaps realizing it, he has never taken the method seriously anyway. Paradoxically, it is often the most firmly institutionalized tenet of faith that is most susceptible to untroubled disregard—in our culture, one must early learn to live with sacrosanct verbal formulas whose import for practical behavior is seldom heeded. I suspect that the primary reasons why null-hypothesis significance testing has attained its current ritualistic status are (*a*) the surcease of methodological insecurity afforded by having an inferential algorithm on the books, and (*b*) the fact that a by-product of the algorithm is so useful, and its end product so obviously inappropriate, that the latter can be ignored without even noticing that this has, in fact, been done. What has given the traditional method its spurious feel of usefulness is that the *first*, and by far most laborious, step in the procedure, namely, estimating the probability of the experimental outcome under the assumption that a certain hypothesis is correct, is also a crucial first step toward what one is genuinely concerned with, namely, an idea of the likelihood of that hypothesis, given this experimental outcome. Having obtained this most valuable statistical information under pretext of carrying through a conventional significance test, it is then tempting, though of course quite inappropriate, to heap honor and gratitude upon the method while overlooking that its actual *result*, namely, a decision to accept or reject, is not used at all.

Toward a More Realistic Appraisal of Experimental Data

So far, my arguments have tended to be aggressively critical—one can hardly avoid polemics when butchering sacred cows. But my purpose is not just to be contentious, but to help clear the way for more realistic techniques of data assessment, and the time has now arrived for some constructive suggestions. Little of what follows pretends to any originality; I merely urge that ongoing developments along these lines should receive maximal encouragement.

For the statistical theoretician, the following problems would seem to be eminently worthy of research:

1. Of supreme importance for the theory of

probability is analysis of what we mean by a proposition's "probability," relative to the evidence provided. Most serious students of the philosophical foundations of probability and statistics agree that the probability of a proposition (e.g., the probability that the General Theory of Relativity is correct) does not, prima facie, seem to be the same sort of thing as the probability of an event-class (e.g., the probability of getting a head when this coin is tossed). Do the statistical concepts and formulas which have been developed for probabilities of the latter kind also apply to hypothesis likelihoods? In particular, are the probabilities of hypotheses quantifiable at all, and for the theory of inverse probability, do Bayes' theorem and its probability-density refinements apply to hypothesis probabilities? These and similar questions are urgently in need of clarification.

2. If we are willing to assume that Bayes' theorem, or something like it, holds for hypothesis probabilities, there is much that can be done to develop the classical theory of inverse probability. While computation of inverse probabilities turns essentially upon the parametric a priori probability function, which states the probability of each alternative hypothesis in the set under consideration prior to the outcome of the experiment, it should be possible to develop theorems which are invariant over important subclasses of a priori probability functions. In particular, the difference between the a priori probability function and the "a posteriori" probability function (i.e., the probabilities of the alternative hypotheses after the experiment), perhaps analyzed as a difference in "information," should be a potentially fruitful source of concepts with which to explore such matters as the "power" or "efficiency" of various statistics, the acquisition of inductive knowledge through repeated experimentation, etc. Another problem which seems to me to have considerable import, though not one about which I am sanguine, is whether inverse-probability theory can significantly be extended to hypothesis-probabilities, given knowledge which is only

probabilistic. That is, can a theory of sentences of form "The probability of hypothesis H, given that E is the case, is p," be generalized to a theory of sentences of form "The probability of hypothesis H, given that the probability of E is q, is p"? Such a theory would seem to be necessary, e.g., if we are to cope adequately with the uncertainty attached to the background assumptions which always accompany a statistical analysis.

My suggestions for applied statistical analysis turn on the fact that while what is desired is the a posteriori probabilities of the various alternative hypotheses under consideration, computation of these by classical theory necessitates the corresponding a priori probability distribution, and in the more immediate future, at least, information about this will exist only as a subjective feel, differing from one person to the next, about the credibilities of the various hypotheses.

3. Whenever possible, the basic statistical report should be in the form of a *confidence interval*. Briefly, a confidence interval is a subset of the alternative hypotheses computed from the experimental data in such a way that for a selected confidence level α, the probability that the true hypothesis is included in a set so obtained is α. Typically, an α-level confidence interval consists of those hypotheses under which the p value for the experimental outcome is larger than $1 - \alpha$ (a feature of confidence intervals which is sometimes confused with their definition), in which case the confidence-interval report is similar to a simultaneous null-hypothesis significance test of each hypothesis in the total set of alternatives. Confidence intervals are the closest we can at present come to quantitative assessment of hypothesis-probabilities (see *technical note*, below), and are currently our most effective way to eliminate hypotheses from practical consideration—if we choose to act as though none of the hypotheses not included in a 95% confidence interval are correct, we stand only a 5% chance of error. (Note, moreover, that this probability of error pertains to the incorrect simultaneous "rejection" of a major part

of the total set of alternative hypotheses, not just to the incorrect rejection of one as in the NHD method, and is a *total* likelihood of error, not just of Type I error.) The confidence interval is also a simple and effective way to convey that all-important statistical datum, the conditional probability (or probability density) function—i.e., the probability (probability density) of the observed outcome under each alternative hypothesis—since for a given kind of observed statistic and method of confidence-interval determination, there will be a fixed relation between the parameters of the confidence interval and those of the conditional probability (probability density) function, with the end-points of the confidence interval typically marking the points at which the conditional probability (probability density) function sinks below a certain small value related to the parameter α. The confidence-interval report is not biased toward some favored hypothesis, as is the null-hypothesis significance test, but makes an impartial simultaneous evaluation of all the alternatives under consideration. Nor does the confidence interval involve an arbitrary decision as does the NHD test. Although one person may prefer to report, say, 95% confidence intervals while another favors 99% confidence intervals, there is no conflict here, for these are simply two ways to convey the same information. An experimental report can, with complete consistency and some benefit, simultaneously present several confidence intervals for the parameter being estimated. On the other hand, different choices of significance level in the NHD method is a clash of incompatible decisions, as attested by the fact that an NHD analysis which simultaneously presented two different significance levels would yield a logically inconsistent conclusion when the observed statistic has a value in the acceptance region of one significance level and in the rejection region of the other.

Technical note: One of the more important problems now confronting theoretical statistics is exploration and clarification of the relationships among inverse probabilities derived from confidence-interval theory, fiducial-probability theory (a special case of the former in which the estimator is a sufficient statistic), and classical (i.e., Bayes') inverse-probability theory. While the interpretation of confidence intervals is tricky, it would be a mistake to conclude, as the cautionary remarks usually accompanying discussions of confidence intervals sometimes seem to imply, that the confidence-level α of a given confidence interval I should not really be construed as a probability that the true hypothesis, H, belongs to the set I. Nonetheless, if I is an α-level confidence interval, the probability that H belongs to I as computed by Bayes' theorem given an a priori probability distribution will, in general, *not* be equal to α, nor is the difference necessarily a small one—it is easy to construct examples where the a posteriori probability that H belongs to I is either 0 or 1. Obviously, when different techniques for computing the probability that H belongs to I yield such different answers, a reconciliation is demanded. In this instance, however, the apparent disagreement is largely if not entirely spurious, resulting from differences in the evidence relative to which the probability that H belongs to I is computed. And if this is, in fact, the correct explanation, then fiducial probability furnishes a partial solution to an outstanding difficulty in the Bayes' approach. A major weakness of the latter has always been the problem of what to assume for the a priori distribution when no pre-experimental information is available other than that supporting the background assumptions which delimit the set of hypotheses under consideration. The traditional assumption (made hesitantly by Bayes, less hesitantly by his successors) has been the "principle of insufficient reason," namely, that given no knowledge at all, all alternatives are equally likely. But not only is it difficult to give a convincing argument for this assumption, it does not even yield a unique a priori probability distribution over a continuum of alternative hypotheses, since there are many ways to express such a continuous set, and what is an equilikelihood a priori distribution under one of these does not necessarily transform into the same under another. Now, a fiducial probability distribution determined over a set of alternative hypotheses by an experimental observation is a measure of the likelihoods of these hypotheses relative to all the information contained in the experimental data, but based on no pre-experimental information beyond the background assumptions restricting the possibilities to this particular set of hypotheses. Therefore, it seems reasonable to postulate that the no-knowledge a priori distribution in classical inverse probability theory should be that distribution which, when experimental data capable of yielding a fiducial argument are now given, results in an a posteriori distribution identical with the corresponding fiducial distribution.

4. While a confidence-interval analysis treats all the alternative hypotheses with glacial impartiality, it nonetheless frequently occurs that our interest is focused on a certain selection from the set of possibilities. In such case, the statistical analysis should also report, when computable, the precise p value of the experimental outcome, or better, though less familiarly, the probability density at that outcome, under each of the major hypotheses; for these figures will permit an immediate judgement as to which of the hypotheses is most favored by the data. In fact, an even more interesting assessment of the postexperimental credibilities of the hypotheses is then possible through use of "likelihood ratios' if one is willing to put his pre-experimental feelings about their relative likelihoods into a quantitative estimate. For let $Pr(H,d)$, $Pr(d,H)$, and $Pr(H)$ be, respectively, the probability of a hypothesis H in light of the experimental data d (added to the information already available), the probability of data d under hypothesis H, and the pre-experimental (i.e., a priori) probability of H. Then for two alternative hypotheses H_0 and H_1, it follows by classical theory that

$$\frac{Pr(H_0, d)}{Pr(H_1, d)} = \frac{Pr(H_0)}{Pr(H_1)} \times \frac{Pr(d, H_0)}{Pr(d, H_1)} \quad \text{Eq. 1}[1]$$

Therefore, if the experimental report includes the probability (or probability density) of the data under H_0 and H_1, respectively, and its reader can quantify his feelings about the

relative pre-experimental merits of H_0 and H_1 (i.e., $Pr(H_0)/Pr(H_1)$), he can then determine the judgment he should make about the relative merits of H_0 and H_1 in light of these new data.

5. Finally, experimental journals should allow the researcher much more latitude in publishing his statistics in whichever form seems most insightful, especially those forms developed by the modern theory of estimates. In particular, the stranglehold that conventional null-hypothesis significance testing has clamped on publication standards must be broken. Currently justifiable inferential algorithm carries us only through computation of conditional probabilities; from there, it is for everyman's clinical judgment and methodological conscience to see him through to a final appraisal. Insistence that published data must have the biases of the NHD method built into the report, thus seducing the unwary reader into a perhaps highly inappropriate interpretation of the data, is a professional disservice of the first magnitude.

Summary

The traditional null-hypothesis significance-test method, more appropriately called "null-hypothesis decision [NHD] procedure," of statistical analysis is here vigorously excoriated for its inappropriateness as a method of *inference*. While a number of serious objections to the method are raised, its most basic error lies in mistaking the aim of a scientific investigation to be a *decision*, rather than a *cognitive* evaluation of propositions. It is further argued that the proper application of statistics to scientific inference is irrevocably committed to extensive consideration of inverse probabilities, and to further this end, certain suggestions are offered, both for the development of statistical theory and for more illuminating application of statistical analysis to empirical data.

---

1. When the numbers of alternative hypotheses and possible experimental outcomes are transfinite, $Pr(d, H) = Pr(H, d) = Pr(H) = 0$ in most cases. If so, the probability ratios in Formula 1 are replaced with the corresponding probability-density ratios. It should be mentioned that this formula rather idealistically presupposes there to be no doubt about the correctness of the background statistical assumptions.

DAVID A. GRANT[1]

10 Testing the Null Hypothesis and the Strategy and Tactics of Investigating Theoretical Models

Testing the null hypothesis, H_0, against alternatives, H_1, is well established and has a proper place in scientific research. However, this testing procedure, when it is routinely applied to comparing experimental outcomes with outcomes that are quantitatively predicted from a theoretical model, can have unintended results and bizarre implications. This paper first outlines three situations in which testing H_0 has conventionally been done by psychologists. In terms of the probable intentions or strategy of the experimenter testing H_0 turns out to be an appropriate tactic in the first situation, but it is inadequate in the second situation, and it is self-defeating with curious implications in the last situation. Alternatives to this conventional procedure are then presented along with the considerations which make the alternatives preferable to testing the usual H_0.

Three Applications of H_0 Testing

Probably the most common application of the tactic of testing H_0 arises when the independent variable has produced a sample difference or

set of differences in the magnitude of the dependent variable. Quantitative predictions of the size of the difference or differences are not available. The experimenter wishes to know whether or not differences of the size obtained could have occurred by virtue of the operation of the innumerable nonexperimental factors conventionally designated as random. He sets up H_0 that the differences are zero; chooses a significance level, α; determines the set of hypotheses alternative to H_0 that he is willing to entertain, H_1; selects an appropriate test statistic, t, F, χ^2, U, T, or the like; and proceeds with the test. Rejection of H_0 permits him to assert, with a precisely defined risk of being wrong, that the obtained differences were not the product of chance variation. Failure of the test to permit rejection of H_0, which, unfortunately, is commonly termed "accepting" H_0, means that the obtained differences or greater ones would occur by chance with a probability greater than α. This situation is straightforward. The experimenter has limited aims. He has asked a simple question, and he has received a simple answer, subject only to those ambiguities which attend all experimental and inductive inference. His tactics are admirably suited to his strategic objective.

Another common but less satisfactory instance of testing H_0 arises when the results of pre-experimental matching or pretesting are to be evaluated. Here the experimenter has measured the dependent variable or some related variable before operation of the independent variable, and he devoutly hopes

1. The author is indebted to Arnold M. Binder, whose arguments inspired him to make explicit some of the issues involved in using conventional analysis of variance procedures in testing the adequacy of a theoretical model. As this paper went through various revisions over a period of time the writer is correspondingly indebted to a number of supporting agencies: the Graduate Research Committee and the College of Letters and Science of the University of Wisconsin, the National Science Foundation, and finally to the Department of Psychology of the University of California, Los Angeles, his host during final preparation of the manuscript.

From *Psychological Review*, Vol. 69, No. 1, pp. 54–61, 1962. Copyright © 1962 by the American Psychological Association, and reprinted by permission.

that the experimental and control groups are alike except for random differences. He is now relieved or chagrined, depending upon whether H_0 is "accepted" or "rejected" as a consequence of his test. Even if H_0 is accepted his relief is tempered by some uneasiness. He knows that he has not proved, and indeed cannot prove, that H_0 is "true." His tactics in testing H_0 seem to be appropriate to the impossible strategic aim of proving the truth of H_0. Certainly, if he had a more reasonable aim he has adopted inappropriate tactics. Utilizing these tactics, the best he can do is to beat a strategic retreat, and if H_0 is accepted he can perhaps point out that he has used a very powerful test and that if there were real differences they were mostly likely very small. Although psychologists have never to my knowledge done so, he might be able to go one step further and point out that his testing procedure would reject H_0 a given percentage of the time, say, 90%, if the "true" difference had been as little as, say, one-tenth of an SD. This sort of statement of the power of a test is a commonplace in acceptance inspection (8, Ch. 13).

With the advent of more detailed mathematical models in psychology (e.g., 3, 4, 7, 9) a new statistical testing situation is arising more and more frequently. The specificity of the predictions and perhaps the whole philosophy behind model construction pose a different kind of statistical problem than those faced by most psychological investigators in the past. It seems obvious that as the use of models becomes more widespread a greater number of investigators will face the problem of evaluating the correspondence between empirical data points and precise numerical predictions of these points. Unfortunately most of the procedures used to date in testing the adequacy of such theoretical predictions set rather bad examples. Probably the least adequate of these procedures has been that in which an H_0 of exact correspondence between theoretical and empirical points is tested against H_1 covering any discrepancy between predictions and experimental results.

Most models predict a considerable number of different aspects of the data, and some of these aspects are predicted with greater success than others (4, Chs. 14, 15, 17, 18). We shall restrict our discussion to the prediction of values along a curve which might be a learning curve. An idealized version of such a typical situation is presented in Figure 1. Here, the

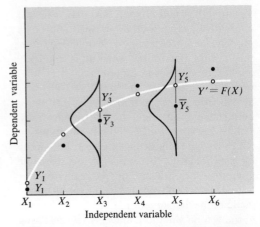

Fig. 1. Idealized situation involving the test of a theoretical function, $Y' = f(X)$. (Theoretical points, Y'_i, are represented by open circles; obtained means, $\bar{Y}_i$, are represented by solid circles.)

dependent variable, Y, is plotted on the vertical axis against the independent variable, X, on the horizontal axis. The theoretical model has led to an expression, $Y' = f(X)$, giving a set of k theoretical predictions, Y'_1, $Y'_2, \ldots, Y'_k$. The experiment has produced k empirical data points, a set of mean values, $\bar{Y}_1, \bar{Y}_2, \ldots, \bar{Y}_k$, corresponding to the values of the independent variable that were investigated, namely, $X_1, X_2, \ldots, X_k$. Individual observations tend to form normal distributions about each of the $\bar{Y}_i$, and these normal distributions tend to have equal σ's for all data points. In further discussion we shall assume that inaccuracies in the manipulation of the independent variable, X, can be ignored. The problem now is to investigate the goodness of fit of the Y'_i to the $\bar{Y}_i$ or the correspondence between the Y'_i and the $\bar{Y}_i$.

The tactics oriented toward accepting H_0 as corroborating the theory involve breaking down the jth individual observation from the general mean of all of the observations, as follows:

$$Y_{ij} - \bar{Y} = (Y_{ij} - \bar{Y}_i) +$$
$$+ (\bar{Y}_i - \bar{Y}'_i) + (Y'_i - \bar{Y}) \qquad \text{Eq. 1}$$

where Y_{ij} is the jth observation in the ith normal distribution, and $\bar{Y}$ is the general mean of all observations.

The total sum of squares may then be partitioned as follows:

$$SS_{\text{Tot}} = SS_{\text{Dev Est}}$$
$$+ SS_{\text{Dev Theory}} + SS_{\text{Theory}} \qquad \text{Eq. 2}$$

where $SS_{\text{Dev Est}}$ is the sum of squares associated with the variation of individual measures from their means, $SS_{\text{Dev Theory}}$ is the sum of squares associated with the systematic departures of empirical data points from the theoretical points, and SS_{Theory} is the sum of squares associated with departures of the theoretical points from the general mean of the whole experiment.

If we suppose that the linear model for the analysis of variance holds, then:

$$Y_{ij} = \mu + T_i + D_i + e_{ij} \qquad \text{Eq. 3}$$

where μ is the population mean for all Y_{ij} over the specific values of the independent variable, X_i; T_i is the departure of the "true" theoretical value of Y'_i from μ; D_i is the discrepancy of the "true" value of $\bar{Y}_i$ from the true value of Y'_i; and e_{ij} is a random element from a normal distribution with a mean of zero and variance, σ_e^2, for all i.

For a fixed set of X_i, the Ts and Ds may be defined so that $\Sigma T_i = \Sigma D_i = 0$. Under H_0 each $D_i = 0$. Under H_i some $D_i \neq 0$, and the variance of the D_i, $\sigma D^2 \neq 0$. This last variance may be termed the true variance of the discrepancies from the theory over the particular set of X_i that was investigated.

The foregoing is a conventional analysis of variance model, and the F ratio of the $MS_{\text{Dev Theory}}$ divided by the $MS_{\text{Dev Est}}$ provides an excellent and powerful test of H_0 against H_1. The number of degrees of freedom for $SS_{\text{Dev Est}}$ will be $k(n-1)$ where n is the number of observations per data point, and the degrees of freedom for $SS_{\text{Dev Theory}}$ will be $k - n_T$, where n_T is the number of degrees of freedom lost in the process of fitting the model to the data. If this F is significant, we reject H_0, concluding that the discrepancies between the $\bar{Y}_i$ and the Y'_i are too great to be accounted for by the observed random variation in the experiment. In this conclusion we accept the 5% or 1% risk implied by our choice of α.

Logical difficulties arise when F fails of significance. H_0 remains tenable but is not proved to be correct. A tenable H_0 provides some support for the theory but only in the negative sense of failing to provide evidence that the theory is faulty. To assert that accepting the H_0 proves that the model provides a satisfactory fit to the data is an inaccurate and misleading statement. We may mean that we are satisfied, but others, especially proponents of other theories, will tend to regard our test as too lenient.

Failure to reject H_0, instead of producing closure, leaves certain annoying ambiguities, but the tactics of testing this particular H_0 imply a strategy that suffers from more serious defects that are readily apparent when the whole conception of testing a theory is carefully considered. To begin with, in view of our present psychological knowledge and the degree of refinement of available theoretical models it seems certain that even the best and most useful theories are not perfect. This means, in terms of the analysis of variance model, there will be some nonzero D_i's. H_0, then, is never really "true." Its "acceptance," rather than "proving" the theory, merely indicates that in this instance the D_i's were too small to be demonstrated by the sensitivity of the experiment in question. The tactics of accepting H_0 as proof and rejecting H_0 as disproof of a theory lead to the anomalous results that a small-scale, insensitive experiment will most often be interpreted as favoring a theory, whereas a large-scale, sensitive experiment will usually yield results opposed to the theory!

Curiously enough, even rejection of H_0 by means of a very stringent experimental test may be quite misleading as far as casting light on the adequacy of the theory is concerned. If the D_i's are very small indeed the theoretical model may be a great improvement over anything else that is available and satisfactory for many purposes even though an extremely sensitive experiment were to reveal the nonzero D_i's. If our task, as scientists, were to test and accept or reject theories as they came off some assembly line the tactics of testing H_0 could be made in a satisfactory manner simply by requiring that the test be "sufficiently" stringent. In fact, our task and our intentions are usually different from testing products; what we are really up to resembles *quality control* rather than *acceptance inspection*, and statistical procedures suitable for the latter are rarely optimal for the former (8, Chs. 1, 13).

Hypothesis Testing versus Statistical Estimation

An analogy will make clear the relation between testing tactics and the intention of the tester. Suppose that I wish to test a parachute; how should I go about it? How I should test depends upon my general intentions. If I want to sell the parachute and am testing it only to be able to claim that it has been tested, and I do not care what happens to the purchaser, then I should give the parachute a most lenient, nonanalytic test. If, however, I am testing the parachute to be sure of it for my own use, then I should subject it to a very stringent, nonanalytic test. But if I am in the competitive business of manufacturing and selling parachutes, then I should subject it to a searching, analytic test, designed to tell me as much as possible about the locus and cause of any failure in order that I may improve my product and gain a larger share of the

parachute market. My contention is that the last situation is the one that is most analogous to that facing the theoretical scientist. He is not accepting or rejecting a finished theory; he is in the long-term business of constructing better versions of the theory. Progress depends upon improvement or providing superior alternatives, and improvement will ordinarily depend upon knowing just how good the model is and exactly where it seems to need alteration. The large D_i's designate the next point of attack in the continuing project of refining the existing model. Therefore attention should be focused upon the various discrepancies between prediction and outcome instead of on the over-all adequacy of the model.

In view of our long-term strategy of improving our theories, our statistical tactics can be greatly improved by shifting emphasis away from over-all hypothesis testing in the direction of statistical estimation. This always holds true when we are concerned with the actual size of one or more differences rather than simply in the existence of differences. For example, in the second instance of hypothesis testing cited at the beginning of this paper, where the investigator tests a pre-experimental difference, he would do better to obtain 95% or 99% confidence interval for the pre-experimental difference. If the interval is small and includes zero, he (and any other moderately sophisticated person) knows immediately that he is on fairly safe ground; but if the interval is large, even though it includes zero, it is immediately apparent that the situation is more uncertain. In both instances H_0 would have been accepted.

Testing a Revised H_0

Before turning to estimation procedures that are useful in examining the correspondence between experimental outcomes and predictions from a mathematical model, I shall digress briefly to outline a statistical testing method which can legitimately be used in appraising the fit of a model to data as shown in Figure 1. Basically the statistical argument in the proper test is reoriented so that rejection of H_0 constitutes evidence favoring the theory. The new H_0 is that the correlation between the predicted values, Y'_i, and the obtained values, $\overline{Y}_i$, is zero, after all correlation due to the fitting process has been eliminated. The alternative, H_1, against which H_0 is tested, is that there is a correlation greater than zero between theoretical and empirical points. The four simple steps required to obtain the necessary F test are as follows:

1. Calculate $t_i = Y'_i - \overline{Y}$ for all i. $\Sigma t_i = 0$.[2]

2. Calculate $SS_{\text{Correspondence}} = n(\Sigma t_i \overline{Y}_i)^2/\Sigma t_i^2$, where n is the number of observations upon which each $\overline{Y}_i$ is based. Negative values of $(\Sigma t_i \overline{Y}_i)$ are treated as zero.

3. Obtain $MS_{\text{Correspondence}} = SS_{\text{Correspondence}}/n_T$, where n_T, the number of degrees of freedom involved in fitting the theoretical points to the empirical data, will ordinarily be the number of linearly independent fitting constants in the mathematical expression of the model.

4. Divide $MS_{\text{Correspondence}}$ by $MS_{\text{Dev Est}}$ to give $F_{\text{Correspondence}}$ which has n_T degrees of freedom for its numerator and $k(n-1)$ degrees of freedom for its denominator, k being the number of $\overline{Y}_i$. The test is one-tailed in the sense that negative values of $\Sigma t_i \overline{Y}_i$ are treated as zero values, so that the probability values of the F distribution must be halved, an unusual procedure with F tests in analysis of variance.

Following the above procedure, rejection of H_0 now means that there is more than random positive covariation between predicted and obtained values of the dependent variable.

This test is admirable in that it puts the burden of proof on the investigator, because a

small-scale, insensitive experiment is unlikely to produce evidence favoring the model. Furthermore, if the model has any merit, the more sensitive the experiment, the more likely it is that a significant F, favoring the theory, will be obtained. Actually, the test is extremely sensitive to virtue in the theory, and therefore in the case of a moderately successful model and a moderately sensitive experiment both this F and the one testing the significance of systematic deviations from the model ($F = MS_{\text{Dev Theory}}/MS_{\text{Dev Est}}$) will tend to be significant. This outcome is no anomaly; it merely indicates that the model predicts some but not all of the systematic variation in the data. In short, progress is being made, but improvement is possible. The fact that simultaneous significance of both Fs, indicating general success and specific failures of a model, should be a commonplace points up the necessity of turning to methods of statistical estimation for a more adequate examination of the workings of a theoretical model.

Practical Estimation Methods for Investigation of Models

As is true of statistical tests, each method of statistical estimation has its advantages and limitations. In the investigation of the adequacy of theoretical curves in psychology there are reasons to believe that the simpler estimation methods have practical advantages over some of the more elegant procedures. To give a fairly complete view of the situation, methods of point and interval estimation of σ_D^2 and of the individual D_i will be described, and a brief evaluation of each method will be given.

Estimating σ_D^2. The variance of the discrepancies between the Y'_i and the $\overline{Y}_i$ condenses into a single number the adequacy of fit of the theoretical model. As such it is an excellent index for the evaluation of the model. The smaller the variance, σ_D^2, the better the model, and vice versa. As an estimate of the size of the discrepancies one might expect in future similar applications of the model,

2. In the unusual event where the general mean of the observations, $\overline{Y}$, is not used as a fitting constant for $Y' = f(X)$, the t_i must be computed as deviations from the mean of all the Y'_i, $\overline{Y}'$. The test will then be insensitive to discrepancies between $\overline{Y}'$ and $\overline{Y}$, and the interpretation will be somewhat equivocal. A separate test of H_0 that $\overline{Y}_{\text{population}}$ equals $\overline{Y}'$, is feasible, but here the experimenter is forced into the illicit posture of seeking to embrace H_0.

σ_{D}^2 is far more informative than any F test. Furthermore σ_{D}^2 is readily estimated in the case of homogeneity of the error variance, σ_{e}^2. The expected values of the relevant mean squares are as follows:

$$\text{Exp}(MS_{\text{Dev Theory}}) = \sigma_{e}^2 + n\sigma_{D^2} \qquad \text{Eq. 4}$$

$$\text{Exp}(MS_{\text{Dev Est}}) = \sigma_{e}^2 \qquad \text{Eq. 5}$$

A maximum likelihood estimate of the variance of the discrepancies, $\hat{\sigma}_{D2}$ is then:

$$\hat{\sigma}_{D}^2 = (MS_{\text{Dev Theory}} - MS_{\text{Dev Est}})/n \quad \text{Eq. 6}$$

The accuracy of this estimator depends upon the number of degrees of freedom associated with $SS_{\text{Dev Theory}}$ and $SS_{\text{Dev Est}}$. The latter rarely poses any practical problem, but the former, in view of the predilection of psychologists for minimizing the number of data points, is quite critical. This is readily apparent when interval estimation of σ_{D}^2 is attempted.

Bross (2) gives a convenient method for accurate approximation of the fiducial interval for σ_{D}^2, and in this case the fiducial and confidence intervals are essentially equal. The method will be outlined below for the 5% interval.

1. Obtain σ_{D}^2 from Equation 6, above. (If the estimate is negative or zero, meaningful limits cannot be obtained.)

2. Find:

$$L = \frac{\dfrac{F}{F_{025(k-n_T,\,k[n-1])}} - 1}{\dfrac{F \cdot F_{025(k-n_T,\,\infty)}}{F_{025(k-n_T,\,k[n-1])}} - 1}$$

where:

$$F = MS_{\text{Dev Theory}}/MS_{\text{Dev Est}}$$

$F_{025(k-n_T,\,[k-n]^1)}$ is the entry in the 2.5% F table (Pearson & Hartley, 1954) for $n_1 = k - n_T$ and $n_2 = k[n-1]$; and $F_{025(k-n_T,\,\infty)}$ is the entry for $n_1 = k - n_T$ and $n_2 = \infty$.

3. Find:

$$L = \frac{\dfrac{F \cdot F_{025(k[n-1],\,k-n_T)} - 1}{F \cdot F_{025(k[n-1],\,k-n_T)}}}{F_{025(\infty,\,k-n_T)}} - 1$$

where $F_{025(k[n-1],\,k-n_T)}$ is the entry in the 2.5% F table for $n_1 = k[n-1]$, and $n_2 = k - n_T$; $F_{025(\infty,\,k-n_T)}$ is the entry for $n_1 = \infty$, and $n_2 = k - n_T$.

4. The upper and lower limits are then $\bar{L}\hat{\sigma}_{D}^2$ and $L\hat{\sigma}_{D2}$, respectively. With less than 15–20 data points these limits will be found to be uncomfortably wide, a fact to bear in mind when designing an experimental test of a theoretical model. For example, in Figure 1, with 6 data points and two degrees of freedom for curve fitting, the limits might plausibly be 0–40, whereas with 14 data points the limits might be 0–12.

Aside from the considerable variability in the estimate of σ_{D2} which can be reduced by increasing the number of data points, there are two other important limitations to the use of estimates of the variance of the discrepancies in evaluating a model. First of all, the population value of σ_{D}^2 is completely dependent upon the particular values of the independent variable, X, which are chosen for the test of the model. Choice of two different sets of Xs could well lead to two entirely different values of σ_{D}^2, and both of these values could be perfectly accurate. Secondly, although σ_{D}^2 gives an over-all index of the adequacy of the model being tested, it condenses so much information into one measure that it does not permit pinpointing the especially large D_i's so that they can be given proper attention in considering revision of the model.

Estimating the D_i. The individual D_i may be estimated as points, or intervals may be established for the D_i, collectively or individually. As before, each method has its good points and its limitations.

Point estimation of the individual D_i's consists simply in comparing the individual data points, the $\bar{Y}_i$, with the fitted curve. It is a crude method, but it has served well in the past and represents the beginning of wisdom. For example, in Figure 1, the model builder might well note that the first three data points lie below the curve and ask himself if there is some special reason for this. He would also note that the greatest discrepancy occurs at

$\bar{Y}_s$, where the neighboring discrepancies are in the other direction. The weakness of this simple method lies in the absence of a criterion which will assist the investigator in deciding which discrepancies should be singled out for further attention and which may be disregarded because they are within the range of expected random variation. This defect is remedied by the interval estimation techniques.

Probably the ideal method of interval estimation is that in which intervals are established for the whole curve in one operation by finding the 95% confidence band. The method takes the theoretical curve as a point of departure, and the result is a pair of curves above and below the theoretical curve, which will tend in the case of random variation to contain between them 95% of the data points. Points lying outside the band are immediately suspect; they are the most promising candidates for attention in the next version of the model. There are two practical difficulties with this method. First, homogeneity of the error variance, σ_e^2, over all the X_i is required. And secondly, because errors in estimation of each fitting parameter must be taken into account, for all but the simplest curves (5, pp. 184–186) the bands may be difficult[3] to obtain. Although the method is elegant, in practice it will rarely represent sufficient improvement over the final method, given below, to justify its use.

The last method seems to me to be the most useful and most robust and most flexible method. It can be widely applied, and the relative ease of application, coupled with its ability to discriminate between significant and random discrepancies make it superior to the other estimation methods. It also possesses the homely virtue of being readily understood. In contrast to the preceding method, this one takes as its point of departure the empirical means, and consists, simply, in computing the 95% confidence limits for each of the $\bar{Y}_i$. If there is homogeneity of variance, the error variance of each mean is taken simply as $\hat{\sigma}_e^2/n$; in cases of suspected heterogeneity, each mean must have its own estimate of error variance. This will, of course, be the variance of the distribution of Y_{ij} for each i, divided by n. When these limits have been obtained, attention is directed to instances where the theoretical curve lies outside the limits. In some cases, the investigator might choose to establish the 80% or 90% limits in order to direct his attention to less drastic departures of the experimental results from the model. Choice of an optimum level for the limits is hard to establish on a general a priori basis, but it is likely that limits narrower than the traditional 95% will be found more useful than the broader limits. Simple as this method is, it is hard to improve upon in actual practice. Instead of giving an almost meaningless over-all acceptance or rejection of a model, it directs attention to specific defects, its functioning improves as the precision of the experimental test is improved, and the investigator can set the confidence coefficient so as to increase its sensitivity to defect at a cost of a fairly well-specified percentage of false positives or wild goose chases. A final and often crucial advantage is that the confidence intervals, based as they are upon the experimental means, can be obtained in cases where the form of the theoretical function does not permit satisfactory estimation of its parameters, and the analysis of variance and confidence bands methods cannot properly be applied.

Summary and Conclusions

In this paper I have attempted to show that the traditional procedure of testing a null hypothesis (H_0) of a zero difference or set of zero differences is quite appropriate to the experimenter's intentions or scientific strategy

3. A sufficient estimate of the error variance of each parameter must be available and independent of the estimates of all other parameters or else the covariances of all parametric estimates must be found and the theoretical function must have continuous first partial derivatives with respect to the parameters in order that the confidence bands may be found in the asymptotic case (11, pp. 207–208). Where an asymptote is involved in the fitting of the theoretical function, satisfactory independent estimators can rarely be obtained.

when he is unable to predict differences of a specified size. When theory or other circumstances permit the prediction of differences of specified size, using these predictions as the values in H_0 is tactically inappropriate, frustrating and self-defeating. This is particularly true when a theoretical curve has been predicted, and H_0 is framed in terms of zero discrepancies from the curve. If rejection of H_0 is interpreted as evidence against the theory and "acceptance" of H_0 is interpreted as evidence favoring the theory, we find that the larger and more sensitive the experiment is, the more likely it will lead to results opposed to the theory; whereas the smaller and less sensitive the experiment, the more likely the results will favor the theory. Aside from this anomaly, which can be corrected by recasting H_0 in terms of a zero covariance between theoretical prediction and experimental outcome, hypothesis testing, as a statistical tactic in this case implies an acceptance-inspection strategy. Acceptance-inspection properly involves examination of finished products with a view to accepting them if they are good enough and rejecting them if they are shoddy enough. The theoretician is not a purchaser but rather he is a producer of goods in a competitive market so that his examination of his theory should be from the standpoint of quality control. His idealized intentions are to detect and correct defects, if possible, so that he can produce a more adequate, more general theoretical model. Because his ideal strategy is not to prove or disprove a theory but rather to seek a better theory, his appropriate statistical tactics should be those involving estimation rather than hypothesis testing.

Examination of alternative techniques available for point or interval estimation of discrepancies between theoretical predictions and experimental outcomes or the over-all variance of these discrepancies suggests stronly that estimation of the confidence intervals for the means found along a theoretical curve is the most practical and most widely applicable general procedure. Other writers have recently emphasized the values of various estimation as opposed to hypothesis testing techniques (e.g. 1, 6, 12) and it is hoped that considerations pointed out by them and points raised in this paper will be helpful to investigators who are in the process of examining theoretical models which lead to specific numeral predictions of experimental outcomes.

References

1. Bolles, R., & Messick, S. Statistical utility in experimental inference. *Psychol. Rep.*, 1958, 4, 223–227.
2. Bross, I. Fiducial intervals for variance components. *Biometrics*, 1950, 6, 136–144.
3. Bush, R. R., Abelson, R. P., & Hyman, R. *Mathematics for psychologists: Examples and problems.* New York: Social Science Research Council, 1956.
4. Bush, R. R., & Estes, W. K. (Eds.) *Studies in mathematical learning theory.* Stanford, Calif.: Stanford Univer. Press, 1959.
5. Cornell, F. G. *The essentials of educational statistics.* New York: Wiley, 1956.
6. Gaito, J. The Bolles-Messick coefficient of utility. *Psychol. Rep.*, 1958, 4, 595–598.
7. Goldberg, S. *Introduction to difference equations.* New York: Wiley, 1958.
8. Grant, E. L. *Statistical quality control.* New York: McGraw-Hill, 1952.
9. Kemeny, J. G., Snell, J. L. & Thompson, G. L. *Introduction to finite mathematics.* Englewood Cliffs, N. J.: Prentice-Hall, 1957.
10. Pearson, E. S., & Hartley, H. O. (Eds.) *Biometrika tables for statisticians.* Cambridge, England: Cambridge Univer. Press, 1954.
11. Rao, C. R. *Advanced statistical methods in biometric research.* New York: Wiley, 1952.
12. Savage, I. R. Nonparametric statistics. *J. Amer. Statist. Ass.*, 1957, 52, 331–344.

ARNOLD BINDER

11 Further Considerations on Testing the Null Hypothesis and the Strategy and Tactics of Investigating Theoretical Models

David A. Grant has argued [Ch. 10 in this book] that it is inappropriate to design experiments such that support for a theory comes from acceptance of the null hypothesis. The present article points out that while this position could be defended in Fisher's approach to testing statistical hypotheses, it could not in the Neyman-Pearson approach or on more general scientific grounds. It is emphasized that one optimally designs experiments with enough sensitivity for rejecting poor theories and accepting useful theories, whether acceptance or rejection of the null hypothesis leads to empirical support. The argument that, in the procedure to which Grant objects, an insensitive experiment is more likely to lead to support for a theory is shown to be only a special case of the argument against bad experimentation.

The arguments in a 1962 article by Grant (15) are directed against experimental designs oriented toward acceptance of the null hypothesis, that is, where support for an empirical hypothesis depends upon acceptance of the null hypothesis. Atkinson and Suppes (1) provide an excellent example of the type of experimental logic to which Grant objects. These investigators postulated a one-stage Markov model for a zero-sum, two-person game. On the basis of the model they predicted, first, the mean proportion of various responses over asymptotic trials and, second, that the probability of State k given States i and j on the two previous trials is equal to the probability of State k given only State j on the immediately preceding trial (i.e., that a one-stage Markov model accounts for the data). The predictions were then compared with the obtained results by means of a series of t tests, in the former case, and a χ^2 test, in the latter. One of the t tests, for exam-

ple, involved a comparison of the predicted proportion of .600 against the observed mean proportion of .605, while another a comparison of a predicted value of .667 and an observed value of .670. Support for the one-stage Markov model was then inferred by the failure of the t tests and the χ^2 to reach the .05 level of significance. That is, support for the empirical model came from acceptance of the null hypotheses. (Other examples may be found in 2, 3, 4, 5, 16, 17, 36, 37.)

To facilitate future discussion it is convenient to refer to the procedure where acceptance of the null hypothesis leads to support for an empirical hypothesis as acceptance-support (a–s), and to the procedure where empirical support comes from rejection of the null hypothesis as rejection-support (r–s).

In addition to the objections to a–s, Grant argues that the method of testing statistical hypotheses may not be a very good idea in any case. He thus argues it is wise to shift

From *Psychological Review*, Vol. 70, No. 1, pp. 107–15, 1963. Copyright © 1963 by the American Psychological Association, and reprinted by permission.

away from the current emphasis in psychological research on hypothesis testing in the direction of statistical estimation.

Statistical Logic

There have been two principal schools of thought in regard to the logical and procedural ramifications of statistical inference. The older of these stems from the writings of Yule, Karl Pearson, and Fisher, while the other comes from the early work of Neyman and Pearson and the more recent developments of Wald. The respective influences of each of these schools on experimental statistics is abundantly evident, but a difficulty in separating these influences is that the actual recommendations for tests and interval estimates in a field like psychology are similar for both.

In the Fisher school one starts the testing process with a hypothesis, called the "null hypothesis," which states that the sample at issue comes from a hypothetical population with a sampling distribution in a certain known class. Using this distribution one rejects the null hypothesis whenever the discrepancy between the statistic and the relevant parameter of the distribution of interest is so large that the probability of obtaining that discrepancy or a larger one is less than the quantity designated α (the significance level). No clear statement is provided for the manner in which the null hypothesis is chosen, but the tests with which Fisher (10) has been associated are in the form where the null hypothesis is equated with the statement "the phenomenon to be demonstrated is in fact absent" (p. 13).

The concept "rejection of the null hypothesis" is therefore unambiguous in the context of Fisher's viewpoint, but what about "acceptance of the null hypothesis?" Fisher (10) provides the following statement "the null hypothesis is never proved or established, but is possibly disproved, in the course of experimentation. Every experiment may be said to exist only in order to give the facts a chance of disproving the null hypothesis" (p. 16). This is not very edifying since one does not expect to prove any hypothesis by the methods of probabilistic inference. Hogben (18) has interpreted these and similar statements of the Yule-Fisher group to mean that a test of significance can lead to one of two decisions: the null hypothesis is rejected at the α level or judgment is reserved in the absence of sufficient basis for rejecting the null hypothesis.

Papers by Neyman and Pearson (27, 28) pointed out that the choice of a statistical test must involve consideration of alternative hypotheses as well as the hypothesis of central concern. They introduced the distinction between the error of falsely rejecting the null hypothesis and the error of falsely accepting it (rejecting its alternative). Neyman and Pearson's (29) general theory of hypothesis testing, based on the concepts Type I error, Type II error, power, and critical region, was presented later.

The possible parameters for the distribution of the random variable or variables in a given investigation are conceptually represented by a set of points in what is called a parameter space. This space is considered to be divided into two or more subsets, but we shall restrict our present discussion to the classical case in which there are exactly two subsets of points.

The statistical hypothesis specifies that the parameter point lies in a particular one of these two subsets while the alternative hypothesis specifies the other subset for the point. A statistical test is a procedure for deciding, on the basis of a set of observations, whether to accept or reject the hypothesis. Acceptance of the hypothesis is precisely the same as deciding that the parameter point lies in the set encompassed by the hypothesis, while rejection of the hypothesis is deciding that the point lies in the other subset. A typical test procedure assigns to each possible value of the random variable (statistic) one of the two possible decisions.

Sets of distributions (or their associated parameters), in this mathematical model, may be considered to correspond to the explanations in the empirical world which may account for the possible outcomes of a given experiment. Empirical hypotheses, which specify values or relationships in the scientific world, are translatable on this basis into statistical hypotheses. But the distinction between empirical and statistical hypotheses is quite important: the former refer to scientific results and relationships, the latter to subsets of points in a parameter space; they are related by a set of correspondences between scientific events and parameter sets.

The term "null hypothesis" does not occur in the writings of many of the advocates of the Neyman-Pearson view. Except for one pejorative footnote I was unable to find the term used by Neyman (23), for example, in any of an extensive array of his publications. In general, these people prefer the term "statistical hypothesis" or simply "hypothesis" in designating the subset of central concern and alternative hypothesis for the other subset. However, null hypothesis has taken on meaning over the years in the context of the Neyman-Pearson tradition among many writers of statistics, particularly those with expository proclivities. In the *Dictionary of Statistical Terms* (20) we find the following definition for null hypothesis: "In general, this term relates to a particular hypothesis under test, as distinct from the alternative hypotheses which are under consideration. It is therefore the hypothesis which determines the Type 1 Error" (p. 202).

An Evaluation[1]

Grant's position in regard to *a–s* is certainly not new or novel since it has been implicit in

1. There is a third viewpoint, represented in the psychological literature by Rozeboom's (31) recent article, from which Grant's position could be evaluated. This viewpoint emphasizes the importance of the a posteriori probabilities of alternative explanations, in the Bayes sense, rather than the decision aspects of experimentation. However, the philosophical and practical problems of this approach remain enormous as is evident in the debates on this and related topics over the years. See, for example,

the writings of Fisher for the past 25 years. Moreover, it has been part of the folklore of statistical advising in psychology at least as far back as my initial exposure to psychological statistics (see Footnote 2). And, in fact, if Grant wishes to argue that his position holds only in the very narrowest interpretation of the Yule-Karl Pearson-Fisher structure, I see no grounds for contesting it. If there are only two possible decisions—reject the null hypothesis or reserve judgment—one would surely not wish to equate the null hypothesis with the empirical hypothesis designating a specific value. Using this logic an investigator could just as well discard as retain a theory when it has led to perfect predictions over a wide range.

In this context I would like to point out that there are many logical difficulties connected with the Fisher formulations which have been brought out dramatically in years of debate (Fisher, 8, 11, 12, 13, 14; Neyman, 23, 24, 25, 26). Moreover there are some people who, while generally sympathetic with the Fisher viewpoint, are quite willing to accept the null hypothesis and conclude that this provides support for an empirical hypothesis (Mather, 21; Snedecor, 33).

Jeffreys (19), Neyman (24), Hogben (18), Savage (32), Chernoff and Moses (6), von Mises (34, 35), and particularly Parzen (30) who discusses the dangers of using Bayesian inverse probability in applied problems. It is typically not the case in basic research that one can assume that an unknown parameter is a random variable with some specified a priori distribution, and in such cases this approach does not presently provide any adequate answers to the problems of hypothesis evaluation.

While of a markedly different philosophical persuasion than the present writer, Rozeboom (31) is equally unsympathetic with the inferential bias represented by Grant. He cuts into an essential component of this bias in the following succinct and effective manner,

Although many persons would like to conceive NHD (the null hypothesis decision procedure) testing to authorize only rejection of the hypothesis, not, in addition, its acceptance when the test statistic fails to fall in the rejection region, if failure to reject were not taken as grounds for acceptance, then NHD procedure would involve no Type II error, and no justification would be given for taking the rejection region at the extremes of the distribution, rather than in its middle (p. 419).

In the pursuit of evaluating Grant's position from the Neyman-Pearson theory we must remember that the null hypothesis is a statistical hypothesis which designates a particular subset of parameter points. Moreover, the null hypothesis and the alternative hypothesis (the other subset) are mutually exhaustive so that rejection of the one implies acceptance of the other; acceptance of a hypothesis being the belief, at a certain probability level, that the subset specified by the hypothesis includes the parameter point. There can be no question about the legitimacy or acceptability of acceptance of the null hypothesis within this purely mathematical scheme since acceptance and rejection are perfectly complementary.

Consequently any interpretative difficulties which result from accepting the null hypothesis must be in the rules for or manner of relating empirical and statistical (null) hypotheses. The null hypothesis is of course that hypothesis for which the probability of erroneous rejection is fixed at α (or set at a maximum of α); the test (critical region) is chosen so as to maximize power for the given α and the alternative hypothesis. Since therein lies the only feature of the process that differentiates the null hypothesis from the other subset, the relating of empirical and statistical hypotheses must be based upon it.

While there are no firm rules for deciding with which of the two subsets a given empirical hypothesis should be associated, there have been certain practices or conventions used by different writers. Neyman (23), for example, suggested a most reasonable convention for relating empirical and statistical hypotheses which is to equate with the null hypothesis that empirical hypothesis for which the error of erroneous rejection is more serious than the error of erroneous acceptance so that the more important error is under the direct control of the experimenter. There are a few other conventions based upon the derivational advantages of fixing α for a simple (rather than a composite) hypothesis, but it is quite clear that Grant has not merely restated any

of these. In fact, Grant's strong statement (15) that "using these predictions as the values in H_0 (the null hypothesis) is tactically inappropriate, frustrating, and self-defeating," [p. 134] indicates that his position is much more than a convention of convenience.

The position which I will develop over the remainder of this paper is not that a–s is preferable to r–s, but that there are no sound foundations for damning a–s. In this process let me initially point out that one can be led astray unless he recognizes that when one tests a point prediction he usually knows before the first sample element is drawn that his empirical hypothesis is not precisely true. Consider testing the hypothesis that two groups differ in means by some specified amount. We might test the hypothesis that the difference in means in 0, or perhaps 12, or perhaps even 122.5. But in each case we are certain that the difference is not precisely 0.0000...ad inf., or 12.0000..., or 122.50000... ad inf.

Recognition of this state of affairs leads to thinking in terms of differences or deviations that are or are not of importance for a given stage of theory construction or of application. Some express this in terms of differences which do and do not have practical importance, but I prefer the term zone of indifference which is used with important implications in sequential analysis. That is, if, for example, the difference in mean performance between two groups is less than, say, ε the two means may be considered equivalent for the given stage of theoretical development. In the case of a prediction of one-third for the proportion of right turns of rats in a maze, one would expect the same courses of action to be followed if the figure were actually .334 or .335. Thus, although we may specify a point null hypothesis for the purpose of our statistical test, we do recognize a more or less broad indifference zone about the null hypothesis consisting of values which are essentially equivalent to the null hypothesis for our present theory or practice.

While the formal procedures for testing

statistical hypotheses are based upon the assumption that the sample size (n) is fixed prior to a consideration of alternative test procedures, the user of statistical techniques is faced with the problem of choosing n and does so with regard for the magnitude of the discriminations which are or are not important for his particular application or level of theory development. In the typical case we choose the conditions of experimentation, including sample size, such that we will reject the null hypothesis with a given probability when the parameter difference is a certain magnitude. This is frequently done very formally in fields like agriculture, although rather informally in psychology. For example, in Cochran and Cox (7) there is an extended discussion of the procedures for choosing the numbers of replications for an experiment on the basis of the practical importance of true differences. Thus, in one of their examples, a difference of 20% of the mean of two values is considered sufficiently important to warrant a sensitive enough experiment to have an .80 probability of detecting it; that is, if the difference is 20% a large enough n is desired to insure that the power of the test is .80. Although it may happen that the required sample size is a function of an unknown distribution and not determinable in advance, it can usually be approximated with the tests used most frequently by psychologists.

The choice of sample size is but one feature in the overall planning to obtain an experiment of the desired precision with due consideration for the level of theory development (including alternate theories), the zones of indifference, and the related consequences of decision. However, such other features as the standard error per unit observation and the design efficiency do not have the flexibility of sample size, and, moreover, are usually chosen to maximize precision for reasons of economy. The choice of optimum sample size applies to all experimental strategies, including the non-objectionable (to Grant) and more usual r–s. It is surely apparent that anyone who wants to obtain a significant difference badly enough can obtain one—if his only consideration is obtaining that significant difference. Accepting that the means, for example, of two groups are never perfectly equal, the difference between them is some value ε. It is obviously an easy matter to choose a sample size large enough, for the ε, such that we will reject the null hypothesis with a given probability. But the difference may be so slight as to have no practical or theoretical consequences for the given stage of measurement and theory construction. As McNemar (22) has recently pointed out, in his objections to the use of extreme groups, significant differences may be obtained even when the underlying correlation is as low as .10 which implies a proportion of predicted variance equal to .01.

After arguing against a–s on the basis of the dangers of tests that tend toward leniency, Grant points out that the procedure may be equally objectionable when the test is too stringent. He illustrates the latter by an example of a theory which is useful though far from perfect in its predictions. This particular point is perfectly in accord with my arguments since it demonstrates the parallelism of a–s and r–s. First, one does not usually want an experiment that is too stringent: in a–s because it may not be desirable to reject a useful, though inaccurate theory; in r–s because one may accept an extremely poor and practically useless theory. Second, one does not want an experiment that is too lenient or insensitive; in a–s because one may accept an extremely poor and practically useless theory; in r–s because it may not be desirable to reject a useful, though inaccurate theory (that is, to accept the null hypothesis which implies rejection of its alternative). The identical terms were chosen in the preceding sentences to dramatize the parallel implications for a–s and r–s of the general desirability of a test that is neither too stringent nor too insensitive. Whether or not the experiment is precise enough is, then, a function of theoretical and practical consequences, and not of whether acceptance or rejection of the null hypothesis leads to support for an empirical theory.

But, one may argue, while there is logical equivalence as stated above, there is not motivational equivalence. That is, while it is agreed that ideally investigators design their experiments (including their choice of sample sizes) in order to be reasonably certain of detecting only differences which are of practical or theoretical importance, in actual practice they are neither so wise nor so pure as to be influenced by these factors to the exclusion of social motivations. And it is indeed much easier to do insensitive rather than precise experimentation. The phenomenon is of course what Grant referred to in his statement.

The tactics of accepting H_0 as proof and rejecting H_0 as disproof of a theory lead to the anomalous results that a small-scale, insensitive experiment will most often be interpreted as favoring a theory, whereas a large-scale, sensitive experiment will usually yield results opposed to the theory! (p. 129).

Perhaps that reflects the essential point of Grant's presentation—merely to caution imprudent experimenters that the combination of personal desire to establish one's hypothesis and the ease of performing insensitive experimentation produce a particularly troublesome interaction.

Before proceeding it should be remembered that scientific considerations may be made secondary to personal desires to establish a theory whether the procedure be $a-s$ or $r-s$ in a perfectly analogous fashion. The only difference involves such practical considerations as the fact that it is usually easier to run 5 or 10 subjects than 100 or 500.

If Grant merely intended this article to convey this obvious warning, I cannot understand the discussions which involve such statements as the following:

Unfortunately most of the procedures used to date in testing the adequacy of such theoretical predictions [from mathematical models] set rather bad examples. Probably the least adequate of these procedures has been that in which an H_0 of exact correspondence between theoretical and empirical points is tested against H_1 covering any discrepancy between predictions and experimental results (p. 128).

If one is pointing out the dangers of using insensitive $a-s$ tests (rather than condemning $a-s$ on logical grounds), one would be expected to object to a particular or general use of $a-s$ only if the use involved insensitive tests. Thus, it might be argued that experimenter WKE obtained support for his quantitative prediction by the use of $a-s$ with a test so insensitive that it could not reasonably detect important discrepancies between predictions and observations. Or, as another fictional example, it might be stated that RRB always used $a-s$ and always found support for his linear models, but his n was uniformly less than 5. But, unless there were almost uniform use of insensitive tests with $a-s$, this cautionary position could not reasonably lead to a condemnation of $a-s$.

As I see it, moreover, the argument against insensitive $a-s$ tests is nothing but a particular form of the more general argument against bad experimentation. It is unquestionably the case that an $a-s$ experiment that is too small and insensitive is poor, but the poorness is a property of the insensitivity and not of the $a-s$ procedure. An $r-s$ experiment that is too small and insensitive is equally poor. Due to the interaction between personal achievement desires and the ease of sloppy experimentation, as referred to previously, it may be necessary to be particularly alert to the usual scientific safeguards when using $a-s$, but that is a trivial matter and hardly worthy of an article.

In summary, it would be perfectly justifiable to argue that n is too small (or even too large) for a particular degree of sensitivity required at a given level of scientific development, but that is far from a proscription of designs where acceptance of the null hypothesis is in some way to the experimenter's social or personal advantage.

Grant's Position from the Viewpoint of Scientific Development

In the process of concluding this discussion I would like to emphasize and expand on certain factors which seem most critical in the process of evaluating scientific theories, as well as to indicate that my objections to Grant's apparent position are justifiable beyond the confines of the Neyman-Pearson theory.

It is surely clear that at various phases in the development of a scientic field one is faced with the problem of deciding about the suitability of different theories. When a discipline is at an early stage of development, knowledge of empirical relationships is crude so that broad isolation of explanatory constructs may be the most that is obtainable. At this stage one might consider as a significant accomplishment the ruling out of the hypothesis that observed differences are chance phenomena. The empirical hypothesis of central concern would be that there is some relationship of unknown magnitude, while its alternative would be the chance or noise explanation.

With increasing sophistication in the discipline the alternative hypotheses may represent different, but more or less equally well-developed theories. One does not choose between theory and chance, but between theory and theory or between theory and theories. Another aspect of increased sophistication is frequently the greater precision in the prediction of empirical results for the various theories.

The decision as to which of the theories is admissible on the basis of the available data may be accomplished directly within the Neyman-Pearson framework, but that is not necessarily the case. Sometimes the choice among theories depends upon a succession of tests of hypotheses or possibly even upon quite informal considerations; as an example of the latter, one theory may lead to a prediction which is perfectly in accord (within rounding errors) with the observations while the other theory is off by quite a margin— a statistical test would be considered foolish indeed. In disciplines that have markedly smaller observational variability than psychology the most common procedure consists of a subjective comparison between predictions and observations. Moreover, the point

that one chooses among alternative hypotheses at various stages of scientific development (whether by statistical methods or otherwise) most certainly does not imply that his efforts stop once he has accepted or rejected a given hypothesis as Grant implies; if the accepted theory, for example, is of any interest he proceeds to make finer analyses and comparisons which may range from orthogonal sub-comparisons in the analysis of variance to intuitive rumination. This provides a basis for objecting to Grant's arguments to the effect that hypothesis testing should be replaced (not supplemented) by estimation. The point is that both are usable, but at different phases of investigation.

I will again refer to the Atkinson and Suppes (1) experiment to illustrate the relative roles of hypothesis testing and subsequent analysis in scientific advancement. Their first strategy was to decide which of two theories—game theory or the Markov model—was most adequate in the given experimental context. This clearly was a problem of testing hypotheses; a choice had to be made and the procedures of estimation could at best provide a substage on the way to the decision. The Markov model was accepted and game theory rejected, as noted above, but this certainly did not lead to a cessation of activity. Instead the investigators initially compared theoretical and observed transition matrices (and found them distinctly different); they then tested the more specific hypothesis of a one-stage Markov model against the alternative of a two-stage model, and finally they investigated the stationarity of the Markov process.

During its early phases, Einstein's general theory of relativity was equivalent to Newtonian theory in the success of explaining various common phenomena and a choice between them could not be made. But the Einstein theory led to certain predictions differing from Newtonian and these in turn led to a series of "crucial" tests. Among these were the exact predictions as to the magnitude of the bending of a light ray from a star by the gravitational field of the sun and the shift of wavelength of light emitted from atoms at the surface of stars. The general theory of relativity, thus, led to predictions which differed from the predictions of the alternative theory (Newton's), and the ultimate correspondence between these predictions and empirical observations (acceptance of no difference between predicted and obtained results) led to support for general relativity. While agreements between theory and observational results have been close they certainly have not been perfect—even physicists have problems of measurement precision and intricacy of mathematical derivation. But to the best judgment of the scientists the closeness of the fit between predictions and observation warrants the conclusion that the data provide support for the theory. Surely, however, despite its tremendous power, physicists do not claim that Einstein's general theory has been proved nor are they convinced that it will not be ultimately replaced by a better theory.

It does not seem reasonable to argue that this method of scientific procedure is not suitable for psychology—just because our measurement precision happens to be lower than in physics and we use statistical tests rather than purely observational comparison.

References

1. Atkinson, R. C., & Suppes, P. An analysis of two-person game situations in terms of statistical learning theory. *J. exp. Psychol.*, 1958, 55, 369–378.

2. Binder, A., & Feldman, S. E. The effects of experimentally controlled experience upon recognition responses. *Psychol. Monogr.*, 1960, 74 (9, Whole No. 496).

3. Bower, G. H. An association model for response and training variables in paired-associate learning. *Psychol. Rev.*, 1962, 69, 34–53.

4. Brody, A. L. Independence in the learning of two consecutive responses per trial. *J. exp. Psychol.*, 1958, 56, 16–20.

5. Bush, R. R., & Mosteller, F. *Stochastic models for learning.* New York: Wiley, 1955.

6. Chernoff, H., & Moses, L. E. *Elementary decision theory.* New York: Wiley, 1959.

7. Cochran, W. G., & Cox, Gertrude M. *Experimental designs.* (2nd ed.) New York: Wiley, 1957.

8. Fisher, R. A. The fiducial argument in statistical inference. *Ann. Eugen.*, 1935, 6, 391–398.

9. Fisher, R. A. *Statistical methods for research workers.* (10th ed.) Edinburgh: Oliver & Boyd, 1948.

10. Fisher, R. A. *The design of experiments.* (5th ed.) Edinburgh: Oliver & Boyd, 1949.

11. Fisher, R. A. The comparison of samples with possibly unequal variances. In, *Contributions to mathematical statistics.* New York: Wiley, 1950.

12. Fisher, R. A. Statistical methods and scientific induction. *J. Roy. Statist. Soc., Ser. B.*, 1955, 17, 69–78.

13. Fisher, R. A. *Statistical methods and scientific inference.* (2nd ed.) Edinburgh: Oliver & Boyd, 1959.

14. Fisher, R. A. Scientific thought and the refinement of human reasoning. *J. Operat. Res. Soc., Japan*, 1960, 3, 1–10.

15. Grant, D. A. Testing the null hypothesis and the strategy and tactics of investigating theoretical models. *Psychol. Rev.*, 1962, 69, 54–61.

16. Grant, D. A., & Norris, Eugenia B. Dark adaptation as a factor in the sensitization of the beta response of the eyelid to light. *J. exp. Psychol.*, 1946, 36, 390–397.

17. Harrow, M., & Friedman, G. B. Comparing reversal and nonreversal shifts in concept formation with partial reinforcement controlled. *J. exp. Psychol.*, 1958, 55, 592–598.

18. Hogben, L. *Statistical theory.* London: Allen & Unwin, 1957.

19. Jeffreys, H. *Scientific inference.* (2nd ed.) Cambridge: Cambridge Univer. Press, 1957.

20. Kendall, M. G., & Buckland, W. R. *A dictionary of statistical terms.* Edinburgh: Oliver & Boyd, 1957.

21. Mather, K. *Statistical analysis in biology.* New York: Interscience, 1943.

22. McNemar, Q. At random: Sense and nonsense. *Amer. Psychologist*, 1960, 15, 295–300.

23. Neyman, J. Basic ideas and theory of testing statistical hypothesis. *J. Roy. Statist. Soc.*, 1942, 105, 292–327.

24. Neyman, J. *Lectures and conferences on mathematical statistics and probability.* (2nd ed.) Washington: United States Department of Agriculture, Graduate School, 1952.

25. Neyman, J. Note on article by Sir Ronald Fisher. *J. Roy. Statist. Soc.*, 1956, 18, 288–294.

26. Neyman, J. Silver jubilee of my dispute with Fisher. *J. Operat. Res. Soc., Japan*, 1961, 3, 145–154.

27. Neyman, J., & Pearson, E. S. On the use and interpretation of certain test criteria for purposes of statistical inference. Part I. *Biometrika*, 1928, 20A, 175–240. (a)

28. Neyman, J., & Pearson, E. S. On the use and interpretation of certain test criteria for purposes of statistical inference. Part II. *Biometrika*, 1928, 20A, 263–294. (b)

29. Neyman, J., & Pearson, E. S. On the problem of the most efficient tests of statistical hypotheses. *Phil. Trans. Roy. Soc., Ser. A*, 1933, 231, 289–337.

30. Parzen, E. *Modern probability theory and its applications*. New York: Wiley, 1960.

31. Rozeboom, W. W. The fallacy of the null-hypothesis significance test. *Psychol. Bull.*, 1960, 57, 416–428.

32. Savage, L. J. *The foundations of statistics.* New York: Wiley, 1954.

33. Snedecor, G. W. *Statistical methods.* (5th ed.) Ames: Iowa State Coll. Press, 1956.

34. von Mises, R. On the correct use of Bayes' formula. *Ann. math. Statist.*, 1942, 13, 156–165.

35. von Mises, R. *Probability, statistics and truth.* (2nd ed.) London: Allen & Unwin, 1957.

36. Weinstock, S. Acquisition and extinction of a partially reinforced running response at a 24-hour intertrial interval. *J. exp. Psychol.*, 1958, 56, 151–158.

37. Witte, R. S. A stimulus-trace hypothesis for statistical learning theory. *J. exp. Psychol.*, 1959, 57, 273–283.

WARD EDWARDS

12 Tactical Note on the Relation Between Scientific and Statistical Hypotheses[1]

Grant, Binder, and others have debated what should be the appropriate relationship between the scientific hypotheses that a scientist is interested in and the customary procedures of classical statistical inference. Classical significance tests are violently biased against the null hypothesis. A conservative theorist will therefore associate his theory with the null hypothesis, while an enthusiast will not—and they may often reach conflicting conclusions, whether or not the theory is correct. No procedure can satisfactorily test the goodness of fit of a single model to data. The remedy is to compare the fit of several models to the same data. Such procedures do not compare null with alternative hypotheses, and so are in this respect unbiased.

Grant (3) [Ch. 10 in this book], Binder (1) [Ch. 11 in this book], and Wilson and Miller (9) have been debating the question of what should be the appropriate relationship between the scientific hypotheses or theories that a scientist is interested in and the statisti-

cal hypotheses, null and alternative, that classical statistics invites him to use in significance tests. Grant rightly notes that using the value predicted by a theory as a null hypothesis puts a premium on sloppy experimentation, since small numbers of observations and large variances favor acceptance of the null hypothesis and "confirmation" of the

1. I am grateful to L. J. Savage, D. A. Grant, and W. R. Wilson for helpful criticisms of an earlier draft.

From *Psychological Bulletin*, Vol. 63, pp. 400–402, No. 6, 1965. Copyright © 1965 by the American Psychological Association, and reprinted by permission.

theory, while sufficiently precise experimentation is likely to reject any null hypothesis and so the theory associated with it, even when that theory is very nearly true. Grant's major recommendation for coping with the problem is to use confidence intervals around observed values; if the theoretical values do not lie within these limits, the theory is suspect. With this technique also, sloppy experimentation will favor acceptance of the theory—but at least the width of the intervals will display sloppiness. Grant also suggests testing the hypothesis that the correlation between predicted and observed values is zero (in cases in which a function rather than a point is being predicted), but notes that an experiment of reasonable precision will nearly always reject this hypothesis for theories of even very modest resemblance to the truth. Binder, defending the more classical view, argues that the inference from outcome of a statistical procedure to a scientific conclusion must be a matter of judgment, and should certainly take the precision of the experiment into account, but that there is no reason why the null hypothesis should not, given an experiment of reasonable precision, be identified with the scientific hypothesis of interest. Wilson and Miller point out that the argument concerns not only statistical procedures but also choice of theoretical prediction to be tested, since some predictions are of differences and some of no difference. Their point seems to apply primarily to loosely formulated theories, since precise theories will make specific numerical predictions of the sizes of differences and it would be natural to treat these as null hypothesis values.

Edwards, Lindman, and Savage (2), in an expository paper on Bayesian statistical inference, have pointed out that from a Bayesian point of view, classical procedures for statistical inference are always violently biased against the null hypothesis, so much so that evidence that is actually in favor of the null hypothesis may lead to its rejection by a properly applied classical test. This fact implies that, other things being equal, a theory is likely to look better in the light of experimental data if its prediction is associated with the alternative hypothesis than if it is associated with the null hypothesis.

For a detailed mathematical exposition of the bias of classical significance tests, see Edwards, Lindman, and Savage (2) and Lindley (4). Lindley has proven a theorem frequently illustrated in Edwards, Lindman, and Savage (2) that amounts to the following. An appropriate measure of the impact of evidence on one hypothesis as against another is a statistical quantity called the likelihood ratio. Name any likelihood ratio in favor of the null hypothesis, no matter how large, and any significance level, no matter how small. Data can always be invented that will simultaneously favor the null hypothesis by at least that likelihood ratio and lead to rejection of that hypothesis at at least that significance level. In other words, data can always be invented that highly favor the null hypothesis, but lead to its rejection by an appropriate classical test at any specified significance level. That theorem establishes the generality and ubiquity of the bias. Edwards, Lindman, and Savage (2) show that data like those found in psychological experiments leading to .05 or .01 level rejections of null hypotheses are seldom if ever strong evidence against null hypotheses, and often actually favor them.

The following example gives the flavor of the argument, though it is extremely crude and makes no use of such tools as likelihood ratios. The boiling point of statistic acid is known to be exactly 50° C. You, an organic chemist, have attempted to synthesize statistic acid; in front of you is a beaker full of foul-smelling glop, and you would like to know whether or not it is indeed statistic acid. If it is not, it may be any of a large number of related compounds with boiling points diffusely (for the example, that means uniformly) distributed over the region from 130° C to 170° C. By one of those happy accidents so common in statistical examples, your thermometer is known to be unbiased and to produce normally distributed errors with a standard deviation of 1°. So you measure the boiling point of the glop, once.

The example, of course, justifies the use of the classical critical ratio test with a standard deviation of 1°. Suppose that the glop really is statistic acid. What is the probability that the reading will be 151.96° or higher? Since 1.96 is the .05 level on a two-tailed critical ratio test, but we are here considering only the upper tail, that probability is .025. Similarly, the probability that the reading will be 152.58° or greater is .005. So the probability that the reading will fall between 151.96° and 152.58°, if the glop is really statistic acid, is .025–.005 = .02.

What is the probability that the reading will fall in that interval if the glop is not statistic acid? The size of the interval is .62°. If the glop is not statistic acid, the boiling points of the other compounds that it might be instead are uniformly distributed over a 40° region. So the probability of any interval within that region is simply the width of the interval divided by the width of the region, .62/40 = .0155. So if the compound is statistic acid, the probability of a reading between 151.96° and 152.58° is .02, while if it is not statistic acid that probability is only .0155. Clearly the occurrence of a reading in the region, especially a reading near its lower end, would favor the null hypothesis, since a reading in that region is more likely if the null hypothesis is true than if it is false. And yet, any such reading would lead to a rejection of the null hypothesis at the .05 level by the critical ratio test.

Obviously the assumption made about the alternative hypothesis was crucial to the calculation. (Such special features as normality, the literal uniformity of the distribution under the alternative hypothesis, and the particular regions and significance levels chosen are not at all important; they affect only the numerical details, not the basic phenomenon.) The narrower the distribution under the alternative hypothesis, the less striking is the paradox; the wider that dis-

tribution, the more striking. That distribution is narrowest if it is a single point, and favors the alternative hypothesis most if that point happens to coincide with the datum. And yet Edwards, Lindman, and Savage (2) show that even a single-point alternative hypothesis located exactly where the data fall cannot bias the likelihood ratio against the null hypothesis as severely as classical significance tests are biased.

This violent bias of classical procedures is not an unmitigated disaster. Many null hypotheses tested by classical procedures are scientifically preposterous, not worthy of a moment's credence even as approximations. If a hypothesis is preposterous to start with, no amount of bias against it can be too great. On the other hand, if it is preposterous to start with, why test it?

The implication of this bias of classical procedures against null hypotheses seems clear. If classical procedures are to be used, a theory identified with a null hypothesis will have several strikes against it just because of that identification, whether or not the theory is true. And the more thorough the experiment, the larger that bias becomes. The scientific conservative, eager to make sure that error is scotched at any cost, will therefore prefer to test his theories as null hypotheses— to their detriment. The scientific enthusiast, eager to make sure that his good new ideas do not die premature or unnecessary deaths, will if possible test his theories as alternative hypotheses—to their advantage. Often, these men of different temperament will reach different conclusions.

The subjectivity of this conclusion is distressing, though realistic. There should be a better, less subjective approach—and there is. The trouble is that in classical statistics the alternative hypothesis is essentially undefined, and so provides no standard by means of which to judge the congruence between datum and null hypothesis; hence the arbitrariness of the .05, .01, and .001 levels, and their lack of agreement with less arbitrary measures of congruence. A man from Mars, asked whether or not your suit fits you, would have trouble answering. He could notice the discrepancies between its measurements and yours, and might answer no; he could notice that you did not trip over it, and might answer yes. But give him two suits and ask him which fits you better, and his task starts to make sense, though it still has its difficulties. I believe that the argument between Grant and Binder is essentially unresolvable; no procedure can test the goodness of fit of a single model to data in any satisfactory way. But procedures for comparing the goodness of fit of two or more models to the same data are easy to come by, entirely appropriate, and free of the difficulties Binder and Grant have been arguing about. (They do have difficulties. Most important, either these models must specify to some extent the error characteristics of the data-generating process, or else a special model of the data-generating process, such as the normality assumption concerning the thermometer in the statistic acid example, must also be supplied. But of course this difficulty is common to all of statistics, and is fully as much a difficulty for the approaches I am rejecting as for those I am espousing.) The likelihood-ratio procedures I advocate do not make use of classical null-hypothesis testing, and so the question of which model to associate with the null hypothesis does not arise. While there is nothing essentially Bayesian about such procedures, I naturally prefer their Bayesian

to their non-Bayesian versions, and so refer you to Savage (6), Raiffa and Schlaifer (5), Schlaifer (7, 8), and Edwards, Lindman, and Savage (2) as appropriate introductions to them. Unfortunately, I cannot refer you to literature telling how to invent not just one but several plausible models that might account for your data.

References

1. Binder, A. Further considerations on testing the null hypothesis and the strategy and tactics of investigating theoretical models. *Psychological Review*, 1963, 70, 107–115.
2. Edwards, W., Lindman, H., & Savage, L. J. Bayesian statistical inference for psychological research. *Psychological Review*, 1963, 70, 193–242.
3. Grant, D. A. Testing the null hypothesis and the strategy and tactics of investigating theoretical models. *Psychological Review*, 1962, 69, 54–61.
4. Lindley, D. V. A statistical paradox. *Biometrika*, 1957, 44, 187–192.
5. Raiffa, H., & Schlaifer, R. *Applied statistical decision theory*. Boston: Harvard University, Graduate School of Business Administration, Division of Research, 1961.
6. Savage, L. J., et al. *The foundations of statistical inference: A discussion*. New York: Wiley, 1962.
7. Schlaifer, R. *Probability and statistics for business decisions*. New York: McGraw-Hill, 1959.
8. Schlaifer, R. *Introduction to statistics for business decisions*. New York: McGraw-Hill, 1961.
9. Wilson, W. R., & Miller, H. A note on the inconclusiveness of accepting the null hypothesis. *Psychological Review*, 1964, 71, 238–242.

DAVID BAKAN

13 The Test of Significance in Psychological Research

The test of significance does not provide the information concerning psychological phenomena characteristically attributed to it; and a great deal of mischief has been associated with its use. The basic logic associated with the test of significance is reviewed. The null hypothesis is characteristically false under any circumstances. Publication practices foster the reporting of small effects in populations. Psychologists have "adjusted" by misinterpretation, taking the p value as a "measure," assuming that the test of significance provides automaticity of inference, and confusing the aggregate with the general. The difficulties are illuminated by bringing to bear the contributions from the decision-theory school on the Fisher approach. The Bayesian approach is suggested.

That which we might identify as the "crisis of psychology" is closely related to what Hogben (20) has called the "crisis in statistical theory." The vast majority of investigations which pass for research in the field of psychology today entail the use of statistical tests of significance. Most characteristically, when a psychologist finds a problem he wishes to investigate he converts his intuitions and hypotheses into procedures which will yield a test of significance, and will characteristically allow the result of the test of significance to bear the essential responsibility for the conclusions which he will draw.

The major point of this paper is that the test of significance does not provide the information concerning psychological phenomena characteristically attributed to it; and that, furthermore, a great deal of mischief has been associated with its use. What will be said in this paper is hardly original. It is, in a certain sense, what "everybody knows." To say it "out loud" is, as it were, to assume the role of the child who pointed out that the emperor was really outfitted only in his underwear. Little of that which is contained in this paper is not already available in the literature, and the literature will be cited.

Lest what is being said in this paper be misunderstood, some clarification needs to be made at the outset. It is not a blanket criticism of statistics, mathematics, or, for that matter, even the test of significance when it can be appropriately used. The argument is rather that the test of significance has been carrying too much of the burden of scientific inference. Wise and ingenious investigators can find their way to reasonable conclusions from data because and in spite of their procedures. Too often, however, even wise and ingenious investigators, for varieties of reasons not the least of which are the editorial policies of our major psychological journals, which we will discuss below, tend to credit the test of significance with properties it does not have.

Logic of the Test of Significance

The test of significance has as its aim obtaining information concerning a character-

From *Psychological Bulletin*, Vol. 66, No. 6, pp. 423–37, 1966. Copyright © 1966 by the American Psychological Association, and reprinted by permission.

istic of a *population* which is itself not directly observable, whether for practical or more intrinsic reasons. What is observable is the *sample*. The work assigned to the test of significance is that of aiding in making inferences from the observed sample to the unobserved population.

The critical assumption involved in testing significance is that, if the experiment is conducted properly, *the characteristics of the population have a designably determinative influence on samples drawn from it*, that, for example, the mean of the population has a determinative influence on the mean of a sample drawn from it. Thus if P, the population characteristic, has a determinative influence on S, the sample characteristic, then there is some licence for making inferences from S to P.

If the determinative influence of P on S could be put in the form of simple logical *implication*, that P implies S, the problem would be quite simple. For, then we would have the simple situation: if P implies S, and if S is false, P is false. There are some limited instances in which this logic applies directly in sampling. For example, if the range of values in the population is between 3 and 9 (P), then the range of values in any sample must be between 3 and 9 (S). Should we find a value in a sample of, say, 10, it would mean that S is false; and we could assert that P is false.

It is clear from this, however, that, *strictly speaking*, one can only go from the denial of S to the denial of P; and not from the assertion of S to the assertion of P. It is within this context of simple logical implications that the Fisher school of statisticians have made important contributions—and it is extremely important to recognize this as the context.

In contrast, approaches based on the theorem of Bayes (1, 3, 14, 22, 34, 35) would allow inferences to P from S even when S is not denied, as S adding something to the credibility of P when S is found to be the case. One of the most viable alternatives to the use

of the test of significance involves the theorem of Bayes; and the paper by Edwards et al. (14) is particularly directed to the attention of psychologists for use in psychological research.

The notion of the null hypothesis[1] promoted by Fisher constituted an advance *within this context* of simple logical implication. It allowed experimenters to set up a null hypothesis complementary to the hypothesis that the investigator was interested in, and provided him with a way of positively confirming his hypothesis. Thus, for example, the investigator might have the hypothesis that, say, normals differ from schizophrenics. He would then set up the *null hypothesis* that the means in the population of all normals and all schizophrenics were *equal*. Thus, the rejection of the null hypothesis constituted a way of *asserting* that the means of the populations of normals and schizophrenics *were different*, a completely reasonable device whereby to affirm a logical antecedent.

The model of simple logical implication for making inferences from S to P has another difficulty which the Fisher approach sought to overcome. This is that it is rarely meaningful to set up any simple "P implies S" model for parameters that we are interested in. In the case of the mean, for example, it is rather that P has a determinative influence on the *frequency* of any specific S. But one experiment does not provide many values of S to allow the study of their frequencies. It gives us *only one* value of S. The *sampling distribution* is conceived which specifies the relative frequencies of all possible values of S. Then, with the help of an adopted *level of significance*, we

---

1. There is some confusion in the literature concerning the meaning of the term null hypothesis. Fisher used the term to designate any exact hypothesis that we might be interested in disproving, and "null" was used in the sense of that which is to be nullified (cf., e.g., 6). It has, however, also been used to indicate a parameter of zero (cf., e.g., 24, p. 15), that the difference between the population means is zero, or the correlation coefficient in the population is zero, the difference in proportions in the population is zero, etc. Since both meanings are usually intended in psychological research, it causes little difficulty.

could, *in effect*, say that S was false; that is, any S which fell in a region whose relative theoretical frequency under the null hypothesis was, say, 5% would be *considered* false. If such an S actually occurred, we would be in a position to declare P to be false, still within the model of simple logical implication.

It is important to recognize that one of the essential features of the Fisher approach is what may be called the *once-ness* of the experiment; the inference model takes as critical that the experiment has been conducted *once*. If an S which has a low probability under the null hypothesis actually occurs, it is taken that the null hypothesis is false. As Fisher (16, p. 14) put it, why should the theoretically rare event under the null hypothesis actually occur to "us"? If it does occur, we take it that the null hypothesis is false. Basic is the idea that "the theoretically unusual does not happen to me."[2] It should be noted that the referent for all probability considerations is neither in the population itself nor the subjective confidence of the investigator. It is rather in a hypothetical population of experiments all conducted in the same manner, but *only one of which is actually conducted*. Thus, of course, the probability of falsely rejecting the null hypothesis if it were true is exactly that value which has been taken as the level of significance. Replication of the experiment vitiates the validity of the inference model, unless the replication itself is taken into account in the model and the probabilities of the model modified accordingly (as is done in various designs which entail replication, where,

however, the total experiment, including the replications, is again considered as *one* experiment). According to Fisher (16, p. 18), "it is an essential characteristic of experimentation that it is carried out with limited resources." In the Fisher approach, the "limited resources" is not only a making of the best out of a limited situation, but is rather an integral feature of the inference model itself. Lest he be done a complete injustice, it should be pointed out that he did say, "In relation to the test of significance, we may say that a phenomenon is experimentally demonstrable when we know how to conduct an experiment which will rarely fail to give us statistically significant results [16, p. 14]." However, although Fisher "himself" believes this, it is *not* built into the inference model.[3]

Difficulties of the Null Hypothesis

As already indicated, research workers in the field of psychology place a heavy burden on the test of significance. Let us consider some of the difficulties associated with the null hypothesis.

1. *The a priori reasons for believing that the null hypothesis is generally false anyway.* One of the common experiences of research workers is the very high frequency with which significant results are obtained with large samples. Some years ago, the author had occasion to run a number of tests of significance on a battery of tests collected on about 60,000 subjects from all over the United States. Every test came out significant. Dividing the cards by such arbitrary criteria as east versus west of the Mississippi River, Maine versus the rest of the country, North versus South, etc., all produced significant differences in means. In some instances, the differences in the sample

2. I playfully once conducted the following "experiment": Suppose, I said, that every coin has associated with it a "spirit"; and suppose, furthermore, that if the spirit is implored properly, the coin will veer head or tail as one requests of the spirit. I thus invoked the spirit to make the coin fall head. I threw it once, it came up head. I did it again, it came up head again. I did this six times, and got six heads. Under the null hypothesis the probability of occurrence of six heads is $(\frac{1}{2})^6 = .016$, significant at the 2% level of significance. I have never repeated the experiment. But, then, the logic of the inference model does not really demand that I do! It may be objected that the coin, or my tossing, or even my observation was biased. But I submit that such things were in all likelihood not as involved in the result as corresponding things in most psychological research.

3. Possibly not even this criterion is sound. It may be that a number of statistically significant results which are *borderline* "speak for the null hypothesis rather than against it (14, p. 235)." If the null hypothesis were really false, then with an increase in the number of instances in which it can be rejected, there should be some substantial proportion of more dramatic rejections rather than borderline rejections.

means were quite small, but nonetheless, the *p* values were all very low. Nunnally (30) has reported a similar experience involving correlation coefficients on 700 subjects. Joseph Berkson (7, pp. 526–527) made the observation almost 30 years ago in connection with chi-square:

I believe that an observant statistician who has had any considerable experience with applying the chi-square test repeatedly will agree with my statement that, as a matter of observation, when the numbers in the data are quite large, the *P*'s tend to come out small. Having observed this, and on reflection, I make the following dogmatic statement, referring for illustration to the normal curve: "If the normal curve is fitted to a body of data representing any real observations whatever of quantities in the physical world, then if the number of observations is extremely large—for instance, on an order of 200,000—the chi-square *P* will be small beyond any usual limit of significance."

This dogmatic statement is made on the basis of an extrapolation of the observation referred to and can also be defended as a prediction from *a priori* considerations. For we may assume that it is practically certain that any series of real observations does not actually follow a normal curve *with absolute exactitude* in all respects, and no matter how small the discrepancy between the normal curve and the true curve of observations, the chi-square *P* will be small if the sample has a sufficiently large number of observations in it.

If this be so, then we have something here that is apt to trouble the conscience of a reflective statistician using the chi-square test. For I suppose it would be agreed by statisticians that a large sample is always better than a small sample. If, then, we know in advance the *P* that will result from an application of a chi-square test to a large sample, there would seem to be no use in doing it on a smaller one. But since the result of the former test is known, it is no test at all.

As one group of authors has put it, "in typical applications ... the null hypothesis ... is known by all concerned to be false from the outset [14, p. 214]." The fact of the matter is that *there is really no good reason to expect the null hypothesis to be true in any population.* Why should the mean, say, of all scores east of the Mississippi be *identical* to all scores west of the Mississippi? Why should any correlation coefficient be *exactly* .00 in the population? Why should we expect the ratio of males to

females be *exactly* 50:50 in any population? Or why should different drugs have *exactly* the same effect on any population parameter (36)? *A glance at any set of statistics on total populations will quickly confirm the rarity of the null hypothesis in nature.*

The reason why the null hypothesis is characteristically rejected with large samples was made patent by the theoretical work of Neyman and Pearson (29). The probability of rejecting the null hypothesis is a function of five factors: whether the test is one- or two-tailed, the level of significance, the standard deviation, the amount of deviation from the null hypothesis, *and the number of observations.* The choice of a one- or two-tailed test is the investigator's; the level of significance is also based on the choice of the investigator; the standard deviation is a given of the situation, and is characteristically reasonably well estimated; the deviation from the null hypothesis is what is unknown; and the choice of the number of cases is in psychological work characteristically arbitrary or expeditious. Should there be any deviation from the null hypothesis in the population, *no matter how small*—and we have little doubt but that such a deviation usually exists—a sufficiently large number of observations will lead to the rejection of the null hypothesis. As Nunnally (30, p. 643) put it,

if the null hypothesis is not rejected, it is usually because the *N* is too small. If enough data are gathered, the hypothesis will generally be rejected. If rejection of the null hypothesis were the real intention in psychological experiments, there usually would be no need to gather data.

2. *Type I error and publication practices.* The Type I error is the error of rejecting the null hypothesis when it is indeed true, and its probability is the level of significance. Later in this paper we will discuss the distinction between *sharp* and *loose* null hypotheses. The sharp null hypothesis, which we have been discussing, is an exact value for the null hypothesis as, for example, the difference between population means being precisely zero. A loose null hypothesis is one in which it is conceived

of as being *around* null. Sharp null hypotheses, as we have indicated, rarely exist in nature. Assuming that loose null hypotheses are not rare, and that their testing may make sense under some circumstances, let us consider the role of the publication practices of our journals in their connection.

It is the practice of editors of our psychological journals, receiving many more papers than they can possibly publish, to use the magnitude of the *p* values reported as one criterion for acceptance or rejection of a study. For example, consider the following statement made by Arthur W. Melton (26, pp. 553–554) on completing 12 years as editor of the *Journal of Experimental Psychology*, certainly one of the most prestigious and scientifically meticulous psychological journals. In enumerating the criteria by which articles were evaluated, he said:

The next step in the assessment of an article involved a judgment with respect to the confidence to be placed in the findings—confidence that the results of the experiment would be repeatable under the conditions described. In editing the *Journal* there has been a strong reluctance to accept and publish results related to the principal concern of the research when those results were significant at the .05 level, whether by one- or two-tailed test. This has not implied a slavish worship of the .01 level, as some critics may have implied. Rather, it reflects a belief that it is the responsibility of the investigator in a science to reveal his effect in such a way that no reasonable man would be in a position to discredit the results by saying that they were the product of the way the ball bounces.

His clearly expressed opinion that nonsignificant results should not take up the space of the journals is shared by most editors of psychological journals. It is important to point out that I am not advocating a change in policy in this connection. In the total research enterprise where so much of the load for making inferences concerning the nature of phenomena is carried by the test of significance, the editors can do little else. The point is rather that the situation in regard to publication makes manifest the difficulties in connection with the overemphasis on the test of

significance as a principal basis for making inferences.

McNemar (25) has rightly pointed out that not only do journal editors reject papers in which the results are not significant, but that papers in which significance has not been obtained are not submitted, that investigators select out their significant findings for inclusion in their reports, and that theory-oriented research workers tend to discard data which do not work to confirm their theories. The result of all of this is that "published results are more likely to involve false rejection of null hypotheses than indicated by the stated levels of significance [p. 300]," that is, published results which are significant may well have Type I errors in them far in excess of, say, the 5% which we may allow ourselves.

The suspicion that the Type I error may well be plaguing our literature is given confirmation in an analysis of articles published in the *Journal of Abnormal and Social Psychology* for one complete year (11). Analyzing 70 studies in which significant results were obtained with respect to the power of the statistical tests used, Cohen found that power, the probability of rejecting the null hypothesis when the null hypothesis was false, was characteristically meager. Theoretically, with such tests, one should not often expect significant results even when the null hypothesis was false. Yet, there they were! Even if deviations from null existed in the relevant populations, the investigations were characteristically not powerful enough to have detected them. This strongly suggests that there is something additional associated with these rejections of the null hypotheses in question. It strongly points to the possibility that the manner in which studies get published is associated with the findings; that *the very publication practices themselves are part and parcel of the probabilistic processes on which we base our conclusions concerning the nature of psychological phenomena.* Our total research enterprise is, at least in part, a kind of scientific roulette, in which the "lucky," or constant player, "wins," that is, gets his paper or papers published. And certainly, going from 5% to 1% does not eliminate the possibility that it is "the way the ball bounces," to use Melton's phrase. It changes the odds in this roulette, but it does not make it less a game of roulette.

The damage to the scientific enterprise is compounded by the fact that the publication of "significant" results tends to stop further investigation. If the publication of papers containing Type I errors tended to foster further investigation so that the psychological phenomena with which we are concerned would be further probed by others, it would not be too bad. But it does not. Quite the contrary. As Lindquist (24, p. 17) has correctly pointed out, the danger to science of the Type I error is much more serious than the Type II error—for when a Type I error is committed, it has the effect of stopping investigation. A highly significant result appears definitive, as Melton's comments indicate. In the 12 years that he edited the *Journal of Experimental Psychology*, he sought to select papers which were worthy of being placed in the "archives," as he put it. Even the strict repetition of an experiment and not getting significance in the same way does not speak against the result already reported in the literature. For failing to get significance, speaking strictly within the inference model, only means that that experiment is inconclusive; whereas the study already reported in the literature, with a low *p* value, is regarded as conclusive. Thus we tend to place in the archives studies with a relatively high number of Type I errors, or, at any rate, studies which reflect small deviations from null in the respective populations; and we act in such a fashion as to reduce the likelihood of their correction.

Psychologist's "Adjustment" by Misinterpretation

The psychological literature is filled with misinterpretations of the nature of the test of significance. One may be tempted to attribute this to such things as lack of proper education, the simple fact that humans may err, and the prevailing tendency to take a cookbook approach in which the mathematical and philosophical framework out of which the tests of significance emerge are ignored; that, in other words, these misinterpretations are somehow the result of simple intellectual inadequacy on the part of psychologists. However, such an explanation is hardly tenable. Graduate schools are adamant with respect to statistical education. Any number of psychologists have taken out substantial amounts of time to equip themselves mathematically and philosophically. Psychologists as a group do a great deal of mutual criticism. Editorial reviews prior to publication are carried out with eminent conscientiousness. There is even a substantial literature devoted to various kinds of "misuse" of statistical procedures, to which not a little attention has been paid.

It is rather that the test of significance is profoundly interwoven with other strands of the psychological research enterprise in such a way that it constitutes a critical part of the total cultural-scientific tapestry. To pull out the strand of the test of significance would seem to make the whole tapestry fall apart. In the face of the intrinsic difficulties that the test of significance provides, we rather attempt to make an "adjustment" by attributing to the test of significance characteristics which it does not have, and overlook characteristics that it does have. The difficulty is that the test of significance can, especially when not considered too carefully, do *some* work; for, after all, the results of the test of significance *are* related to the phenomena in which we are interested. One may well ask whether we do not have here, perhaps, an instance of the phenomenon that learning under partial reinforcement is very highly resistant to extinction. Some of these misinterpretations are as follows:

1. *Taking the* p *value as a "measure" of significance.* A common misinterpretation of the test of significance is to regard it as a "measure" of significance. It is interpreted as the answer to the question "How significant

is it?" A p value of .05 is thought of as less significant than a p value of .01, and so on. The characteristic practice on the part of psychologists is to compute, say, a t, and then "look up" the significance in the table, taking the p value as a *function of* t, and thereby a "measure" of significance. Indeed, since the p value is inversely related to the magnitude of, say, the difference between means *in the sample*, it can function as a kind of "standard score" measure for a variety of different experiments. Mathematically, the t is actually very similar to a "standard score," entailing a deviation in the numerator, and a function of the variation in the denominator; and the p value is a "function" of t. If this use were explicit, it would perhaps not be too bad. But it must be remembered that this is using the p value as a *statistic descriptive of the sample alone*, and does not automatically give an inference to the population. There is even the practice of using tests of significance in studies of total populations, in which the observations cannot by any stretch of the imagination be though of as having been randomly selected from any designable population.[4] Using the p value in this way, in which the statistical inference model is even hinted at, is completely indefensible; for the single function of the statistical inference model is making inferences to populations from samples.

The practice of "looking up" the p value for the t, which has even been advocated in some of our statistical handbooks (e.g., 23 p. 117; 39, p. 129), rather than looking up the t for a given p value, violates the inference model. The inference model is based on the presumption that one *initially* adopts a level of significance as the specification of that probability which is too slow to occur to "us," as Fisher has put it, in this one instance, and under the null hypothesis. A purist might speak of the "delicate problem ... of fudging with a posteriori alpha values [levels of significance (21, p. 165)]," as though the levels of signifi-

cance were initially decided upon, but rarely do psychological research workers or editors take the level of significance as other than a "measure."

But taken as a "measure," it is only a measure of the sample. Psychologists often erroneously believe that the p value is "the probability that the results are due to chance," as Wilson (43, p. 230) has pointed out; that a p value of .05 means that the chances are .95 that the scientific hypothesis is correct, as Bolles (9) has pointed out; that it is a measure of the power to "predict" the behavior of a population (39, p. 107); and that it is a measure of the "confidence that the results of the experiment would be repeatable under the conditions described," as Melton put it. Unfortunately, none of these interpretations are within the inference model of the test of significance. Some of our statistical handbooks have "allowed" misinterpretation. For example, in discussing the erroneous rhetoric associated with talking of the "probability" of a population parameter (in the inference model there is no probability associated with something which is either true or false), Lindquist (24, p. 14) said, "For most practical purposes, the end result is the same as if the 'level of confidence' type of interpretation is employed." Ferguson (15, p. 135) wrote, "The .05 and .01 probability levels are descriptive of our degree of confidence." There is little question but that sizable differences, correlations, etc., in *samples*, especially samples of reasonable size, speak more strongly of sizable differences, correlations, etc., in the population; and there is little question but that if there is real and strong effect in the population, it will continue to manifest itself in further sampling. However, these are inferences which *we* may make. They are outside the inference model associated with the test of significance. The p value within the inference model is only the value which we take to be as how improbable an event could be under the null hypothesis, which we judge will not take place to "us," in this one experiment. *It is not a "measure" of the goodness of the other inferences which we*

---

4. It was decided not to cite any specific studies to exemplify points such as this one. The reader will undoubtedly be able to supply them for himself.

might make. It is an a priori condition that we set up whereby we decide whether or not we will reject the null hypothesis, not a measure of significance.

There is a study in the literature (32) which points up sharply the lack of understanding on the part of psychologists of the meaning of the test of significance. The subjects were 9 members of the psychology department faculty, all holding doctoral degrees, and 10 graduate students, at the University of North Dakota; and there is little reason to believe that this group of psychologists was more or less sophisticated than any other. They were asked to rate their degree of belief or confidence in results of hypothetical studies for a variety of p values, and for n's of 10 and 100. That there should be a relationship between the average rated confidence or belief and p value, as they found, is to be expected. What is shocking is that these psychologists indicated substantially greater confidence or belief in results associated with the larger sample size for the same p values! According to the theory, especially as this has been amplified by Neyman and Pearson (29), the probability of rejecting the null hypothesis for any given deviation from null and p value *increases* as a function of the number of observations. The rejection of the null hypothesis when the number of cases is small speaks for a more dramatic effect in the population; and if the p value is the same, the probability of committing a Type I error remains the same. Thus one can be more confident with a small n than a large n. The question is, how could a group of psychologists be so wrong? I believe that this wrongness is based on the commonly held belief that the p value is a "measure" of degree of confidence. Thus, the reasoning behind such a wrong set of answers by these psychologists may well have been something like this: the p value is a measure of confidence; but a larger number of cases also increases confidence; therefore, for any given p value, the degree of confidence should be higher for the larger n. The wrong conclusion arises from the erroneous character of the first premise, and from

the failure to recognize that the p value is a function of sample size for any given deviation from null in the population. The author knows of instances in which editors of very reputable psychological journals have rejected papers in which the p values and n's were small on the grounds that there were not enough observations, clearly demonstrating that the same mode of thought is operating in them. Indeed, rejecting the null hypothesis with a small n is indicative of a strong deviation from null in the population, the mathematics of the test of significance having already taken into account the smallness of the sample. Increasing the n increases the probability of rejecting the null hypothesis; and in these studies rejected for small sample size, that task has already been accomplished. These editors are, of course, in some sense the ultimate "teachers" of the profession; and they have been teaching something which is patently wrong!

2. *Automaticity of inference.* What may be considered to be a dream, fantasy, or ideal in the culture of psychology is that of achieving complete automaticity of inference. The making of inductive generalizations is always somewhat risky. In Fisher's *The Design of Experiments* (16, p. 4), he made the claim that the methods of induction could be made rigorous, exemplified by the procedures which he was setting forth. This is indeed quite correct in the sense indicated earlier. In a later paper (17, p. 74), he made explicit what was strongly hinted at in his earlier writing, that the methods which he proposed constituted a relatively *complete* specification of the process of induction:

That such a process of induction existed and was possible to normal minds, has been understood for centuries; it is only with the recent development of statistical science that an analytic account can now be given, about as satisfying and complete, at least, as that given traditionally of the deductive processes.

Psychologists certainly took the procedures associated with the t test, F test, and so on, in this manner. *Instead* of having to engage in inference themselves, they had but to "run the tests" for the purpose of making inferences, since, as it appeared, the statistical tests were analytic analogues of inductive inference. The "operationist" orientation among psychologists, which recognized the contingency of knowledge on the knowledge-getting operations and advocated their specification, could, it would seem, "operationalize" the inferential process simply by reporting the details of the statistical analysis! It thus removed the burden of responsibility, the chance of being wrong, the necessity for making inductive inferences, from the shoulders of the investigator and placed them on the tests of significance. The contingency of the conclusion upon the experimenter's decision of the level of significance was managed in two ways. The first, by resting on a kind of social agreement that 5% was good, and 1% better. The second in the manner which has already been discussed, by not making a decision of the level of significance, but only reporting the p value as a "result" and a presumably objective "measure" of degree of confidence. But that the probability of getting significance is also contingent upon the number of observations has been handled largely by ignoring it.

A crisis was experienced among psychologists when the matter of the one- versus the two-tailed test came into prominence; for here the contingency of the result of a test of significance on a decision of the investigator was simply too conspicuous to be ignored. An investigator, say, was interested in the difference between two groups on some measure. He collected his data, found that Mean A was greater than Mean B in the sample, and ran the ordinary two-tailed t test; and, let us say, it was not significant. Then he bethought himself. The two-tailed test tested against *two* alternatives, that the population Mean A was greater than population Mean B and vice versa. But then, he really wanted to know whether Mean A was greater than Mean B. Thus, he could run a one-tailed test. He did this and found, since the one-tailed test is more powerful, that his difference was now significant.

Now here there was a difficulty. The test of significance is not nearly so automatic an inference process as had been thought. It is manifestly contingent on the decision of the investigator as to whether to run a one- or two-tailed test. And somehow, making the decision *after* the data were collected and the means computed, seemed like "cheating." How should this be handled? Should there be some central registry in which one registers one's decision to run a one- or two-tailed test before collecting the data? Should one, as one eminent psychologist one suggested to me, send oneself a letter so that the postmark would prove that one had pre-decided to run a one-tailed test? The literature on ways of handling this difficulty has grown quite a bit in the strain to somehow overcome this particular clear contingency of the results of a test of significance on the decision of the investigator. The author will not attempt here to review this literature, except to cite one very competent paper which points up the intrinsic difficulty associated with this problem, the *reductio ad absurdum* to which one comes. Kaiser (21, p. 160, 161), early in his paper, distinguished between the *logic* associated with the test of significance and other forms of inference, a distinction which, incidentally, Fisher would hardly have allowed: "The arguments developed in this paper are based on logical considerations in statistical inference. (We do not, of course, suggest that statistical inference is the only basis for scientific inference)." But then, having taken the position that he is going to follow the logic of statistical inference relentlessly, he said (Kaiser's italics): "*we cannot logically make a directional statistical decision or statement when the null hypothesis is rejected on the basis of the direction of the difference in the observed sample means.*" One really needs to strike oneself in the head! If Sample Mean A is greater than Sample Mean B, and there is reason to reject the null hypothesis, in what other direction can it reasonably be? What kind of logic is it that leads one to believe that it could be otherwise than that Population

Mean A is greater than Population Mean B? We do not know whether Kaiser intended his paper as a *reductio ad absurdum*, but it certainly turned out that way.

The issue of the one- versus the two-tailed test genuinely challenges the presumptive "objectivity" characteristically attributed to the test of significance. On the one hand, it makes patent what was the case under any circumstances (at the least in the choice of level of significance, and the choice of the number of cases in the sample), that the conclusion is contingent upon the decision of the investigator. An astute investigator, who foresaw the results, and who therefore predecided to use a one-tailed test, will get one *p* value. The less astute but honorable investigator, who did not foresee the results, would feel obliged to use a two-tailed test, and would get another *p* value. On the other hand, if one decides to be relentlessly logical within the logic of statistical inference, one winds up with the kind of absurdity which we have cited above.

3. *The confusion of induction to the aggregate with induction to the general.* Consider a not atypical investigation of the following sort: A group of, say, 20 normals and a group of, say, 20 schizophrenics are given a test. The tests are scored, and a *t* test is run, and it is found that the means differ significantly at some level of significance, say 1%. What inference can be drawn? As we have already indicated, the investigator could have insured this result by choosing a sufficiently large number of cases. Suppose we overlook this objection, which we can to some extent, by saying that the difference between the means in the population must have been *large enough* to have manifested itself with only 40 cases. But still, what do we know from this? The *only* inference which this allows is that the mean of all normals is different from the mean of all schizophrenics in the populations from which the samples have presumably been drawn at random. (Rarely is the criterion of randomness satisfied. But let us overlook this objection too.)

The common rhetoric in which such results are discussed is in the form "Schizophrenics differ from normals in such and such ways." The sense that both the reader and the writer have of this rhetoric is that it has been justified by the finding of significance. Yet clearly it does not mean *all* schizophrenics and *all* normals. All that the test of significance justifies is that *measures of central tendency of the aggregates* differ in the populations. The test of significance has *not* addressed itself to anything about the schizophrenia or normality which characterizes *each* member of the respective populations. Now it is certainly possible for an investigator to develop a hypothesis about the nature of schizophrenia *from which he may infer* that there should be differences between the means in the populations; and his finding of a significant difference in the means of his sample would add to the credibility of the former. However, that 1% which he obtained in his study bears only on the means of the populations, and is not a "measure" of the confidence that he may have in his hypothesis concerning the nature of schizophrenia. There are *two* inferences that he must make. One is that of the sample to the population, for which the test of significance is of some use. The other is from his inference concerning the population to his hypothesis concerning the nature of schizophrenia. The *p* value does not bear on this second inference. The psychological literature is filled with assertions which confound these two inferential processes.

Or consider another hardly atypical style of research. Say an experimenter divides 40 subjects at random into two groups of 20 subjects each. One group is assigned to one condition and the other to another condition, perhaps, say, massing and distribution of trials. The subjects are given a learning task, one group under massed conditions, the other under distributed conditions. The experimenter runs a *t* test on the learning measure and again, say, finds that the difference is significant at the 1% level of significance. He may then say in his report, being more careful than the psychologist who was studying the difference between normals and schizophrenics (being more "scientific" than his clinically-interested colleague), that "the mean in the population of learning under massed conditions is lower than the mean in the population of learning under distributed conditions," feeling that he can say this with a good deal of certainty because of his test of significance. But here too (like his clinical colleague) he has made *two* inferences, and not one, and the 1% bears on the one but not the other. The statistical inference model certainly allows him to make his statement for the population, but only for *that* learning task, and the p value is appropriate only to that. But the generalization to "massed conditions" and "distributed conditions" beyond that particular learning task is a second inference with respect to which the p value is not relevant. The psychological literature is plagued with any number of instances in which the rhetoric indicates that the p value does bear on this second inference.

Part of the blame for this confusion can be ascribed to Fisher who, in *The Design of Experiments* (16, p. 9), suggested that the mathematical methods which he proposed were exhaustive of scientific induction, and that the principles he was advancing were "common to all experimentation." What he failed to see and to say was that after an inference was made concerning a population parameter, *one still needed to engage in induction* to obtain meaningful scientific propositions.

To regard the methods of statistical inference as exhaustive of the inductive inferences called for in experimentation is completely confounding. When the test of significance has been run, the necessity for induction has hardly been completely satisfied. However, the research worker knows this, in some sense, and proceeds, as he should, to make further inductive inferences. He is, however, still ensnarled in his test of significance and the presumption that *it* is the whole of his inductive activity, and thus mistakenly takes a low p value for the measure of the validity of his *other* inductions.

The seriousness of this confusion may be seen by again referring back to the Rosenthal and Gaito (32) study and the remark by Berkson which indicate that research workers believe that a large sample is better than a small sample. We need to refine the rhetoric somewhat. Induction consists in making inferences from the particular to the general. It is certainly the case that as confirming particulars are added, the credibility of the general is increased. However, *the addition of observations to a sample is*, in the context of statistical inference, *not the addition of particulars* but the modification of what is *one particular* in the inference model, the sample aggregate. In the context of statistical inference, it is not necessarily true that "a large sample is better than a small sample." For, as has been already indicated, obtaining a significant result with a small sample suggests a larger deviation from null in the population, and may be considerably more meaningful. Thus more particulars are better than fewer particulars on the making of an inductive inference; but not necessarily a larger sample.

In the marriage of psychological research and statistical inference, psychology brought its own reasons for accepting this confusion, reasons which inhere in the history of psychology. Measurement psychology arises out of two radically different traditions, as has been pointed out by Guilford (18, pp. 5 ff.) and Cronbach (12), and the matter of putting them together raised certain difficulties. The one tradition seeks to find propositions concerning the nature of man in *general*—propositions of a general nature, with each *individual a particular* in which the general is manifest. This is the kind of psychology associated with the traditional experimental psychology of Fechner, Ebbinghaus, Wundt, and Titchener. It seeks to find the laws which characterize the "generalized, normal, human, adult mind [10 p. 413]." The research strategy associated with this kind of psychology is straightforwardly inductive. It seeks inductive generalizations which will apply to *every* member of a designated class. A single particular in which a generalization fails forces a rejection of the generalization, calling for either a redefinition of the class to which it applies or a modification of the generalization. The other tradition is the psychology of individual differences, which has its roots more in England and the United States than on the continent. We may recall that when the young American, James McKeen Cattell, who invented the term *mental test*, came to Wundt with his own problem of individual differences, it was regarded by Wundt as *ganz Amerikanisch* (10, p. 324).

The basic datum for an individual-differences approach is not anything that characterizes *each* of two subjects, but the *difference between them*. For this latter tradition, it is the *aggregate* which is of interest, and not the general. One of the most unfortunate characteristics of many studies in psychology, especially in experimental psychology, is that the data are treated as aggregates while the experimenter is trying to infer general propositions. There is hardly an issue of most of the major psychological journals reporting experimentation in which this confusion does not appear several times; and in which the test of significance, which has some value in connection with the study of aggregates, is not interpreted as a measure of the credibility of the general proposition in which the investigator is interested.

The distinction between the aggregate and the general may be illuminated by a small mathematical exercise. The methods of analysis of variance developed by Fisher and his school have become techniques of choice among psychologists. However, at root, the methods of analysis of variance do not deal with that which any two or more subjects may have in common, but consider only *differences between* scores. This is all that is analyzed by analysis of variance. The following identity illustrates this clearly, showing that the original total sum squares, of which everything else in any analysis of variance is simply the partitioning of, is based on the literal difference between each pair of scores (cf. 2). Except for *n*, it is the only information used

from the data:

$$
\sum_{i=1}^{n} (X_i - \bar{X})^2 = \frac{1}{2} \left[\frac{(X_1 - X_2)}{1} \right]^2 + \frac{2}{3} \left[\frac{(X_1 - X_3) + (X_2 - X_3)}{2} \right]^2 + \ldots + \frac{n-1}{n} \left[\frac{(X_1 - X_n) + \ldots + (X_{n-1} - X_n)}{n-1} \right]^2.
$$

Thus, what took place historically in psychology is that instead of attempting to *synthesize* the two traditional approaches to psychological phenomena, which is both possible and desirable, a syncretic combination took place of the methods appropriate to the study of aggregates with the aims of a psychology which sought for general propositions. One of the most overworked terms, which added not a little to the essential confusion, was the term "error," which was a kind of umbrella term for (at the least) variation among scores from different individuals, variation among measurements for the same individual, and variation among samples.

Let us add another historical note. In 1936, Guilford published his well-known *Psychometric Methods* (18). In this book, which became a kind of "bible" for many psychologists, he made a noble effort at a "Rapprochement of Psychophysical and Test Methods" (p. 9). He observed, quite properly, that mathematical developments in each of the two fields might be of value in the other, that "Both psychophysics and mental testing have rested upon the same fundamental statistical devices [p. 9]." There is no question of the truth of this. However, what he failed to emphasize sufficiently was that mathematics is so abstract that the same mathematics is applicable to rather different fields of investigation without there being any necessary further identity between them. (One would not, for example, argue that business and genetics are essentially the same because the same arithmetic is applicable to market research and in the investigation of the facts of heredity.) A critical point of contact between the two traditions was in connection with scaling in which Cattell's principle that "equally often noticed differences are equal unless always or never noticed [18]" was adopted as a fundamental assumption. The "equally often noticed differences" is, of course, based on aggregates. By means of this assumption, one could collapse the distinction between the two areas of investigation. Indeed, this is not really too bad if one is alert to the fact that *it is* an assumption, one which even has considerable pragmatic value. As a set of techniques whereby data could be analyzed, that is, as a set of techniques whereby one could *describe* one's findings, and then make inductions about the nature of the psychological phenomena, that which Guilford put together in his book was eminently valuable. However, around this time the work of Fisher and his school was coming to the attention of psychologists. It was attractive for several reasons. It offered advice for handling "small samples." It offered a number of eminently ingenious new ways of organizing and extracting information from data. It offered ways by which several variables could be analyzed simultaneously, away from the old notion that one had to keep everything constant and vary only one variable at a time. It showed how the effect of the "interaction" of variables could be assessed. But it also claimed to have mathematized induction! The Fisher approach was thus "bought," and psychologists got a theory of induction in the bargain, a theory which seemed to exhaust the inductive processes. Whereas the question of the "reliability" of statistics had been a matter of concern for some time before (although frequently very garbled), it had not carried the burden of induction to the degree that it did with the Fisher approach. With the "buying" of the Fisher approach the psychological research worker also bought, and then overused, the test of significance, employing it as the measure of the significance, in the largest sense of the word, of his research efforts.

Sharp and Loose Null Hypothesis

Earlier, a distinction was made between sharp and loose null hypotheses. One of the major difficulties associated with the Fisher approach is the problem presented by sharp null hypotheses; for, as we have already seen, there is reason to believe that the existence of sharp null hypotheses is characteristically unlikely. There have been some efforts to correct for this difficulty by proposing the use of loose null hypotheses; in place of a single point, a region being considered null. Hodges and Lehmann (19) have proposed a distinction between "statistical significance," which entails the sharp hypothesis, and "material significance," in which one tests the hypothesis of a deviation of a stated amount from the null point instead of the null point itself. Edwards (13, pp. 30–31) has suggested the notion of "practical significance" in which one takes into account the meaning, in some practical sense, of the magnitude of the deviation from null together with the number of observations which have been involved in getting statistical significance. Binder (8) [Ch. 11] has equally argued that a subset of parameters be equated with the null hypothesis. Essentially what has been suggested is that the investigator make some kind of a decision concerning "How much, say, of a difference makes a difference?" The difficulty with this solution, which is certainly a sound one technically, is that in psychological research we do not often have very good grounds for answering this question. This is partly due to the inadequacies of psychological measurement, but mostly due to the fact that the answer to the question of "How much of a difference makes a difference?" is not forthcoming outside of some particular practical context. The question calls forth another question, "How much of a difference makes a difference *for what*?"

Decisions versus Assertions

This brings us to one of the major issues within the field of statistics itself. The problems of the research psychologist do not generally lie within practical contexts. He is rather interested in making assertions concerning psychological functions which have a reasonable amount of credibility associated with them. He is more concerned with "What is the case?" than with "What is wise to do?" (cf. 33).

It is here that the decision-theory approach of Neyman, Pearson, and Wald (Neyman, 27, 28; Neyman & Pearson, 29; Wald, 40, 41, 42) becomes relevant. The decision-theory school, still basing itself on some basic notions of the Fisher approach, deviated from it in several respects:

1. In Fisher's inference model, the two alternatives between which one chose on the basis of an experiment were *reject* and *inconclusive*. As he said in *The Design of Experiments* (16, p. 16), " the null hypothesis is never proved or established, but is possibly disproved, in the course of experimentation." In the decision-theory approach, the two alternatives are rather *reject* and *accept*.

2. Whereas in the Fisher approach the interpretation of the test of significance critically depends on having one sample from a *hypothetical* population of experiments, the decision-theory approach conceives of, is applicable to, and is sensible with respect to numerous repetitions of the experiment.

3. The decision-theory approach added the notions of the Type II error (which can be made only if the null hypothesis is accepted) and power as significant features of their model.

4. The decision-theory model gave a significant place to the matter of what is concretely lost if an error is made in the practical context, on the presumption that accept entailed one concrete action, and reject another. It is in these actions and their consequences that there is a basis for deciding on a level of confidence. The Fisher approach has little to say about the consequences.

As it has turned out, the field of application par excellence for the decision-theory approach has been the sampling inspection of mass-produced items. In sampling inspection, the acceptable deviation from null can be specified; both accept and reject are appropriate categories; the alternative courses of action can be clearly specified; there is a definite measure of loss for each possible action; and the choice can be regarded as one of a series of such choices, so that one can minimize the overall loss (cf. 5). Where the aim is only the acquisition of knowledge without regard to a specific practical context, these conditions do not often prevail. Many psychologists who learned about analysis of variance from books such as those by Snedecor (37) found the examples involving log weights, etc. somewhat annoying. The decision-theory school makes it clear that such practical contexts are not only "examples" given for pedagogical purposes, but actually are essential features of the methods themselves.

The contributions of the decision-theory school essentially revealed the intrinsic nature of the test of significance beyond that seen by Fisher and his colleagues. They demonstrated that the methods associated with the test of significance constitute not an assertion, or an induction, or a conclusion calculus, but a decision- or risk-evaluation calculus. Fisher (17, p. 70) has reacted to the decision-theory approach in polemic style, suggesting that its advocates were like "Russians [who] are made familiar with the ideal that research in pure science can and should be geared to technological performance, in the comprehensive organized effort of a five-year plan for the nation." He also suggested an American "ideological" orientation: "In the U. S. also the great importance of organized technology has I think made it easy to confuse the process appropriate for drawing correct conclusions, with those aimed rather at, let us say, speeding production, or saving money."[5] But perhaps a more reasonable way of looking at this is to regard the decision-theory school to have explicated what was already implicit in the work of the Fisher school.

Conclusion

What then is our alternative, if the test of significance is really of such limited appropri-

[5] For a reply to Fisher, see Pearson (31).

ateness as has been indicated? At the very least it would appear that we would be much better off if we were to attempt to *estimate* the magnitude of the parameters in the populations; and recognize that we then need to make other inferences concerning the psychological phenomena which may be manifesting themselves in these magnitudes. In terms of a statistical approach which is an alternative, the various methods associated with the theorem of Bayes which was referred to earlier may be appropriate; and the paper by Edwards et. al. (14) and the book by Schlaifer (35) are good starting points. However, that which is expressed in the theorem of Bayes alludes to the more general process of inducing propositions concerning the non-manifest (which is what the population is a special instance of) and ascertaining the way in which that which is manifest (which the sample is a special instance of) bears on it. This is what the scientific method has been about for centuries. However, if the reader who might be sympathetic to the considerations set forth in this paper quickly goes out and reads some of the material on the Bayesian approach with the hope that thereby he will find a *new basis for automatic inference*, this paper will have misfired, and he will be disappointed.

That which we have indicated in this paper in connection with the test of significance in psychological research may be taken as an instance of a kind of essential mindlessness in the conduct of research which may be, as the author has suggested elsewhere (4), related to the presumption of the non-existence of mind in the subjects of psychological research. Karl Pearson once indicated that higher statistics were only common sense reduced to numerical appreciation. However, that base in common sense must be maintained with vigilance. When we reach a point where our statistical procedures are substitutes instead of aids to thought, and we are led to absurdities, then we must return to the common sense basis. Tukey (38) has very properly pointed out that statistical procedures may take our attention away from the data, which constitute the ultimate base

for any inferences which we might make. Robert Schlaifer (35, p. 654) has dubbed the error of the misapplication of statistical procedures the "error of the third kind," the most serious error which can be made. Berkson has suggested the use of "the interocular traumatic test, you know what the data mean when the conclusion hits you between the eyes [14, p. 217]." We must overcome the myth that if our treatment of our subject matter is mathematical it is therefore precise and valid. Mathematics can serve to obscure as well as reveal.

Most importantly, we need to get on with the business of generating *psychological* hypotheses and proceed to do investigations and make inferences which bear on them; instead of, as so much of our literature would attest, testing the statistical null hypothesis in any number of contexts in which we have every reason to suppose that it is false in the first place.

References

1. Bakan, D. Learning and the principle of inverse probability. *Psychological Review*, 1953, 60, 360–370.
2. Bakan, D. The general and the aggregate: A methodological distinction. *Perceptual and Motor Skills*, 1955, 5, 211–212.
3. Bakan, D. Clinical psychology and logic. *American Psychologist*, 1956, 11, 655–662.
4. Bakan, D. The mystery-mastery complex in contemporary psychology. *American Psychologist*, 1965, 20, 186–191.
5. Barnard, G. A. Sampling inspection and statistical decisions. *Journal of the Royal Statistical Society* (B), 1954, 16, 151–165.
6. Berkson, J. Some difficulties of interpretation encountered in the application of the chi-square test. *Journal of the American Statistical Association*, 1938, 33, 526–542.
7. Berkson, J. Tests of significance considered as evidence. *Journal of the American Statistical Association*, 1942, 37, 325–335.
8. Binder, A. Further considerations on testing the null hypothesis and the strategy and tactics of investigating theoretical models. *Psychological Review*, 1963, 70, 101–109.
9. Bolles, R. C. The difference between statistical hypotheses and scientific hypotheses. *Psychological Reports*, 1962, 11, 639–645.

10. Boring, E. G. *A history of experimental psychology.* (2nd ed.) New York: Appleton-Century-Crofts, 1950.

11. Cohen, J. The statistical power of abnormal-social psychological research: A review. *Journal of Abnormal and Social Psychology,* 1962, 65, 145–153.

12. Cronbach, L. J. The two disciplines of scientific psychology. *American Psychologist,* 1957, 12, 671–684.

13. Edwards, A. L. *Experimental design in psychological research.* New York: Rinehart, 1950.

14. Edwards, W., Lindman, H., & Savage, L. J. Bayesian statistical inference for psychological research. *Psychological Review,* 1963, 70, 193–242.

15. Ferguson, L. *Statistical analysis in psychology and education.* New York: McGraw-Hill, 1959.

16. Fisher, R. A. *The design of experiments.* (4th ed.) Edinburgh: Oliver & Boyd, 1947.

17. Fisher, R. A. Statistical methods and scientific induction. *Journal of the Royal Statistical Society* (B), 1955, 17, 69–78.

18. Guilford, J. P. *Psychometric methods.* New York: McGraw-Hill, 1936.

19. Hodges, J. L., & Lehman, E. L. Testing the approximate validity of statistical hypotheses. *Journal of the Royal Statistical Society* (B), 1954, 16, 261–268.

20. Hogben, L. *The relationship of probability, credibility and error: An examination of the contemporary crisis in statistical theory from a behaviourist viewpoint.* New York: Norton, 1958.

21. Kaiser, H. F. Directional statistical decision. *Psychological Review,* 1960, 67, 160–167.

22. Keynes, J. M. *A treatise on probability.* London: Macmillan, 1948.

23. Lacey, O. L. *Statistical methods in experimentation.* New York: Macmillan, 1953.

24. Lindquist, E. F. *Statistical analysis in educational research.* Boston: Houghton Mifflin, 1940.

25. McNemar, Q. At random: Sense and nonsense. *American Psychologist,* 1960, 15, 295–300.

26. Melton, A. W. Editorial. *Journal of Experimental Psychology,* 1962, 64, 553–557.

27. Neyman, J. Outline of a theory of statistical estimation based on the classical theory of probability. *Philosophical Transactions of the Royal Society* (A), 1937, 236, 333–380.

28. Neyman, J. "Inductive behavior" as a basic concept of philosophy of science. *Review of the Mathematical Statistics Institute,* 1957, 25, 7–22.

29. Neyman, J., & Pearson, E. S. On the problem of the most efficient tests of statistical hypotheses. *Philosophical Transactions of the Royal Society* (A), 1933, 231, 289–337.

30. Nunnally, J. The place of statistics in psychology. *Education and Psychological Measurement,* 1960, 20, 641–650.

31. Pearson, E. S. Statistical concepts in their relation to reality. *Journal of the Royal Statistical Society* (B), 1955, 17, 204–207.

32. Rosenthal, R., & Gaito, J. The interpretation of levels of significance by psychological researchers. *Journal of Psychology,* 1963, 55, 33–38.

33. Rozeboom, W. W. The fallacy of the null-hypothesis significance test. *Psychological Bulletin,* 1960, 57, 416–428.

34. Savage, L. J. *The foundations of statistics.* New York: Wiley, 1954.

35. Schlaifer, R. *Probability and statistics for business decisions.* New York: McGraw-Hill, 1959.

36. Smith, C. A. B. Review of N. T. J. Bailey, *Statistical methods in biology. Applied Statistics,* 1960, 9, 64–66.

37. Snedecor, G. W. *Statistical methods.* (4th ed.; orig. publ. 1937) Ames, Iowa: Iowa State College Press, 1946.

38. Tukey, J. W. The future of data analysis. *Annals of Mathematical Statistics,* 1962, 33, 1–67.

39. Underwood, B. J., Duncan, C. P., Taylor, J. A., & Cotton, J. W. *Elementary statistics.* New York: Appleton-Century-Crofts, 1954.

40. Wald, A. Contributions to the theory of statistical estimation and testing hypotheses. *Annals of Mathematical Statistics,* 1939, 10, 299–326.

41. Wald, A. *Statistical decision functions.* New York: Wiley, 1950.

42. Wald, A. *Selected papers in statistics and probability.* New York: McGraw-Hill, 1955.

43. Wilson, K. V. Subjectivist statistics for the current crisis. *Contemporary Psychology,* 1961, 6, 229–231.

WARNER WILSON   HOWARD L. MILLER
AND JEROLD S. LOWER[1]

14 Much Ado about the Null Hypothesis[2]

Edwards has charged that classical statistics, in contrast to Bayesian statistics, is always violently biased against the null hypothesis. Edwards has advised the conservative classical investigator that he should, therefore, always identify his theory with the null hypothesis, so as minimize specious claims for theoretical support. This paper reinterprets the so-called bias in terms of differential assumptions about the nature of the alternatives which must be considered; its main purpose, however, is to point out that insensitive experiments, in contrast to sensitive ones, are always biased for, rather than against, the null hypothesis. It is this 2nd bias (which exists independently of the 1st) that prompts the conservative investigator not to identify his theory with the null hypothesis.

Grant (6) [Ch. 10 in this book] and Binder (1) [Ch. 11] have clarified the fact that two strategies can be used in theory testing. First, one can identify the theory under test with the null hypothesis and claim support for the theory if the null hypothesis is accepted. The second, presumably more orthodox and traditional, approach is to identify the theory under test with the alternative hypothesis and claim support for the theory if the null hypothesis is rejected. Binder has referred to these two approaches as acceptance support and rejection support strategies. In this paper, however, the authors will follow Edwards (4) [Ch. 12, pp. 143–147] and speak of "identifying one's theory with the null hypothesis" and basing support on the acceptance of the null versus "identifying with the alternative hypothesis" and basing support on the rejection of the null and, of

course, the subsequent acceptance of the alternative.

Binder (1) has ably pointed out that either strategy may be used effectively under some circumstances. Wilson and Miller (8, 9) have joined with Grant, however, in arguing that it is generally better to identify with the alternative and, hence, base support for a theory on the rejection of some null hypothesis. These writers pointed out that while the probability of *rejecting* the null hypothesis wrongly is held constant, for example, at the .05 level, the probability of *accepting* the null hypothesis wrongly varies with the precision of the experiment. To the extent that error is large, the study in question is biased for the null hypothesis and for any theories identified with it. According to this view, the conservative, cautious approach is to identify one's theory with the alternative hypothesis.

This essentially orthodox (Fisherian) view of classical statistical procedures has seemed so reasonable to the present authors that they were surprised to find Edwards, who identifies himself with Bayesian statistics, taking a dramatically opposed view. Edwards' article

1. The order of authorship should not be interpreted as implying a greater contribution on the part of the senior author.
2. The authors wish to express their thanks to Ward Edwards for his personal communications with them and for the patient forbearance he has demonstrated in attempting to help clarify the ideas that are discussed in this paper.

From *Psychological Bulletin*, Vol 67, No. 3, pp. 188–96, 1967. Copyright © 1967 by the American Psychological Association, and reprinted by permission.

is only one of several considering the relative virtues of classical versus Bayesian statistics (see 2, for an excellent review). Edwards' article seems especially important, however, due to the fact that it strongly urges changes in the tactics of the orthodox classical statistician—changes which might prove to be ill-advised in some cases and impossible in others. Edwards' (4, p. 143) paper seems to make or imply the following points: (*a*) Classical procedures, in fact, "are always violently biased against the null hypothesis [p. 143]." (*b*) The cautious, conservative approach, therefore, is to identify one's theory with the null hypothesis and, hence, base support for one's theory on the acceptance of the null hypothesis. (*c*) The ideal solution, however, is to compare the goodness of fit of several models to the same data, thus avoiding the whole problem of null hypothesis testing.

Edwards apparently believes that a Bayesian analysis is always feasible or that if it is not, the experiment in question is not worth doing. The present writers do not agree with this point. They do, however, find much that is admirable in Edwards' position and certainly agree that Bayesian procedures are to be preferred—when they can be used. The purpose of the present paper, therefore, is not to disagree with Edwards so much as to suggest clarification and qualification.

In connection with Point *a*, it is conceded that Edwards is commenting on differences between classical and Bayesian statistics that really exist. It is suggested, however, that the term "bias" is perhaps not the best way to sum up these differences. A Bayesian analysis typically assumes that the datum comes from a null distribution or from some other distribution. Classical statistics assumes that the datum comes from a null distribution or from some one of all other possible distributions. The assumption that the datum may come from *any* distribution does, indeed, always increase the apparent probability that it comes from some distribution other than the null. The difference lies in the nature of the alternatives which are to be taken into account. Classical

procedures happen to assume that all possible alternatives must be taken into account. Granted this assumption, any bias for or against the null is then expressed by the probability level, which, even in the case of the .05 level, clearly favors the null.

In relation to Point *b*, it is suggested that the bias for theories identified with the null hypothesis in imprecise experiments, which Grant talked about, exists independently of and is logically distinct from the bias against the null hypothesis which Edwards talked about. Even when Edwards' bias *against* the null hypothesis exists, it does not imply the absence of Grant's bias *for* the null hypothesis. These considerations make the choice of tactics more complex than Edwards' article indicated. Edwards' (4) tactical advice was that, "If classical procedures are to be used, a theory identified with a null hypothesis will have several strikes against it. . . . And the more thorough the experiment, the larger that bias becomes [p. 145]." An attempt will be made to show that this advice is valid only in experiments of extreme precision, a type presumably rare in psychology. As experiments become imprecise, just the opposite tactical advice becomes appropriate.

In relation to Point *c*, it is suggested that no matter how many models we may have, many people will still find null hypotheses which will seem to them to need testing.

Is Classical Statistics Always Biased against the Null Hypothesis?

Edwards' first point was that classical statistics is always violently biased against the acceptance of the null hypothesis. He argued persuasively for this point in several different ways. He presented, for one thing, the following example, which supposedly illustrates the bias. This example and other points made by Edwards will be considered here in hopes that the discussion will help clarify the circumstances under which classical procedures can and cannot meaningfully be said to be biased, and also give some indication of how often inappropriate rejections of the null hypothesis may, in fact, occur.

The following example gives the flavor of the argument, though it is extremely crude and makes no use of such tools as likelihood ratios. The boiling point of statistic acid is known to be exactly 50°C. (Presumably this number was intended to be 150°C.) You, an organic chemist, have attempted to synthesize statistic acid; in front of you is a beaker full of foul-smelling glop, and you would like to know whether or not it is indeed statistic acid. If it is not, it may be any of a large number of related compounds with boiling points diffusely (for the example, that means uniformly) distributed over the region from 130° C. to 170° C. By one of those happy accidents so common in statistical examples, your thermometer is known to be unbiased and to produce normally distributed errors with a standard deviation of 1°. So you measure the boiling point of the glop, once.

The example, of course, justifies the use of the classical critical ratio test with a standard deviation of 1°. Suppose that the glop really is statistic acid. What is the probability that the reading will be 151.96° or higher? Since 1.96 is the .05 level on a two-tailed critical ratio test, but we are here considering only the upper tail, that probability is .025. Similarly, the probability that the reading will be 152.58° or greater is .005. So the probability that the reading will fall between 151.96° and 152.58°, if the glop is really statistic acid, is .025 − .005 = .02.

What is the probability that the reading will fall in the interval if the glop is not statistic acid? The size of the interval is .62°. If the glop is not statistic acid, the boiling points of the other compounds that it might be instead are uniformly distributed over a 40° region. So the probability of any interval within that region is simply the width of the interval divided by the width of the region, .62/40 = .0155. So if the compound is statistic acid, the probability of a reading between 151.96° and 152.58° is .02, while if it is not statistic acid that probability is only .0155. Clearly the occurrence of a reading in that region, especially a reading near its lower end, would favor the null hypothesis, since a reading in that region is more likely if the null hypothesis is true than if it is false. And yet, any such reading would lead to a rejection of the null hypothesis at the .05 level by the critical ratio test [p. 144].

If we follow the mode of analysis Edwards used, that of comparing an area of the null distribution to an area of the alternative distribution, we can note first that the probability of actually rejecting the null when the data in fact favor it is quite low, even in this contrived example. It would seem that we would reject the null when the data actually favor it when the observation falls in the interval 151.96–152.40. When the null is true, the data will fall in this interval, or in the corresponding lower interval, only about 3% of the time.

In addition, the type of analysis Edwards used has two aspects that seem intuitively unappealing: (a) *All* outcomes have a low probability under the alternative hypotheses, and (b) this probability is equally low no matter where an observation occurs. For example, if a datum occurs at 150° the implied inference is that the probability of a hit in this segment of .62 is .62/40 or .0155; likewise, if a datum occurs at 169° the implied inference is that the probability of a hit in this segment of .62 is still .62/40 or .0155.

Another way of looking at this example avoids both of the aspects noted above. Suppose, for simplification, that 1.96 is rounded off to 2.00. The null hypothesis then implies that the observations should fall in a segment of 4° between 148° and 152° 95% of the time. Suppose the actual reading is 152°. The probability of a hit as far as 2° away from 150°, if the null is true, is only .05; therefore, the null is rejected. It would seem that in order to test the alternative hypothesis, one could ask, "What is the probability of a hit as close as 2° to 150° if the acid is not statistic?" The answer would seem to be 4/40 or .10. It would seem, then, that a reading of 151.96° or 152° is more probable if the null hypothesis is false, and rejection of the null would seem appropriate after all. Perhaps, then, the bias is not as prevalent as Edwards would lead us to believe. Indeed, if a person working at the .05 level of confidence is to run any danger of rejecting the null when the data actually support it, it would seem that the width of the distribution under the alternative hypothesis must be more than 80 standard deviations. The present authors will leave it up to Edwards to show that situations of this sort occur frequently enough to justify concern.

The reader may wish to note, however, that

the apparent bias in classical procedures can be manipulated at will. If either a broad alternative distribution or a small error term is assumed, the bias will be increased.

Lindley (7), another Bayesian, presumably had just such considerations in mind when he stated that data can always be invented that highly favor the null hypothesis yet lead to its rejection by a properly applied classical test. Although such data can be invented, it is still meaningful to ask whether such data are inevitable or even likely in reality. By assuming a wide enough alternative, a bias can be created; however, in reality the alternative distribution is supposedly based on some theoretical or empirical consideration, and its width cannot be set arbitrarily. Error terms, on the other hand, can be reduced, even in reality, by the expedient of collecting more cases. However, in order for a reduced error term to lead inevitably to a bias, it is necessary to assume that as the error term is reduced, the absolute deviation from chance becomes less, so that the probability of the deviation's occurrence remains constant. This convenient constancy of probability in the face of a shrinking error term cannot be expected in reality. Consider again the statistic acid example, assuming a deviation of 2° and an error term of 1°. As indicated above, the probability of a hit at 152° is .05 under the null and .10 under the alternative. In real life, any observation is more likely than not to be near the true value, so if data are collected until the error term becomes .1°, the mean value of all the observations may still be near 152°. Now the probability under the alternative would still be .10, but the probability under the null would have become far, far less, since the critical ratio would now be 20. Thus, although it is necessary to admit that data can always be invented which will make a classical test look biased, it is also possible to point out that such data are not necessarily obtainable in reality and that certainly it is also easy to invent data that make classical tests look unbiased.

The considerations up to this point seem to support the assertion that classical statistics if blindly applied will sometimes be biased against the null hypothesis. Support for the assertion that classical statistics is always biased seems lacking. Instead, it appears that the extent of such bias depends in great part on the width of the alternative distribution relative to the width of the null distribution.

In further exploring Edwards' position, it may be noted that Edwards conceded that the bias becomes less as the relative width of the alternative distribution decreases. He firmly insisted, however, that no matter how narrow the alternative distribution, the bias will persist. Edwards seems to have come to this conclusion through an inappropriate comparison of probability levels with likelihood ratios.

The likelihood ratio is the ratio of one probability density (at the point of the data) to another. In a case such as the acid example, the Bayesian would apparently rather base his conclusions on the likelihood ratio than on the probability level, and the present authors would have no objection so far as such cases are concerned. In commenting on the relation of likelihood ratios to classical significance tests, Edwards (4) said:

Even a single-point alternative hypothesis located exactly where the data fall [the form of alternative distribution that most violently biases the likelihood ratio against the null hypothesis] cannot bias the likelihood ratio against the null hypothesis as severely as classical significance tests are biased [p. 145].

Whether we formally use likelihood ratios (ratios of ordinates) or simply other ratios of conditional probabilities (areas), what Edwards was saying seems to have a certain surface validity. If we consider only the probability (or probability density at a point) under one distribution, the null hypothesis, and do not take into consideration how likely this event might be under some specified alternative distribution, we are biasing ourselves against our null hypothesis by comparing it essentially to all possible alternatives instead of comparing it to just one. It seems to us that this is exactly what the classical statistician *intends* to do. If we have a clearly defined alternative, and we can say that "reality" must be one or the other, then we can justify a likelihood ratio or some similar procedure. If we do not have such alternative models, we cannot invent them to avoid a theoretical bias.

Edwards, Lindman, and Savage (5) implied that in any inference based on statistics, the decision involved must be a joint function of a prior probability estimate (what you thought before about the likelihood of your hypothesis), the likelihood ratio, and the payoff matrix (the relative rewards and costs of being right and wrong about your hypothesis). Edwards seemed to imply that "classical statisticians" use no such considerations. It is doubtful that this is so. For one thing, a choice of significance level can, under some circumstances, be construed as a prior probability estimate—not the subjective one of the individual scientist but an admittedly arbitrary attempt to standardize a bias against alternative hypotheses (not altogether different from a bias for the null). It appears to be a deliberate attempt to offer a standardized, public method of objectifying an individual scientist's willingness to make an inference. An undisputed goal of science is objectivity—public reproducibility. To introduce, into inferential statistics, a methodology dependent on partially subjective estimates of probability would seem to undermine this goal.

It is apparently impossible to say whether the choice of low probability levels implies a low prior probability or a payoff matrix biased for retention of the null hypothesis, but one or both seem implicit. The natural tendency is for investigators to believe that their hypotheses are correct and that the world can ill afford to ignore them. If such subjective inclination were allowed full sway, experimentation could become superfluous, and science might well degenerate into controversy. Classical statistics wisely resolves prior probability and payoff considerations in a conservative and standard rather than in a subjective and variable manner.

In answer to the obvious criticism concerning the subjectivity of invented alternative hypotheses, Edwards[3] stated essentially that a scientist always has some information regarding alternatives. Bayesian statistics considers this information; classical statistics does not. It seems that the bias that Edwards was discussing is a function of the failure to use (assume?) this additional information. In point of fact, the choice of one particular alternative distribution with which to compare the null excludes other possible alternatives. It is precisely this exclusion (which may be justifiable under some circumstances) which increases the probability that you will accept the null.

In this section we have attempted to discuss such questions as "Are classical procedures biased against the null hypothesis?" and "How often might such a bias result in rejections of the null when the data actually favor it or discredit it only weakly?" We see no reason to view classical procedures as biased against the null in any absolute sense —the opposite seems to be the case. We see no reason to view classical procedures as biased against the null hypothesis relative to Bayesian statistics since this comparison is at best unsatisfactory due to the difference in the procedures which are used and in the information which is assumed to be available. We can concede only that under special conditions, including presumably a specifiable alternative distribution, blind use of a classical analysis might result in a rejection of the null when a defensible Bayesian analysis, considering only the specifiable alternative, might show that the data actually support the null. We know of not one real-life instance in which the above has been demonstrated. It would seem to us that circumstances making such errors likely are not frequent, and it is suggested that the burden of proof is on those who think that such errors

3. W. Edwards, personal communication, October 1966.

occur frequently—in the literature, as opposed to in the examples used in articles written by Bayesians.

Should the Scientific Conservative Always Identify His Theory with the Null Hypothesis?

Edwards' second main point was that if one does use classical statistics, the more conservative strategy is to identify one's theory *not* with the alternative hypothesis—as Wilson, Miller, and Grant advocated—but with the null hypothesis. This point, too, is apparently incorrect. What is more, even if the first point, about classical statistics being always biased, were correct, the second point would not necessarily follow. In order to see the actual independence of the two points, it is helpful to realize that if something is biased, it is biased relative to something else. Edwards presumably meant that classical statistics is always biased relative to Bayesian statistics.

On the other hand, when Grant, Wilson, and Miller said that an insensitive experiment is biased for the acceptance of the null hypothesis and any theory identified with it, they meant that an insensitive experiment is biased relative to a sensitive one. A classical analysis can be biased against the null in comparison to a Bayesian analysis, and an insensitive experiment can still be biased for the null in comparison to a sensitive experiment. The two biases exist independently. What is more, the bias for the null hypothesis in insensitive experiments is just as true with a Bayesian analysis as with a classical analysis.

The following example (see Table 1) is offered as an illustration of the bias in insensitive versus sensitive experiments—a bias which, prior to the Edwards article, the present writers would have considered not in need of illustration. The example views experiments as perfectly sensitive or as completely insensitive; null hypotheses as true or false; and theories as identified with the alternative and supported if the null is rejected, or as

identified with the null and supported if the null is not rejected.

Edwards said that if you are a conservative, that is, if you wish to minimize undeserved successes, you should always identify your theory with the null. Wilson, Miller, and Grant said that in the case of insensitive experiments, such as are common in psychology, just the opposite tactic is to be recommended to the conservative. Table 1 indicates the number of deserved and undeserved successes achieved by theorists depending on whether they do identify with the alternative or with the null. Overall, identification with the null clearly promotes success for one's theory, a total of 285 (out of 400) successes versus 115 for those who identify with the alternative. The same is true in the case of total undeserved successes. Those who identify with the null get a total of 95 undeserved successes (out of 200) versus 10 for those who identify with the alternative. The most dramatic difference occurs, of course, in the case of insensitive experiments. The score is 95 illegitimate successes for those who test their theories as null hypotheses and only 5 for those who test their theories as alternative hypotheses. Hopefully, no one will wish to attempt to reconcile these outcomes with Edwards' (4) assertion: "The scientific conservative, eager to make sure that error is scotched at any cost, will therefore (always) prefer to test his theories as null hypotheses—to their detriment [p. 145]."

The authors would like to concede, however, that in recommending continued use of classical statistics combined with identification of theories with alternative hypotheses, they are operating on the basis of several beliefs which are not mathematically demonstrable.

Perhaps the most critical belief in this context is that most experiments in psychology are insensitive. It may be noted that a conservative would not favor identification with the alternative on the basis of Table 1 unless he held this belief. In a perfectly sensitive experiment, only identification with the alternative leads to accepting one's theory

Table 1. Limits of deserved and undeserved successes assuming identification with the null versus the alternative in perfectly sensitive and insensitive experiments

	Identification of theory with the null		Identification of theory with the alternative	
	Percentage deserved successes	Percentage undeserved successes	Percentage deserved successes	Percentage undeserved successes
Sensitive experiments				
True null	95	0	0	5
False null	0	0	100	0
Insensitive experiments				
True null	95	0	0	5
False null	0	95	5	0

when it is false. This would occur because no matter how small the error, t's of 1.96 and greater will occur 5% of the time. These writers would point out, however, that in very sensitive experiments, specious deviations from chance, though technically significant, would be so small that they would hardly mislead anyone. It might also be argued that belief in ESP, for example, survives partly on just such deviations. Such a consideration might justify more concern about such errors, greater use of the .01 or .001 significance level, and greater interest in likelihood ratios when meaningful ones can be computed.

Although the good showing of "acceptance support" in sensitive experiments is in its favor, it should still be noted that, seemingly, grounds are seldom available for deciding if experiments are going to be sensitive. In the face of this inevitable equivocality, investigators are encouraged to identify their theories with the alternative and so put an upper limit on error of 5% rather than 95%. One is not justified, after all, in assuming that favorable circumstances—true theories and sensitive experiments—will occur generally. A sensible strategy must assume the possibility of unfavorable circumstances—false theories and insensitive experiments—and must provide protection against these unfavorable circumstances.

Intuitively, it might seem impossible to base any inference, or express any bias, on the basis of a completely insensitive experiment. This consideration, however, is just the point of the objection to identification with the null. Identification with the null allows one to base positive claims for theoretical confirmation on the acceptance of the null hypothesis, which is, of course, virtually assured ($p = .95$) in the completely insensitive experiment.

Yet another consideration relates to the fact that it makes relatively little difference which approach you use in precise experiments. With great precision, you cannot go too far wrong. As experiments become imprecise, however, the tactical choice makes an increasingly large difference. All the more reason, therefore, for the conservative to choose the tactic that protects him even when experiments are imprecise.

The second belief is that statistics can sometimes reveal facts worth knowing even if they are not apparent to the naked eye. The relationships between smoking and lung cancer and between obesity and heart disease are examples. It is true that statistics may lead one to be overly optimistic about the importance of effects that are more significant than important, and certainly this tendency is to be deplored. On the other hand, although the human observer, unbeguiled by statistics, may indeed discount many trivial effects, he may also infer strong effects when only a trivial effect or no effect at all is present. Many people are, in the opinion of these authors, overly optimistic about the existence of ESP and the efficacy of psychotherapy. This overoptimism exists, however, in spite of statistics, not because of them.

Those who favor the so-called interocular

test should realize that situations in which effects are large relative to error will yield their secrets quickly. This consideration suggests that investigators will inevitably spend most of their time on ambiguous situations in which the effects of interest are small relative to the precision of measurement so far achieved. Statistics will be needed in such situations.

The third belief is that false positives are more damaging than false negatives. In the present context, this statement means that it is worse to view a false theory as already proved than to view a true theory as not yet proved. This belief is widespread (see, e.g., 3) and will not be belabored here. Granted the belief that false positives cause more trouble, identification of one's theory with the alternative is only natural. The traditional .05 significance level then limits the investigator to 5% error no matter how insensitive his experiments and no matter how false his hypotheses. When one identifies his theory with the null, however, the natural conservatism inherent in the traditional use of small probability levels works for, rather than against, hasty claims for support. Indeed, if an investigator identifies his theories with the null and if his theories are false, his number of false positives approaches not 5%, but 95%, as his experiments become increasingly imprecise.

The fourth belief is that many null hypotheses are worth testing. Edwards questioned this belief by suggesting that most null hypotheses are obviously false and that the testing of them is, therefore, meaningless. One of several possible replies is that the real question is frequently not whether the data deviate from the null, but whether the deviation is positive or negative. In such a case the testing of the null is obviously meaningful.

If the conservative investigator believes that false positives are the greater threat and that his experiment will be insensitive, he will surely choose to identify his theory with the null hypothesis. On the other hand, none of the beliefs discussed so far necessarily

justifies a preference for probability levels over likelihood ratios, and likelihood ratios are, in fact, strongly recommended whenever it is possible to compute them. The last belief, however, is that in most psychological experiments it is not possible to use a Bayesian approach based on likelihood ratios. The calculation of a ratio requires at least one specifiable alternative distribution. In most psychology experiments, no grounds are available for arriving at such a distribution. In such cases, classical statistics appears to be the only alternative, and, under this condition, the possibility of classical statistics being biased relative to Bayesian statistics is a meaningless issue.

Naturally, classical statisticians as well as Bayesian statisticians should consider alternative distributions. The point is that such considerations may or may not yield enough information to clearly justify a Bayesian analysis. So long as such information is often, if not usually, lacking, Edwards' rejection of classical approaches seems premature.

Edwards implied, to be sure, that investigators using classical tests have often rejected true null hypotheses without real evidence even when Bayesian statistics were potentially available. Bayesians could perhaps make a definite contribution by analyzing a number of published experiments and pointing out instances in which classical statistics has led to null hypotheses rejection when a potentially available Bayesian analysis would not have. It seems entirely possible, however, that such examples might be hard to find. At least they seem to be conspicuously absent from Bayesian critiques. It is also suggested that it would be most instructive if Bayesians would supply a precise alternative distribution to accompany any of the following null hypotheses, which are presented as typical psychological problems: (a) partially reinforced subjects extinguish at the same rate as continuously reinforced subjects; (b) patients show no change on tests of adjustment as a function of counseling; (c) punishment does not influence response rate; and (d) students working with teaching machines learn no faster and no better than students reading ordinary textbooks. Furthermore, the likelihood ratio, even if available, is not likely to disagree with the classical test unless the alternative distribution is very broad. If the meaningful alternative is not uniform, as it was in the statistic acid example, but instead has a mode or modes somewhere in the neighborhood of the null value, the likelihood ratio and significance test are even more likely to point in the same direction.

Another tactical point that merits attention is the question of whether a null hypothesis rejection resulting from a sensitive experiment should always be viewed as a legitimate success. As Table 1 indicates, if a null hypothesis is false, a sufficiently sensitive experiment will always reject it, and theories identified with the alternative will always be supported. Table 1 views such successes as legitimate. The possibility always exists, however, that the difference, though real, may be so slight that recording it in the literature is a complete waste of effort. The present writers think that the indiscriminant cataloguing of trivial effects is, in fact, a major problem in psychology today, and they would certainly regret it if their position was in any way interpreted as encouraging this unfortunate practice. On the other hand, as Wilson and Miller have pointed out, one must weigh one problem against another. If investigators identify their theories with the alternative hypothesis, they may be tempted to run *many* subjects and report theories to be true, even though the theories have no predictive utility. On the other hand, if investigators identify their theories with the null hypothesis, they may be tempted to run *few* subjects and report theories to be true, even though they are completely false. The present writers find no difficulty in deciding that they would prefer to confront investigators with the first temptation rather than the second.

A consideration of the problem of accepting trivial effects does not, therefore, greatly modify this paper's inclination towards identification with the alternative hypothesis in combination with the use of classical tests. This strategy may not be the best imaginable, but it is still often the best available, and it is recommended to the scientific conservative.

In summing up this section, we wish to remind the reader that Edwards apparently recommended that investigators switch to Bayesian techniques altogether. He went on to say, however, that if one *does* use classical statistics, the more conservative tactic, that is, the tactic that minimizes erroneous claims for theoretical support, is identification with the null. Our perspective on this advice can be summed up very briefly: If a conservative is a person who wishes to abandon a tactic that puts a ceiling on error of 1 in 20 and adopt instead a tactic that puts a ceiling on error of 19 in 20, then this is excellent advice.

Does the Development of Multiple Models Avoid the Need for Null Hypothesis Testing?

Edwards' last point was that the better tactic is to compare your data to several plausible models, and hence avoid null hypothesis testing altogether. Multiple models seem thoroughly desirable, and it seems worthwhile to note that in a traditional two-tailed test, classical statistics always implies three families of models: one predicting no difference, one predicting a positive difference, and one predicting a negative difference. On the other hand, it is hard to see how multiple models avoid the need for null hypothesis testing. Again an example from Edwards' paper (4) may be helpful.

A man from Mars, asked whether or not your suit fits you, would have trouble answering. He could notice the discrepancies between its measurements and yours, and might answer no; he could notice that you did not trip over it, and might answer yes. But give him two suits and ask him which fits you better, and his task starts to make sense [p. 225].

But ask him if he's sure of his decision or

if he might reverse it if he saw you model the suits again, and you have a null hypothesis to test. In other words, although on one occasion one model (suit) was judged to fit the data (you) better, one must still ask if the difference in fit is significant relative to the potential sources of error. However stated and however tested, this question still seems to constitute a null hypothesis. Bayesian statistics may offer a meaningful alternative to null hypothesis testing, but it will take more than this example to convince the present authors.

Are Undefined Alternative Hypotheses the Fault of Classical Statistics?

From the current vantage point, the classical bias against the null hypothesis does not appear as obvious as Edwards' bias against classical statistics. It is instructive to note one aspect of the rationale behind Edwards' (4) bias: "The trouble is that in classical statistics the alternative hypothesis is essentially undefined, and so provides no standard by means of which to judge the congruence between datum and null hypothesis [p. 145]." Edwards seemed to see the absence of a specifiable alternative as a shortcoming of classical procedure. It seems appropriate to point out that, in fact, the absence of a well-defined alternative is not a vice of classical statistics. The absence of a well-defined alternative is a problem, a problem which is unavoidable in many cases, a problem which Bayesian statistics presumably cannot handle, and also a problem which classical statistics is especially designed to avoid.

Summary

Some of the main points of the position of the present writers may be summed up as follows: (a) Identification with the alternative limits erroneous claim for theoretical support to 5%; identification with the null limits such errors to 95%. The conservative is, therefore, presumably better advised to identify with the alternative. (b) Classical procedures assume that only the null distribution can be specified and ask if the data are from this distribution or some other. Bayesian procedures assume that two distributions can be specified, and ask if the data are from the null distribution or the alternative. Granted the difference in procedure and in the information assumed, discussion of a bias in one procedure relative to the other seems of dubious meaningfulness. (c) Granted the information assumed by classical procedures, they shown an absolute bias in favour of the null hypothesis.

References

1. Binder, A. Further considerations on testing the null hypothesis and the strategy and tactics of investigating theoretical models. *Psychological Review*, 1963, 70, 107–115.
2. Binder, A. Statistical theory. *Annual Review of Psychology*, 1964, 15, 277–310.
3. Campbell, D. T. Methodological suggestions from a comparative psychology of knowledge processes. *Inquiry*, 1959, 2, 152–182.
4. Edwards, W. Tactical note on the relation between scientific and statistical hypotheses. *Psychological Bulletin*, 1965, 63, 400–402.
5. Edwards, W., Lindman, H., & Savage, L. J. Bayesian statistical inference for psychological research. *Psychological Review*, 1963, 70, 193–242.
6. Grant, D. A. Testing the null hypothesis and the strategy and tactics of investigating theoretical models. *Psychological Review*, 1962, 69, 54–61.
7. Lindley, D. V. A statistical paradox. *Biometrika*, 1957, 44, 187–192.
8. Wilson, W., & Miller, H. The negative outlook. *Psychological Reports*, 1964, 15, 977–978. (a)
9. Wilson, W. R., & Miller, H. A note on the inconclusiveness of accepting the null hypothesis. *Psychological Review*, 1964, 71, 238–242. (b)

ROLFE LaFORGE

15 Confidence Intervals or Tests of Significance in Scientific Research?

David Bakan's generally well-taken comments are criticized on the grounds that the procedures he recommended are typically more difficult to manage than those procedures whose management by psychologists he criticized. In particular, more attention to procedures for constructing confidence intervals and computing the power of tests of hypotheses is recommended, within the Neyman-Pearson approach to statistical inference. Both neo-Bayesian procedures and inexplicit, intuitive procedures are opposed.

David Bakan's (1) [Ch. 13 in this book] criticism of statistical practice common in psychological research is for the most part well taken; however, his recommendation that psychological investigators should turn to neo-Bayesian procedures seems ill-advised. If the clarity of the Neyman-Pearson approach cannot be managed by psychological editors and teachers, the complexities of the neo-Bayesians are hardly to be recommended as standard operating procedure. Moreover, two major considerations were somewhat slighted in Bakan's discussion.

First, confidence regions (usually intervals) for estimation of unknown parameters are integral features of the Neyman-Pearson approach to statistical inference and *are* appropriate for most scientific research and reporting. Bakan's [p. 159] passing recommendation of estimation does not make the reader aware that such an alternative exists within the decision-theoretic Neyman-Pearson formulation, nor does it enable the reader to find a description of such interval-estimation methods. Among other texts, those by Dixon and Massey (2), Hays (4), Stilson (9), and Guenther (3) contain adequate presentations of confidence-interval estimation at an elementary level.

Second, Bakan contrasted the applicability of the Neyman-Pearson approach in operations research (of which sampling inspection, cited by Bakan, is a special instance) with its supposed lack of applicability in scientific research. In point of fact, the introduction of a decision-theoretic model into operations research does not enable the systems analyst to organize a technological system automatically, any more than it enables the researcher to make scientific inferences automatically. Introduction of the decision-theoretic model does mean that the investigator has specified the relevant parameters of the situation, identified the kinds of errors he may make, and calculated how likely he is to make these errors in the situation is of a given, well-specified kind. As a result, both he and his reader are better able to estimate the effects of possible changes in the situation. That is, one of the most beneficial contributions of the Neyman-Pearson approach to hypothesis testing was its emphasis on the central importance of the *performance characteristics* (operating characteristics) of statistical tests. In fact, Neyman (7, p. 11) used these terms to *define* "the scope of mathematical statistics. Mathematical statistics is a branch of probability. It deals with problems relating to performance characteristics

From *Psychological Bulletin*, Vol. 68, No. 6, pp. 446–47, 1967. Copyright © 1967 by the American Psychological Association, and reprinted by permission.

of rules of inductive behavior based on random experiments." Unfortunately, most articles in psychological journals fail to evidence any explicit concern with the performance characteristic of the significance tests employed. This failure is the more surprising in view of the fact that elementary discussions of methods for rapid calculation of the power of commonly used tests have been available for some time (e.g., 2; 3). More extensive charts for calculating power can be found in Scheffé (8) and still more extensive tables are scheduled to be published by the Bureau of Standards. By simply introducing the concept of *power* (one kind of performance characteristic), one can clarify the nature of experimental design sufficiently to show that many proposed experiments must be revised if they are likely to be of any value, that many past experiments should never have been done as they were done, and that something is seriously wrong with the operations of our current research-publication system (as Bakan himself has done).

Perhaps the most serious criticism of Bakan's generally helpful paper is that it may be taken by some as a license to substitute common sense for an explicit statement of one's interpretative model. An explicit (hopefully, mathematical) model makes public the investigator's assumptions, deductions, and inferential processes; the intuitive, common-sense approach to scientific research has none of these virtues—in fact, used by itself it does not offer much. Unfortunately, equally great minds often have opposite intuitive perceptions of the essential nature of a situation; it was to just this problem that Neyman's (e.g., 7) penetrating analysis of the nature of statistical inference was directed. That Bakan criticized Kaiser's (5) exposition of the fundamental criterion of the decision-theoretical model (to minimize a defined function of the probability of error under well-defined circumstances) on the basis of a common-sense identification of a *statistic* with a *parameter* suggests that Neyman's analysis still has relevance.

References

1. Bakan, D. The test of significance in psychological research. *Psychological Bulletin*, 1966, 66, 423–437.
2. Dixon, W. J., & Massey, F. J. *Introduction to statistical analysis.* (2nd ed.) New York: McGraw-Hill, 1957.
3. Guenther, W. C. *Concepts of statistical inference.* New York: McGraw-Hill, 1965.
4. Hays, W. L. *Statistics for psychologists.* New York: Holt, Rinehart & Winston, 1963.
5. Kaiser, H. F. Directional statistical decisions. *Psychological Review*, 1960, 67, 160–167.
6. Neyman, J. *First course in probability and statistics.* New York: Holt, 1950.
7. Neyman, J. *Lectures and conferences on mathematical statistics and probability.* (2nd ed.) Washington, D. C.: United States Department of Agriculture Graduate School, 1952.
8. Scheffé, H. *The analysis of variance.* New York: Wiley, 1959.
9. Stilson, D. W. *Probability and statistics in psychological research and theory.* San Francisco: Holden-Day, 1966.

C. ALAN BONEAU

16 A Comparison of the Power of U and t Tests[1]

In a recent paper (2), the author summarized the results of a number of theoretical and empirical studies dealing with the effects of violations of assumptions underlying the t test. It was concluded that the t test is remarkably unaffected by the two common violations: sampling from populations having unequal variances and sampling from non-normal distributions. One who uses the t test can be reasonably sure that the probability of rejecting a true null hypothesis is close to the alpha value he selects for his experiment even though he may have misgivings about the assumptions upon which the t test is based. As a result of these considerations, a recommendation was made in the previous paper to the effect that even when the assumptions are not met (except under special conditions) the t test and the F test on means of the analysis of variance be used without those attendant feelings of turpitude which can be attributed to an introjection of the strictures of the proponents of nonparametric methods.

This recommendation was based upon an assumption that the t and F tests, because they make effective use of the information in the sample and have other desirable properties, should be more powerful techniques than nonparametric competitors. (For readable explanations and discussions of the power of a test see among others (12) or (13).) That is to say, if the null hypothesis is false—if there are true differences between means—the t test should signal the detection of small differences by yielding significant results more frequently than should comparable non-parametric methods.

1. The author wishes to express appreciation to Thomas M. Gallie for his cooperation and assistance.

Theoretically, the t test is more powerful than any of the usually utilized tests when the assumptions underlying it are met. It is also true, however, that when sampling is from certain nonnormal distributions, other tests may be more powerful than the t test. The Wilcoxon-Mann-Whitney U test (14, 10) for example, in one pathological case, theoretically is infinitely more powerful than the t test. Theoretically also, the power of the U test is never less than .83 of that of the t test (7). In fact even in the case for which the t test is designed (normality and equal variances) the U test by one measure of the relative power of the two tests is 95% as powerful as the t test (7).

Such theoretical statements about relative power of tests are based upon mathematical limiting processes involving conditions which are not representative of most practical situations, for example, infinitely large sample sizes and arbitrarily small differences between population means: (4, 7, 11). Statements as to the relative efficiency in general of various nonparametric competitors of the t test are scattered throughout the literature ((4, 7, 9, 11), to mention only the relatively accessible ones). They seem not, however, to have permeated effectively that hard core of statistical lore which the research psychologist musters in an attempt to wrest truth from chaff.

The present paper is intended to present the facts (culled from the literature as well as manufactured for the purpose) about the power of the t test and, in particular, how that power compares with the power of a specific nonparametric competitor in various practical situations. This presentation is meant to temper in part the implications of the previous

From *Psychological Review*, Vol. 69, No. 3, pp. 246–56, 1962. Copyright © 1962 by the American Psychological Association, and reprinted by permission.

paper (2) that the *t* test should be used whenever possible. It would seem that here, as in other areas of human endeavor, a little discretion may pay off.

Attention will be focused upon the *U* test, a worthy protagonist whose principal strengths vis-à-vis the *t* test have already been mentioned. The *U* test, or equivalent versions of procedures based upon ranked scores, has been invented several times in the history of statistics, first by Deuchler (3), but later by Wilcoxon (14), Mann and Whitney (10), among others. (See 8, for historical discussion.) As used in the present context, the statistic *U* is computed by determining the number of scores in the second sample which are exceeded by each score in the first sample. The sum of all such counts summed over the scores in the first sample is called *U*, tables for which have been developed by Mann and Whitney (10), extended by Auble (1), and made readily accessible by Siegel (12). Wilcoxon's *T* test (14), although limited to equal-size samples, gives exactly equivalent results even though it is computed in a different fashion.

The null distribution of *U* may be derived from the assumption that ranks are assigned to the two samples on a random basis such that every combination of ranks among samples is equally likely. For example, given that n_1, the first sample size, is 2 and n_2 is 3, the first possible values of the two ranks in the first sample (assuming no ties) are 1 and 2, 1 and 3, 1 and 4, 1 and 5, 2 and 3, 2 and 4, 2 and 5, 3 and 4, 3 and 5, and finally, 4 and 5. By the definition above, these lead to *U* values of 6, 5, 4, 3, 4, 3, 2, 2, 1, and 0, respectively. If all of these combinations are equally likely—the two samples came from the same distribution for example—the probability of getting values as extreme as 6 or 0 by chance is the sum of the individual probabilities:

$$1/10 + 1/10 = 1/5$$

By the logic of statistical decisions, however, one attributes extreme values of *U* not to these accidents of random sampling which occur with known probability if the null hypothesis is true, but to actual differences between the distributions. In actuality, differences in distribution usually lead to non-equally-likely combinations of ranks. Ranks 1 and 2 occur together with relatively greater frequency as the difference between the means of the populations increases and as a result more frequent extreme *U* values occur. For this reason *U* is generally considered to be a test of displacement or shift of distributions, the main focus being on differences in central tendency. Note also that discrepancies of variance tend also to produce non-equally-like combinations of ranks. If two populations have the same mean, the values 1 and 5 tend more to occur together as the size of the variance of the first increases relative to the size of that of the second. However, these combinations give rise to middling values of *U* and hence are ignored, in effect, by the *U* test. We shall see, however, that there are cases for which differences in distribution other than central tendency affect the value of *U*.

One further statement might be made about the sensitivity of the *U* test in specific cases. Since essentially it is based only upon ranks, first and last scores get rank 1 and *n* whether they are close to the mean or several standard deviations away. Thus the occasional score which is apparently not in the distribution but which furnishes no real justification for exclusion is treated as a member of the in-group by the *U* test but as the pariah it may well be by the *t*.

The method of the present paper is quite similar to the approach followed by the author in the previous paper dealing with the probability of rejecting the null hypothesis if it is true. In that study populations having specified characteristics were constructed and the values of *t* arising from the differences between means of random samples drawn from them were computed. The empirical probability of rejecting the null hypothesis was obtained by determining the proportion of sample *t* values falling outside the ordinary tabled values for the appropriate number of degrees of freedom (i.e., falling in the region of rejection). Since the null hypothesis was indeed true, these empirical probabilities or proportions could be compared with the nominal values to determine the effects of modifying the specified characteristics of the populations in such a way as to violate the assumptions underlying the *t* test. In the present study, the concern is with the proportion of obtained *t*'s and *U*s falling in the region of rejection (or critical region) when the null hypothesis is false—when there is a built-in, specified difference between means. To generate this information, the only required addition to the previous *t* test program is a provision for changing the mean of the first sample to any value desired.

The program using the IBM 650 Electronic Data Process System for generating *t*'s from random deviates was discussed in detail in the previous paper (2). To summarize briefly, 10-digit random numbers were generated by a multiplication process. These were converted into random deviates from a specified population by a table-look-up procedure; the random deviates were injected into the computing formula for the *t* test for the difference between means of two independent samples; and the resulting *t* value was sorted and tallied on an internally contained table within the computer.

The program designed for the present study for the *U* test utilized the existing random number and random deviate generating procedures. The value of *U* was computed by the simple expedient of subtracting every score in the first sample from every score in the second sample and counting the number of minus signs which resulted. This number is *U* by definition. The possibility for a tie was ignored since the expected rate of ties was approximately one per thousand *U*s, a rate which, while significant, would seem to have little effect on the observed results. As in the *t* program, the obtained *U* values were sorted and tallied on an internally contained table which was punched out in card when the desired number of *U*s from the specified populations was reached.

Results

Since the results of the study will be expressed in terms of empirical power functions, the investment of a small amount of space to elaborate on the method of their determination may be in order at this point.

For any given set of conditions, i.e., combinations of means, variances, and distributions, the result of the computer procedure is a set of *t*'s or *U*s which may be arranged in a frequency distribution. Figure 1 shows two such distributions. The distributions are of *t*'s obtained on the basis of sample sizes of 15 from normal populations having a variance of 1.0. One of the distributions shown, that centered around the *t* value of zero, arose when the means of the two samples were both equal to zero. For the other distribution, that centered around 2.8 and shaded, the difference between the means of the two samples was equal to 1.0, that is, equal to one standard deviation. The vertical lines divide the range of possible *t* values into two regions. The unhatched region marks off those values of *t* which result in a decision to *accept* (or fail to reject) the null hypothesis at the .05 level. The hatched regions, those values of *t* which result in a decision to *reject* the null hypothesis at that level. As can be seen, when the null hypothesis is true most of the obtained *t*'s fall in the region of acceptance. The proportion which fall in the region of rejection, in this case .049, we have called the empirical alpha level.

Sometimes a decision is made to accept a false null hypothesis, the so-called beta error. In Figure 1, such an error would be made in the case of those values of *t* from the shaded distribution which fall in the region of acceptance. On the other hand, decisions to reject the null hypothesis when it is indeed false occur for that proportion of the *t*'s from the shaded distribution which fall in the region of rejection, in this case .737. It is this proportion which we call the empirical power of the test under the given conditions. It should be noted that both the empirical

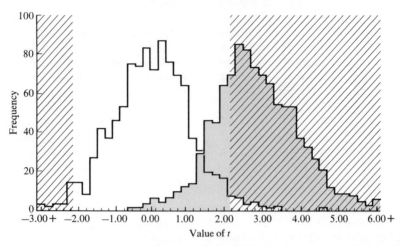

Fig. 1. Empirical t distribution for mean difference of (a) 0.00 (unshaded area) and (b) 1.00 (shaded area) for sample sizes of 15. (The hatched area is the region of rejection for the .05 level of significance.)

alpha and the empirical power are estimates of the exact theoretical values which obtain for these conditions.

The data of the present study are empirical power values considered as functions of the actual difference between population means. We shall consider separately, the functions for the one- and two-tailed tests and for the .05 and .01 values of alpha. The figures which will be presented will, for a given set of conditions, depict such functions for both that t and U tests so that visual comparisons may be made.

One further thing should be said about nomenclature before results are presented. As in the previous paper, the conditions of sampling will be symbolically represented. For example, N(2,1)5-N(0,1)15 indicates that the first sample is from a normal population N with a mean of 2 and a variance of 1, the sample size being 5. In this instance, the second sample is from a normal distribution having a mean of 0, a variance of 1, and the sample size is 15. In the text and figures, we will use the variable "x" for the value of the first mean to indicate that it takes on the several values necessary for the $\mu_1 - \mu_2$ values on the abscissa. In all cases the value of the mean of the second distribution is zero. One

thousand Us and t's were obtained for each condition.

NORMAL DISTRIBUTIONS: HOMOGENEOUS
VARIANCES

First to be considered are the cases in which the sizes of both samples are the same. Figure 2 depicts the various empirical power functions obtained when the condition of sampling is

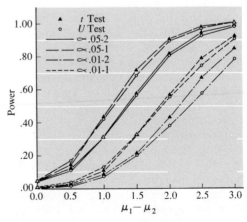

Fig. 2. Empirical power functions for U and t tests with sampling scheme N(x,1)5-N(0,1)5.

N(x,1)5-N(0,1)5. Because of the discrete nature of the U distribution, exact alpha values of .05 and .01 are not possible. When both samples sizes are 5, the following alpha values obtained from tables are used: .056 for the two-tailed test and .048 for the one-tailed test in place of .05, and .008 for both the one- and two-tailed test in place of .01.

A number of interesting facts can be observed in Figure 2. First is the expected superiority of the one-tailed test to the two-tailed test. Of prime importance for the present paper is the remarkable lack of difference in power of the t and U tests over the range of values presented. Only in the case of the two-tailed at the .008 level does the t test seem to exhibit a definite superiority and here only for gross difference between the means. In most of the other cases, the differences between the obtained points are well within the margin of sampling error (i.e., not significantly different). This would indicate that although the t test is theoretically a uniformly (over all mean differences) most powerful test, the margin over the U test is not very much. Because of this power property of the t test under these conditions, the points at which the U test shows a superiority must be attributed to sampling error. It is also clear that the alpha values ($\mu_1 - \mu_2 = 0$) are virtually identical and are approximately the theoretical values expected.

Increasing both sample sizes from 5 to 15 tends, as shown in Figure 3, to increase the power of the test, but to leave virtually unaffected the things which we have said about the smaller sizes. For example, at the .05 level for a one-tailed test, the power of both tests for a difference between means of 1.0 is around .42 for sample sizes of 5, and .85 for sample of size 15.

Still maintaining the condition of sampling from a normal distribution with equal variances of the parent populations, we may allow the sample sizes to be different, 5 as opposed to 15, and generate another series of curves, Figure 4. The results are similar to those preceding, with the power for the one-tailed

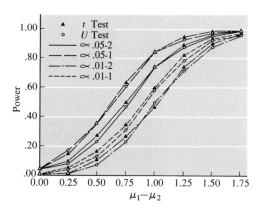

Fig. 3. Empirical power functions for U and t tests for sampling scheme N(x,1)15-N(0,1)15.

test at the .05 level and a mean difference of 1.0 being in this case about .60. This, too, is to be expected since the power of the test among other things is an increasing function of the difference between the means but a decreasing function of the expected standard error of the difference between means where

$$\sigma_{\bar{x}_1 - \bar{x}_2} = \sqrt{\sigma_1{}^2/n_1 + \sigma_2{}^2/n_2}$$

Figure 4 shows more clearly than any of the preceding graphs the superiority of the t test to the U test, but the largest obtained difference is only .12, and being the largest probably overestimates the true difference.

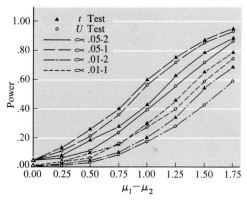

Fig. 4. Empirical power functions for U and t tests for sampling scheme N(x,1)5-N(0,1)15.

The results we have observed thus far are for conditions in which the assumptions underlying the *t* test are satisfied. Under these conditions we know that theoretically the *t* test is the most powerful test of the difference between two means. The power functions and relations between the powers of the two tests obtained in this study are comparable with those found in several sources (4, 5, 6, to name a few). Thus they contribute only a confirmation of the general method and at the same time furnish a graphical demonstration of the fact that, while less powerful than the *t* test, the *U* test performs quite well in those situations for which the *t* test is expressly suited.

When the assumptions of the *t* test are not fulfilled, it is not necessarily a most powerful test. Moreover, as stated earlier, there are theoretical conditions for which the *t* test is considerably less powerful than other tests including the *U* test. The remainder of this paper will compare power functions for the *U* and *t* tests for those violations of assumptions which arise from various combinations of the three distributions, the two variances, and the two sample sizes which have been selected for the study. We will determine whether the power functions for the *t* test show any drastic deviations from those power functions we have already seen, and we shall discover those cases, if any, for which the *U* test performs better than does the *t* test. This, of course, must be within the limitations imposed by the selection of conditions.

NORMAL DISTRIBUTIONS: HETEROGENEOUS
VARIANCES

Initially, we shall proceed by examining the effect of violating the assumption of homogeneity of variances with normal distribution. In the previous study, it was determined that inequality of variances up to at least a ratio of 1 to 4 produced a very little effect in alpha provided the sizes of the two samples are the same. If the sample sizes are different, gross disturbances in alpha occur.

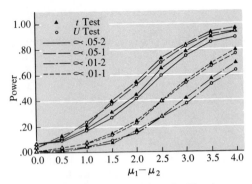

Fig. 5. Empirical power functions for *U* and *t* tests for sampling scheme N(x,1)5-N(0,4)5.

Figure 5, depicting the equal-sample-size case (*n* = 5), reveals that for *t* the alpha is relatively undisturbed and power also seems little affected. It should be noted that the relatively low power for Figure 5 (and for some following figures) for a given mean difference is to be attributed to a change in the standard error of the difference between means occasioned by the change in σ_2 from 1 to 4. For a given mean difference in standard error units, the power remains essentially the same. For example, the true standard error of the difference between means for the case N(x,1)5-N(0,4)5 is .63, while for the case (x,1)5-N(0,4)5 it is 1.0. A mean difference of 2.0 (2 standard errors) in Figure 5 shows the power of the two-tailed *t* test at the .056 level to be approximately .45. On Figure 2, a mean difference of 1.26 (2 standard errors) shows the comparable power to be approximately .44. In terms of the true standard error of the difference between sample means, then, the power of the *t* test seems relatively unaffected by violating the homogeneity of variances assumption.

Likewise, the power of the *U* test is maintained, but at a level again slightly less powerful than the *t* test. Similar results (not shown) obtain when both sample sizes are changed to 15.

Introducing heterogeneity of sample size as well as heterogeneity of variance produces discrepancies which might be predicted

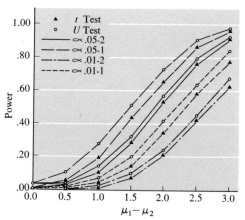

Fig. 6. Empirical power functions for U and t tests for sampling scheme N(x,1)5-N(0,4)15.

from what is already known about the effect of this condition on the alpha level. Figures 6 and 7 portray these effects for the two possible combinations of variance and sample size considered, N(x,1)5-N(0,4)15 and N(x,4)5-N(0,1)15 respectively. The first thing to observe in these figures is that effect on the alpha level (the power for a mean difference of zero). In Figure 6 the alpha is for all curves less than the nominal values of .05 and .01, although the magnitude of the difference for the U curves is less than those for t. The actual values observed are as follows: (one-tailed

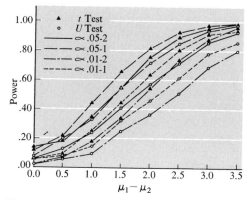

Fig. 7. Empirical power functions for U and t tests for sampling scheme N(x,4)5-N(0,1)15.

test-.05 level) $t = .010$; $U = .029$; (two-tailed test-.05 level) $t = .009$; $U = .027$; (one-tailed test-.01 level) $t = .002$; $U = .005$; (two-tailed test-.01 level) $t = .001$; $U = .004$. The power functions reflect the fact that while nominally at a .05 level, the tests are actually operating at a reduced alpha value. At the reference value, a mean difference equal to two standard errors, the power of the two-tailed .05-level t test is approximately .24, while the power for the comparable U test is about .28. Both of these values are much less than the values of about .45 which obtained under the other conditions. We may conclude that the conditions of heterogeneity of variances and sample sizes which produced Figure 6 have affected the alpha level of both U and t, U to a lesser extent, however, than t. Since the alpha level for the U test under these conditions is greater than that for the t test, the resulting power functions should and do reflect a superiority of U to t. What we are observing is the power curve for t for an alpha level of about .01 and for U of about .03 when we consider, for example, the curves which were constructed on the basis of the normal boundaries of the region of rejection for the .05 level of alpha.

We may make exactly the same comparisons for the results depicted in Figure 7, but note that the effects are in the opposite direction to those found in Figure 6. For example, the alpha values obtained are all greater than the nominal values, and again the distortion to the t values is greater than those for U. For this case—N(x,4)5-N(0,1)15—the actual alpha values observed are: (one-tailed test-.05 level) $t = .115$; $U = .081$; (two-tailed test-.05 level) $t = .145$; $U = .064$; (one-tailed test-.01 level) $t = .048$; $U = .020$; (two-tailed test-.01 level) $t = .058$; $U = .021$. Considering the reference point used earlier, the empirical power of the two-tailed test with alpha equal to .05 for a difference between means equal to two standard errors of the difference between means, we find these values to be .75 for t and .52 for U. And as before, the power curves behave as if they were the power curves for the observed value of alpha, the curves for *t* being considerably above those for *U* at all points.

We may conclude that violating the assumption of homogeneity of variance if the underlying distributions are normal has little effect on either the alpha level or the power of the *t* or the *U* test as long as sample sizes are the same. The violation of this assumption coupled with heterogeneous sample sizes changes the alpha level of both the *t* and the *U* tests and produces power functions which seemingly are roughly appropriate for the true alpha level rather than the nominal one. The *U* test seems much less disturbed by this particular violation than does the *t* test, but it is by no means true that the *U* test is completely unaffected as would seem to be implied by the term "nonparametric". Rather it seems to behave much as does the *t* test, but somewhat less sensitively to the violation of the assumption of homogeneity.

NONNORMAL DISTRIBUTIONS

At this point we will examine the empirical power functions for the *t* and the *U* tests when sampling for at least one sample is from nonnormal distributions. In this way we will observe the effects, if any, on the functions if one or both of the parent populations is exponential, or if one or both of the parent populations is rectangular. From an examination of the empirical alpha for the *t* test, we already know what the effects of sampling from a rectangular distribution are minimal on alpha. When the exponential distribution is involved, however, some perturbations in alpha may occur because of differences in skewness of the two distributions. The magnitude of these disturbances as seen in the earlier study was progressively lessened as sample size increased. At sample sizes of 25, the effect was virtually unnoticeable.

These earlier observations are confirmed in this study. Figure 8, for example, depicts the the results of sampling from two rectangular distributions—R(x,1)5-R(0,1)5. Alpha is ap-

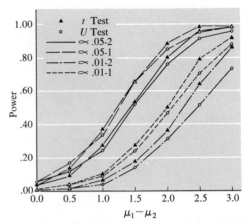

Fig. 8. Empirical power functions for *U* and *t* tests for sampling scheme R(x,1)5-R(0,1)5.

proximately the correct value for both levels for both tests. In this figure, it appears that the power of *t* is quite generally greater than that for *U*, but never by much except for the .01 level. Indeed, it would seem that for small differences between means, say, 0.5, *U* may be superior to *t*. Similar results (not shown) were obtained when both sample sizes were increased to 15.

The next distribution to be examined occurs when both samples are taken from exponential distributions as in Figure 9—E(x,1)5-E(0,1)5. The empirical alpha values are in the

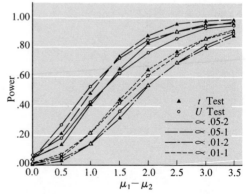

Fig. 9. Empirical power functions for *U* and *t* tests for sampling scheme E(x,1)5-E(0,1)5.

appropriate ranges. Here again, for small differences between the means, the *U* test seems consistently more powerful than the *t* test, but this advantage disappears with greater mean differences. All in all one may conjecture that when both distributions have the same shape, even though not normal, the power functions of the *t* and *U* tests have a relatively constant relationship. In most instances, the *t* test is slightly more powerful than the *U* test, as we have observed in most of our examples.

All of the foregoing power functions have come from combinations of distributions which produce essentially symmetric distribution of *t* and *U* when the null hypothesis is true (zero difference between means). We might expect more severe disturbances in power functions in those cases which, because of basic asymmetries in the observed *t* distributions, exhibited discordant obtained alpha values in the previous study. As may be recalled, the asymmetric distributions arose when the two parent populations differed in skew, one normal, the other exponential, for example. It was true, however, that increasing the sample size greatly diminished the asymmetries since the underlying probability mechanisms tend to normalize the distribution of *t* as sample size increases.

It is such conditions, probably not too uncommon in the experience (or at least the imagination) of the research worker, which motivate a desire to seek statistical tools which exhibit fewer allergic reactions to violations of assumptions.

Because of these considerations, it is interesting to compare the power functions of the *t* and the *U* test under such conditions of sampling. Figure 10 makes the comparisons for the case of exponential and normal distributions with samples of size 5—E(x,1)5-N(0,1)5. First to be noted are the discrepancies in the obtained alpha values for the one-tailed tests due to the asymmetrical distribution of *t* and, surprisingly enough, for *U*. The .048-one-tailed values are .022 for *U*, .014 for *t*. Likewise, the .008-one-tailed values are .002 for *U*,

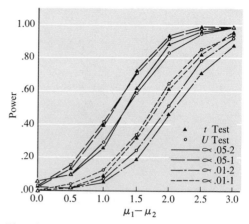

Fig. 10. Empirical power functions for *U* and *t* tests for sampling scheme E(x,1)5-N(0,1)5.

.001 for *t*. This is to be contrasted with the two-tailed values which are relatively close to the nominal values—the .056-two-tailed value for U is .049, for *t* it is .068; and the .008-two-tailed value for *U* is .014, for *t*, .011. These results for *t* are comparable to those found in the previous study. Thus we find that when considering alpha, *t* and *U* both are affected by sampling from populations which differ in skew, although it is possible that the effect on *U* is less than that on *t*.

A further examination of Figure 10 reveals that the empirical power functions for *U* are, with one or two exceptions, higher than the power functions for *t*, but the advantage is slight.

As mentioned previously, increasing the sample size tends to normalize the distribution of *t* in the null case, the effect being to lessen the discrepancy of nominal and obtained values for the one-tailed test. Figure 11 presents the curves for the increased sample size case—E(x,1)15-N(0,1)15. As before, our attention is first directed to the zero-mean-difference points, and as expected, the values for *t* have become closer to the nominal values— one-tailed test, .037 for .05 level, and .006 for .01 level; two-tailed test, .044 for .05 level and .012 for .01 level. Increasing the sample

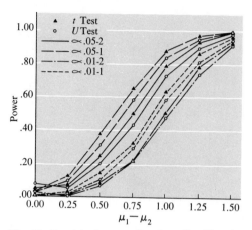

Fig. 11. Empirical power functions for U and t tests for sampling scheme E(x,1)15-N(0,1)15.

size to 15, however, does not seem to improve the performance of the U test. For the one-tailed U test, the obtained alpha values are .016 for the .05 level, and .000 for the .01 level. For the two-tailed test, the obtained alpha values again seem to be higher than the nominal values—.068 for the .05 level, and .019 for the .01 level. In Figure 11, we note that the power functions for the U test are almost invariably below those for the t test.

A notable phenomenon occurs for the .05-level, two-tailed U test. This particular curve shows a decrease in power from 0 mean difference to 0.25 before starting up again. While sampling error may well account for the dip, it is certainly possible for a test to be "biased", the technical term for such an occurrence. In fact there is no reason to believe that the U test as a test for mean differences should not be biased. The U test is only fortuitously a test for mean differences, being fundamentally a test for differences between distributions. As we have seen it is less sensitive to some kinds of differences between distribution than others, being perhaps maximally sensitive to differences in central tendency of two distributions. But there are many measures of central tendency, the mean and the median, for example. We

know that the mean and median are different in skewed distributions. In the combination of distributions with which Figure 11 is concerned, namely, exponential and normal, it is possible for medians to be the same for the two distributions which necessitates that the means be different and vice versa. For the t test which explicitly evaluates differences in sample means this seems to present no problem. The U test, however, may well be more sensitive to median differences and thus show the bias when used as a test for differences between means.

Other combinations of distributions which were explored in no way change the general picture which we have continually observed. We may summarize that picture as follows: In general the t test is more powerful than the U test, but never by much. Based on the evidence we have seen, one might conjecture that over a long series of experiments involving distributions of the kind we have used, a consistent use of the t test might result in, say, 5% more rejections of a false null hypothesis than would a consistent application of the U test. There are many other kinds of distributions arising in research, however, for which this statement need not apply. Depending upon one's inclinations, such a conclusion could be interpreted as ample grounds for habitual use of either of the two tests. There are, as we have seen, other considerations. As a general rule we might say that the t test seems to provide the appropriate power curve for the actual alpha level involved, whereas, the U test shows more variability in its power functions. That is to say that if the actual (not the nominal) alpha is .05, the power curve for the t test in most cases is probably very similar to the power function for the theoretical case for the .05 level; it is also to say that the statement is not nearly so true of the U test. This property of the t test is useless, however, unless we know what the actual alpha is. In cases when assumptions are violated we will not. It is true that the violations of the assumptions underlying the t test can produce large discrepancies between nominal and actual alpha when the sample sizes are other than nearly equal. This in itself contraindicates the use of the *t* test in these instances. A further somewhat surprising consideration is that the *U* test is not truly distribution free. It is always sensitive to differences in distributions, and sometimes seems more affected by differences (other than mean differences) than is the *t* test.

If one final word is to be said it might be that one should not avoid using the *t* test (provided relevant considerations have been made) solely on the grounds that it is subject to error when assumptions are violated and that the *U* test is not subject to error under the same conditions. Both of the statements are unreasonable in view of the data. One should not, however, refrain from using the *U* test in place of the *t* test on the grounds that it is considerably less powerful than the *t* test. This is simply not true.

References

1. Auble, D. Extended tables for the Mann-Whitney statistic. *Bull. Inst. Educ. Res., Ind. U.*, 1953, 1 (2).
2. Boneau, C. A. The effects of violations of assumptions underlying the *t* test. *Psychol. Bull.*, 1960, 57, 49–64.
3. Deuchler, G. Über die Methoden der Korrelationsrechnung in der Pädagogik und Psychologie. *Z. Pädag. Psychol.*, 1914, 15, 114–131, 145–159, and 229–242.
4. Dixon, W. J. Power under normality of several nonparametric tests. *Ann. math. Statist.*, 1954, 25, 610–614.
5. Dixon, W. J., & Massey, F. J. *Introduction to statistical analysis.* (2nd ed.) New York: McGraw-Hill, 1957.
6. Ferris, C. D., Grubbs, F. E., & Weaver, C. L. Operating characteristics for the common statistical tests of significance. *Ann. math. Statist.*, 1946, 17, 178–197.
7. Hodges, J. L., & Lehman, E. L. The efficiency of some nonparametric competitors of the *t*-test. *Ann. math. Statist.*, 1956, 27, 324–335.
8. Kruskal, W. H. Historical notes on the Wilcoxon unpaired two-sample test. *J. Amer. Statist. Ass.*, 1957, 52, 356–360.
9. Lehman, E. L. The power of rank tests. *Ann. math. Statist.*, 1953, 24, 23–43.
10. Mann, H. B., & Whitney, D. R. On a test of whether one of two random variables is stochastically larger than the other. *Ann. math. Statist.*, 1947, 18, 50–60.
11. Mood, A. M. On the asymptotic efficiency of certain nonparametric two-sample tests. *Ann. math. Statist.*, 1954, 25, 514–522.
12. Siegel, S. *Nonparametric statistics: For the behavioral sciences.* New York: McGraw-Hill, 1956.
13. Walker, H. M., & Lev, J. *Statistical inference.* New York: Holt, 1953.
14. Wilcoxon, F. Individual comparisons by ranking methods. *Biometrics*, 1945, 1, 80–83.

3

The One-Tail, Two-Tail Controversy

When an investigator uses null-hypothesis decision procedures to test some proposition he states that there will be some statistically significant difference between the scores of two (or more) groups. If the investigator predicts that the mean of one group will be greater than the mean of a second group he is employing a one-tail (or one-sided) statistical test. If he does not predict the direction of the difference but merely predicts that there will be some statistically significant difference between the two groups he employs a two-tail (or two-sided) statistical test.

In a paper entitled, "Two Kinds of Experiments Distinguished in Terms of Statistical Operations," M. Marks differentiated between those investigators who appropriately make use of two-tail tests of significance and those who should make use of one-tail tests, and suggested that behavioral scientists make more use of one-tail tests. In his article, "A Note on One-Tailed and Two-Tailed Tests," W. Hick objected to the use of one-tailed tests, and the one-tail, two-tail controversy followed. In an attempt to resolve the conflict Kimmel offered some criteria for the use of the one-tailed test.

From these discussions the student can learn much about the issues involved in the selection of a one-tailed or two-tailed statistical test.

MELVIN R. MARKS

17 Two Kinds of Experiment Distinguished in Terms of Statistical Operations

The work which a scientist does when he is "finding out" something has been variously called research, investigation, study, inquiry, examination, etc. Underwood (9) dichotomizes experimental problems into the "I-wonder-what-would-happen" and the "I-bet-this-would-happen" types. Mann[1] selects for distinction the terms "inquiry" and "research": The former proceeds without theory, whereas the latter is generated by theory and is reflexive, i.e., the results of research modify the constructs of the basic theoretical matrix. Both Underwood and Mann point out that basically there is a difference between just "finding-out," and "finding-out-if-a-hypothesis-is-consistent-with-fact." From this standpoint a distinction might be made on the basis of necessity for

1. From unpublished seminar discussions.

control. In "finding-out" control might be dispensed with, since control must always be with respect to something, and in "finding-out" that something is what is sought. On the contrary, in "finding-out-if- . . . ," control is necessary to evaluate results properly.

The writer believes that some sort of distinction is necessary, that it is best made in terms of statistical operations, and that it has important implications for the validity of conclusions drawn from results. What is needed first are two terms relatively free of connotations bearing on possible distinctions. While "inquiry" has been little used, "research" has been overused—and in a wide variety of meanings. To avoid ambiguity, the terms "experimentation$_I$," and "experimentation$_{II}$" have been selected.

From *Psychological Review*, Vol. 58, pp. 179–84, 1951. Copyright © 1951, by the American Psychological Association, and reprinted by permission.

A brief review of the statistical concepts relevant to the distinction will be helpful. Most current texts discuss them in part, but it is believed that the synthesis proposed here is new. At any rate such synthesis should be of value to those psychologists engaged in "experimentation" who have not found time to peruse thoroughly the introductory material of the more advanced statistical texts.

Statistical Hypothesis. This is any testable assumption about parametric values. Typical parameters are population mean, population variance, difference between two population means, etc. As examples, we might make several statistical hypotheses about the populations from which two sample groups, say *A* and *B*, were drawn:

"There is no difference between the means of the populations from which *A* and *B* were drawn"—algebraically,

$$(m_A - m_B) - 0 = 0. \qquad \text{Eq. 1}$$

"The population means of *A* and *B* differ by 5 points."

$$(m_A - m_B) - 5 = 0, \qquad \text{Eq. 2}$$

or, more generally,

$$(m_A - m_B) - K = 0$$
$$(K = \text{any constant}). \qquad \text{Eq. 3}$$

Note that in each of the three equations, the quantity $(m_A - m_B)$ is given a positive sign. In effect, a definite prediction is being made about the direction of the difference in magnitudes. A completely generalized equation,

$$(|m_A - m_B|) - K = 0, \qquad \text{Eq. 4}$$

states, "the absolute difference between the means of the populations from which *A* and *B* were drawn does not differ from some constant *K*."

It is assumed frequently that equation 4 represents the classical "null hypothesis." Actually, equations 1, 2, and 3 are null hypotheses as well. In each case the hypothesis is that the parametric difference between some assumed difference and a given constant is zero. In each instance the right side of the equation is the null which is to be tested.

Level of Confidence, Statistical Significance, etc. When the test of a statistical hypothesis yields an estimate of the probability that the null is tenable, it is customary to say that the results are "significant" if the associated probability, *p*, is less than some value chosen arbitrarily in advance of the test. For the purpose of this paper the statement, "significant at the 5 per cent level," means that the hypothesis tested was of the form of equations 1, 2, 3, or 4, and that the associated $p < .05$.

Type I Error. Suppose that *A* and *B* are each groups of 11 children for whom I.Q.s have been determined. Let the mean difference in I.Q. be 4.172, and the standard error of that difference be 2. With these data, $t = 2.086$, $d.f. = 20$, and $p = .05$. An investigator using the 5 per cent level would conclude that there is a significant difference. Two possibilities exist; either there is a difference in the population means, or there is not. If, actually, there is a difference, his conclusion would be correct; if, actually, there is no difference, *i.e.*, both groups come from the same population, he has erroneously falsified the null. The false rejection of the null hypothesis is called a Type I Error. Note that the probability of occurrence of a Type I Error is determined absolutely by the level of confidence adopted. In the example the 5 per cent level was chosen; hence, by definition, there are 5 chances in 100 of a random fluctuation which would lead to a *t* significant at that level.

Type II Error. This may be illustrated by recasting our example. Suppose that the two groups of children came from populations whose means differed by 2 I.Q. points; that the difference between the means of the samples was also 2 points (*i.e.*, "perfect" sampling), and that the standard error estimated from the sample difference was again 2 points. In this case, $t = 1$, $d.f. = 20$, $p > .30$. The same investigator would conclude erroneously that the null was tenable. The failure to reject the false null is called a Type II Error.

The *power* of a statistical test is defined as the probability that a Type II Error will *not* occur. Unlike the case of the Type I Error, the probability of a Type II Error cannot be fixed by the investigator, since it is a function of three variables, only two of which are under the investigator's control. The variables are: 1) the sample size; as N increases probability of Type II Error decreases (power increases), *i.e.*, a parametric difference is more likely to be found if the sample is large; 2) the probability of Type I Error (per cent level of confidence chosen by the investigator); as the level increases (in the sense that a 5 per cent level is an increase over the 1 per cent level), probability of Type II Error decreases (power increases), *i.e.*, it is more likely that a parametric difference will be detected with the 5 per cent level than with the 1 per cent level; 3) the relative magnitude of the parametric difference; as the magnitude (in standard error units) increases, probability of Type II Error decreases (power increases), *i.e.*, if the population difference is large it is likely that such difference will be detected in the sampling .

It is obvious that variable 3 above is unknown to the investigator. It should be noticed that, unless the hypothesis tested includes a definitive statement of the relative magnitude of the parametric difference, the power of the test is indeterminate. For example, given the hypothesis that $m_A > m_B$, without qualification as to the magnitude of the difference, the power cannot be computed; but, if m_A and m_B are assigned definite values, the power may be computed. Neyman and Tokarska (7) have tabulated the power of the t-test for various levels of confidence (Type I Error), sample sizes, and parametric differences. For example, with 20 *d.f.* at the 5 per cent level, if the parametric difference is 4.12 standard error units, power = .99, *i.e.*, probability of Type II Error = .01; with 1.70 parametric difference, power decreases to .50; with .39 units of parametric difference, power decreases to .10. Increase in power with increase in N is slight. For infinite *d.f.*,

at the 5 per cent level, 3.97 units of parametric difference give power of .99; 1.64 give power of .50, and .36 give power of .10. Johnson (5, p. 68) cites several papers where power functions of other tests are tabulated.

Two-Tailed Tests. In the two examples concerning the difference in group I.Q., the *sign* of that difference was not stipulated. Those examples were tests of the null expressed as in equation 4. The sign of t was not at issue; m_A could have exceeded m_B or vice versa. Tests made on this basis are called two-tailed tests, because both tails of the symmetrical distribution of t or x/σ are considered in determining the associated probability. The tables of t and x/σ are misleading in that only positive values of the statistic are tabulated, but the associated probabilities are for two-tailed tests. Although the distribution of Chi^2 is not symmetrical, here too tabular probabilities are for two-tailed tests, *i.e.*, the probability of frequency discordance in *either* direction from the hypothetical; note, however, that Chi^2, being a sum of squares, is necessarily always positive. Similarly, the F-ratio is always positive, but here too, tabled values refer to probabilities of chance *plus or minus* differences among the means of the treatments—thus the F-test as usually used is a two-tailed test.

One-Tailed Tests. Suppose that, in the example concerning the children's I.Q.s the investigator had predicted *before* the measurements were taken that $m_A > m_B$. The experimental hypothesis would fail obviously if $m_A < m_B$, by no matter how slight an amount. The investigator in making his test should exclude exactly half of the values which t might have, since he is interested only in the occurrence of t's which bear a positive sign. This is quite legitimate since, in effect, he has agreed that all negative t's will indicate an insignificant difference. His question is, given that m_A does exceed m_B, is the difference too great to be attributed to chance variation at the level of confidence selected. The two-tailed test does not apply here, since only positive values of t are considered. The hypothesis is properly evaluated by using only one tail of the sampling distribution. The t sought is that which might occur 10 per cent of the time if the null were true, since 5 per cent, or half of the possible values, would occur in the positive direction. This $t = \pm 1.725$, since $+1.725$ would occur by chance 5 per cent of the time. Recall that the 5 per cent value for the two-tailed test is 2.086, and it will be seen that the investigator is much more likely to detect the parametric difference if he uses the one-tailed test.

The one-tailed test leads to a similar increase in power with other statistical tests as well. For the sampling distribution of x/σ, ± 1.96 and ± 2.58 are the values required for the 5 per cent and 1 per cent levels, respectively, when a two-tailed test is employed; for the one-tailed test the corresponding values are 1.65 and 2.33. When using the Chi^2 and F-tables with a one-tailed test, the value of the statistic which has an associated probability *double* that of the level of confidence selected is the value which must be reached for falsification of the null. That value is always less than would have been required if a two-tailed test were used.

We are now prepared to examine, or better to define, the distinction between experimentation$_I$ and experimentation$_{II}$. *Experimentation$_I$ is that form of experiment to which two-tailed tests of the data are appropriate; experimentation$_{II}$ is that form of experiment to which one-tailed tests of the data are appropriate.*

It follows that a) preëxperimental predictions and b) use of one-tailed tests are severally necessary and together sufficient for experimentation$_{II}$. The *intention* of the experimenter is *not* the controlling factor. Thus, if he decides to do experimentation$_{II}$ but either fails to make a prediction or employs a two-tailed test he is actually engaged in experimentation$_I$. Conversely, if he decides on experimentation$_I$, but predicts the direction of his results and employs a one-tailed test, he is actually engaged in experimentation$_{II}$.

The experimental distinctions are not mere verbal quibbles. We may exemplify their importance first with a fictitious problem, then with illustrations chosen from psychological literature.

Suppose that the investigator of group differences in I.Q. found that his sample means differed by 3.9 I.Q. points, and that the standard error of the mean differences was again 2.0. On these data $t = 1.95$. If we suppose further that group B had been given special coaching designed to "increase" I.Q., while group A had been maintained as a control, it would appear that the investigator thought he was engaged in experimentation$_{II}$. However, unaware of the distinction made here, he consults the t-table and finds that the obtained value of 1.95 falls short of the 2.086 required for the 5 per cent level. He concludes that the special treatment given to group B was ineffective in increasing I.Q. Actually, by using the right test (one-tailed), he would fulfill the requirements for experimentation$_{II}$, and his results would be significant at the indicated level.

It is not difficult to find instances where investigators have done experimentation$_I$, under the illusion that they were doing experimentation$_{II}$. Tinker (8) had Ss read two forms of his Speed of Reading Test, the first under "ordinary" conditions, the second while the reading table was vibrated mechanically. He predicted that vibration would cause fatigue which would in turn lead to a decrement in reading speed. His results bore out the prediction. He also used a control group who read both forms under "ordinary" conditions. Here there was a critical ratio of 2.52 in favor of the first reading. He employed a two-tailed test at the 1 per cent level and found the difference could be attributed to chance (2.58 was needed). He might have predicted that there would be some fatigue in the second reading, even though the table was not being vibrated. Such predicted decrement with a one-tailed test would have been significant at the 1 per cent level. Tinker's results with the control group amount to experimentation$_I$, not experimentation$_{II}$.

Kircheimer, Axelrod and Hickerson (6) studied college students who: 1) changed their majors and a) were counseled, b) were not counseled; and 2) did not change their majors and a) were counseled, b) were not counseled. They predicted that, of the groups who changed majors, those who were also counseled would show the greatest increase in grade point average. The critical ratio (in the direction of the prediction) was 1.84. The writers said that this was significant at the 7 per cent level, and had they employed a 5 per cent level criterion, the result would not have been significant statistically. Had they employed a one-tailed test as they should, the result would clearly have been significant at the 5 per cent level. These writers too have failed to draw the distinction between experimentation$_I$ and experimentation$_{II}$ and their results have appeared less critical thereby.

Gagné (4) predicted that, when highly similar items were grouped together, learning of serial lists would be accomplished in a shorter time than when such items were separated. The results were in the predicted direction with a critical ratio of 1.69. Gagné stated that the probability of occurrence of a deviation in the expected direction was 4.6 per cent. He correctly used a one-tailed test. Had he used the two-tailed test and adopted the 5 per cent level, he would not have found significant differences, and the prediction would appear to have failed. He rightly distinguished between experimentation$_I$ and experimentation$_{II}$.

The example concerned with Tinker's results was predicated on the basis that the direction of the decrement in reading decrement *could* have been predicted *before* the data were in. It must be emphasized that the one-tailed test is not justified unless the prediction is made prior to the data. If an investigator begins a study with preconceptions of results, and on studying those results generates a theory which will account for them, he cannot accept such afterthoughts as predictions, *i.e.*, switch—on the spot—from a two-tailed to a one-tailed test and pride himself on

doing experimentation$_{II}$. He can *use* the results to predict *future* data. If he makes the switch after collecting the data, he has, in effect, increased the probability of committing a Type I Error without realizing it. If he uses the 5 per cent level on a one-tailed test, this is equivalent to the 10 per cent level with a two-tailed test, and he has unwittingly doubled his level of confidence: a dangerous departure from scientific conservatism. Burke (1) and Cronbach (2) have pointed out the inflation of level of confidence which occurs with either adding more subjects on the basis of already gathered data, or "shopping around" in compiled data for comparisons which are likely to show significant differences.

The experimenter$_{II}$ is in possession of a statistical tool not at the disposal of the experimenter$_I$. He is not limited to the prediction of results in a particular direction, but he may frame his hypothesis in such a manner that the magnitude of the parametric difference is included as well. For example, again referring to the comparison of group I.Q.s mentioned previously, the research worker might use an hypothesis of the form of equation 3, where the stipulated difference attributable to the "coaching" may be arbitrarily small. In this case, if the null remains tenable in light of the data, the theory is not rejected, whereas in experimentation$_I$, the null is of the form of equation 1 and, if there were theory, that theory would appear to have failed. This tool should be used with caution. No theory is particularly valuable if it predicts differences which are impracticably small. For instance, if the same coaching were expected to increase I.Q. by .5 points, the theory might remain tenable but the question "So what?" suggests itself. In this vein, Edwards (3) has distinguished "practical" from "statistical" significance. The experimenter$_{II}$ should ever attempt to increase the power of his tests. If he is at liberty to set up experimental situations he should endeavor to maximize parametric differences since these contribute to test power. It follows that, in new areas experimentation$_{II}$ might wisely be limited to the comparison of extreme instances, rather than include the attempted distinction of subtle differences.

In summary, experimentation$_{11}$—as distinguished from experimentation$_1$—is characterized by predictions and one-tailed tests of significance. It has inherently greater statistical power and increases the productivity of investigation.

References

1. Burke, C. J. The effect of postponed decisions on statistical tests. Paper read at 22nd annual meeting of the Mid-western Psychological Association.

2. Cronbach, L. J. Statistical methods applied to Rorschach scores: a review. *Psychol. Bull.*, 1949, 46, 393–429.
3. Edwards, A. L. *Experimental design in psychological research.* New York: Rinehart, 1950.
4. Gagné, R. M. The effect of sequence of presentation of similar items on the learning of paired associates. *J. exp. Psychol.*, 1950, 40, 61–73.
6. Kircheimer, B. A., Axelrod, D. W., & Hickerson, G. X., Jr. An objective evaluation of counseling. *J. appl. Psychol.*, 1949, 33, 249–257.
5. Johnson, P. O. *Statistical methods in research.* New York: Prentice-Hall, 1949.
7. Neyman, J., & Tokarska, B. Errors of the second kind in testing Student's hypothesis. *J. Amer. statist. Assn.*, 1936, 31, 318–326.
8. Tinker, M. A. Effect of vibration on reading. *Amer. J. Psychol.*, 1948, 51, 386–390.
9. Underwood, B. J. *Experimental psychology.* New York: Appleton-Century-Crofts, 1949.

LYLE V. JONES

18 Tests of Hypotheses: One-Sided *vs.* Two-Sided Alternatives

Psychological literature abounds with experimental studies which utilize statistical tests of the significance of differences between two groups of subjects. Most of these studies present tests based upon either the distribution of Student's *t* or upon the distribution of χ^2. Since the comparison of an experimental group with a control group of subjects is so fundamental to the experimental method, and since statistical tests of significance are appropriate for testing hypotheses regarding differences between two groups of subjects, it would seem important to correct a common misconception concerning the application of these tests of hypotheses.

One model for a test of significance of mean difference, the more familiar model, is that in which we test the null hypothesis, H_0,

against a set of two-sided alternatives, H_1. We might formalize this test,

$$H_0 : \mu_1 - \mu_2 = 0$$

$$H_1 : \mu_1 - \mu_2 \neq 0,$$

where μ_1 is the mean of the population represented by one sample and μ_2 is the mean of the population represented by a second sample. Assuming scores X_1, from the first population, and scores X_2, from the second, both to be distributed normally, and assuming the population standard deviations to be equal, we may find

$$t = \frac{\bar{X}_1 - \bar{X}_2}{s\sqrt{\dfrac{1}{N_1} + \dfrac{1}{N_2}}},$$

From *Psychological Bulletin*, Vol. 49, pp. 43–46, 1952. Copyright © 1952 by the American Psychological Association, and reprinted by permission.

where

$$s = \sqrt{\frac{\sum_{i=1}^{N_1} (X_{1i} - \bar{X}_1)^2 + \sum_{j=1}^{N_2} (X_{2j} - \bar{X}_2)^2}{N_1 + N_2 - 2}}$$

and N_1 and N_2 are the numbers of individuals in the samples from the first and second populations.[1] Having stipulated a desired confidence level, α, we may enter the t table[2] with $N_1 + N_2 - 2$ degrees of freedom and a p-value equal to α to find a critical value of t, t_c. If the absolute value of the observed t exceeds t_c, we reject H_0 in favor of H_1; otherwise, we accept H_0. In Figure 1 appears a distribution

not, in psychological research, our hypotheses have a *directional* character. We are interested in whether or not a given diet *improves* maze performance in the rat. We hypothesize that the showing of a particular motion picture to a group of individuals would lead to a *more tolerant* attitude toward certain racial minorities. We wish to test whether or not anxious subjects will respond *more actively* than normal subjects to environmental changes which might be perceived as threatening. In each case, theoretical considerations allow the postulation of the direction of experimental effects. The appropriate experimental test is one which takes this into account, a test of the

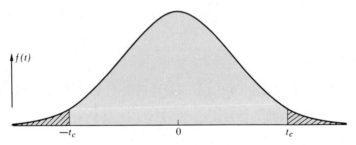

Fig. 1. The Two-Tailed Test Model

of t showing, graphically, the nature of this decision. This distribution corresponds to the sampling distribution of mean differences, under the null hypothesis. For any value of t to the right of t_c or to the left of $-t_c$, we reject H_0. The two shaded tails of the distribution, taken together, make up α per cent of the total areas under the curve.

   The model above, the test of the null hypothesis against two-sided alternatives, is the one used most often by investigators in psychology. Yet in many cases, probably in most cases, it is not the test most appropriate for their experimental problems. More often than

null hypothesis against a one-sided alternative.
   In the one-sided case we test H_0 against H_1, where

$$H_0 : \mu_1 - \mu_2 = 0$$
$$H_1 : \mu_1 - \mu_2 > 0.$$

Under the identical assumptions of the two-sided model we may calculate t as before. Again a confidence level, α, is stipulated. The distinction between the one-sided test and the two-sided test arises in the determination of the critical value, t_c. In the present case this critical value is found by entering the t table with $N_1 + N_2 - 2$ degrees of freedom, as before, but with a p-value equal to 2α. If our observed t is greater than this t_c we reject H_0 in favor of H_1; if t is less than t_c we accept H_0. The t distribution in Figure 2 exemplifies this procedure. A value of t

1. Of course, if the two samples are not independently selected, we should make use of the correlation between them in the determination of t.
2. R. A. Fisher and F. Yates, *Statistical Tables for Biological, Medical and Agricultural Research*, Edinburgh: Oliver and Boyd, 1938.

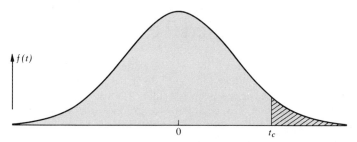

Fig. 2. The One-Tailed Test Model

to the right of t_c leads to the rejection of H_0, the acceptance of H_1. While the shaded area under the curve once again represents α per cent of the total area, the shaded portion is restricted, in this case, to one tail of the distribution.

It might be noted that with this formulation of the one-tailed test there is no allowance for the possibility that the true difference, $\mu_1 - \mu_2$, is negative. In the type of problem for which the one-tailed test is suited, such a negative mean difference is no more interesting than a zero difference. In fact, the hypotheses for the one-sided case might be

$$H_0 : \mu_1 - \mu_2 \leqq 0$$
$$H_1 : \mu_1 - \mu_2 > 0.$$

In order to determine a sampling distribution under H_0 we should consider the "worst" of the infinite alternatives under H_0, i.e., that alternative which would make the decision between H_0 and H_1 a most difficult one. Clearly, the decision would be more difficult if the true mean difference were zero than if the true difference were any negative value. Hence we would proceed exactly as in the preceding one-tailed case, utilizing, for our test, the distribution of t based upon the same sampling distribution of mean differences as

before. The confidence level should be doubled to provide the p-value for entering a table to find a critical t_c, òr, if it is desired to ascertain the p-value corresponding to an observed t, the correct value is one-half that given in the typical table of t.

While the one-tailed test has been exemplified here as a test of mean difference, based upon the t distribution, it is limited in application neither to mean difference problems nor to the t statistic. Indeed, wherever an alternative to the null hypothesis is stated in terms of the direction of expected results, the one-tailed test is applicable.

The failure, among psychologists, to utilize the one-tailed statistical test, where it is appropriate, very likely is due to the propagation of the two-tailed model by writers of text books in psychological statistics. It is typical, in such texts, to find little or no attention given to one-tailed tests.[3] Since the test of the null hypothesis against a one-sided alternative is the most powerful test for all directional hypotheses, it is strongly recommended that the one-tailed model be adopted wherever its use is appropriate.

3. One notable exception occurs in A. L. Edwards' *Experimental Design in Psychological Research*, where the two cases are clearly differentiated.

W. E. HICK

19 A Note on One-Tailed and Two-Tailed Tests

The following remarks were provoked by the recent paper by Marks[1] [Ch. 17 in this book] on this subject. Although the impracticability, in most cases, of deciding just what level of significance is "significant" makes it superfluous to fuss about minor inaccuracies, the difference between one-tailed and two-tailed tests can be serious. Moreover, the problem of which to use in a given case does give an appreciable amount of trouble to the research worker. It appears to me that the interpretation given by Marks errs on the unsafe side.

In the first place, it should be clearly understood—though Marks, perhaps inadvertently, implies the opposite—that it makes no difference *when* a theory or hypothesis is conceived, as far as its logical content and implications are concerned. Logic is timeless; it does not, and cannot, matter whether a theory was conceived before, during, or after the experiment; it may be suggested by the data, or it may be revealed in a dream. A hypothesis derived from the data may be expected to fit the data, more or less; but the statistical calculations are intended to show how well or how badly it does fit, and, in the vast majority of cases, to show this on the assumption that personal opinions and collateral evidence are set on one side.

This is quite separate from the subtraction of degrees of freedom when parameters of the chance hypothesis are calculated from the data. When we do this, we are not depending on the data to provide the chance hypothesis, but to tell us which of a certain family of such hypotheses will act as the most stringent

1. M. R. Marks, Two kinds of experiment distinguished in terms of statistical operations. *Psychol. Rev.*, 1951, 58, 179–184.

test. Ideally, we should choose the hypothesis which best fits the data, with the exception that it must have no preferential tendency to produce the effect in question—e.g., a deviation of the mean, or something of that kind. If we can exclude this chance hypothesis, then we can *a fortiori* exclude all others, since they are less likely. This is the step which requires us to deduct degrees of freedom, because it is only this step which gives us any appreciable amount of information from the data. To be able to reject one chance hypothesis tells us nothing, since there is an infinity of others; but to be able to reject a whole class really means something, and the data must pay.

However, though robbing the data in this way affects the statistical significance, it does not appear to have anything to do with the problem of one-tailed and two-tailed tests. To deal with this, we must first consider the statistical question asked—namely, "Could my results reasonably be due to chance, or must I assume that they were due to some cause or systematic bias?" Or, since the experimenter is not necessarily required to make up his mind on this point, he may go no further than the question, "What is the probability, on the chance hypothesis, of my results occurring?"

Now this, unfortunately, is just what the ordinary statistical methods fail to answer explicitly. As is well known, the probability of the particular sample depends, not only on the shape of the distribution, but also on the number of possible alternative samples. On the other hand the P of the ordinary significance test is, strictly speaking, a probability irrelevant to the question of whether the chance hypothesis should be rejected on

From *Psychological Review*, Vol. 59, pp. 316–18, 1952. Copyright © 1952 by the American Psychological Association, and reprinted by permission.

the grounds of unlikelihood. The best we can say of it is that it happens, in the ordinary cases, to be vaguely related to what we want to know.

If the reader doubts this, he has only to consider what "significance" he would attach to the occurrence of an observation in, say, a 5 per cent slice at the end of a rectangular distribution. Obviously such an event would not give us the least grounds for rejecting the hypothesis, and, in fact, there is no significance test, in the ordinary sense, for this distribution, except for the trivial case of an observation right outside it. This is almost a *reductio ad absurdum*, but it serves to emphasize that P, though it is a probability, is not the one which, by itself, makes us view the chance hypothesis with suspicion.

In the Neyman and Pearson theory of critical regions P has a definite place. But some statisticians think this theory approaches the problem from the wrong end. It is certainly difficult, and often impossible, to apply. If then we are compelled in practice to use some rough and ready method, which is the least rough and the most ready? It is clear that the actual sample probability is what matters, and it is possible to make some sense of it by dividing it by the probability of the most probable sample. This relative probability answers the question, "How much less likely are my results than what I should have expected on the chance hypothesis?" However, this also leads to absurdity in special cases, and we must admit that there is no easy method that is quite foolproof.

The essence of the ordinary P, correctly used, is that it is the class probability of a critical region composed solely of all the samples whose individual probabilities are below a certain critical level. The distribution may go up and down like a mountain range, but wherever the curve falls below this level, there is a piece of the critical region in that place. This is not the case, incidentally, for the tabular probabilities of Chi^2, which are only the probabilities of *exceeding* a given value. Marks states that these probabilities are for

two-tailed tests, but this is only true in the rather different sense that they refer indiscriminately to positive or negative discrepancies. But the Chi^2 distribution has a short tail as well as a long one, and both should properly be included in the critical region. As it is, we just have to remember that small values are "suspicious."

In attempting to justify the one-tailed test, Marks appears to regard as equivalent such states of mind as *knowing* that, say, a negative deviation cannot occur except by chance, not being interested if it does, guessing that a positive deviation will occur, and so on. What the experimenter is interested in has nothing to do with the case. What he guesses is relevant, if he can show that it is a rational guess and can assess it in terms of probability. What he knows for certain is still more important. If he knows that a negative bias is impossible, it means that no negative deviation, however great, will shake his faith in "pure chance" as the cause of it. If he is in as strong a position as that, of course he is entitled to put the whole critical region in the positive tail and call it a one-tailed test. What he is doing is to accept a more lenient degree of significance, though it is difficult to see why he should bother with this form of test at all; if the bias cannot be negative, there is little risk of it being exactly zero.

But suppose he is only moderately sure that the bias is positive; is he to do a one-and-a-half-tailed test, or something like that? By all means, if he can assess his prior knowledge in terms of fractions of a tail, except that it then follows that there are not just two kinds of experimentation, as Marks suggests, but one for every degree of prior expectancy.

It is far better to carry out the statistical work in the ordinary way, without tampering with the critical region, and let prior probability (or any other relevant consideration) determine what level of significance you will regard as decisive. You can still believe in a positive deviation more readily than a negative one, if you like; but you do not confuse the issue for others who may have different ideas.

MELVIN R. MARKS

20 One- and Two-Tailed Tests

Hick, in "A Note on One-Tailed and Two-Tailed Tests" (1) [Ch. 19 in this book], purports to vitiate the recommendations made by me in a recent paper (2) [Ch. 18 in this book]. I think a reply is indicated.

1. My paper was not intended to precipitate a controversy over the philosophical foundations of mathematical statistics. It *was* intended to show that, by taking advantage of available statistical techniques, the experimenter could increase the precision of his investigation by recognizing and minimizing the incidence of Type I and Type II errors. The paper was expository rather than argumentative, a restatement rather than a presentation *de novo*. All statements made therein relative to the testing of hypotheses have the acceptance of statisticians generally.

2. The experimenter's decision to adopt a particular level of confidence is not made with reference to statistical considerations. Such a decision depends entirely on the assessment of the likelihood of Type I and Type II errors and the practical importance to be attached to their occurrence. Thus, the propriety of the one- or two-tailed test depends only upon the nature of the hypothesis to be tested —not on the level of confidence adopted.

3. Although logic is timeless, the "personal equation" of the experimenter is not. The legitimate use of particular data for the test of a particular hypothesis *does* depend on why (the basis for), if not when, the hypothesis was formulated. Hick says, " . . . it does not and cannot matter whether a theory (read hypothesis) was conceived before, during, or after the experiment; it may be suggested by the data, or it may be revealed in a dream." Now this statement is true in *all* respects *if*

conclusions about the tenability of the hypothesis are to be restricted to the data at hand. But if these conclusions are to be extrapolated, we must strike the phrase, "it may be suggested by the data." For consider, with reference to any particular data, if the hypothesis is to proceed from the data, the best hypothesis is that the data are as they are. In such case, we might solemnly aver that they are as they are by definition, and never bother to test any hypothesis. We shall always be right, if only we select the hypothesis carefully enough—until the next time!

4. Hick challenges, at least implicitly, the Neyman and Pearson theory as it applies to critical regions. The pros and cons of such a controversy have no place in this discussion. However, it may be stated that, when the critical region selected is appropriate to the hypothesis being tested, then the level of confidence (by definition) is known exactly; and the probability that a Type II error will occur (false acceptance of the null hypothesis) is minimized.

5. Hick's remark on my treatment of the chi-square test has merit. Technically, the term "two-tailed," as applied to the chi-square distribution, refers to the actual tails of that distribution—i.e., the regions of exceptionally large and exceptionally small values of chi square. However, it is still legitimate to cut the level of confidence in half when we predict direction of frequency discordance. This is so because when we eliminate exactly half of the possible values of chi square (that half corresponding to frequency discordances in the unwanted direction), we also eliminate half of the Type I errors.

6. The same remarks apply, with some-

From *Psychological Review*, Vol. 60, No. 3, pp. 207–8, 1953. Copyright © 1953 by the American Psychological Association, and reprinted by permission.

what less force, to the indicated use of the F test. Bendig[1] has pointed out that only one tail of the F distribution is tabled—i.e., values of F equal to or greater than unity. When I discussed the increased precision which could be achieved by predicting the hierarchy of magnitude of the means, I was referring to the fact that, in the case of simple classification analysis of variance with only two columns (when $t^2 = F$), the number of Type I errors is cut in half when the negative values of t are eliminated beforehand. The number of Type I errors would be reduced still further in the case of

1. Personal communication.

more than two columns (variables) if the ordering of the means was predicted beforehand, although in such case power would suffer—i.e., the chances of committing a Type II error would increase since a slight inversion from the predicted order would necessitate rejection of the experimental hypothesis.

References

1. W. E. Hick, A note on one-tailed and two-tailed tests. *Psychol. Rev.*, 1952, 59, 316–318.
2. M. R. Marks, Two kinds of experiment distinguished in terms of statistical operations. *Psychol. Rev.*, 1951, 58, 179–184.

C. J. BURKE

21 A Brief Note on One-Tailed Tests

Concurrent with the recent discussions of one-tailed and two-tailed tests by Hick (4) [Ch. 19 in this book], Jones (5) [Ch. 18—page references to this chapter], and Marks (8) [Ch. 20], there has been a disturbing increase in the use of one-tailed tests in student experimental reports as well as in published and not-yet-published manuscripts. While the popularity of one-tailed tests is undoubtedly attributable in part to the overwillingness of psychologists as a group to make use of the statistical recommendations they have most recently read, there seems to be a certain residual of bad logic, so far as both statistics and psychology are concerned, which merits examination. The writer takes the position already taken by Hick (4) in all important essentials but the argument to be presented differs, at least in emphasis, from that of Hick. It should be noted that some tests, χ^2 and F for example, are naturally single-ended.

Nothing said here should be construed so as to apply to them.

Both Jones (5) and Marks (8) seem to the writer to confuse somewhat two quite different notions—that an experimental hypothesis is often directional and that an experimenter may be willing to accept a deviation of any size in the unexpected direction as consonant with the null hypothesis. We shall consider two quotations from Jones.

The model above, the test of the null hypothesis against two-sided alternatives, is the one used most often by investigators in psychology. Yet in many cases ... it is not the test most appropriate for their experimental problems. More often than not, in psychological research, our hypotheses have a *directional* character ... theoretical considerations allow the postulation of the direction of experimental effects. The appropriate experimental test is one which takes this into account, a test of the null hypothesis against a one-sided alternative [18, p. 194].

From *Psychological Bulletin*, Vol. 50, No. 5, pp. 384–87, 1953. Copyright © 1953 by the American Psychological Association, and reprinted by permission.

It is a fact that many hypotheses in psychological research, experimentally conceived, are directional for the investigator conducting the experiment, but it does not follow from this that one-sided tests should be used in experimental reports.

To amplify these considerations we point out that there are, in many experiments, two statistical decisions to be made and two different levels of confidence may be involved. The first is the decision made by the individual experimenter who frequently plans one experiment from his evaluation of a previous one. We concede that here a one-tailed test is often proper. The second is the decision which determines the place of his findings in the literature of psychology. Here the one-tailed test seems inadmissible. It is the second type of decision with which we are concerned. Marks (8) has in essence repeated from statistical sources a discussion of the Type I and Type II errors which shows that the decisions made in any statistical interpretation depend only upon the underlying populations and the rule of procedure used. Any comparison of alternative rules of procedure must take into account errors of both types, the error of rejecting a hypothesis when it is true and the error of failing to reject it when it is false, but the underlying statistical considerations do not provide automatically a criterion for the selection of one rule over another. Such a criterion is to be sought in the number and kinds of errors the experimenter will tolerate. Roughly, an acceptable criterion is to make the over-all number of errors as small as possible and at the same time to render large and serious errors relatively impossible. Within the class of hypotheses which are considered to be directional it is likely that a one-tailed test might yield a smaller over-all number of errors than a two-tailed test, but there is, under the single-tailed rule, no safeguard whatsoever against occasional large and serious errors when the difference is in the unexpected direction. If one is less willing to commit a large error than to commit a small one, it does not follow from the theory of testing statistical

hypotheses that the experimenter's expectation of a given direction for the result necessarily makes the one-tailed test desirable.

To advance this point in our case against the use of the one-tailed test in the public report, we next take up the second quotation from Jones.

It might be noted that with this formulation of the one-tailed test there is no allowance for the possibility that the true difference . . . is negative. In the type of problem for which the one-tailed test is suited, such a negative mean difference is no more interesting than a zero difference [5, p. 272].

This statement is perfectly correct.[1] If we consider it carefully we discover its import to be that the investigator should use a one-tailed test when he is willing to accept a difference in the unexpected direction, *no matter how large*, as consonant with the hypothesis of zero difference. This is quite a different matter from using a one-tailed test whenever the direction of the difference is predicted, on some grounds or other, in advance. It is to be doubted whether experimental psychology, in its present state, can afford such lofty indifference toward experimental surprises.

The questions raised by the one-tailed test are to be answered finally by considering the effect of general use of this procedure on the content of psychological literature. The writer cannot agree with Hick (4) that its use makes little difference since there is no practical rule for deciding what "significance" really is. In some super-scientific world this point might be well taken, but there is evidence that in our workaday world (where we sometimes read only the concluding sections of reports) it does make a difference whether the investigator has stated that his results were significant. The controversy over the Blodgett effect is a case in point (1, 2, 6, 7, 9, 10, 11, 12).

Remembering that the problem of testing a statistical hypothesis is a statistical problem in which each individual experiment is viewed

1. In his subsequent discussion, Jones spoils the force of this point by confusing hypotheses to be tested with classes of hypotheses to be guarded against as alternatives.

only as a member of a class of similar experiments and recalling that the properties of any statistical test are determined solely by the procedure followed and by the populations underlying the class, it is pertinent to inquire into the effects of widespread adoption of one-tailed tests upon the literature. The writer believes the following statements to be reasonable forecasts.

1. The discovery of new psychological phenomena will be hindered. Our literature abounds with instances in which the outcome of a given experiment has differed reliably and sharply from expectation. These experiments are usually of great interest—new psychological concepts arise from them. Our science is not yet so mature that these can be expected to occur infrequently. The most recent instance, known to the writer, of conflicting results from experiments thought to be highly similar was reported by Underwood (13) at the 1952 meetings of the American Psychological Association. From any careful examination of contemporary psychological literature we must conclude that nowhere in the field can we have sufficient a priori confidence in the outcome of any genuinely new experiment to justify the neglect of differences in the unexpected direction.

2. There will be an increase in barren controversy. Fruitless controversies arise from unreliable results. Conclusions at low levels of confidence tend to be unreliable, and the adoption of one-tailed tests is equivalent to a general lowering of levels of confidence. At a time of severe journal overload this is especially pernicious. There is no substitute in statistical methodology for the carefully designed and controlled experiment in which any important difference between groups will show up at a high enough level of confidence to insure a certain reliability in the conclusion.

3. Abuses will be rampant. It is no criticism of the position held on statistical grounds by Jones and Marks to point out that the considerations involved in the choice of a one-tailed test are really rather delicate. A nice instance of what can happen is seen in an experimental report by Gwinn (3). Gwinn reports two experiments which are not markedly different from each other. They turn out in opposite directions, and, by appropriate selection of the position of his "critical tail," Gwinn establishes significance and near significance (1 per cent and 8 per cent levels, approximately) for his results on the basis of one-tailed tests.

The moral can be pointed with advice. We counsel anyone who contemplates a one-tailed test to ask of himself (before the data are gathered): "If my results are in the wrong direction and significant at the one-billionth of 1 per cent level, can I publicly defend the proposition that this is evidence of no difference?" If the answer is affirmative we shall not impugn his accuracy in choosing a one-tailed test. We may, however, question his scientific wisdom.

References

1. Blodgett, H. C. The effect of the introduction of a reward upon maze performance of rats. *Univer. Calif. Publ. Psychol.*, 1929, 4, 113–134.
2. Blodgett, H. C. Reynolds' repetition of Blodgett's experiment on "latent" learning. *J. exp. Psychol.*, 1946, 36, 184–186.
3. Gwinn, G. T. Resistance to extinction of learned fear drives. *J. exp. Psychol.*, 1951, 42, 6–12.
4. Hick, W. E. A note on one-tailed and two-tailed tests. *Psychol. Rev.*, 1952, 59, 316–318.
5. Jones, L. V. Tests of hypotheses: one-sided vs. two-sided alternatives. *Psychol. Bull.*, 1952, 49, 43–46.
6. Kendler, H. H. Some comments on Thistlethwaite's perception of latent learning. *Psychol. Bull.*, 1952, 49, 47–51.
7. Maltzman, I. The Blodgett and Haney types of latent learning experiment: reply to Thistlethwaite. *Psychol. Bull.*, 1952, 49, 52–60.
8. Marks, M. R. Two kinds of experiment distinguished in terms of statistical operations. *Psychol. Rev.*, 1951, 58, 179–184.
9. Meehl, P. E., & MacCorquodale, K. A failure to find the Blodgett effect and some secondary observations on drive conditioning. *J. comp. physiol. Psychol.*, 1951, 44, 178–183.
10. Reynolds, B. A repetition of the Blodgett experiment on "latent" learning. *J. exp. Psychol.*, 1945, 35, 504–516.

11. Thistlethwaite, D. A critical review of latent learning and related experiments. *Psychol. Bull.*, 1951, 48, 97–129.

12. Thistlethwaite, D. Reply to Kendler and Maltzman. *Psychol. Bull.*, 1952, 49, 61–71.

13. Underwood, B. J. The learning and retention of serial nonsense lists as a function of distributed practice and intralist similarity. Paper read at Amer. Psychol. Ass., Washington, D. C., September, 1952.

LYLE V. JONES

22 A Rejoinder on One-Tailed Tests

In a recent issue of this journal, Burke (1) [Ch. 21 in this book] criticizes earlier discussions of one-tailed and two-tailed tests (3, 4, 5) [Ch. 19, Ch. 18, Ch. 17], and suggests need for caution in the application of one-tailed statistical tests to psychological research designs. The writer is in accord with several implications of Burke's note. As is true for most statistical designs, abuses would be reduced markedly were the test model completely specified and justified in terms of the purpose of investigation, before data are viewed by the investigator. To be guided by the data in the specification of hypotheses and statistical tests is a grave breach of the rules of experimental verification (cf. 6) [Ch. 20].

The argument presented by Burke, however, is more than a plea for careful consideration of the choice of test models for given experimental problems. It is stated that the selection of a one-tailed test model requires that an investigator be willing to "publicly defend the proposition ... of no difference" if results actually show a large difference in the direction opposite to that predicted (21, p. 201). The proposition appears indefensible, since it demands arguing that a particular observed difference, no matter how large, is only a sampling departure from zero. If accepted, Burke's argument should lead to universal avoidance of one-tailed tests.

Consider the following experimental problems, selected for simplicity as single variable designs: *a*) On the basis of a certain behavioral theory, we might predict that an experimental condition imposed upon subjects in the population under study would raise the mean level of performance on a given task. The theory provides a prediction (an alternative hypothesis) that the mean for the experimental group population will exceed the mean for the control group population. The hypothesis under test is that the mean for the experimental population is the same as or less than that for the control population. We should like a statistical test that will yield a decision: either the data are consistent with the hypothesis under test, or we reject the hypothesis in favor of the alternative. *b*) In a field of applied psychology a new diagnostic technique is developed and is to be adopted if, and only if, we are confident that it is better than the current technique which would be replaced. Assuming the availability of a suitable criterion, the two techniques are applied to comparable samples or to the same sample; interest resides in the extent to which the parametric proportion of successful predictions using the new technique exceeds that using the old. A statistical test is to supply a decision: either the new technique is no more adequate than the old, or the new technique is more adequate.

From *Psychological Bulletin*, Vol. 51, No. 6, pp. 585–86, 1954. Copyright © 1954 by the American Psychological Association, and reprinted by permission.

For the class of problems illustrated by these two examples, the hypothesis under test is not simply one of no difference. We wish to test the hypothesis that the algebraic difference between parametric mean performance under experimental and control conditions is zero *or negative* against the alternative hypothesis that the difference is positive. It is meant to stress this formulation of the one-tailed statistical test with the greatest possible emphasis. With this formulation, it is apparent that acceptance of the hypothesis under test does not demand defense of a proposition of no difference: the observed difference, whether negative, zero, or slightly positive, simply does not allow acceptance of the alternative hypothesis at the level of stringency (values of α and β) chosen for the test.

In a footnote, Burke (1) [p. 200] criticizes this formulation as it appeared earlier (4) [p. 202] on the grounds that it confuses hypotheses to be tested with hypotheses to be guarded against as alternatives. To the contrary, this statement of the problem clarifies the nature of the hypothesis under test. The hypothesis to be tested is[1]

$$H_0 : \mu_e - \mu_c \leqq 0,$$

where μ_e is the population mean for the experimental condition, μ_c is the population mean for the control condition, and the experimental prediction yields an alternative hypothesis,

$$H_1 : \mu_e - \mu_c > 0.$$

Burke's primary argument seems to rest upon the contention that "there is, under the single-tailed rule, no safeguard whatsoever against occasional large and serious errors when the difference is in the unexpected direction" (1) [p. 200]. Our formulation of the

1. An equivalent formulation of the one-tailed test model, of which the writer was unaware at the time of his earlier note, is that proposed by Dixon and Massey (2, pp. 100–104).

hypothesis under test completely resolves this difficulty, for no error is committed when that hypothesis is accepted on the basis of a large observed difference in the unexpected direction. The event is one of a class of events consistent with the hypothesis tested.

If one were to retain the alternative hypothesis, H_1, above, and to adopt a two-tailed statistical test, accepting H_1 when there were observed large differences between the means *in either direction*, his position would be unenviable. For, following the rules of his test, he would have to reject the hypothesis under test in favor of the alternative, even though an observed difference, $\mu_e - \mu_c$, was a substantial negative value.

The remaining discussion by Burke consists of pragmatic arguments against the adoption of one-tailed tests. The arguments appear valid only under the assumption that every application of the one-tailed test is an abuse of experimental methodology. Certainly, if (*a*) the test model is specified completely (including specification of the confidence level to be adopted) before the data are gathered, and if (*b*) the purpose of the test is only to determine whether a particular directional prediction is supported by the data, then the one-tailed test not only is appropriate, but it is in error to use a two-tailed test model.

References

1. Burke, C. J. A brief note on one-tailed tests. *Psychol. Bull.*, 1953, 50, 384–387.
2. Dixon, W. J., & Massey, F. J., Jr. *Introduction to statistical analysis.* New York: McGraw-Hill, 1951.
3. Hick, W. E. A note on one-tailed and two-tailed tests. *Psychol. Rev.*, 1952, 59, 316–318.
4. Jones, L. V. Tests of hypotheses: one-sided vs. two-sided alternatives. *Psychol. Bull.*, 1952, 49, 43–46.
5. Marks, M. R. Two kinds of experiment distinguished in terms of statistical operations. *Psychol. Rev.*, 1951, 58, 179–184.
6. Marks, M. R. One- and two-tailed tests. *Psychol. Rev.*, 1953, 60, 207–208.

C. J. BURKE

23 Further Remarks on One-Tailed Tests[1]

In the discussion of one-tailed tests there are a number of issues which have not been clearly separated. An effort will here be made to separate them.

Two Types of Models

Psychologists have used two different types of models in interpreting their data: statistical models and specifically psychological models. The two types have been employed in different ways and for entirely different purposes. Statistical models have been used to determine whether data are intrinsically interesting or, in other words, whether the data indicate relationships between psychological variables. Psychological models have been utilized in attempts to organize the knowledge attained in various areas of the field.

Early uses of statistical methods mixed the psychological and statistical models. The substantive biases of the experimenter led him to seek out, with each set of data, those statistical techniques which supported his views and to neglect the techniques which did not. Gradually, it was recognized that the function of the statistical model was prior to and separate from the function of the substantive model. Cognizant of the fallibility of their data and the greater fallibility of their theories, psychologists developed the view that data should be interpreted without the intrusion of the biases, however well founded, of the experimenter, and accordingly accepted certain statistical procedures as conventions. The advocates of one-tailed tests would take us a large step backward, for they openly

1. The writer thanks his colleagues, A. M. Binder and W. K. Estes, for their suggestions after reading an earlier draft of this reply.

favor the mixing of the statistical and substantive models.

Any psychological theory worth bothering with will generate a number of predictions which can be directly checked against experimental data. Such direct determination of the consistency of data with the model is the only proper test of a psychological theory. In a check of this kind, there is a point by point verification of the theory, and strictly speaking, no statistical model is necessary, This does not mean that there should be no statistical interpretation of the data; it is usually wise to make the ordinary statistical interpretation prior to the theoretical check—to determine whether the data show enough to warrant a theoretical analysis. If, in any given experiment, a theory provides only a directional prediction, there seems to be nothing wrong with our traditional procedure of first establishing the presence of a difference between groups and subsequently noting its direction. A statistical model should enter directly into the verification of a substantive theory only when it is based on a null hypothesis with respect to the residuals of the data from theoretical predictions.

A statistical model can be viewed as a technique for assessing the reliability of an experiment without repeating it. The question answered by a statistical test is whether or not the sample obtained is a member of a certain class of samples. This class is usually defined by the null hypothesis to be tested and by the conditions under which the experiment would be repeated, if repetition were undertaken; frequently certain supplementary parametric assumptions must be made. Since an experiment can be repeated without any appeal to a body of substantive theory, no

From *Psychological Bulletin*, Vol. 51, No. 6, pp. 587–90, 1954. Copyright © 1954 by the American Psychological Association, and reprinted by permission.

such appeal need ever be made for the purposes of statistical analysis. Experiments are often designed from theoretical consideration, and the conditions of repetition may, therefore, be dictated by a substantive model. In some analysis of variance designs there may be freedom in the choice of an error term. This freedom indicates that the single experiment which has been performed, even in conjunction with a null hypothesis, does not define a unique class of repetitions. When this is the case, appeal to substantive theory may lead to the choice of a proper error term, and this appeal may seem to involve a direct intrusion of substantive theory upon the statistical interpretation. As we have put the matter, however, it is readily seen that in this instance the theory does no more than define the conditions under which the experiment would be repeated.

The One-Tailed Test in Theoretical Statistics

Properly described, the concept of a one-tailed test is clear and free from any objection on mathematical grounds. There is no disagreement on this point. Disagreement on what constitutes a proper description of a one-tailed test centers specifically on the nature of the hypothesis that is tested. Jones has emphasized his conviction that the hypothesis of a nonpositive difference is tested against the alternative of a positive difference. I have stated that a null hypothesis is tested with safeguards against only a subset of the possible alternatives.

As it now stands, the mathematical theory of testing statistical hypotheses requires that the hypothesis under test lead to the calculation of a level of confidence. (Until the onslaught of the one-tailers, books in psychological statistics cautioned us to test only "exact" hypotheses.) If we ask Jones to exhibit his calculation of the level of confidence in a one-tailed test, we shall probably discover that he bases the calculation on the distribution obtained under the null hypothesis. Then,

according to the usual statistical logic, he is in fact testing the null-hypothesis against selected alternatives. The comments of my earlier note were made within this framework.

An easy modification of statistical logic can make the one-tailed test of a nonpositive difference tenable. Since the probability that he rejects the hypothesis of a nonpositive difference when it is true can, in his procedure, never exceed the level of confidence calculated under the null hypothesis, Jones can declare that he has a bound on his level of confidence even though he does not know its precise value. Utilizing this bound, he can set up consistent rules for one-tailed interpretation of the hypothesis he has stated.

The two paragraphs above present what seem to be the only two positions open to Jones. Whichever he accepts, I am in complete accord with him so far as mathematical statistics goes, for both are clear and statistically defensible. Yet his succinct assertion that I advocate universal avoidance of one-tailed tests is correct. The locus of disagreement is to be found in practice, not in theory.

Applied Problems

In applied problems like Jones's example of the drugs, it is often true that certain practices or routines will be changed if, and only if, an experiment yields a reliable difference *in a specified direction*—if the new is reliably better than the old. For problems like this, Jones maintains that the two-tailed test is inappropriate. Verbally his argument proceeds well, but before we accept it, let us note that problems of this kind have never given any difficulty—we have always understood what we did and why. Let Jones use his one-tailed test at the 5 per cent confidence level to analyze data from a large number of such experiments. We shall analyze the same data using a two-tailed test of the null hypothesis but permitting ourselves a luxuriously loose 10 per cent confidence level. Being sensible men, we shall not advocate a change to the new routine if the old one proves reliably superior. Unless we wish to differentiate a null from a negative difference (we might, for example, consider a replication necessary unless the null hypothesis were rejected), the two procedures will obviously lead to the same recommendations with every set of data. Thus, they have identical consequences for the immediate practical decision.

For myself, I do not much care whether one uses a one-tailed or two-tailed model in such applications. Since the choice of a level of confidence is arbitrary and since identical decisions will always be made, we have complete equivalence between the one-tailed model and a doubled level of confidence in our traditional procedure. It would be wrong for either Jones or me to pretend that compelling reasons exist for preferring one of these ways of talking about applied experiments over the other. Any appeal to the risks of the two kinds of errors is little more than an uninteresting parlor game. Since no gain results, there seems to be insufficient reason for changing the traditional two-tailed interpretation, but this is not a very strong objection. In my earlier note, I conceded the admissibility of the one-tailed test for the experimenter's own laboratory planning; I am quite willing to add the applied experiment to the list.

The Public Literature

There do seem to be compelling reasons why the use of one-tailed tests in our permanent reports must be rejected. These reasons are of two kinds: one kind residing in the nature of the scientific enterprise and the functions of the experimental literature, and the other associated with the debasing effect upon the literature that is almost certain to result from adopting one-tailed tests.

Experimental scientists must have for data a permanent respect that transcends their passing interest in the stories they make up about their data. Science is a public enterprise. These are statements to which most experi-

mental scientists would subscribe. One-tailed tests violate both the spirit and the letter of these statements. Interest in whether a relationship is found between two variables in a given experiment is seldom confined to those who share the theoretical preconceptions of the experimenter, and the right to discuss experimental data in relation to a particular theory does not remove the obligation to interpret the experiment according to rules that can be accepted by the reader who rejects your views as well as by the reader who shares them. Our experience has shown that experimental results can be viable for years after they are first reported even when the experiments are designed on the basis of moribund theoretical considerations. Let us consider our obligation to future psychologists who might not be able to understand why we were so naive in 1954 as to predict *that* direction for our experimental results. Why should we put needless difficulties in the way of any reader, present or future?

Why, particularly, when the change over to one-tailed test is almost certain to gain nothing and lose much? Jones asserts that my dire forecasts on the effects of one-tailed tests on our literature are predicated on the assumption that every one-tailed test is a misuse. Here he has missed the fundamental point of my argument. As in applied experiments, there is pragmatic equivalence between using the one-tailed test and doubling the level of confidence in the two-tailed test, for if the discrepancy is in the expected direction, the power of these two tests is identical, and experiments should be, and usually are, set up with power as a foremost consideration.

Most psychologists would resist the general adoption of the 10 per cent level for rejecting hypotheses. Such a low level of aspiration would lead to a decreased number of subjects per experiment and thus accomplish a gradual attrition in the soundness of our reported conclusions. This is precisely what will happen if there is general, and editorial, acceptance of the one-tailed test.

Concluding Remarks

A diminution in the quality of our psychological literature may be of little moment to the theoretical statistician but must be of grave concern to the experimental psychologist. Once they have the assurance of the mathematical statistician that the procedure is logically defensible, experimenters seem so eager to employ one-tailed tests that, sociologically speaking, I have lost the argument almost before it has been joined. Of course, the procedure is mathematically sound, but psychologists are mistaken if they believe the mathematical statistician can speak with special authority in the matter. The decision is for use alone; it is for us to ponder whether, in the interpretation of our data, the one-tailed test is wise. We are drifting into an unfortunate decision, and I, for one, wish to enter a plea for a little less methodology and a little more wisdom. We expound a distinction between experimental hypotheses and statistical hypotheses to our beginning students; let us maintain the distinction for ourselves.

HERBERT D. KIMMEL

24 Three Criteria for the Use of One-Tailed Tests

Examination of the recent literature on the question of when to use one-tailed tests of significance in psychological research reveals a state of unresolved disagreement. A variety of differing opinions (1 [Ch. 21], 2 [Ch. 23], 5 [Ch. 19], 7 [Ch. 18], 8 [Ch. 22], 9 [Ch. 17], 10, pp. 62–63) have been presented, ranging from Burke's (2) exhortation that psychologists should never report one-tailed tests in the public literature to Jones' (8) statement that we may not only do so, but, in certain instances, we will be in error if we fail to do so.

It is by no means necessary for psychologists to agree on all matters of importance to them. Disagreement regarding methodological considerations, however, especially when they bear on how and when propositions shall be accepted as true or rejected as false, should not be permitted to persist indefinitely. The argument is not settled by noting, as Burke (2) does, that the increased use of one-tailed tests may result in the one-tailers scoring a sociological victory almost before the controversy has begun. Actually, this observation by Burke does not coincide completely with the fact that many responsible investigators have continued to employ two-tailed tests (in situations calling for one-tailed tests according to Jones' view) long after the opening of the one-tailed avenue.[1]

1. An example of an experiment with an explicit directional hypothesis, but employing a two-tailed test, is reported by Davitz (3). This experimenter reasoned that the injection of tetraethylammonium prior to extinction trials would inhibit the punishing effect of the emotional response under study and, consequently, would result in faster extinction in the experimental animals than in a placebo-injected control group. Instead, Davitz found that the experimental group extinguished slower than the control group, the difference in mean number of trials being significant at the 5 per cent level using a two-tailed test. A one-tailed hypothesis in this experiment (as would have been urged by Jones) would have made it impossible to evaluate the significance of the obtained

From *Psychological Bulletin*, Vol. 54, No. 4, pp. 351–53. Copyright © 1957 by the American Psychological Association, and reprinted by permission.

In attempting to arrive at a set of acceptable criteria for the use of one-tailed tests, it is important to note that the argument is not one of mathematical statistics but primarily one of experimental logic. Burke and Jones would agree that one-tailed tests should be used to test one-tailed hypotheses; their disagreement concerns when one-tailed hypotheses should and should not be made.

Before proceeding to the proposed criteria, it would be of value to consider the difference between one- and two-tailed hypotheses from a view-point that has not been stressed by previous writers. All concerned agree that a given mean difference in the hypothesized direction is "more significant"[2] under a one-tailed hypothesis (in the correct direction) than under a two-tailed hypothesis. This is due to the fact that there are exactly twice as many chances of committing a type 1 error, with a given mean difference, under a two-tailed hypothesis. The important consideration is that this gain does not accrue without concomitant loss. Even psychology has its law of conservation of energy.

The price that is paid in return for the increased power of one-tailed tests over two-tailed tests stems from the fact that two-tailed null hypotheses are actually more specific than their one-tailed counterparts. A two-tailed null hypothesis can be rejected by a large observed difference in either direction but a one-tailed null hypothesis cannot be rejected by a difference in the unpredicted direction, no matter how large this difference may be. This means that an experimenter using a one-tailed hypothesis *cannot* conclude that an extreme difference in the unpredicted

direction is reliably different from zero difference. This limitation cannot be shrugged off by the comment, "We have no interest in a difference in the opposite direction." Scientists are interested in empirical fact regardless of its relationship to their preconceptions.

The meaning of this limitation is exemplified even in applied studies; e.g., those intended to answer the question whether a new product is "better" than the current product. It would be desirable to be able to conclude that the new product is not only "not better" (which is all that failure to reject a one-tailed null hypothesis permits[3]), but, in fact, "poorer." The decision not to market the proposed new product would follow from either conclusion, it is true, but the additional information available as a result of rejecting a two-tailed null hypothesis from the unexpected side could very well indicate a course of behavior quite different from that indicated by the mere inability to reject a specific one-tailed null hypothesis.

It is hoped that the following criteria will be acceptable to psychological investigators as a group and will be adopted conventionally as a guide. The ultimate consequence of our present state of ambiguity on this matter can only be confusion and subsequent retrogression to a more primitive level of scientific communication and understanding.

Criteria for the Use of One-Tailed Tests

1. Use a one-tailed test when a difference in the unpredicted direction, while possible, would be psychologically meaningless. An example of this situation might be found in the comparison of experimental and control groups on a skilled task for which only the experimental group has received appropriate training. The experiment would have to be

difference. A study by Hilgard et al. (6), on the other hand, stated a one-tailed hypothesis in a situation in which a difference in the unpredicted direction could have been predicted with as much justification on the basis of previous work. They obtained a difference in their predicted direction that was significant at the 5 per cent level using a one-tailed test. Their rejection of the null hypothesis on the basis of the difference they obtained is the equivalent of loosening the conventional 5 and 1 per cent standards.

2. That is to say, by chance, the unidirectional event is half as probable as the bidirectional; thus its occurrence, being half as likely, is twice as significant.

3. As Fisher (4) has pointed out, an experimenter never "accepts" the null hypothesis, he merely fails to reject it on the basis of his data. This is one reason why the null hypothesis in a particular experiment should be stated as specifically as possible.

designed in such a way as to eliminate all known conditions that could produce opposite results (e.g., not testing immediately after training to avoid fatigue effects, not testing too long after training to avoid memory loss effects, etc.). Since a difference in the unpredicted direction will have been declared beforehand to have no possible meaning (in terms of previous data and present operations) one-tailed hypotheses could not undergo metamorphosis into two-tailed hypotheses to permit testing the significance of differences in the unpredicted direction.

2. Use a one-tailed test when results in the unpredicted direction will, under no conditions, be used to determine a course of behavior different in any way from that determined by no difference at all. This situation is exemplified by the applied study discussed above, in which a new product is compared with one already on the market.

3. Use a one-tailed test when a directional hypothesis is deducible from psychological theory but results in the opposite direction are not deducible from coexisting psychological theory. If results in the opposite direction are explainable in terms of the constructs of existing theory, no matter how divergent from the experimenter's theoretical orientation this theory may be, the statistical hypothesis must be stated in a way that permits evaluation of opposite results. If this criterion were not already implicitly accepted by psychologists, crucial experiments could never be performed.

It should be apparent that the three criteria stated above are actually slightly differing reflections of the same underlying precept. Neither the ethical nor the logical decisions of individual scientists can be prescribed before-hand by any set of standards, no matter how all-pervasive these standards may seem at a given moment. The three criteria proposed above, however, are offered as temporary guideposts until such time as a new set of temporary criteria supersede them. Proponents of one-tailed tests, such as Jones (7, 8), cannot complain that the use of these criteria will reduce the number of one-tailed tests to near zero, without admitting that these tests have been misused in the past. Opponents of one-tailed tests, such as Burke (1, 2), should welcome this attempt to limit the use of one-tailed tests to those infrequent situations provided for by the proposed criteria.

References

1. Burke, C. J. A brief note on one-tailed tests. *Psychol. Bull.*, 1953, 50, 384–387.
2. Burke, C. J. Further remarks on one-tailed tests. *Psychol. Bull.*, 1954, 51, 587–590.
3. Davitz, J. R. Decreased autonomic functioning and extinction of a conditioned emotional response. *J. comp. physiol. Psychol.*, 1953, 46, 311–313.
4. Fisher, R. A. *The design of experiments.* London: Oliver and Boyd, 1947.
5. Hick, W. E. A note on one-tailed and two-tailed tests. *Psychol. Rev.*, 1952, 59, 316–318.
6. Hilgard, E. R., Jones, L. V., & Kaplan, S. J. Conditioned discrimination as related to anxiety. *J. exp. Psychol.*, 1951, 42, 94–99.
7. Jones, L. V. Tests of hypotheses: One-sided vs. two-sided alternatives. *Psychol. Bull.*, 1952, 49, 43–46.
8. Jones, L. V. A rejoinder on one-tailed tests. *Psychol. Bull.*, 1954, 51, 585–586.
9. Marks, M. R. Two kinds of experiment distinguished in terms of statistical operations. *Psychol. Rev.*, 1951, 58, 179–184.
10. McNemar, Q. *Psychological statistics.* New York: Wiley, 1955.

MARVIN R. GOLDFRIED

25 One-Tailed Tests and "Unexpected" Results[1]

There has been much controversy (1 [Ch. 21], 2 [Ch. 23], 4 [Ch. 19], 5 [Ch. 18], 6 [Ch. 22], 8 [Ch. 17], 9 [Ch. 20]) regarding the use of the one-tailed test of significance. The important question debated is not *if* it should be used, but rather *when* it should be used. Kimmel (7) has recently attempted to resolve the controversy by suggesting criteria for the use of one-tailed tests. He maintains that one-tailed tests may be used when results in the opposite direction: *a*) will not be used to determine any new course of behavior, *b*) will be psychologically meaningless, or *c*) cannot be deduced by any psychological theory, while an outcome in the expected direction can. It is these last two instances that will be dealt with in this paper.

When an experimenter uses a one-tailed test and finds that his results are in disagreement with his prediction (i.e., if they are in the opposite direction and would have been statistically significant had a two-tailed test been used), he can do one of several things. One course of action is simply to ignore these findings. In practical problems (e.g., deciding whether or not to introduce new machinery for production), this approach, which is consistent with Kimmel's first criterion, is quite acceptable. With regard to this practice in psychology, on the other hand, Burke has quite correctly pointed out that "It is to be doubted whether experimental psychology, in its present state, can afford such lofty indifference toward experimental surprises" [Ch. 21, p. 200]. Because an outcome is not deducible from any *existing* theory does not mean that it could not be deduced from

future theories. The implicit assumption in this practice is that no new theoretical approaches will be advanced in the future, and that the task of psychology as a science is to confirm the presently existing theories. A similar criticism might be made of Kimmel's criterion of unpredicted differences being "psychologically meaningless." He defines the "possible meaning" of a difference in the unpredicted direction " . . . in terms of previous data and present conditions" [Ch. 24, p. 209]. Whether or not it is "possible" for a given proposition to have meaning, however, depends upon whether or not it is capable of confirmation (3). It seems that what Kimmel is referring to when he speaks of the "possible meaning" of a given outcome is actually the degree to which a proposition regarding this outcome (i.e., one that states that such an event does not fit into an existing psychological theory) has been confirmed. Thus, since "psychological meaningfulness" in this sense will change as our knowledge increases, criticisms made of the criterion of theoretical predictability apply here as well.

The experimenter might, on the other hand, wish to take cognizance of his unexpected findings. To do so, however, he must adopt the procedure of changing his original null hypothesis. Instead of testing the hypothesis that $\mu_1 \le \mu_2$ (one-tailed), he might test the hypothesis that $\mu_1 = \mu_2$ (two-tailed).[2] However, if this practice is adopted, there will be an *increase* in the probability of making a Type I error. This results from the combination of the

---

1. The writer is greatly indebted to K. H. Kurtz for his critical evaluation of this paper.

2. Some experimenters might make the even greater change in their null hypothesis by testing $\mu_1 \ge \mu_2$ (one-tailed, but in the opposite direction).

From *Psychological Review*, Vol. 66, No. 1, pp. 79–80, 1959. Copyright © 1959 by the American Psychological Association, and reprinted by permission.

probability of committing a Type I error when using the original null hypothesis with the probability associated with the new null hypothesis. For example, suppose one has adopted the .05 level of significance when using a one-tailed test; the probability of making a Type I error is thus .05 (the probability associated with the critical region in the given tail). If the null hypothesis is changed to account for the difference which is statistically significant in the opposite direction, what is actually being used now is a two-tailed test. Was this to be used originally (i.e., before the study was conducted), the probability of the experimenter committing a Type I error would be .05 (.025 being associated with the critical point in each direction). Since this null hypothesis has been adopted after the decision had been made to use a one-tailed test (with its associated probability of making this error), the probability of this researcher committing a Type I error is now .075 (i.e., .05 when $H_0 : \mu_1 \leq \mu_2$ plus .025 related to the "unexpected" direction when $H_0 : \mu_1 = \mu_2$). It should also be noted that even an experimenter who believes he has the option to use such a procedure is operating under the .075 level of significance—whether or not he has occasion to test a difference in the "unexpected" direction. Thus, whether he knows it or not, such an investigator is using a two-tailed test with one tail twice as large as the other.

Another possible course of action would be to repeat the experiment, now using a two-tailed test. Assuming that the errors of measurement are not significantly greater in this replication and this experimenter obtains the same results, he may now conclude that his findings in the previously unexpected direction are significant. Thus, the decision to use a one-tailed test may result in the necessity of repeating the study if results appear in the opposite direction.

The above considerations indicate that the criteria of theoretical predictability and psychological meaninglessness are not as decisive

as they may appear to be. Three possible courses of action available when results occur in the unpredicted direction each present difficulties.[3] *Ignoring* differences in the "unexpected" direction leads to the omission of findings which may have important theoretical significance, and thus stifles any fresh theoretical thinking that might have otherwise emerged. If the differences *are* recognized by switching to a two-tailed test within a given study, psychology as a science may unwittingly be led to operate under conclusions with a lower level of statistical significance. The third approach, repeating the experiment and applying a two-tailed test to this new set of data, might be undesirable in terms of the time, expense, etc, that would be involved. The decision to use a one-tailed test should thus be made in light of the difficulties with which the investigator is confronted when the results occur in the "unexpected" direction.

References

1. Burke, C. J. A brief note on one-tailed tests. *Psychol. Bull.*, 1953, 50, 384–387.
2. Burke, C. J. Further remarks on one-tailed tests. *Psychol. Bull.*, 1954, 51, 587–590.
3. Carnap, R. The two concepts of probability. In H. Feigl & M. Brodbeck (Eds.), *Readings in the philosophy of sicence*. New York: Appleton-Century-Crofts, 1953. Pp. 438–455.
4. Hick, W. E. A note on one-tailed and two-tailed tests. *Psychol. Rev.*, 1952, 59, 316–318.
5. Jones, L. V. Tests of hypotheses: One-sided vs. two-sided alternatives. *Psychol. Bull.*, 1952, 49, 43–46.
6. Jones, L. V. A rejoinder on one-tailed tests. *Psychol. Bull.*, 1954, 51, 585–586.
7. Kimmel, H. D. Three criteria for the use of one-tailed tests. *Psychol. Bull.*, 1957, 54, 351–353.
8. Marks, M. R. Two kinds of experiment distinguished in terms of statistical operations. *Psychol. Rev.*, 1951, 58, 179–184.
9. Marks, M. R. One- and two-tailed tests. *Psychol. Rev.*, 1953, 60, 207–208.

3. Whether or not there exist any other possible approaches requires further analysis.

H. J. EYSENCK

26 The Concept of Statistical Significance and the Controversy about One-Tailed Tests

Several controversial papers regarding the uses and abuses of the one-tailed test of significance have recently appeared (1 [Ch. 21], 2 [Ch. 23], 3 [Ch. 25], 4 [Ch. 19], 5 [Ch. 18], 6 [Ch. 22], 8 [Ch. 17], 9 [Ch. 20]). As Goldfried (3) points out, "the important question debated is not *if* it should be used, but rather *when* it should be used." It is suggested here that most of the disagreements emerging from this controversy stem from a misunderstanding of the term "significance," and it is further suggested that the same misunderstanding runs through many discussions of two-tailed tests as well. It will be suggested that in the sense in which Goldfried's statement is meant, it has been the wrong question which has been debated; neither one-tailed nor two-tailed tests should be used at all in the sense envisaged by most of the writers quoted.

The outcome of the statistical examination of experimental results is always stated in terms of the probability of disconfirmation of the null hypothesis; the set of values which these *p* values can take is continuous in the interval from 0 to 1. It is customary to take arbitrary *p* values, such as .05 and .01, and use them to dichotomize this continuum into a *significant* and an *insignificant* portion. This habit has no obvious advantage, if what is intended is merely a restatement of the probability values; these are already given in any case and are far more precise than a simple dichotomous statement. Indeed, gross absurdities result from taking these verbal statements too seriously; the difference between a C.R. of 1.90 and another of 2.00 is quite negligible,

yet one falls on one side of the dichotomy, the other on the other side. This has led to such summary statements as: "almost significant," or "significant at the 10% level." If the verbal dichotomous scale is not satisfactory—as it clearly is not—the answer surely is to keep to the continuous *p* scale, rather than subdivide the verbal scale.

However, surplus meaning has accrued to the word "significant," and it has become a shibboleth which divides the successful from the unsuccessful research. It is frequently interpreted as almost guaranteeing reproducibility of results, while failure to reach significance is interpreted as disconfirmation. Hence the urgent desire to achieve respectability and significance by one-tailed tests, if need be, and the argument regarding when the cachet of "significance" can be bestowed upon a research result. Yet the argument, and the achievement or nonachievement of significance, do not alter the facts of the case, which are contained in the statement of the *p* value of the results. Anything beyond these facts depends upon interpretation, and is subjective; it does not alter the facts of the case in the slightest.

As an example of the necessity of interpretation, consider the a priori probability of the conclusion. Suppose that an experiment on ESP were carried out with all the precautions which human ingenuity can devise, so that even the most sceptical had to agree that no fault could be found with the experimental design. *Suppose* also that a *p* value of .05 were achieved. Would this be considered 'signifi-

From *Psychological Review*, Vol. 67, No. 4, pp. 269–271, 1960. Copyright © 1960 by the American Psychological Association, and reprinted by permission.

cant,' in the sense of guaranteeing reproducibility? Critics would point out quite rightly that where the a priori probability is very low, as in this case, much higher *p* values would be required to carry significance. Logicians are agreed that interpretation of experimental results must call on all available knowledge about the subject in question; a priori probability is a kind of summary statement of much of this knowledge. It cannot be overlooked in arriving at a conclusion regarding "significance" when the term carries the surplus meaning indicated.

That interpretation comes into the problem very much is clear when we look at such conditions as those suggested by Kimmel (7 [Ch. 24]) as criteria for the use of one-tailed tests. He suggests, for instance, that they may be used if results in the opposite direction would be psychologically meaningless or could not be deduced from any psychological theory. These are obviously not objective criteria, but depend on what the author (or reader) considers psychologically meaningless, or the kind of theory he may hold. Opinions will differ, and consequently some readers will agree to the use of the one-tailed test in a particular case, other will not. Thus to some readers the results will appear *significant*, to others *insignificant*.

The whole argument seems to be about *words*, not about *facts*: Is the word "significant" to be used in a given situation, or is it not? This would only matter if the word carried some objective meaning not contained in the probability figures; we have argued that it does carry surplus meaning, but that this is not of an objective kind. Consequently, nothing important is changed by omitting the term altogether in the report, leaving interpretation to the reader. After all, the only true proof of reproducibility is reproduction! Verbal assertions of "significance" have no more meaning than the *droit du pour* at the court of Louis XIV.

The solution is to separate quite clearly and decisively the *objective statement of the probability of disproof* of the *null hypothesis*

(by means of a two-tailed test), and the *subjective evaluation and interpretation of the results*. The reader would be able to accept the first statement as a statement of fact and would then be able to judge for himself the arguments presented by the author regarding the *meaning* of these facts. These arguments might be based on results of previous experiments, predictions made on the basis of more or less widely accepted theories, numbers of cases involved, a priori lack of acceptability of the conclusions, and other similar grounds; an explicit statement of the arguments would enable the reader to decide for himself the acceptability of the conclusions in a manner precluded by the simple statement of one-tailed probability. *A statement of one-tail probability is not a statement of fact, but of opinion, and should not be offered instead of, but only in addition to, the factual two-tailed probability*; if it is offered at all, it should be accompanied by a full statement of the arguments in favor of its facilitating a more meaningful interpretation of the data. In the writer's opinion, it would be better to drop such statements of one-tailed probability altogether and rely entirely on appropriate argumentation to establish the meaning of the observed (two-tailed) probabilities.

Implicit in this recommendation is the corollary that the mechanical evaluation of experimental results in terms of "significant" and "not significant" be dropped outright. Interpretation is implicit in the statement of one-tailed probabilities, but it is also implicit in the statement of two-tailed probabilities if these are *automatically* interpreted as being significant or not significant, with all the surplus meaning carried by these terms. The experimenter should give his (two-tailed) *p* values and then proceed to argue regarding the acceptability of the conclusions on the basis already indicated. There have appeared in the literature solemn discussions about the possible causes for discrepancies between two experiments, one of which gave significant, the other insignificant results; yet the respective *t* values were almost identical, one lying just on the one side, the other just on the other side, of the arbitrary 5% line. Such arguments are unrealistic and would be avoided if p values were compared, rather than verbal statements. Two experiments giving p values of .048 and .056 are in excellent agreement, although one is significant, while the other is not.

To summarize the main point of this note briefly, we would say that verbal statements regarding "significance" are at best super-erogatory restatements in an inconvenient dichotomous form of results already properly stated in terms of a continuous system of p values; at worst they carry unjustified surplus meaning of an entirely subjective kind under the guise of an objective and mathematically meaningful statement. Subjective judgements of reproducibility cannot reasonably be based on the mechanical application of a rule of thumb whose only usefulness lies in the elementary instruction of undergraduates lacking in mathematical background; if they are to be made at all they demand complex consideration of a priori probabilities. It is suggested that the accurate and factual statement of probabilities (two-tailed) should be mandatory

and that all subjective considerations, arguments, and judgments should be clearly separated from such factual statements. It is implied that judgments of "significance" belong with the subjective side, and it is also implied that the calculation of p values on the basis of one-tailed tests has no place in psychology.

References

1. Burke, C. J. A brief note on one-tailed tests. *Psychol. Bull.*, 1953, 50, 384–387.
2. Burke, C. J. Further remarks on one-tailed tests. *Psychol. Bull.*, 1954, 51, 587–590.
3. Goldfried, M. R. One tailed tests and "unexpected" results. *Psychol. Rev.*, 1959, 66, 79–80.
4. Hick, W. E. A note on one-tailed and two-tailed tests. *Psychol. Rev.*, 1952, 59, 316–318.
5. Jones, L. V. Tests of hypotheses: One-sided and two-sided alternatives. *Psychol. Bull.*, 1952, 49, 43–46.
6. Jones, L. V. A rejoinder on one-tailed tests. *Psychol. Bull.*, 1954, 51, 585–586.
7. Kimmel, H. D. Three criteria for the use of one-tailed tests. *Psychol. Bull.*, 1957, 54, 351–353.
8. Marks, M. R. Two kinds of experiment distinguished in terms of statistical operations. *Psychol. Bull.*, 1951, 58, 179–184.
9. Marks, M. R. One- and two-tailed tests. *Psychol. Rev.*, 1953, 60, 203–208.

HENRY F. KAISER

27 Directional Statistical Decisions

This paper has two purposes. First, we shall point out a seemingful common logical error in the statistical interpretation given results of two-sided tests of statistical hypotheses. A correct interpretation of the traditional two-sided test would appear to make this classic procedure of essentially negligible interest. Second, we shall outline an appropriate treatment of the problem with which two-sided statistical tests seem concerned and contrast

this procedure with the one-sided test. Throughout the paper, we shall indicate the relationship of our discussion to the prolonged controversy on one-sided tests versus two-sided tests (1 [Ch. 21], 2 [Ch. 22], 4 [Ch. 25], 5 [Ch. 19], 7 [Ch. 18], 8 [Ch. 22], 10 [Ch. 24], 12 [Ch. 17], 13 [Ch. 20]).

The arguments developed in this paper are based on logical considerations in statistical inference. (We do not, of course, suggest that

From *Psychological Review*, Vol. 67, No. 3, pp. 160–67, 1960. Copyright © 1960 by the American Psychological Association, and reprinted by permission.

statistical inference is the only basis for scientific inference.) Our statistical interpretation and development stem primarily from the decision-theoretic position of Wald (17, 18).

The Nondirectional Two-Sided Test

Consider the traditional two-sided test. For example, we wish to test the null hypothesis:

$$H_2: \mu_X - \mu_Y = 0$$

against the obvious two-sided alternative:

$$H_{13}: \mu_X - \mu_Y \neq 0$$

where μ_X and μ_Y are the population means of the normally distributed random variables X and Y, and where $\sigma_X = \sigma_Y = \sigma$ is unknown.[1] This, of course, is an example of the classic t test.

The error in statistical interpretation of perhaps the majority of those who have used this test lies in the decision or statement made if the null hypothesis is rejected. When this occurs obviously we accept the alternative hypothesis that the population means are different. While this is correct, *we cannot logically make a directional statistical decision or statement when the null hypothesis is rejected on the basis of the direction of the difference in the observed sample means.* Our a priori alternative hypothesis merely states a nondirectional difference; logically, then, we may only state or decide upon a nondirectional difference if this alternative is accepted.

It seems difficult to imagine a problem for which this traditional test could give results of interest. To find a difference or a "significant" effect and not be able to decide in which direction this difference or effect lies, seems a sterile way to do business. One escape would be to conduct the traditional nondirectional two-sided test, and then if the alternative hypothesis is accepted, to gather new data and attempt to decide upon the direction provoked by the original non-directional two-

1. Our designation of the null hypothesis as H_2 rather than H_0 is unconventional; however, the exposition seems logically clearer if we use the subscripts 1, 2, and 3 to refer to negative, zero, and positive differences, respectively.

sided affair with the appropriate one-sided test. This two-stage procedure, while correct, obviously wastes data. A more efficient, single-stage procedure is described in the section after next.

The Directional Two-Sided Test

Consider the one-sided test. We wish, for example, to test the null hypothesis:

$$H_{12}: \mu_X - \mu_Y \leq 0$$

against the one-sided alternative:

$$H_3: \mu_X - \mu_X > 0$$

One point of confusion concerning the above statement of the null hypothesis sometimes occurs because traditionally the definition of a null hypothesis has been restricted to the hypothesis of no difference— e.g., our H_2 of the previous section. Under the latter interpretation, the one-sided test would be for deciding between the null hypothesis H_2 and the alternative H_3— leaving the left flank unguarded. Statistically, this restriction is not necessary; a statistical hypothesis simply is a statement about the probability distribution(s) of observable random variable(s) (15, p. 250). Any such statement, such as our H_{12} above, if it is the hypothesis being tested (in the sense that falsely rejecting it may occur with maximum probability given by the level of significance) is then a null hypothesis (15, p. 259). The well-entrenched adjective "null" is probably misleading for it implies an unnecessary restriction on statements of hypotheses to be tested.

On the other hand, Burke (1, 2) has argued not unconvincingly that stating the null hypothesis in a one-sided test as a nonpositive difference may often be scientifically naive; the difference between the scientific hypotheses corresponding to H_1 and H_2 may be such that it would not be wise (extrastatistically) to toss them into the same null pot, where they remain indistinguishable.

Of course, with the one-sided test we are

in the much more palatable position than with the traditional two-sided test of being able to make a directional statistical decision if the alternative hypothesis is accepted.

The Directional One-Sided Test

Let us say we are interested in making a directional decision if we attain "statistical significance" and yet wish to guard against differences in both directions. This section outlines a solution of this problem for the example considered here, statistical decisions about differences between population means of normally distributed random variables with equal variance.

To do this we consider briefly the notion of a statistical decision function (17). A statistical decision function prescribes a correspondence between one of k possible decisions as a function of n possible observational outcomes (15, p. 10). In applied statistics n is usually infinite; for example, in our problem the possible values of t are the $n = \infty$ possible outcomes. On the other hand, in conventional applied statistics k is usually either two or infinite; when k is two, we have hypothesis testing using two-valued statistical decision functions, and when k is infinite we have the problem of estimation (deciding along a continuum of points or intervals). Either of the t tests considered in the two previous sections uses a two-valued statistical decision function or, less solemnly, is a two-decision procedure, because in each case there are two, and only two, possible decisions contemplated: a decision to accept (not reject) the null hypothesis or a decision to accept the alternative. The two two-decision procedures are different, of course, both because of the nature of the hypotheses tested and because of the different correspondence established between the possible outcomes and the two decisions; i.e., the critical regions or tail(s) for the two tests are different for rejecting the null hypothesis.

Wald's (16, 17) contribution of the notion of a statistical decision function integrates into a single general theory what prior to 1939 were thought of as two more or less distinct branches of statistics, hypothesis testing and estimation. In this most general framework, conventional hypothesis testing is represented by two-valued statistical decision functions while estimation involves statistical decision functions of infinitely many values.

However, there is no reason why we should not consider the zone in between: k-decision procedures, $2 < k < \infty$. And this is precisely what we shall do to give a correct single-stage solution to the directional two-sided decision problem. For this problem requires a *three*-valued statistical decision function (11); we wish to decide among

$$H_1 : \mu_X - \mu_Y < 0$$

and

$$H_2 : \mu_X - \mu_Y = 0$$

and

$$H_3 : \mu_X - \mu_Y > 0$$

The difference between the traditional nondirectional two-sided test and the directional two-sided test proposed in this section may be seen by considering the possible errors which may occur in making a wrong decision. For the classic nondirectional test, only two errors are possible: *a*) the error of deciding that there is a difference, when, in fact, the null hypothesis is true—an error of the first kind (α error), or *b*) the error of not detecting that the null hypothesis is false, i.e., deciding that there is no difference when in fact there is—an error of the second kind (β error). The four possible situations may be represented conveniently in the following four-fold table:

		Nature	
		H_2	H_{13}
Decision about Nature	H_2	correct decision	β error
	H_{13}	α error	correct decision

For the directional test of this section, there are six possible errors. They may readily be

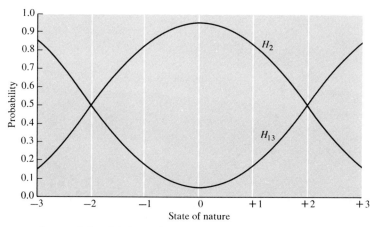

Fig. 1. Performance characteristic of the non-directional two-sided test with $\alpha = .05$. State of Nature in units of the standard error of the difference between the means. Rule of inductive behavior (for large samples): decide upon H_2 when $-1.960 \leq t \leq +1.960$, decide upon H_{13} when $|t| > +1.960$.

seen as the off-diagonal cells in the following nine-fold table.

		Nature		
		H_1	H_2	H_3
	H_1	correct decision	α_{12} error	γ_{13} error
Decision about Nature	H_2	β_{21} error	correct decision	β_{23} error
	H_3	γ_{31} error	α_{32} error	correct decision

Any one of the possible errors in the above table is symbolized uniquely by the subscripts used: the first subscript indicates which hypothesis is decided upon, while the second indicates the hypothesis which obtains in Nature. We have added the unnecessary α, β, and γ, to provide comparability with the notation used in classical hypothesis testing. Thus, the α_{12} and α_{32} errors are similar to the α error in the usual two-decision problem; either involves making a false decision of difference when there is none. The β_{21} and β_{23} errors are similar to the β error; either involves not not detecting a difference. The particularly

repugnant γ_{13} and γ_{31} errors—"errors of the third kind"—have no parallel in classical hypothesis testing, as these "gamma errors" involve deciding upon a difference in the wrong direction.[2]

The difference between the directional and nondirectional two-sided tests may be illustrated quantitatively if we contrast their *performance characteristics*. The performance characteristic of a k decision procedure is the system of k functions, each of which gives the probability, as a function of the model describing the state of Nature, of accepting one of the k decisions contemplated (15, p. 11). Figure 1 shows the performance characteristic for the classic nondirectional two-sided (equal tails) t test with level of significance α ($= .05$). It consists of two functions, each giving the probability of deciding upon the hypothesis (H_2 or H_{13}) indicated.[3] Note that the two functions are redundant; the curve giving the probability of accepting H_2, Wald's operating characteristic, is complementary to the curve

2. Mosteller (14) seems to have coined the expression "errors of the third kind."
3. Dixon and Massey (3, Ch. 14) and Walker and Lev (18, pp. 161–167) give excellent elementary discussions of how these functions may be computed.

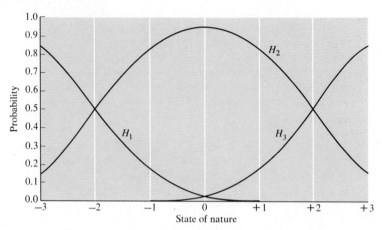

Fig. 2. Performance characteristic of the directional two-sided test with $\alpha_{12} = \alpha_{32} = .025$. State of Nature in units of the standard error of the difference between the means. Rule of inductive behavior (for large samples): decide upon H_1 when $t < -1.960$, decide upon H_2 when $-1.960 \leq t \leq +1.960$, decide upon H_3 when $t > +1.960$.

giving the probability of accepting H_{13}, the Neyman-Pearson power function. More generally, of course, any performance characteristic has this sort of redundancy: since the k possible decisions are mutually exclusive and jointly exhaustive, the probability of making any $k-1$ of them is sufficient to give the desired information.

Figure 2 shows the three functions of the performance characteristic of our three-decision procedure, the directional two-sided test. For this illustration the probability of making each of the α_{12} and α_{32} errors has been set at one-half the level of significance used for Fig. 1; this makes it convenient to compare the directional and nondirectional two-sided tests when the directional test is carried out under the guise of the traditional nondirectional test with level of significance α. Several comparisons of this three-decision procedure with the traditional test seem worth mentioning. When $\alpha_{12} = \alpha_{32} = \frac{1}{2}\alpha$, comparing Figs. 1 and 2:

1. The probability of accepting the null hypothesis H_2 is the same for either test for all states of Nature.

2. The probability of correctly accepting either H_1 or H_3 in the directional test is less than the probability of correctly accepting H_{13} in the non-directional test, and, for a given state of Nature, this loss of power is equal to the probability of making the nasty error of the third kind.

3. The probability of making a gamma error is always less than $\frac{1}{2}\alpha$.

An alternative treatment for the directional two-sided problem would be to make the probabilities of each of the α_{12} and α_{32} errors traditional values, like .05 or .01, rather than the .025 or .005 generated by an incorrect interpretation of the nondirectional test.

Discussion

It seems obvious that the traditional two-sided test should almost never be used. If, as is typical, not rejecting the null hypothesis is a result of little scientific concern, then this test may be said never to give results of direct scientific interest because accepting the non-directional alternative H_{13} is merely a gener-

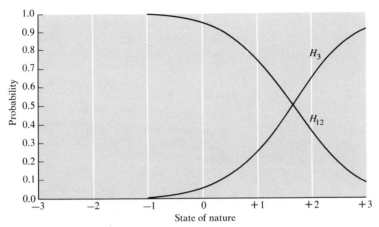

Fig. 3. Performance characteristic of the directional one-sided test with $\alpha = .05$. State of Nature in units of the standard error of the difference between the means. Rule of inductive behavior (for large samples): decide upon H_{12} when $t \leq +1.645$, decide upon H_3 when $t > +1.645$.

ator of directional alternative hypotheses.[4]

Since we are proposing that almost without exception the directional two-sided test should replace the traditional nondirectional test, it seems appropriate to contrast the one-sided test with this three-decision procedure. The performance characteristic of the one-sided test is given in Fig. 3. The level of significance ($\alpha = .05$) in this illustration is the same as in Fig. 1. In comparing Figs. 2 and 3, then, we compare the one-sided test with the three-decision procedure where $\alpha_{12} = \alpha_{32} = \frac{1}{2}\alpha$. The loss of performance engendered by guarding both sides with the directional two-

4. When the alternative hypothesis is so nonspecific as the nondirectional H_{13}, a compelling argument (9) may be made not to test hypotheses at all—that a more appropriate statistical procedure is estimation, e.g., for our problem, first find a point estimate for $\mu_X - \mu_Y$ and then determine a confidence interval about this point. Indeed, it might be argued that even the directional alternatives H_1 and H_3 are too non-specific relative to the null hypothesis H_2, because their dimensionality in the parameter space is greater than that of H_2. A completely "balanced" or "symmetric" theory of testing hypotheses would seem logically to require that all k hypotheses under consideration have the same dimensionality in the parameter space. Such symmetry for our procedure could occur if H_1 and H_3 were chosen as specific negative and positive differences rather than any positive and negative differences.

sided test is readily seen. Only from the traditional point of view of correctly accepting the null hypothesis, or controlling errors of the first kind, is the two-sided test as good; the two-sided test is markedly less powerful (in the Neyman-Pearson sense) than the one-sided test for correctly rejecting the null hypothesis in the "right" direction, from the viewpoint of the one-sided test. Also, with the two-sided test, there is always the possibility of the repulsive gamma errors.

To equate the power of the directional two-sided test with that of the one-sided test with level of significance α, it is sufficient to use this three-decision procedure with $\alpha_{12} = \alpha_{32} = \alpha$. Compare Figs. 3 and 4.

A nice feature of this comparison is that there is no difference in the critical values to t in the tail corresponding to the alternative hypothesis for the one-sided test. See Fig. 5. Thus the traditional and delicate problem of changing the number of sides in midstream and/or fudging with a posteriori alpha values cannot arise. The distinction between these two tests lies in whether differences in the "wrong" direction, from the viewpoint of the one-sided test, can lead to a decision in this direction. For the three-decision procedure

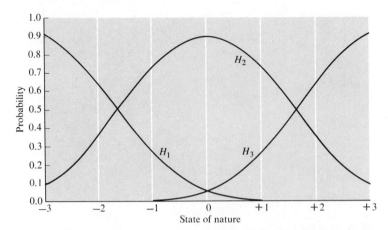

Fig. 4. Performance characteristic of the directional two-sided test with $\alpha_{12} = \alpha_{32} = .05$. State of Nature in units of the standard error of the difference between the means. Rule of inductive behavior (for large samples); decide upon H_1 when $t < -1.645$, decide upon H_2 when $-1.645 \leq t \leq +1.645$, decide upon H_3 when $t > +1.645$.

proposed in this paper, this may happen; for the traditional one-sided test, it may not, as the null hypothesis there includes all non-positive differences. At first glance, then, it might seem that one would always prefer the three-decision procedure because it guards against differences in both directions— differences which of course may be decided

upon directionally. It is suggested that this argument is not to be taken lightly; consult Burke (1, 2) for an extended and convincing defense of the scientific desirability of procedures which will detect differences in both directions.

However, the choice is not completely clear cut. Consider again Fig. 4, the performance

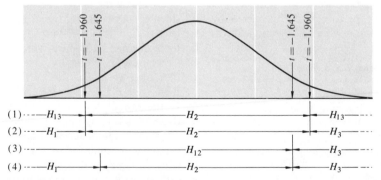

Fig. 5. Ranges of values of t (for large samples) leading to the decision indicated for four statistical tests. The numbers in parentheses at the left are the same as the numbers of the above figures giving the performance characteristics of these tests: (1) nondirectional two-sided test with $\alpha = .05$, (2) directional two-sided test with $\alpha_{12} = \alpha_{32} = .025$, (3) directional one-sided test with $\alpha = .05$, (4) directional two-sided test with $\alpha_{12} = \alpha_{32} = .05$.

characteristic of the three-decision procedure where $\alpha_{12} = \alpha_{32} = \alpha$. In comparing Figs. 3 and 4, one traditionally serious disadvantage of the directional two-sided test obtains: in the unlikely event that the null hypothesis H_2 is true, i.e., the population mean difference is exactly equal to zero, then the probability of accepting this null hypothesis is only $1 - \alpha_{12} - \alpha_{32} = 1 - 2\alpha$ for the two-sided test as compared with probability $1 - \alpha$ of accepting H_{12} when the one-sided test is used.

We have not attempted to settle the scientific issue of one-sided versus two-sided tests. However, it is hoped that the problem has been recast so as to eliminate confusion arising from failing to distinguish directional from nondirectional two-sided tests. As for the scientific issues briefly outlined in this section, a more detailed and perhaps more compelling defense of either test may be found in the papers referred to in the first paragraph of this paper, if it is remembered that these writers are almost certainly referring to our three-decision procedure when speaking of two-sided tests.

Notes

The directional two-sided test proposed in this paper need not necessarily be developed explicitly as a three-decision procedure. An alternative approach would be simultaneously to make two one-sided tests (6): H_{12} against H_3 and H_{23} against H_1. If both these two-decision procedures are carried out simultaneously and with the same data, at level of significance α, it is readily seen that we have exactly the equivalent of the three-decision procedure illustrated and described in Fig. 4.

It is perhaps worth pointing out that it is surely not necessary and may not always be best to set $\alpha_{12} = \alpha_{32}$ in our directional two-sided test; after all, the α_{12} and α_{32} errors may entail very different consequences. Indeed, we may envision a continuum of possible partitions of $\alpha_{12} + \alpha_{32}$ from a left tail critical one-sided test through the equal tails three-decision procedure described in this paper to a right tail critical one-sided test.

It has been convenient to discuss problems about differences between means. The rationale and application of the three-decision procedure outlined above may easily be extended to other problems involving other parameters where the traditional alternative hypothesis lies on both sides of the null hypothesis.

Finally, it might also be noted that the statistical notion of the number of sides or "tails" bears no necessary relation to the scientific notion of whether the test is directional or non-directional. For example, the one-sided t test is directional scientifically and one-sided statistically, while most traditional F and chi square tests are nondirectional scientifically and one-sided statistically. As such, directional decisions cannot properly be made with such F and chi square tests and they are to be thought of merely as hypothesis generators for scientifically more explicit statistical decision procedures.

References

1. Burke, C. J. A brief note on one-tailed tests. *Psychol. Bull.*, 1953, 50, 384–387.
2. Burke, C. J. Further remarks on one-tailed tests. *Psychol. Bull.*, 1954, 51, 587–590.
3. Dixon, W. J., & Massey, F. J. *Introduction to statistical analysis.* (2nd ed.) New York: McGraw-Hill, 1957.
4. Goldfried, M. R. One-tailed tests and "unexpected" results. *Psychol. Rev.*, 1959, 66, 79–80.
5. Hick, W. E. A note on one-tailed and two-tailed tests. *Psychol. Rev.*, 1952, 59, 316–318.
6. Hodges, J. L., & Lehmann, E. L. Testing the approximate validity of statistical hypotheses. *J. Roy. statist. Soc., Lond., Ser. B (Methodological)*, 1954, 16, 261–268.
7. Jones, L. V. Tests of hypotheses: one-sided vs. two-sided alternatives. *Psychol. Bull.*, 1952, 49, 43–46.
8. Jones, L. V. A rejoinder on one-tailed tests. *Psychol. Bull.*, 1954, 51, 585–586.
9. Jones, L. V. Statistical theory and research design. *Annu. Rev. Psychol.*, 1955, 6, 405–430.
10. Kimmel, H. D. Three criteria for the use of one-tailed tests. *Psychol. Bull.*, 1957, 54, 351–353.

11. Lehmann, E. L. Some principles of the theory of testing hypotheses. *Ann. math. Statist.*, 1950, 21, 1–26.
12. Marks, M. R. Two kinds of experiments distinguished in terms of statistical operations. *Psychol. Rev.*, 1951, 58, 179–184.
13. Marks, M. R. One- and two-tailed tests. *Psychol. Rev.*, 1953, 60, 207–208.
14. Mosteller, F. A *k*-sample slippage test for an extreme population. *Ann. math. Statist.*, 1948, 19, 58–65.
15. Neyman, J. *First course in probability and statistics*. New York: Holt, 1950.
16. Wald, A. Contributions to the theory of statistical estimation and testing hypotheses. *Ann. math. Statist.*, 1939, 10, 299–326.
17. Wald, A. *Statistical decision functions*. New York: Wiley, 1950.
18. Walker, H. M., & Lev, J. *Statistical inference*. New York: Holt, 1953.

SECTION 4

Bayesian Statistics

In an article of Section 2, W. Rozeboom argued against the use of null-hypothesis decision procedures and advocated the use of Bayesian procedures. Some of the ideas expressed by Rozeboom had been considered previously, for the notion that data and statistical procedures can be used to alter the beliefs of scientists has been with us for some time, ever since the mathematician Thomas Bayes proved his now-famous theorem more than two hundred years ago. The interest in the use of this probabilistic model lay relatively dormant until recently. At the present time some statisticians and behavioral scientists are intensely interested in what have come to be called Bayesian statistics or Bayesian procedures.

The first article of this section is Chapter 2 of R. A. Fisher's book, *Statistical Methods and Scientific Inference*, which discusses the history and substance of Bayes's theorem. The material by R. Schlaifer consists of the first two chapters of his book, *Introduction to Statistics for Business Decisions*, which is an elementary introduction to the notions of Bayesian statistics. The articles by Pitz and Overall are specific examples of the use of Bayesian techniques.

R. A. FISHER

28 The Early Attempts and Their Difficulties

Thomas Bayes

For the first serious attempt known to us
to give a rational account of the process of
scientific inference as a means of understanding the real world, in the sense in which this
term is understood by experimental investigators, we must look back over two hundred
years to an English clergyman, the Reverend
Thomas Bayes, whose life spanned the first
half of the eighteenth century. It is indeed only
in the present century, with the rapid expansion of those studies which are collectively
known as Statistics, that the importance of
Bayes' contribution has come to be appreciated. *The Dictionary of National Biography* (13),
representing opinion current in the last quarter
of the nineteenth century, does not include
his name. The omission is the more striking
since this work of reference does include a
notice of his father, Joshua Bayes (1671–1746).
While the father was no doubt a learned and

eloquent preacher, still, in his own time, his
son Thomas was for twenty years a Fellow of
the Royal Society, and therefore known also
as a not inconsiderable mathematician.
Indeed, his mathematical contributions to the
Philosophical Transactions show him to have
been in the first rank of independent thinkers,
very well qualified to attempt the really revo-
lutionary task opened out by his posthumous
paper "An Essay towards solving a problem
in the doctrine of chances," which appeared
in the *Philosophical Transactions* (1) in 1763,
not long after his death in 1761.

It is entirely appropriate that this first
attempt should have been made at this time.
For more than a century the learned world
had been coming to regard deliberate experimentation as the fundamental means to "The
Improvement of Natural Knowledge," in the
words chosen by the Royal Society. With Isaac
Newton, moreover, and such men as Robert

Boyle, the possibility of formulating natural law in quantitative terms had been brilliantly exhibited. The nature of the reasoning process by which appropriate inferences, or conclusions, could be drawn from quantitative observational data was ripe for consideration. The prime difficulty lay in the uncertainty of such inferences, and it was a fortunate coincidence that the recognition of the concept of probability, and its associated mathematical laws, in its application to games of chance, should at the same time have provided a possible means by which such uncertainty could be specified and made explicit. In England such a publication as Abraham de Moivre's *Doctrine of Chances* (9) must have been a very immediate stimulus to Bayes' reflexions on this subject.

Bayes' Essay was communicated to the Royal Society some time after his death by his friend Richard Price. Price added various demonstrations and illustrations of the method, and seems to have replaced Bayes' introduction by a prefatory explanation of his own. It is to be regretted that we have not Bayes' own introduction, for it seems clear that Bayes had recognized that the postulate used in his demonstration would be thought disputable by a critical reader, and there can be little doubt that this was the reason why his treatise was not offered for publication in his own lifetime. Price evidently laid less weight on these doubts than did Bayes himself; on the other hand he very fully appreciated the importance of what Bayes had done, or attempted, for the advancement of experimental philosophy; although the central theorem of the essay is framed in somewhat academic and abstract terms, without expatiating on the large consequences for human reasoning which would flow from its acceptance.

It contains also an element of artificiality, which has obscured its understanding, and which, I believe, is capable of being removed (6).

The most important passage of Price's introductory letter is as follows (1, p. 370):

In an introduction which he has writ to this Essay, he says, that his design at first in thinking on the subject of it was, to find out a method by which we might judge concerning the probability that an event has to happen, in given circumstances, upon supposition that we know nothing concerning it but that, under the same circumstances, it has happened a certain number of times, and failed a certain other number of times. He adds, that he soon perceived that it would not be very difficult to do this, provided some rule could be found according to which we ought to estimate the chance that the probability for the happening of an event perfectly unknown, should lie between any two named degrees of probability, antecedently to any experiments made about it; and that it appeared to him that the rule must be to suppose the chance the same that it should lie between any two equidistant degrees; which, if it were allowed, all the rest might be easily calculated in the common method of proceeding in the doctrine of chances. Accordingly, I find among his papers a very ingenious solution of this problem in this way. But he afterwards considered, that the *postulate* on which he had argued might not perhaps be looked upon by all as reasonable; and therefore he chose to lay down in another form the proposition in which he thought the solution of the problem is contained, and in a *scholium* to subjoin the reason why he thought so, rather than to take into his mathematical reasoning anything that might admit dispute.

The actual mathematics of Bayes' theorem may be expressed very briefly in modern notation.

If in $a + b$ independent trials it has been observed that there have been a successes and b failures, then if p were the hypothetical probability of success in each of these trials, the probability of the happening of what has been observed would be

$$\frac{(a+b)!}{a!\,b!}\,p^a(1-p)^b;\qquad \text{Eq. 1}$$

but if in addition we know, or can properly postulate, that p itself has been chosen by an antecedent random process, such that the probability of p lying in any infinitesimal range dp between the limiting values 0 and 1 is equal simply to

$$dp,\qquad \text{Eq. 2}$$

then the probability of the compound event of p lying in the assigned range, and of the observed numbers of successes and failures occurring will be the product of these two expressions, namely

$$\frac{(a+b)!}{a!\,b!}\,p^a(1-p)^b\,dp. \qquad \text{Eq. 3}$$

But, from the data, such a compound event has happened for some element or other of those into which the total range from 0 to 1 may be divided, so that the probability that any particular one should have happened in fact is the ratio,

$$\frac{\dfrac{(a+b)!}{a!\,b!}\,p^a(1-p)^b\,dp}{\dfrac{(a+b)!}{a!\,b!}\displaystyle\int_0^1 p^a(1-p)^b\,dp}, \qquad \text{Eq. 4}$$

of which the denominator, involving a complete Eulerian integral, is equal $1/(a+b+1)$.

The finite probability that p should lie between any assigned limits u and v may therefore be expressed as the incomplete integral

$$\frac{(a+b+1)!}{a!\,b!}\int_u^v p^a(1-p)^b\,dp. \qquad \text{Eq. 5}$$

The postulate which Bayes regarded as questionable is represented above by the equation 2. The greater part of Bayes' analysis is concerned with approximate forms for the discussion of these integrals, and is of historical rather than mathematical interest for the modern reader. How explicit Bayes is in introducing his critical postulate is shown by his own introductory remarks.

The crucial theorem, proposition 8, comes in the second section of the essay, and is preceded by a special explanatory foreword (1, p. 385):

SECTION II

Postulate 1. I suppose the square table or plane $ABCD$ to be made and levelled, that if either of the balls O or W be thrown upon it, there shall be the same probability that it rests upon any one equal part of the plane as another, and that it must necessarily rest somewhere upon it.

2. I suppose that the ball W shall be first thrown, and through the point where it rests a line os shall be drawn parallel to AD, and meeting CD and AB in s and o; and that afterwards the ball O shall be thrown $p+q$ or n times, and that its resting between AD and os after a single throw be called the happening of the event M in a single trial. These things supposed,

Lemma 1. The probability that the point o will fall between any two points in the line AB is the ratio of the distance between the two points to the whole line AB. (The proof occupies two pages, with an examination of incommensurability after the manner of the fifth book of Euclid's elements.)

Lemma 2. The ball W having been thrown, and the line os drawn, the probability of the event M in a single trial is the ratio Ao to AB.

After a short proof there follow the enunciation of proposition 8 and its demonstration. A single figure is used to represent the square table and the construction upon it, and also outside the square, a graph representing the function,

$$\frac{(a+b)!}{a!\,b!}\,p^a q^b, \qquad p+q=1,$$

for all values of p from 0 to 1. The latter is used to give geometrical significance to the analytic integrals used above.

In broaching the boundaries of an entirely new field of thought by means of a single illustrative theorem, pregnant as it was, Bayes left untouched many distinctions of importance to its discussion in the future. In respect to the nature of the concept of probability very diverse opinions have been expressed. In particular, although perhaps all would agree that the word denotes a measure of the strength of an opinion or state of judgment, some have insisted that it should properly be used only for the expression of a state of rational judgement based on sufficient objective evidence, while others have thought that equality of probability may be asserted merely from the indifference of, or the absence of *differentiae* in, the objective evidence, if any, and therefore from the total absence of objective evidence, if there were none.

Bayes evidently held the first of these opinions and framed a definition suited—in my view—to show 1) that he was not thinking merely of games of chance, and, 2) at the same time that his concept of probability was that of the mathematicians, such as Montmort (10) and de Moivre, who had treated largely of gambling problems, in which the equality of probability assigned to numerous possible events and combinations of events is a consequence of the assumed perfection of the apparatus and operations employed.

Bayes' definition is (1, p. 376): "5. The *probability of any event* is the ratio between the value at which an expectation depending on the happening of the event ought to be computed, and the value of the thing expected upon its happening. 6. By *chance* I mean the same as probability." There is no room for doubt that Bayes would have regarded the "expectation" to which he referred as capable of verification to any required approximation, by repeated trials with sufficiently perfect apparatus. Subject to the latent stipulation of fair use, or of homogeneity in the series of tests, his definition is therefore equivalent to the limiting value of the relative frequency of success.

On the contrary Laplace, who needed a definition wide enough to be used in the vastly diverse applications of the *Théorie analytique*, manifestly inclined to the second view (1820).

La théorie des hasards consiste à réduire tous les évènemens du même genre, à un certain nombre de cas également possibles, c'est-à-dire, tels que nous soyons également indécis sur leur existence; et à déterminer le nombre de cas favorables à l'évènement dont on cherche la probabilité. Le rapport de ce nombre à celui de tous les cas possibles, est la mesure de cette probabilité qui n'est ainsi qu'une fraction dont le numérateur est le nombre des cas favorables, et dont le dénominateur est le nombre de tous les cas possibles.

This differs a little from the form used in 1812:

La théorie des probabilités consiste à réduire tous les évènemens qui peuvent avoir lieu dans une circonstance donnée, à un certain nombre de cas également possibles, c'est-à-dire tels que nous soyons également indécis sur leur existence, et à déterminer parmi ces cas, le nombre de ceux qui sont favorables à l'évènement dont on cherche la probabilité. Le rapport de ce nombre à celui de tous les cas possibles, est la mesure de cette probabilité qui n'est donc qu'une fraction dont le numérateur est le nombre des cas favorables, et dont le dénominateur est celui de tous les cas possibles.

It is seen that Laplace effectively avoids any objective definition, first by using the term *possible* in a context in which *probable* could be used, without explaining what difference, if any, he intends between the two words, and secondly by his indication that equal possibility could be judged without cogent evidence.

In consequence of this difference of concept, Bayes' attempt is exposed to different types of criticism in his own hands and in those of Laplace. While I have, for myself, no doubt that Bayes' definition is the more satisfactory, being not only in accordance with the ideas upon which the *Doctrine of Chances* of his own time was built, but in connecting the comparatively modern notion of *probability*, which seems to have been unknown to the Islamic and to the Greek mathematicians, with the much more ancient notion of an *expectation*, capable of being bought, sold and evaluated, nevertheless it would merely confuse the discussion to give further reasons for this opinion; the difficulties to which Bayes' approach was eventually found to lead can be easily expressed in terms of the notions which he himself favoured.

Whereas Laplace defined probability by means of the enumeration of discrete units, Bayes defined a continuous probability distribution, by a formula for the probability between any pair of assigned limits. He did not, however, consider the metric of his continuum. For in stating his prime postulate in the form that the chance *a priori* of the unknown probability lying between p_1 and p_2, should be equal to $p_2 - p_1$ he might, so far as cogent evidence is concerned, equally have taken any monotonic function of p, such as

$$\phi = \tfrac{1}{2}\cos^{-1}(1 - 2p), \quad p = \sin^2 \phi,$$

and postulated that the chance that ϕ should lie between ϕ_1 and ϕ_2 should be

$$\frac{2}{\pi}(\phi_2 - \phi_1),$$

so that, instead of inserting the probability *a priori* as

$$dp,$$

it would have appeared in the analysis as

$$\frac{2}{\pi}d\phi = \frac{1}{\pi\sqrt{pq}}.dp, \quad q = 1 - p, \text{ Eq. 6}$$

a postulate or assumption rather more favourable to extreme values of the unknown p, near to 0 or 1, at the expense of more central values.

Bayes' introduction of an expression representing probability *a priori* thus contained an arbitrary element, and it was doubtless some consciousness of this that led to his hesitation in putting his work forward. He removes the ambiguity formally by means of the auxiliary experiment with the ball W, and in Chapter V it is shown that such an auxiliary experiment can sometimes be realized in practice.

A more important question, however, is whether in scientific research, and especially in the interpretation of experiments, there is cogent reason for inserting a corresponding expression representing probabilities *a priori*. This practical question cannot be answered peremptorily, or in general, for certainly cases can be found, or constructed, in which valid probabilities *a priori* exist, and can be deduced from the data. More frequently, however, and especially when the probabilities of contrasted scientific theories are in question, a candid examination of the data at the disposal of the scientist shows that nothing of the kind can be claimed.

George Boole

The superb pre-eminence of Laplace as a mathematical analyst undoubtedly inclined mathematicians for nearly fifty years to the view that the logical approach adopted by him had removed all doubts as to the applicability in practice of Bayes' theorem. That this was indeed Laplace's view may be judged from his reference to the position of Bayes in the history of the subject (7, p. cxxxvii).

Bayes dans les *Transactions philosophiques* de l'année 1763, a cherché directement la probabilité que les possibilités indiquées par des expériences déjà faites, sont comprises dans des limites données; et il y a parvenu d'une manière fine et très ingénieuse, quoiqu'un peu embarrassée.

I imagine that the hint of criticism in the last phrase is directed against Bayes' hesitation to regard the postulate he required as axiomatic. It will be noticed in the sequel that discussion turned on just this question of its axiomatic nature, and not on the question, more natural to an experimental investigator, of whether, in the particular circumstances of the investigation, the knowledge implied by the postulate was or was not in fact available. It is the submission of the author that actual familiarity with the processes of scientific research helps greatly in the understanding of scientific data, and has in the present century clarified the issue by bringing into prominence the factual question, rather than the abstract question of axiomatic validity. It was not, however, until the weight of opinion among philosophical mathematicians had turned against the supposed axiom that the controversy could come to be examined in this more realistic manner.

Simple examples are provided by genetic situations. In Mendelian theory there are black mice of two genetic kinds. Some, known as homozygotes (*BB*), when mated with brown yield exclusively black offspring; others, known as heterozygotes (*Bb*), while themselves also black, are expected to yield half black and half brown. The expectation from a mating between two heterozygotes is 1 homozygous black, to 2 heterozygotes, to 1 brown. A black mouse from such a mating has thus, prior to any test-mating in which it may be used, a known probability of 1/3 of being homozygous, and of 2/3 of being heterozygous. If, therefore, on testing with a brown mate it yields seven offspring, all being black, we have a situation perfectly analogous to that set out by Bayes in his proposition, and can develop the counterpart of his argument, as follows:

The prior chance of the mouse being homozygous is 1/3; if it is homozygous the probability that the young shall be all black is unity; hence the probability of the compound event of a homozygote producing the test litter is the product of the two number, or 1/3.

Similarly, the prior chance of it being heterozygous is 2/3; if heterozygous the probability that the young shall be all black is $1/2^7$, or $1/128$; hence the probability of the compound event is the product, 1/192.

But, one of these compound events has occurred; hence the probability after testing that the mouse tested is homozygous is

$$1/3 \div \left(\frac{1}{3} + \frac{1}{192} \right) = 64/65,$$

and the probability that it is heterozygous is

$$1/192 \div \left(\frac{1}{3} + \frac{1}{192} \right) = 1/65.$$

If, therefore, the experimenter knows that the animal under test is the offspring of two heterozygotes, as would be the case if both parents were known to be black, and a parent of each were known to be brown, or, if, both being black, the parents were known to have produced at least one brown offspring, cogent knowledge *a priori* would have been available, and the method of Bayes could properly be applied. But, if knowledge of the origin of the mouse tested were lacking, no experimenter would feel he had warrant for arguing as if he knew that of which in fact he was ignorant, and for lack of adequate data Bayes' method of reasoning would be inapplicable to his problem.

It is evidently easier for the practitioner of natural science to recognize the difference between knowing and not knowing than this seems to be for the more abstract mathematician. The traditional line of thought running from Laplace to, for example, Sir Harold Jeffreys in our own time would be to argue that, in the absence of relevant genealogical evidence, there being only two possibilities, mutually exclusive, and with no prior information favouring one rather than the other, it is axiomatic that their probabilities *a priori* are equal, and that Bayes' argument should be applied on this basis. This is to treat the problem, in which we have no genealogical evidence, exactly *as if* the mouse to be tested were known to have been derived from a

mating producing half homozygotes and half heterozygotes.

In spite of the high prestige of all that flowed from Laplace's pen, and the great ability and industry of his expositors, it is yet surprising that the doubts which such a process of reasoning from ignorance must engender should begin to find explicit expression only in the second half of the nineteenth century, and then with caution. That extraordinary work, *The Laws of Thought*, by George Boole (2) appeared in 1854. Its twentieth chapter is given to problems of causes, and of this the second half to problems in which (p. 320) we "may be required to determine the probability of a particular cause, or of some particular connection among a system of causes, from observed effect". A hint of Boole's point of view appears in the opening words of Section 20:

It is remarkable that the solutions of the previous problems are void of any arbitrary element. We should scarcely, from the appearance of the data, have anticipated such a circumstance. It is, however, to be observed, that in all those problems the probabilities of the *causes* involved are supposed to be known *a priori*. In the absence of this assumed element of knowledge, it seems probable that arbitrary constants would *necessarily* appear in the final solution.

The cases chosen by Boole to illustrate this view are two: *a*) The Reverend J. Michell (8) had calculated that if stars of each magnitude were dispersed at random over the celestial sphere, there would very rarely occur so many apparent double stars or clusters as those actually observed by astronomers. *b*) The planes of revolution of the planets of the solar system are more nearly coincident than could often occur if these planes had been assigned at random. Instead of treating these calculations, as would now generally be done, as *tests of significance* overthrowing the theory of random dispersal, and therefore all cosmological theories implying random dispersal (disposing of this hypothesis without reference to, or consideration of, any alternative hypothesis which might be actually or conceivably brought forward); instead of this, it had been thought proper to discuss each question as one in inverse probability, and Boole has no difficulty in showing that as such it requires two elements really unknown, namely the probability *a priori* of random dispersal, and, secondly, the probability, in the aggregate of alternative hypotheses, of the observed frequency of conjunctions being realized. As he says on p. 367, "Any solutions which profess to accomplish this object, either are erroneous in principle, or involve a tacit assumption respecting the above arbitrary elements."

Again in Section 22:

Are we, however, justified in assigning to [these two unknowns] particular values? I am strongly disposed to think that we are not. The question is of less importance in the special instance than in its ulterior bearings. In the received applications of the theory of probabilities, arbitrary constants do not explicitly appear; but in the above, and in many other instances sanctioned by the highest authorities, some virtual determination of them has been attempted. And this circumstance has given to the results of the theory, especially in reference to questions of causation, a character of definite precision, which, while on the one hand it has seemed to exalt the dominion and extend the province of numbers, even beyond the measure of their ancient claim to rule the world; on the other hand has called forth vigorous protests against their intrusion into realms in which conjecture is the only basis of inference. The very fact of the appearance of arbitrary constants in the solutions of problems like the above, treated by the method of this work, seems to imply, that definite solution is impossible, and to mark the point where inquiry ought to stop.

On page 370:

It has been said, that the principle involved in the above and in similar applications is that of the equal distribution of our knowledge, or rather of our ignorance—the assigning to different states of things of which we know nothing, and upon the very ground that we know nothing, equal degrees of probability. I apprehend, however, that this is an arbitrary method of procedure.

And finally, on page 375:

These results only illustrate the fact, that when the defect of data is supplied by hypothesis, the solutions will, in general, vary with the nature of the hypotheses assumed; so that the question still remains, only more definite in form, whether the principles of the theory of probabilities serve to guide us in the election of such hypotheses. I have already expressed my conviction that they do not—a conviction strengthened by other reasons than those above stated. ... Still it is with diffidence that I express my dissent on these points from mathematicians generally, and more especially from one who, of English writers, has most fully entered into the spirit and the methods of Laplace; and I venture to hope, that a question, second to none other in the Theory of Probabilities in importance, will receive the careful attention which it deserves.

These quotations, which I have picked out from the rather lengthy mathematical examples which Boole developed are sufficient to exhibit unmistakably his logical point of view. He does not, indeed, go so far as to say that no statements in terms of mathematical probability can properly be based on data of the kind considered, but he is entirely clear in rejecting the application to these cases of the method of arriving at such statements which, in the absence of appropriate data, introduced values of the probabilities *a priori* supported only by a questionable axiom.

His phrase, moreover, on supplying by hypothesis what is lacking in the data, points to an abuse very congenial to certain twentieth-century writers.

John Venn and the Rule of Succession

An immediate inference from Bayes' theorem assigning the frequency distribution

$$\frac{(a+b+1)!}{a!\,b!}\, p^a(1-p)^b\, dp \qquad \text{Eq. 7}$$

to the probability of success of an event, supposed constant, after *a* successes have been observed in $a+b$ independent trials, is to calculate the probability of success of a new trial, of the same kind as the others and, like them, independent. For this we have only to multiply the frequency element above by *p* and integrate between the limits 0 and 1. The result takes the simple form

$$(a+1)/(a+b+2), \qquad \text{Eq. 8}$$

and this inference came to be known as the Rule of Succession; it is often quoted in the form taken when $b = 0$, as leading to the probability $(a+1)/(a+2)$.

It should be emphasized, as it has sometimes passed unnoticed, that such a rule can be based on Bayes' theorem only on certain conditions. It requires that i) the record of a successes out of $a+b$ trials constitutes the whole of the information available; ii) the successive trials are independent in the sense that the success or failure of one trial has no effect in favouring the success or failure of subsequent tests, which have in each case the same probabilities.

During the long period over which its correctness was unquestioned, the Rule of Succession had been eagerly seized upon by logicians as providing a solid mathematical basis for inductive reasoning. In his *Logic of Chance* (14), Venn, who was developing the concept of probability as an objective fact, verifiable by observations of frequency, devotes a chapter to demolishing the Rule of Succession, and this, from a writer of his weight and dignity, had an undoubted effect in shaking the confidence of mathematicians in its mathematical foundation.

Venn, however, does not discuss its foundation, and perhaps was not aware that it had a mathematical basis demonstrated by Laplace; that like other mathematical theorems it contained stipulations specific for its validity; and that in particular it rested upon the supposed, though disputable, axiom used for the demonstration of Bayes' proposition. As in other cases in which a work of demolition is undertaken with great confidence, there is no doubt that Venn in this chapter uses arguments of a quality which he would scarcely have employed had he regarded the matter as one open to rational debate.

After giving instances of not very unreasonable inferences drawn by Laplace and De Morgan with the aid of the Rule, Venn writes (14, p. 180):

Let us add an example or two more of our own. I have observed it rain three days successively,—I have found on three separate occasions that to give my fowls strychnine has caused their death,—I have given a false alarm of fire on three different occasions and found the people come to help me each time.

These examples seem to be little more than rhetorical sallies intended to overwhelm an opponent with ridicule. They scarcely attempt to conform with the conditions of Bayes' theorem, or of the rule of succession based upon it. In the last case the reader is to presume, the same neighbours having been deceived on three occasions, that on the fourth they will be for this reason less ready to exert themselves; that is to say, the successive trials are not even conceived to be independent. Objection could be made on the same ground to the first example, which is perhaps particularly unrealistic in that three rainy days are postulated to comprise the whole of the subject's experience of days wet or fine. Perhaps the example could be repaired by making him arrive by air in a region of unknown climate; if so, Bayes' postulate implies that the region has been chosen at random from an aggregate of regions in each of which the probability of rain is constant and independent from day to day, while this probability varies from region to region in an equal distribution from 0 to 1. If applied to cases in which this information is lacking the inference is not indeed ridiculous, though I should agree with Venn that it would often be found to be mistaken, if put to the test of repeated trials, and it can scarcely be doubted that Bayes would have taken the same view. A climate without the unnatural feature of independence of weather from day to day, and therefore without conforming to the conditions of Bayes' theorem, might yet justify the Rule of Succession, in the limited form here used, if the proportion of all rainy days falling in spells of n successive rainy days were

$$\frac{4n}{(n+1)(n+2)(n+3)}; \qquad \text{Eq. 9}$$

and it is clearly a question of ascertainable fact, and not of personal predilection, whether the climate of any part of the world conforms to such a rule.[1]

1. While this simple distribution suffices to justify the Rule of Succession when applied to experience of only wet or of only fine days, the general form of the rule requires that the spells of wet and fine weather must

The standardization of drugs by an experimental assay of their potency often involves the determination of the 50% lethal dose, or, that which, with the population of animals sampled for testing, will have a probability of 50% of killing in each case. The rhetorical force of Venn's example lies in the presumption that much more than the 50% lethal dose of strychnine was employed, but a valid criticism of Bayes' theorem through the failure of the Rule of Succession requires a less cavalier treatment of the example. If, for example, 50 strengths of dose were made up at concentrations capable of killing 1%, 3%, ..., 99% of the animals to be tested, and if each experiment consisted in choosing one of these doses, with equal probability, and applying this dose to each of four hens chosen at random; of ascertaining first if each of three of these hens had died, and if so of predicting that the fourth would die also, the proportion of successes would agree closely with the fraction 4/5 given by the rule of succession. If, on the contrary, the doses were spaced in toxic content between the 1% and the 99% dosages, either in arithmetical or in geometrical progression, the forecast, though by no means a ridiculous estimate, would doubtless be somewhat in error. *Knowledge* of the experimental conditions might thus justify the rule, though it cannot rationally be based on ignorance of them.

It seems that in this chapter Venn was to such an extent carried away by his confidence

---

be arranged to fulfil further conditions. Thus the frequency with which two successive spells are of u and v days respectively must be

$$\frac{6(u+1)!(v+1)!}{(u+v+3)!}, \qquad \text{Eq. 10}$$

consistent with the marginal frequency for u and v

$$\frac{12(u!)}{(u+3)!}. \qquad \text{Eq. 11}$$

Three successive spells of lengths u, v and w, in that order, have frequency

$$\frac{6(v+2)!(u+w)!}{(u+v+w+3)!}, \qquad \text{Eq. 12}$$

while four spells of lengths t, u, v, w will have a frequency

$$\frac{6(t+v+1)!(u+w+1)!}{(t+u+v+w+3)!} \qquad \text{Eq. 13.}$$

that the rule of induction he was criticizing was indefensible in many of its seeming applications, and by his eagerness to dispose of it finally, that he became uncritical of the quality of the arguments he used. A most serious lapse of a general character appears on page 181 at the beginning of Section 9:

It is surely a mere evasion of the difficulty to assert, as is sometimes done, that the rule is to be employed in those cases only in which we do not know anything beforehand about the mode and frequency of occurrence of the events. The truth or falsity of the rule cannot be in any way dependent upon the ignorance of the man who uses it. His ignorance affects himself only, and corresponds to no distinction in the things.

Taken in its sweeping generality such an argument seems to imply that the extent of the observational data available can have no bearing on the nature or precision of our inferences from them; that a jury ignorant of certain facts ought to give the same verdict as one to whom they have been presented! The precise specification of our knowledge is, however, the same as the precise specification of our ignorance. Certainly, the observer's knowledge or ignorance may have no effect on external objects, but the extent of the observations to which his reasoning is applied does make a selection of those material systems to which he imagines his conclusions to be applicable; and the objective frequencies observed in such selected systems may depend, and indeed must depend if inductive reasoning have any validity, on the observational basis by which the selection is effected, and on which the reasoning is based.

It is certain that Venn understood this in respect of the inductive process generally, and that nothing but inadvertence can have led him to develop, in criticizing "the rule," a mode of argument fatal equally to all inferences based on experience.

Perhaps the most important result of Venn's criticism was the departure made by Professor G. Chrystal in eliminating from his celebrated textbook of *Algebra* (3) the whole of the traditional material usually presented under the headings of *Inverse Probability* and of the

Theory of Evidence. Chrystal does not discuss the objections to this material, but expresses the opinion that "many of the criticisms of Mr. Venn on this part of the doctrine of chances are unanswerable. The mildest judgement we could pronounce would be the following words of De Morgan himself, who seems, after all, to have 'doubted': 'My own impression derived from this and many other circumstances connected with the analysis of probabilities, is, that the mathematical results have outrun their interpretation.' " (Chapter xxxvi, p. 604.)

It should be noted that De Morgan's remark has been quoted clean out of its context; that he was not writing on inverse probability, nor even on the theory of evidence, but about the curiously ubiquitous success of methods based on the Normal law of errors, even when applied to cases in which such a law is not accurately plausible. In fact the passage (from the Fourth Appendix, the title of which is "On the average result of a number of observations") goes on:

and that some simple explanation of the force and meaning of the celebrated integral, whose values are tabulated at the end of this work, will one day be found to connect the higher and lower parts of the subject with a degree of simplicity which will at once render useless (except to the historian) all the works hitherto written.

In reality, the introduction of the inverse method was to De Morgan (11, p. vi) one of the most important advances to be recorded in the history of the theory of probability. I have already quoted his opinion to this effect, in the introduction to my book on *The Design of Experiments* (5):

There was also another circumstance which stood in the way of the first investigators, namely, the not having considered, or, at least, not having discovered the method of reasoning from the happening of an event to the probability of one or another cause. The questions treated in the third chapter of this work could not therefore be attempted by them. Given an hypothesis presenting the necessity of one or another out of a certain, and not very large, number of consequences, they could determine the chance that any given one or other of those consequences should arrive; but given an event as having happened, and which might have been the consequence of either of several different

causes, or explicable by either of several different hypotheses, they could not infer the probability with which the happening of the event should cause the different hypotheses to be viewed. But, just as in natural philosophy the selection of an hypothesis by means of observed facts is always preliminary to any attempt at deductive discovery; so in the application of the notion of probability to the actual affairs of life, the process of reasoning from observed events to their most probable antecedents must go before the direct use of any such antecedent, cause, hypothesis, or whatever it may be correctly termed. These two obstacles, therefore, the mathematical difficulty, and the want of an inverse method, prevented the science from extending its views beyond problems of that simple nature which games of chance present.

If he ever checked the reference to his quotation, therefore, Chrystal was scarcely playing fair. His case as well as Venn's illustrates the truth that the best causes tend to attract to their support the worst arguments, which seems to be equally true in the intellectual and in the moral sense.

The Meaning of Probability

Whatever view may be preferred on the controversial issues which the quotations set out above have been selected to illustrate, it is evident beyond question that highly competent, or even illustrious, mathematicians had formed upon them quite irreconcilable opinions; and this appearance of inability to find a common ground is not lessened by a perusal of what has been written in our own century.

Since there is no reason to doubt the purely mathematical ability of these writers, it is natural to suspect a semantic difficulty due to an imperfect analysis of words regarded as being too simple to be elucidated by further examination, such as the word "probability" itself. Of course, each writer has "defined" this word to his own satisfaction. Mathematical definition is, however, often no more than a succinct statement of the axioms to be applied when the word occurs in deductive mathematical reasoning, and may pay less attention than is needed to the conditions of the correct applicability of the term in the real world. It is these conditions of applicability which are properly the concern of those responsible for Applied Mathematics.

Indeed, I believe that a rather simple semantic confusion may be indicated as relevant to the issues discussed, as soon as consideration is given to the meaning that the word probability must have to anyone so much practically interested as is a gambler, who, for example, stands to gain or lose money, in the event of an ace being thrown with a single die. To such a man the information supplied by a familiar mathematical statement such as: "If a aces are thrown in n trials, the probability that the difference in absolute value between a/n and $1/6$ shall exceed any positive value ε, however small, shall tend to zero as the number n is increased indefinitely," will seem not merely remote, but also incomplete and lacking in definiteness in its application to the particular throw in which he is interested. Indeed, by itself it says nothing about that throw. It is obvious, moreover, that many subsets of future throws, which may include his own, can be shown to give probabilities, in this sense, either greater or less than $1/6$. Before the limiting ratio of the whole set can be accepted as applicable to a particular throw, a second condition must be satisfied, namely that before the die is cast no such subset can be *recognized*. This is a necessary and sufficient condition for the applicability of the limiting ratio of the entire aggregate of possible future throws as the probability of any one particular throw. On this condition we may think of a particular throw, or of a succession of throws, as a *random* sample from the aggregate, which is in this sense subjectively homogeneous and without recognizable stratification.

Makers of the standard apparatus of games of chance, dice, cards, roulettes, etc., take great care to satisfy both the requirements of a sufficiently specific statement of what is meant by probability. If either the long-run frequencies were faulty, or, in particular, if there were any means of foreseeing, even to a limited extent, the outcome of their use in a particular case, the apparatus, or, perhaps, the method of using them, would be judged defective for the purpose for which they were made.

This fundamental requirement for the applicability to individual cases of the concept of classical probability shows clearly the role of subjective ignorance, as well as that of objective knowledge in a typical probability statement. It has been often recognized that any probability statement, being a rigorous statement involving uncertainty, has less factual content than an assertion of certain fact would have, and at the same time has more factual content than a statement of complete ignorance. The *knowledge* required for such a statement refers to a well-defined aggregate, or population of possibilities within which the limiting frequency ratio must be exactly known. The necessary *ignorance* is specified by our inability to discriminate any of the different sub-aggregates having different limiting frequency ratios, such as must always exist. Laplace's definition of probability, in which he actually speaks of "événements," is so worded that this necessary stipulation of ignorance in respect of particular events can be transferred to *hypotheses*, so as to imply in Boole's words "the assigning to different states of things of which we know nothing, and upon the very ground that we know nothing, equal degrees of probability." Has Laplace not in fact passed unawares from proposition (*a*) below to proposition (*b*)?

(*a*) A possible outcome must be assigned equal probabilities in different future throws, because we can draw no relevant distinction between these in advance.

(*b*) Hypotheses must be judged equally probable *a priori* if no relevant distinction can be drawn between them.

How extremely conservative was the tradition of mathematical teaching is shown by the slowness with which the opinions of Boole, Venn and Chrystal were appreciated. The reluctance naturally felt to abandoning a false start was certainly enhanced by the fact that, so far as the problem of scientific induction was concerned, nothing had been put forward to replace that which had been taken away.

The gap seems to have been felt only sub-consciously. In many cases it must have been clear that it was possible for data of great value to the formation of our scientific ideas to be presented, and yet for there to be no defensible basis, in the light of the criticisms which had been made, for the application of Bayes' theorem. Many mathematicians must have felt that with a proper restatement, the theorem, or one fulfilling the same purpose in inductive reasoning, could be set on its feet again. Indeed, the two leading statisticians in England at the beginning of the twentieth century, K. Pearson (12) and F. Y. Edgeworth (4, p. 387) both put forward attempts, dis-cordant indeed and both abortive, to justify the mode of reasoning in which no doubt each had been brought up, but which had since been discredited.

The reader of this preliminary chapter will have seized my meaning if he perceives that the different situations in which uncertain inferences may be attempted admit of logical distinctions which should guide our procedure. That it may be that the data are such as to allow us to apply Bayes' theorem; or, secondly, that we may be able validly to apply a test of significance to discredit a hypothesis the ex-pectations from which are widely at variance with ascertained fact. If we use the term rejection for our attitude to such a hypothesis, it should be clearly understood that no irreversible decision has been taken; that, as rational beings, we are prepared to be con-vinced by future evidence that appearances were deceptive, and that in fact a very remark-able and exceptional coincidence had taken place. Such a test of significance does not authorize us to make any statement about the hypothesis in question in terms of mathe-matical probability, while, none the less, it does afford direct guidance as to what elements we may reasonably incorporate in any theories we may be attempting to form in explanation of objectively observable phenomena. Thirdly,

the logical situation we are confronted with may admit of the consideration of a series, or, more usually, of a continuum of hypotheses, one of which *must* be true, and among which a selection may be made, and that selection justified, so far as may be, by statistical reasoning. The stasis or deadlock which had set in by the end of the century has been, I shall hope to show, in fact, released by the consideration of these diverse possibilities.

References

1. T. Bayes (1763). An essay towards solving a problem in the doctrine of chances. *Phil. Trans. Roy. Soc.*, vol. 53, p. 370.
2. G. Boole (1854). *The Laws of Thought.* Dover Publications, Inc., New York (n.d.), with original pagination.
3. G. Chrystal (1886). *Algebra.* Adam and Charles Black, London.
4. F. Y. Edgeworth (1908). On the probable errors of frequency-constants. *J. Roy. Stat. Soc.*, vol. 71, pp. 381–397.
5. R. A. Fisher (1935–1953). *The Design of Experiments.* Oliver and Boyd, Edinburgh.
6. R. A. Fisher (1958). Mathematical probability in the natural sciences. *18th Int. Congr. of Pharm. Sciences.* Brussels, Sept. 1958.
7. P.-S. marquis de Laplace (1812, 1820). Théorie analytique des probabilités. Paris. 1st ed., p. 178. 3rd ed. (1820), preface, p. iv.
8. J. Michell (1767). An inquiry into the probable parallax, and magnitude of the fixed stars, from the quantity of light which they afford us, and the particular circumstances of their situation. *Phil. Trans.*, vol. 57, pp. 234–264.
9. A. de Moivre (1718, 1738, 1756). *Doctrine of Chances.*
10. P. De Montmort (1708, 1714). Essai d'analyse sur les jeux de hazards.
11. A. De Morgan (1838). *An Essay on Probabili-ties and on their Application to Life Contin-gencies and Insurance Offices.* Longman and Co., London.
12. K. Pearson (1920). The fundamental problem of practical statistics. *Biometrika*, vol. 13, pp. 1–16.
13. *The Dictionary of National Biography.* Oxford University Press.
14. J. Venn (1866, 1876). *The Logic of Chance.* Macmillan and Co., London.

R. SCHLAIFER

29 The Meaning of Probability

The Problem of Decision under Uncertainty

When all of the facts bearing on a business decision are accurately known—when the decision is made "under certainty"—careless thinking is the only reason why the decision should turn out, after the fact, to have been wrong. But when the relevant facts are not all known—when the decision is made "under uncertainty"—it is impossible to make sure that every decision will turn out to have been right in this same sense. Under uncertainty, the businessman is forced, in effect, to gamble. His previous actions have put him in a position where he *must* place bets, hoping that he will win but knowing that he may lose. Under such circumstances, a right decision consists in the choice of the best possible bet, whether it is won or lost after the fact. The following examples are typical of situations in which business decisions must be made and judged in this way.

An Inventory Problem. A retailer is about to place an order for a number of units of a perishable commodity which spoils if it is not sold by the end of the day on which it is stocked. Each unit costs the retailer $1; the retail price is $5. The retailer does not know what the demand for the item will be, but he must nevertheless decide on a definite number of units to stock.

A Scrap-allowance Problem. A manufacturer has contracted to deliver at least 100 good pieces of a nonstandard product at a fixed price for the lot. He feels virtually sure that there will be some defectives among the first 100 pieces produced; and since setting up for a second production run to fill out a shortage would cost a substantial amount of money, he wishes to schedule some additional pieces on the original run as a scrap allowance. On the other hand, once 100 good pieces have been produced the direct manufacturing cost of any additional production will be a total loss, and therefore he does not wish to make the scrap allowance excessively large. If the manufacturer knew exactly how many pieces would have to be produced in order to get exactly 100 good pieces, it would be easy to set the "right" size for the production order; but he must decide on some definite size for the order even though he does not know the "right" size.

An Investment Problem. A manufacturer is about to tool up for production of a newly developed product. This product can be manufactured by either of two processes, one of which requires a relatively small capital investment but high labor cost per unit produced while the other will have much lower labor costs but requires a much greater investment. The former process will thus be the better one if sales of the product are low while the latter will be better if sales are high; but the manufacturer must choose between the two processes without knowing what his sales will actually be.

A Marketing Problem. The brand manager for a certain grocery product is considering a change of package design in the hope that the new package will attract more attention on the shelf and thereby increase sales. He has done a certain amount of store testing and has found that during the test weeks sales of the new package were greater than sales of the old in some stores but that the contrary was true in

This material appears as Chapter I in *Introduction to Statistics for Business Decisions*, Robert Schlaifer, Professor of Business Administration, Harvard University (New York: McGraw-Hill Book Company, Inc., 1961). It is reproduced here by specific permission of the copyright holder, The President and Fellows of Harvard College.

other stores. He still feels uncertain whether adoption of the new package will increase or decrease his total national sales, but he must nevertheless either decide on one package or the other or else decide to spend more money on additional testing; in the latter case he must decide whether he should simply continue the test for a few more weeks in the same stores he has already used or spend still more money to draw new stores into his sample.

THE PAYOFF TABLE

The essential characteristics of all four of these problems, and of all problems which we shall study in this course, are the following.

1. A choice must be made among several possible *acts*.
2. The chosen act will ultimately lead to some definite profit (possibly negative), but for at least some of the acts the amount of this profit is unknown because it will be determined by some *event* which cannot be predicted with certainty.

The first step in analyzing any such problem is to lay out all the possible acts and all their possible consequences in some systematic fashion, and we shall do this for the inventory problem as an example.

In the inventory problem, an "act" is a decision to stock some particular number of units; the "event" is the number of units which the customers will actually demand. If we suppose that the retailer's space limits the number of units stocked to a maximum of 5, then remembering that each unit stocked costs $1 while each sale brings in $5 of revenue we can describe the whole problem by a table like Table 1, where each column corresponds to a particular act while each row corresponds to a particular event. Such a table is known as a *payoff table*.

COMPARISON OF ACTS

If we compare any two acts (columns) in Table 1, we see that one of the two will be more profitable if certain events occur while the other will be more profitable if other events occur; but when we actually choose among these acts we are implicitly if not explicitly making a single, unconditional evaluation of each act. We are saying that in some sense one of the acts is "better" than any of the others.

The Minimax Principle. One *possible* way of evaluating acts under uncertainty is to follow the so-called *minimax* principle, according to which the decision maker should look only at the *worst* possible consequence of each act and then choose the act for which the worst consequences is *least bad*. He should, in other words, *mini*mize the *max*imum damage which the world can do him. Use of the minimax principle has been seriously advocated for problems involving sampling, but we can see its basic implications very clearly by applying it to the problem of Table 1. What it says there is that the retailer should choose the act "stock 0," since with this act the worst that can happen is that he will make no money, whereas any other act *might* result in an actual *loss* of money. Observe that, since the same conclusion would apply to any other item the retailer might stock, the minimax principle implies that the retailer should simply go out of business.

The Principle of Weighing the Possibilities. We shall examine another version of the minimax principle in Chapter 4 and find that it too leads to completely intolerable results. Any sensible businessman will of course immediately reject not only the minimax principle but *any* purely *arbitrary* principle of action under uncertainty and will say that even though the retailer cannot predict demand with *certainty* he ought to know enough about his business and the product in question to have some convictions about what the demand *is likely to be*. If after weighing all the available information the retailer decides that there is very little chance that customers will demand less than 3 or more than 4 units, he will conclude that the only reasonable act is to stock either 3 or 4 units. Choice between these two acts will be a little more complex, since the

Table 1. Payoff table for the inventory example

Event	Act (number of units stocked)					
(number demanded)	0	1	2	3	4	5
0	$0	− $1	− $2	− $3	− $4	− $5
1	0	+ 4	+ 3	+ 2	+ 1	0
2	0	+ 4	+ 8	+ 7	+ 6	+ 5
3	0	+ 4	+ 8	+12	+11	+10
4	0	+ 4	+ 8	+12	+16	+15
5 or more	0	+ 4	+ 8	+12	+16	+20

larger stock will be only $12 − $11 = $1 less profitable than the smaller if there is a demand for only 3 units while it will be all of $16 − $12 = $4 more profitable if 4 units are demanded. Consequently the retailer will want to stock 4 units even if he believes that the chance of a demand for 4 is somewhat less than the chance of a demand for 3; it is only if he believes that the chance of a demand for 4 is relatively *very* slight that he will reduce his stock to 3 units.

Now this informal kind of reasoning works very well when the decision problem is relatively simple, but one quickly becomes confused when the problem is even slightly more complex. Even in our very simple example, it will be hard for the retailer to see through to a satisfying conclusion if he thinks that there is a substantial chance that demand may have any of three or four different values, and in larger problems of the same sort he may well consider a hundred or a thousand different values as possible. What we would like to do, therefore, is find some way of *systematizing* the kind of analysis which a reasonable man uses in simple problems so that it can be effectively applied in more complex problems.

If we look back at the reasoning used by our hypothetical retailer, we see that in essence he proceeded in two steps: he first gave a numerical *value* to the consequence of each possible act given each possible event, but he then attached more *weight* to the consequences corresponding to certain events (demand 3 or 4) than he did to the others. This suggests that it may be possible to systematize the reasoning underlying *any* decision under uncertainty by proceeding as follows:

1. Attach a definite numerical *value* to the consequence of every possible act given every possible event.
2. Attach a definite numerical *weight* to every possible event.
3. For each act separately, use these weights to compute a *weighted average* of all the values attached to that act.
4. Select the act whose weighted-average value is highest.

Our hope is that we can find rules for using the businessman's own knowledge and beliefs in carrying out steps 1 and 2 in such a way that he will *want* to choose the act with the highest computed value instead of relying on mere inspection of a mass of numbers and informal reasoning of the kind described above. If we are to have confidence in these rules in complex situations, they must yield values which seem reasonable to us when applied in very simple situations, and for this reason many of the examples which we shall use in developing these rules will be artificial ones which avoid the complexities of practical business decisions in order to present their really essential features in the simplest possible form. Because the heart of the problem is the uncertainty concerning the event, we shall begin by developing the rules for attaching weights to events.

Events

Before we even start to assign numerical weights to a set of events some one of which will determine the consequence of any act we choose, we obviously must have in mind a clear and complete description of the events which may occur. We usually have considerable latitude in defining the possible events in a given problem, but certain rules must be followed if we are to avoid hopeless confusion.

COLLECTIVELY EXHAUSTIVE EVENTS

If before we started to analyze the inventory problem of Table 1 the retailer had told us that he was absolutely convinced that there would be a demand for at least 2 units, we could just as well have simplified Table 1 by eliminating the rows describing the consequences of the events "demand 0" and "demand 1." In general, impossible events may be totally disregarded if it is convenient to do so, and it is to be emphasized that there is no need to "prove" that an event is impossible before it is eliminated. Our object is to arrive at results which the businessman *wants to accept*, and therefore an event is impossible for our purposes whenever the businessman wants to treat it as impossible.

It is obvious, on the other hand, that we must keep *all* the *possible* events in mind in analyzing any decision problem, since if we fail to include some of the possible events in the payoff table the corresponding consequences will not be duly considered in evaluating the various acts. The same thing can be stated the other way around: the basic list of events must be complete in the sense that *some one of the events on the list is bound to occur*. The events on such a list are called *collectively exhaustive*.

MUTUALLY EXCLUSIVE EVENTS

In the inventory example of Table 1, demand for each specific number of units from 0 to 4 inclusive was treated as a separate event but demands for all numbers of units above 4 were treated as constituting the same event "demand for 5 or more." Obviously we *could* have treated a demand for exactly 5 units as a separate event and assigned it a separate line

in Table 1, and similarly for any larger number of units, but nothing was to be gained by so doing because for every act under consideration the consequences of the event "demand for 5" were identical to the consequences of the event "demand for 6" or the event "demand for 7" and so forth.

Careless grouping of events can easily lead to confusion, however. It is obvious that potentially separate events must not be grouped if their consequences differ for any act under consideration. We cannot treat "demand for 3 or 4" or "demand for 4 or more" as a single event in constructing a payoff table for our inventory example. What is often less obvious is that we must not have events with *overlapping definitions* on our list even if it is possible to give a clear description of the consequences of all acts in terms of such a list.

Suppose, for example, that we are given a choice of one or the other of two tickets in a lottery to be conducted by drawing one ball from an urn containing four kinds of balls: dotted red, striped red, dotted green, and striped green. The first ticket entitles the holder to a prize of value V if the ball drawn from the urn is either red or striped; the second entitles the holder to the same prize if the ball is dotted green. Table 2 gives a perfectly clear

Table 2

	Act (choice of ticket)	
Event	1	2
Red	V	0
Striped	V	0
Dotted green	0	V

description of the conditions under which the prize will be awarded, but confusion is bound to arise if we base our analysis of this decision problem on this table because the events "red" and "striped" will *both* occur if a striped red ball is drawn. To illustrate the difficulty by an extreme case, suppose that we know that *all* the red balls are striped and that all the striped balls are red. Then the events "red" and "striped" are really the same event counted twice, and any weight which we attach to this event will be counted twice in evaluating the acts under consideration.

This kind of difficulty can be avoided by basing our analysis on any of the three lists of events shown in Table 3, since the occurrence

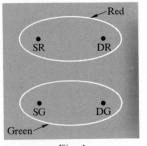

Fig. 1

Table 3

A	B	C
Striped red	Red	Red or striped
Dotted red	Striped green	Dotted green
Striped green	Dotted green	
Dotted green		

of any one event on any of these lists means that *no other event on the same list can possibly occur*. The events on any such list are said to be *mutually exclusive*.

ELEMENTARY AND COMPOUND EVENTS

The importance of mutual exclusiveness is so great that it is worth the trouble to find a way of visualizing it. The events on list *A* of Table 3 are obviously mutually exclusive because they have been defined without any grouping at all—balls which differ in *any* respect have been classified as separate events in this list. These four events will be called the *elementary events* of this problem.

Any set of *elementary* events can be visualized as a set of *points* in a diagram like Figure 1, 2, or 3, where the points represent the four elementary events of list *A* in Table 3. Events such as "red" or "striped" can then be visualized as corresponding to a *group of points* representing elementary events: the events "red" and "green" are depicted in Figure 1, the events "striped" and "dotted" in Figure 2. Such events will be called *compound events*, and it is obvious that

Two compound events are mutually exclusive if they contain no elementary events in common.

In Figure 3 we illustrate the difficulty with the events used in Table 2: the point corresponding to the elementary event "striped red" is included in *both* the compound events "red" and "striped."

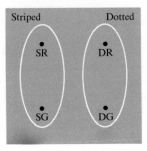

Fig. 2

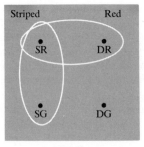

Fig. 3

The Basic Rules Governing the Assignment of Weights

We are now ready to develop rules for using a definite number to represent the weight which a decision maker attaches to each of the events in a set of mutually exclusive and collectively exhaustive events. Since we propose to use these numbers in computing weighted averages, our rules must be such that these weighted averages will "make sense"—i.e., they must be such that the decision maker will *want* to choose the act with the highest weighted-average value. On the other hand, this is the *only* way in which we shall use these weights; and if we find that the requirement just stated can be met by more than one set of rules, we are free to choose the one which is most convenient.

To see whether we do have any such choice, let us review the way in which any weighted average is computed. In the first two columns of Table 4a we show a set of four values with a weight attached to each value; the meaning of the values and the weights is irrelevant for our present purpose. The weighted average is computed in three steps:

1. Each value is multiplied by its weight to form the products shown in the third column of Table 4a.
2. Both the weights and the products are added to obtain the sums shown at the bottoms of their respective columns.
3. The sum of the products is divided by the sum of the weights to obtain the weighted average.

Observe now that exactly the same weighted average is obtained in Table 4b by using weights each of which is one-tenth as large as the corresponding weight in Table 4a. It is obvious that this example can be generalized: dividing every weight in a set by the same nonzero number has no effect on any weighted average computed by use of these weights. In other words, *weighted averages are affected by the proportions among the weights attached to the values being averaged but not by the absolute sizes of the weights.*

This means that we are free to specify that the weights assigned to a set of mutually exclusive and collectively exhaustive events shall add up to any amount we choose, and unless we do make such a specification it will be possible to represent the same beliefs by many different sets of weights. If we allow this, confusion is bound to arise, and we shall

therefore adopt the following *fundamental convention* as the first of our basic rules for assigning weights to events:

Rule 1. The sum of the weights assigned to any set of mutually exclusive and collectively exhaustive events shall be 1.

The choice of 1 rather than some other number for the specified total is purely a matter of convenience; it eliminates the need to divide by the sum of the weights in order to convert the sum of products into a weighted average.

Table 4a

Value	Weight	Product
3	2	6
2	1	2
7	3	21
5	4	20
	10	49

Weighted average $= \dfrac{49}{10} = 4.9$

Table 4b

Value	Weight	Product
3	.2	.6
2	.1	.2
7	.3	2.1
5	4	2.0
	1.0	4.9

Weighted average $= \dfrac{4.9}{1.0} = 4.9$

Having adopted this fundamental convention, we are now ready to develop rules which *must* be observed in assigning weights if the resulting weighted averages are to make sense. In so doing it will be well to have an extremely simple decision problem actually before us, and we may as well use the same problem which we have already used to illustrate the concept of mutually exclusive events. Three lists of collectively exhaustive and mutually exclusive events suitable for analysis of this problem were shown in Table 3; payoff tables based on two of these three lists are shown in Tables 5a and 5b.

Let us first consider the problem of evaluating ticket number 2. Since this ticket pays off only if the event "dotted green" occurs, three facts are immediately obvious about the value we will assign to this ticket.

1. If we are absolutely convinced, for whatever reason, that the ball will *not* be dotted green, we will value the ticket at 0.
2. If we are absolutely convinced that the ball *will* be dotted green, we will value the ticket at V—it is just as good as the prize itself.
3. If we are uncertain about the event, we will value the ticket at something between 0 and V.

Table 5a

	Act (*choice of ticket*)	
Event	1	2
Striped red	V	0
Dotted red	V	0
Striped green	V	0
Dotted green	0	V

Table 5b

	Act (*choice of ticket*)	
Event	1	2
Red or striped	V	0
Dotted green	0	V

Now if we assign numerical weights to the events in Table 5a or 5b and use these to compute a weighted average of the values in the column describing ticket number 2, this weighted average will be simply V times the weight we assign to the event "dotted green"— recall that by Rule 1 the sum of the weights assigned to all the events in either table must be 1 and therefore that as in Table 4b the sum of products is left unchanged when it is divided by the sum of the weights. But if this is so, then our weighted-average valuation will agree with the three direct valuations listed just above only if we assign weight 0 to an event which we believe impossible, weight 1 to an event which we believe certain, and some

intermediate number to any doubtful event. We thus arrive at our second fundamental rule:

Rule 2. The weight assigned to any event shall be a number between 0 and 1 inclusive, 0 representing complete conviction that the event will not occur and 1 representing complete conviction that it will occur.

We now turn our attention to the valuation of ticket number 1. If we compute a weighted average of the values in the column describing ticket number 1 in Table 5a, we will have the sum of three terms:

$V \times$ weight of "striped red,"
$V \times$ weight of "dotted red,"
$V \times$ weight of "striped green,"

and this sum is equal to V times the sum of the three weights. If on the other hand we compute a weighted average of the values in the corresponding column of Table 5b, we will have simply V times the weight of the compound event "red *or* striped." We conclude that the weight assigned to the event "red or striped" must be the sum of the weights assigned to the three mutually exclusive events of which it is composed, and we generalize this example to obtain our last basic rule:

Rule 3. If two or more mutually exclusive events are grouped into a single event, the weight attached to this single event shall be equal to the sum of the weights attached to the original events.

Observe that this rule does *not* hold for events which are not mutually exclusive. Suppose, for example, that for some reason or other we have assigned the weights shown in Table 6 to the four mutually exclusive events

Table 6

Event	*Weight*
Striped red	.4
Dotted red	.3
Striped green	.2
Dotted green	.1
	——
	1.0

of Table 5a. We can use Rule 3 to show that the weight assigned to "red" must be $.4 + .3 = .7$ or to show that the weight assigned to "striped" must be $.4 + .2 = .6$, but we *cannot* add these two results to obtain $.7 + .6 = 1.3$ for the weight to be assigned to "red or striped"; if we do, we are double-counting the .4 weight originally assigned to the event "striped red."

The Standard Lottery

Although the three basic rules which we have derived above may seem so broad that they fail to specify exactly what set of numbers should be used as the weights in any given problem of decision under uncertainty, we shall now see that this is not so. In any situation there will exist one and only one set of weights which will both comply with these rules and express the decision maker's attitudes toward a set of collectively exhaustive and mutually exclusive events.

Suppose that we are offered a free chance at a prize of value V under the following conditions. Balls numbered 1 to 100 have been placed in an urn and one of these balls has then been drawn and put in a closed box. We are presented with 100 tickets numbered from 1 to 100 and are allowed to choose one of them. If the number we choose matches the number on the ball which has been drawn from the urn, we will receive the prize; if not, we receive nothing. Suppose further that even though the prize is one which we are extremely anxious to win, we do not feel that it is worth the slightest effort to look for a ticket with any particular number on it; we simply take the first one which comes to hand.

In such a situation we shall say that *in our opinion* the 100 possible events are *equally likely*. Notice very carefully that we do not and *cannot* "prove" that the events are "in fact" equally likely: the fact is that the ball which has been drawn has some one particular number and no other. But even though anyone who *knew* which ball has been drawn would not be indifferent among the 100 tickets, *our* decisions must be based on what *we* know or believe about the facts of the world—they *cannot* be based on the unknown truth about these facts. Therefore if *we* are indifferent in the way described, then *for us* the 100 events are equally likely *by definition*.

Now if our state of mind as just described is to be described by numerical weights attached to the 100 possible events 1, 2, . . . , 100, it is clear that *these weights must all be equal*. If the sum of these 100 equal numbers is to be 1, as required by Rule 1, it is also clear that the number attached to each event must be 1/100. Rule 3 then tells us that events such as "ball number 2 or 7" must have weight $1/100 + 1/100 = 2/100$, that events such as "any ball numbered between 1 and 37 inclusive" must have weight 37/100, and so forth. Thus while Rule 2 specified only that the weight attached to any event must be a number between 0 and 1 inclusive, we have found a way of selecting a specific number within this range to describe our attitude toward any conceivable event in this lottery.

What is more important, a *businessman can find the unique set of weights which describes his attitudes in a more complex situation by using a lottery of this sort as a standard of comparison.* In order to decide what weight to assign to the event "demand 0" in our inventory example, the retailer can imagine that he is given a choice between a certain number of tickets in the standard lottery with a prize of value V as described above and the right to receive *this same prize* in the event of "demand 0." If in his opinion the right to receive this prize in the event of "demand 0" has exactly the same value as 18 tickets in the standard lottery, then *by definition* he considers these two events equally likely and he should assign weight 18/100 to the event "demand 0." (It goes without saying that if the standard lottery with 100 balls does not offer a fine enough division, the retailer can substitute a similar lottery with more balls. If he feels that the right to receive the prize in case of demand 0 is worth more than 18 tickets but less than 19 in a lottery with 100 equally likely events, he may decide that it is equivalent to 183 tickets in a lottery with 1000 equally likely events.)

Having assigned a weight to the event "demand 0," the retailer can proceed in the same way to assign weights to all the other events in Table 1. These weights must of course be such that their total is 1, and therefore what the retailer is really doing is placing the set of collectively exhaustive and mutually exclusive events shown in Table 1 into one-to-one correspondence with a set of collectively exhaustive and mutually exclusive events in the standard lottery. When he is through, the event "demand 0" will correspond, say, to the event "ball numbered between 1 and 18 inclusive," the event "demand 1" to balls 19 to 52, and so forth. It is perhaps worth remarking that we are in no sense assuming that a businessman will actually be as ready to gamble on balls drawn from an urn as to make decisions concerning his regular business. We are simply assuming that a rational person can with practice *think abstractly about his feelings of certainty and uncertainty in any given situation*, regardless of any feelings he may have about any other aspects of the situation.

Logical Consistency and the Mathematical Theory of Probability

In addition to checking to see that the weights assigned to the events of Table 1 obey the fundamental convention expressed by Rule 1, the retailer may do well to check whether he is satisfied with some of the logical consequences which result when Rule 3 is applied to these weights. It is easy to assign either too small or too large a weight to an individual event in a long list of events, and after assigning weight .18 to "demand 0" and weight .34 to "demand 1" the retailer may find that the weight .18 + .34 = .52 which he has thus *implicitly* assigned to the compound event "demand less than 2" is not what he would have assigned if he had thought directly about that event. If so, he must reconcile this *logical inconsistency* before proceeding further with the analysis of his problem.

In many problems such checks for logical consistency are of really crucial importance. To cite a very simple but famous example, the mathematician D'Alembert assigned weight 1/3 to the occurrence of one heads in two tosses of a coin, arguing that the pair of tosses must produce 0, 1, or 2 heads and that in his opinion these three events were equally likely. To see whether we would share this attitude we may reason as follows. An *elementary* event of a pair of tosses of a coin is described by stating the results of each of the two tosses in the order in which they occurred. If we use *HT* to denote the elementary event "heads on first toss, tails on second toss" and similar notation for all the other possibilities, the four possible elementary events of the double toss are *HH, HT, TH,* and *TT*. If we feel that *these* four events are equally likely and therefore assign weight 1/4 to each of them, we can add the weights assigned to *HT* and *TH* and find that we have implicitly assigned weight 1/2 rather than 1/3 to the compound event "one heads." To state the conclusion the other way around, D'Alembert implicitly assigned the same total weight to the *two* events *HT* and *TH* that he assigned to each of the single events *HH* and *TT*.

Assignments of weights in more complex problems are still more in need of this kind of check. As a practical business example, consider the scrap-allowance problem which was sketched at the beginning of this chapter. The actual payoff table for this problem is too complex to discuss at this point, but it is easy to see that because a new setup will be required if less than 100 good pieces are produced on the first run, it will be necessary to assign weights to such events as "more than 80 defectives in a production run of 180 pieces." An elementary event of a run of 180 pieces can be described by a sequence of 180 *g*'s and *d*'s, *g* denoting a good piece and *d* a defective; and in some cases the manufacturer may be able to check any weight he assigns directly to the event "more than 80 defectives" by assigning weights to these elementary events just as we assigned weights to sequences such as *HT* in order to check D'Alembert's probability. To consider only the simplest possible case, suppose that the manufacturer feels that any one of the 180 pieces is as likely to be defective as it is to be good and assigns *equal* weight to every possible elementary event. The weight which he has implicitly assigned to the event "more than 80 defectives" can then be computed by simply counting the total number of possible sequences of 180 *g*'s and *d*'s, counting the number of sequences which contain more than 80 *d*'s, and dividing the latter of these two counts by the former.

It is true that this counting would take a very great deal of time, since it can be shown that the total number of sequences is roughly 1 followed by 54 zeros and a substantial fraction of these sequences contains more than 80 *d*'s. Fortunately, however, actual counting is unnecessary. By the use of simple mathematical short cuts which we shall study later in the course, we can very quickly determine that 922/1000 of the total number of sequences contain more than 80 *d*'s and therefore that the weight which has implicitly been assigned to the even "more than 80 defectives" is .922. We shall also see later in the course that these same mathematical short cuts can be used to compute implicit probabilities when the businessman does not think that each piece produced is as likely to be defective as it is to be good, even though the reasoning about the weights to be assigned to the elementary events is more complex in that case.

The whole body of mathematical short cuts used in computations of this kind is known as the *theory of probability*. Like any *mathematical* "theory," the theory of probability is simply a set of logical deductions from certain basic axioms; the axioms of this particular theory are the following:

1. A probability is a number between 0 and 1 assigned to an event.
2. The sum of the probabilities assigned to a set of mutually exclusive and collectively exhaustive events must be 1.
3. The probability of an event which is composed of a group of mutually exclusive events is the sum of their probabilities.

We are justified in using the theory of probability to calculate "weights" in the way in which we have just used it because we have agreed to assign weights in accordance with these three axioms; the axioms are simply our three "basic rules" for assigning weights presented in slightly different language and with the order of the first and second rules reversed. Henceforth we shall use the word *probability* in exactly the same sense that we have hitherto used the word "weight."

Relative Frequency and the Rational Assessment of Probabilities

Although we have just seen that the theory of probability can be used to show that certain probabilities are mutually inconsistent and although we have said that such inconsistencies must be reconciled before final assignments of probabilities are made, we have as yet said nothing about the way in which a reasonable man will reconcile the inconsistencies he discovers. We have seen that it is inconsistent to assign probability 1/3 to the event "one heads" and at the same time to assign probability 1/4 to each of the events *HT* and *TH*, but we have given no reason for preferring either one of these assignments to the other. It is to this problem that we now turn our attention.

In our original discussion of the meaning of "weights" or probabilities, we emphasized that any probability is necessarily an expression of a personal judgment and is therefore necessarily *subjective* in the sense that two reasonable men may assign different probabilities to the same event. This by no means implies, however, that a reasonable man will assign probabilities *arbitrarily*.

Reasonable men base the probabilities which they assign to events in the real world on their experience with events in the real world, and when two reasonable men have had roughly the same experience with a certain kind of event they assign it roughly the same probability.

OVERWHELMING COMMON EXPERIENCE

As an extreme example of this principle, consider the assessment of the probability of heads on the toss of a coin which has been very carefully inspected and found to be perfectly symmetric and which is to be tossed in such a way that it will spin an extremely large number of times before it falls. Although we may or may not have had direct experience with this particular coin and this particular tossing procedure, almost everyone has observed that other coins tossed in more or less the same way seem to turn up heads roughly half of the time. We have further observed that although the ratio of heads to tosses is often very far from 1/2 in short sequences of tosses, it is usually much closer to 1/2 in long sequences. Still further, we have observed that heads occur about as frequently on tosses which follow heads as on tosses which follow tails, and more generally that heads occur about half the time *whatever* the pattern of heads and tails on previous tosses. Finally, all this experience with coins agrees with our experience with other symmetric objects—all the above statements apply to the event "ace" on the roll of a perfectly symmetric die if 1/6 is substituted for 1/2, and so forth.

On the basis of all this experience we proceed to construct a *physical* theory of the behavior of a tossed coin; in other words, we proceed to make *predictions* about the behavior of a tossed coin. This theory asserts that the fraction of tosses resulting in heads is almost certain to be almost exactly 1/2 if the coin is tossed indefinitely, and it asserts further that in a very long run half the heads will be followed by heads, half the runs of two heads will be followed by a third head, and so forth. We expect, furthermore, that any reasonable man either will adopt this same theory on the basis of his own experience or will adopt it as soon as he is informed of the very great amount of experience which other people have had on the point.

Now such a theory or model of the real world says nothing directly about the *probability* of heads. It predicts what would happen in a very large number of tosses and says nothing whatever about any individual toss. Such a prediction is exactly analogous to a prediction that the average diameter of parts produced by a certain machine will be 1.037 inches, and it is obvious that a predicted average diameter and a probability are not the same thing. On the other hand, a reasonable man will clearly take account of long-run relative frequency in assigning probabilities. If he believes that a certain coin would fall heads half the time when tossed repeatedly under a certain set of conditions, and if he has no way of predicting which particular tosses will be heads, he will assign probability 1/2 to the event "heads" on any one toss—he will pay neither more nor less for a chance at a prize conditional on heads on a particular toss than he will pay for a chance at the same prize conditional on tails. In general, we shall assume it to be a characteristic of rational behavior that:

> If a person assessing the probability of a given event under a given set of conditions feels absolutely sure that the event would occur with relative frequency p in a very great number of trials made under these same conditions, he will assign probability p to the event.

It is important to make clear the meaning of the words "under these same conditions." In one sense it is tautologically true that if conditions were *really* the same from trial to trial, the same event would always occur. If a coin were tossed several times in *exactly* the same way, it would either always fall heads or always fall tails. What we actually mean when we say that conditions are "the same" is that there is no *observable* difference from one trial to the next which *enables us to predict* the fall of the coin on any particular trial.

We are now able to say something definite about the probability which it is reasonable to assign to "one heads" in D'Alembert's problem. If we have adopted a model of coin behavior in which heads occur in the long run on one-half of all tosses and in which half the heads are followed by heads, and so forth, it is easy to see that in a long run of *pairs* of tosses the events *HH*, *HT*, *TH*, and *TT* will each occur 1/4 of the time. Any reasonable man who has adopted this model of the behavior of a given coin will therefore assign the same probability to each of these events and therefore must assign probability 1/2 rather than 1/3 to the compound event "one heads." In actual practice, we would not even go through the process of first assigning a probability directly to "one heads" and then checking this against the implications of probabilities assigned to the four elementary events. We know in advance that our assignment of probabilities to the elementary events can be based on experience which is extremely extensive in comparison with the number of times that we have tossed a coin twice and counted the number of heads in the pair of tosses, and therefore we would start by assigning probabilities to the elementary events and stop when we had computed the probability which we had thus implicitly assigned to the event "one heads."

In more complex problems such as the scrap-allowance example we will proceed in the same general way: we will ask the businessman to assign probabilities to those events on which his experience bears most directly and we will then use the theory of probability to compute the probabilities of the events with which he has had less extensive experience. It is for this reason and this reason alone that the theory of probability is of use in making practical business decisions:

The theory of probability allows the businessman to assign probabilities to those events on which his experience and judgment bear most directly rather than to the events which will actually determine the profit or cost of his decision but with which he has had little or no direct experience.

LIMITED EXPERIENCE

It is only rarely that experience with a given kind of event will be as overwhelming as it is for "heads" on the toss of a coin, but even when experience is limited it is still a guide to the rational assessment of probabilities. Suppose, for example, that we wish to assess the probability of ace on the roll of a die which has been deformed in such a way that it is no longer symmetric. In this situation general experience with rolled objects will usually lead a reasonable person to adopt a model of die behavior which is like the coin model except that the fraction of aces is unknown. Our experience is sufficient to lead us to predict that in the long run the relative frequency of ace will become and remain nearly equal to *some* fraction *p*, that ace will be followed by ace with this *same* relative frequency, and so forth; but our experience is *not* adequate for a prediction of the exact value of this frequency.

Obviously such a model does *not* tell us exactly what probability to assign to ace. We can say that *if* we had had enough experience with the die to feel sure that the long-run relative frequency of ace would be .15, *then* we would assign probability .15 to ace on any one roll, and so forth; but our problem is not to make statements of this sort. If the consequences of a decision depend on the occurrence of ace on the next roll of the die, we must assess the probability of this event in the light of whatever experience we actually have. Two reasonable people may well disagree concerning the probability to be assigned to ace in a situation like this, since neither of them will have had any great amount of experience with the behavior of a die deformed in exactly the way this one is. Observe, however, that this does not mean that there is *no* relevant experience: if the deformation of the die is slight, we will *not* consider a person reasonable if he assigns probability .01 or .99 to ace.

LEARNING FROM ADDITIONAL EXPERIENCE

The case of the perfectly symmetric coin and the case of the deformed die differ not only in the amount of agreement to be expected in the initial assessment of the probabilities of heads or ace but also in the way in which further experience affects any one individual's assessments of these same probabilities on subsequent trials.

In the case of the perfectly symmetric coin, we might still assess the probability of heads on the next toss at 1/2 even though we had just observed a large number of consecutive heads or tails; our model of the long-run behavior of the coin rests on an extremely great amount of evidence and we may consider this new evidence negligible in comparison. In the case of the asymmetric die, on the contrary, we will use any experience we gather by rolling the die to modify the probability we originally assigned to ace. Notice, however, that we usually will *not* simply equate the probability of ace to the fraction of aces observed in a limited number of rolls. If we roll the die once and it comes up ace, we will not assign probability 1 to ace; if we roll it six times and get no ace, we will not assign probability 0 to ace.

Our assessment of the probability of ace will continue to be substantially influenced by our observation of the shape of the die, and the relative importance we attach to the observed shape of the die in comparison with the importance we attach to the observed frequencies is necessarily a matter of subjective judgment.

APPLICATION TO BUSINESS PROBLEMS

In exceptional circumstances the probabilities involved in a business problem can be simply equated to "known" relative frequencies in the way probability 1/2 is assigned to heads on the toss of a very symmetric coin. If 50 per cent of the last 100,000 parts produced by some machine have been defective, if we have no reason either in theory or in observation to believe that defectives occur in "streaks," and

if a new production run is to be made under the same conditions as all these past runs, we will be strongly tempted to adopt a model of the behavior of the machine which is exactly like the model of coin behavior discussed above. We will be willing to predict that 50 per cent of all future parts will be defective, that 50 per cent of the defectives will be followed by defectives, etc., and we will not change these predictions whatever the pattern of quality in the next few hundred pieces produced. We will then be *justified* in assigning equal probabilities to all possible elementary events in the way we did [on pp. 238–42].

In the majority of cases, however, the problem will not be so simple. If the machine is new or has just been repaired, or if a new operator is employed or a slightly off-standard batch of raw material is received, we will be in the same position that we are when we assess the probability of ace on a slightly deformed die. The probability assigned to defective on the first piece will depend on "judgment" in the sense that two reasonable men may well assign different values. This probability will be revised as more experience is gained, and again judgment will determine the relative weights given to the observed frequencies on the one hand and to other kinds of evidence on the other.

MENTAL PROCESSES AND RELATIVE FREQUENCY

The examples which we have discussed above of the way in which models predicting relative frequencies can be of use in assessing probabilities all involved the relative frequencies of physical phenomena, but the same kind of argument can be of use in connection with mental phenomena. Frequency models of mental processes usually involve uncertainty about the actual value of the long-run frequency in exactly the same way that most frequency models of physical processes do; but in both cases the frequency model is useful even though it is not completely decisive. The value of a large tract of timber is often assessed by having it visually inspected by an experienced timber cruiser whose judgment has previously been calibrated by comparing his estimates of the amount of timber in a number of tracts with accurate measurements made on the same tracts. The probability that his present estimate will be low by 10 per cent, say, is then assessed largely on the basis of the relative frequency of errors of this magnitude on previous occasions.

In the same way a sales manager who bases sales forecasts on his "feel of the market" can very usefully be treated as a "process." If we have extensive records of the errors he has made in his past forecasts, we will assess the probability that his current forecast will be low by 10 per cent almost entirely on the basis of the relative frequency with which this event occurred in past forecasts. If on the other hand we have very little previous experience with his forecasts, or if the nature of the product or the market has been radically changed, we will have to make much larger use of other kinds of experience in assessing this probability, just as we have to depart from exclusive reliance on observed frequencies when we assess probabilities concerning the performance of a new machine or of an old machine under new conditions.

Relative Frequency and the Mathematical Theory of Probability

If we think back to the three axioms of the mathematical theory of probability as stated [on p. 245], we will see that relative frequencies—either those predicted for the long run or those actually observed in a finite number of trials—are numbers which agree with these axioms. The relative frequency of any event is a number between 0 and 1 inclusive, the sum of the relative frequencies of all possible events is 1, and the relative frequency of a compound event such as "either ace or deuce" is the sum of the relative frequencies of the mutually exclusive events of which it is composed.

This means that the theory of probability can be used to deduce relative frequencies

from other relative frequencies in exactly the same way that it can be used to deduce probabilities (i.e., subjective weights) from other probabilities. When we first discussed the scrap-allowance example [on p. 244], we assumed that the manufacturer assigned equal *probability* to every possible elementary event, i.e., to every possible sequence of 180 g's and d's, and from these probability assignments we deduced that the probability of the compound event "more than 80 defectives" was .922. We pointed out [on p. 248], however, that the assignment of equal probabilities to the elementary events was warranted only on the basis of a "model" of the production process which implies that these events would occur with equal *relative frequencies* in a very great number of runs of 180 pieces, and this gives us an alternative way of expressing the same calculation. Given that the elementary events occur with equal relative frequencies, the theory of probability can be used to show that the *relative frequency* of the compound event "more than 80 defectives" must be .922; we can then assess the probability of this compound event by equating it to its *own* relative frequency.

A relationship of this kind between probabilities and relative frequencies can be imagined even in a problem where the probabilities of the elementary events have *not* been assessed by reference to any frequency model. In other words, we can *visualize* all the probabilities involved in *any* problem as being equal to relative frequencies in an imaginary sequence of trials whether or not the particular trial with which we are dealing is of such a nature that it could conceivably be repeated. Since relations among actual numbers of events are easier to grasp than relations among abstract numbers called probabilities, we shall often make use of this device to "explain" the results of calculations involving probabilities; but the student must always remember that such "explanations" do not imply either that probabilities *are* relative frequencies or that they are necessarily *equal* to *real* relative frequencies.

R. SCHLAIFER

30 Expected Value and Utility

At the beginning of the previous chapter we said that any problem of decision under uncertainty can always be described by a pay-off table in which there is a column for every possible *act* and a row for every possible *event;* each cell in the table describes the *consequence* of a particular act given a particular event. We said that we would try to find a way of choosing among the acts in the fact of uncertainty concerning the events by:

1. Assigning a definite numerical *value* to every consequence (every cell in the table),
2. Assigning a definite numerical *weight* to every event,
3. Evaluating each act by taking a *weighted average* of all the different values which might result from that act.

In the remainder of the chapter we concentrated our attention on the second of these three steps; we now go on to consider how we can carry out the first step in such a way that the result of the third step will in fact be a "correct" guide to action.

Definitions of Conditional and Expected Value

Conditional Value. Each of the values which have to be assigned in step 1 of the procedure outlined just above is the value which some particular act will have *on condition* that some particular event occurs, and therefore these values will be called *conditional values.* We define

Conditional value of an act given a particular

event: the value which the person responsible for a choice among acts attaches to the consequence which that particular act will have if that particular event occurs.

Expected Value. After probabilities have been assigned to events in step 2 of the procedure we propose to use, step 3 consists in obtaining a *single* value for each act by taking a weighted average of all the various conditional values of that act, each conditional value being weighted by the *probability* that the act will in fact have that value. The standard name for an average in which all possible values are weighted by their probabilities is *expected value;* we define

Expected value of an act: a weighted average of *all* the conditional values of the act, each conditional value being weighted by its probability.

Such a weighted average is also called the *expectation* of the conditional values of the act.

Mistakes are bound to occur unless we adopt some kind of systematic procedure for the actual computation of expected values according to the definition just given. We have already said that the analysis of any decision problem must start by 1) drawing up a *payoff table* showing the *conditional value* of every act given every event and 2) assigning a *probability* to every event in the payoff table. After both these steps have been completed, we shall take the acts of the payoff table *one at a time* and compute the expected value of each one on a work sheet like the one shown in Table 1, filling out this work sheet according to the following rules:

1. List every possible *event* in column 1.
2. Enter the *probability* of each event in column 2.
3. Enter the *conditional value* of the act given each event in column 3.
4. For each event *multiply* probability times conditional value and enter the product in column 4, *taking care to preserve the algebraic sign.*
5. *Add* the products in column 4 *with due regard to algebraic sign.*

Table 1.

Computation of the expected value of an act

Event	Probability	Value Conditional	Expected
A	.3	+5	+1.50
B	.3	+3	+ .90
C	.4	−4	−1.60
	1.0		+ .80

Expected Monetary Value

The definition of expected value which we have given above applies no matter what *kind* of value is assigned to each consequence in a decision problem. If in an inventory problem like the one discussed at the beginning of the preceding chapter we take the net cash receipts shown in Table 1 there as representing the value of each consequence, then a computation like the one illustrated in Table 1 above will give us the expected net cash receipts of any act. If we value each consequence according to the number of units sold, application of the same rules of computation will give us the expected number of units sold; and so forth. We now turn to our real problem, which is to find out exactly how each consequence must be valued if the businessman is to feel that the act with the highest expected value is really the act he wants to choose.

Our first inclination, of course, is to think that at least in most business problems the value of a consequence can properly be represented by a sum of money, and our first step will be to inquire to what extent this proposition is true. What we shall see is that while expected monetary value is in fact a valid guide to action in the great majority of practical business problems, there are some very important problems in which it would be an extremely misleading guide.

THE IMPORTANCE OF THE INDIVIDUAL'S ATTITUDE TOWARD RISK

Consider two businessmen each of whom believes that if he submits the proper proposal he has a 50-50 chance of being awarded a contract which is sure to yield a $35,000 gross profit, and suppose that preparation of the proposal will cost either of these men $10,000 out of pocket. The expected monetary value of the act "submit the proposal" is shown in Table 2 to be a positive $7500 for either of these two men while the corresponding figure for not making the proposal is obviously $0, and yet the two men may quite reasonably come to opposite conclusions. If one of them is extremely hard pressed for cash and could easily be bankrupted by the loss of $10,000, he may well decide to let this opportunity go; if the other man has adequate working capital he may with equally good reason decide to make the proposal.

This example obviously implies that there

Table 2. Expected monetary value of making the proposal

Event	Probability	Monetary value Conditional	Expected
Get contract	$\frac{1}{2}$	+ $25,000	+ $12,500
Do not get contract	$\frac{1}{2}$	− 10,000	− 5,000
	1		+ $7,500

are situations in which expected monetary value is not a valid guide to action if by "valid" we mean a guide which accords with the businessman's own judgment and preferences, but if we look a little more closely we will see that it implies much more than this. What must be decided is simply whether it is worth risking a loss of $10,000 in order to have an even chance of a $25,000 profit, and there is *no conceivable* computation or method of analysis which will be of the least help to anyone in making such a decision—it *must* turn *entirely* on a direct expression of personal preference.

Table 3. Description of act "Submit the Proposal"

Event	Consequence	Probability
A	+ $25,000	.1
B	+ 20,000	.1
C	+ 15,000	.1
D	+ 10,000	.1
E	+ 5,000	.1
F	− 10,000	.5
		1.0

The student may well ask at this point how we propose to help a businessman in any situation whatever if we can be of no help at all in a situation as simple as the one just described, and the question deserves an answer before we proceed further. The answer is this: we propose to show the businessman how he can make a fully reasoned analysis of a *very complex* decision problem—one in which there are many possible acts each of which has many possible consequences—by in effect reducing this very complex problem to a number of separate problems every one of which is just as simple as the one we have just discussed.

Suppose, for example, that our two businessmen are given the opportunity of submitting proposals for another contract and that in this case they both assign to the act "submit the proposal" the whole set of possible consequences and associated probabilities shown in Table 3. Comparison of this table with Table 2 shows that the act "submit" is clearly less

desirable in the present example than in the original example, and consequently the businessman who was hard pressed for cash and therefore refused to submit the proposal in the original example can quickly arrive at the same conclusion in the present example; in other words, he can solve a complex decision problem by referring it to a simple decision problem in which he can easily see exactly what is at stake. The choice is by no means so clear for the other businessman, however, and he *will* be substantially aided if we can find some systematic technique of analysis which in effect reduces his complex problem to a simple problem in which he can see exactly what is at stake. We shall now investigate the conditions under which the computation of expected monetary value will be a suitable technique.

CONDITIONS UNDER WHICH EXPECTED MONETARY VALUE IS A VALID GUIDE TO ACTION

If we think for a moment about what we know about the way in which businessmen in fact make very simple decisions under uncertainty, we will realize that whether or not they formally compute expected monetary value they act in accordance with expected monetary value when the amounts at stake are not too large. If a businessman believes that there is 1 chance in 1000 that his million-dollar plant will burn down during the next year, he may be willing to pay $1500 as a premium for an insurance policy even though the expected monetary value of his loss if he does not insure is only $1000; but if the same businessman believes that he runs a 1-in-1000 chance of suffering $100 worth of damage to his machinery because of tramp iron in a particular batch of raw material, he is very likely to be unwilling to pay a cent more than the $.10 expected value of this loss for insurance against it. Remembering that a cash outlay is to be given a minus sign, we see that in the former case he chooses an act with a monetary value of − $1500 even though the alternative act has the greater monetary value − $1000 but that in the latter case he says that he will take the act with expected monetary value − $.10 if the monetary value of the other act is the least amount lower.

This general kind of behavior is not restricted to situations in which the monetary values of all possible consequences are negative or at best zero. A businessman with net assets of $500,000 who must choose between a deal which is certain to result in a profit of $50 and another which in his eyes is equally likely to result in a profit of $0 or a profit of $110 is likely to choose the latter act in accordance with the fact that its expected monetary value is $55; but if this same businessman is given the happy opportunity to choose between a deal which is certain to net him $5 million and another which has equal chances of yielding $0 and $11 million, he is very likely to take the $5 million.

To sum up: businessmen tend to treat acts which must have one or the other of just two possible consequences as being "really worth" their expected monetary value as long as the worst of the two consequences is not too bad and the best of the consequences is not too good. This immediately suggests that a businessman who must evaluate an act or acts with a great number of possible consequences can decide whether or not he should use expected monetary value as the basis of his evaluation by looking only at the best and the worst of the consequences and asking himself whether he would act in accordance with expected monetary value if these were the *only* possible consequences. More specifically, it would seem reasonable for a man faced with a very complex decision problem to decide whether or not he should take expected monetary value as his guide by applying the following very simple

Test for the Validity of Expected Monetary Value as a Guide to Action: Expected monetary value should be used as the decision criterion in any real decision problem, however complex, if the person responsible for the decision would use it as his criterion in choosing between 1) an act which is certain to result in receipt or payment of a definite amount of cash and 2) an act which will result in either the *best* or the *worst* of all the possible consequences of the real decision problem.

Later in the chapter we shall see that the correctness of this rule can be "proved" in the sense that we can show that any person who does not follow the rule will end up by making choices which in the opinion of most reasonable people are logically inconsistent.

As an illustration of the application of this rule, let us return to the businessman who must decide whether or not to submit a proposal for a contract when the possible consequences of this act are as described in Table 3. The best and worst possible consequences of this act are + $25,000 and − $10,000; and since the consequence of not submitting the proposal is certain to be $0, the two consequences previously named are the best and worst of the entire decision problem. As an initial test, the businessman can therefore ask himself the following question: "Suppose that *I* had to choose between 1) receiving a definite amount of cash and 2) being awarded a contract such that *I* assigned probability 1/2 to the consequence + $25,000 and probability 1/2 to the consequence − $10,000, making the expected monetary value of the contract $7500. Would *I* (*a*) prefer the contract to the cash if the specified amount of cash was less than $7500 and (*b*) prefer the cash to the contract if the specified amount of cash was over $7500?" If the answer to this question is yes, expected monetary value will almost certainly be a correct guide to this businessman's action in his real problem; but in principle he must go on to ask himself whether he would answer yes to *any* question of this type *whatever* the probability he assigned to the $25,000 profit. He should, for example, suppose that he had already signed a contract with probability .1 assigned to the consequence + $25,000 and probability .9 assigned to − $10,000, so that the expected monetary value of the contract was $- \$6500$, and then ask himself whether in fact he would (a) prefer to pay any amount of cash less than $6500 for a release rather than perform the contract but (b) prefer to perform the contract rather than pay any sum greater than $6500 for a release.

If the businessman's answer to any of these questions is no, a little common sense is required. Such an answer implies that expected monetary value will not give an *exactly accurate evaluation* of any act which may result in the $25,000 profit or the $10,000 loss, but this does not mean that expected monetary value will necessarily lead to the *wrong choice of act*. In our example, the expected monetary value of the act "submit the proposal" is $+ \$2500$, as shown in Table 4, and this is very substantially greater than the value $0 of the act

Table 4

Event	Probability	Monetary value Conditional	Expected
A	.1	+ $25,000	+ $2500
B	.1	+ 20,000	+ 2000
C	.1	+ 15,000	+ 1500
D	.1	+ 10,000	+ 1000
E	.1	+ 5,000	+ 500
F	.5	− 10,000	− 5000
	1.0		+ $2500

"do not submit the proposal." If then the businessman feels that he would value a contract which gave him even chances of $+ \$25,000$ and $- \$10,000$ at only slightly less than its expected monetary value of $+ \$7500$, he can feel quite sure that the act "submit the proposal" in the real problem is better than an act which is certain to have the value $0 even though he could not be sure that it would be better than an act which was certain to have the value $2400.

DELEGATION OF ROUTINE DECISION MAKING

Systematic use of expected monetary value actually simplifies practical business decisions even more than this example suggests, and for two reasons.

1. The person who is ultimately responsible for a certain class of decisions does not have to look at each decision problem individually in order to decide whether expected monetary value is a proper guide to action, as we can easily see by considering the decision which had to be made by the retailer of the example originally discussed at the beginning of the preceding chapter. This retailer will presumably have larger numbers of decisions of exactly this same kind to make daily, and he can settle the question of the validity of expected monetary value as a guide to all these decisions once and for all by simply asking himself how large the worst possible loss and the greatest possible profit would have to be before he would *refuse* to use expected monetary value as a guide in a simple two-consequence problem. If he has $10,000 of working capital, he may well decide that he would take expected monetary value as a guide in any inventory-control problem where the worst possible loss did not exceed, say, $100 and where the greatest possible profit did not exceed, say, $500. If his preferences are of this sort, then a simple statement of policy to this effect will enable his subordinates to solve virtually all of his stock-control problems without having to ask him any further questions about the "value of money," while at the same time he can feel absolutely sure that his preferences are respected.

2. In principle, the person ultimately responsible for a class of risky decisions must himself evaluate the probabilities or weights which he himself attaches to the various possible events in any problem, but this evaluation can also be delegated in the great majority of practical business problems. In most routine problems the executive would follow some systematic procedure for assessing these probabilities if he did assess them himself; and whenever this is true he can delegate the assessment by simply prescribing the assessment procedure or even the general type of assessment procedure to be used. Thus probabilities may be assessed in routine inventory-control problems by examining the

record of demand over the past several periods and using this record in some systematic way; probabilities in routine quality-control problems may be assessed by standard statistical procedures which we shall study later in this course, and so forth.

Once the executive has specified the range of problems within which he wants to have expected monetary value taken as a guide to action and the procedures by which probabilities are to be assessed in routine situations, he will be free to make a careful personal analysis of those problems where such an analysis is really worth the effort: problems in which the possible losses and gains are so great that expected monetary value ceases to be a proper guide to action, and problems in which business judgment of a kind not expected of clerks and statisticians is required to assess the probabilities of the events.

Expected Utility

In the remainder of this chapter we shall study the problem of choice in situations where the amounts at stake are so large that the test described in the preceding section tells the businessman that he should *not* use expected monetary value as a guide to action, and we shall see that even in these situations the businessman can reach a fully reasoned solution of the most complex problem by deciding how he would want to act in a number of very simple problems. More specifically, we shall see that his decisions in the simple problems can be used as the basis for assigning a *utility value* to each possible consequence in the real problem and that once this has been done the real problem can be solved by the mere mechanical computation of the *expected utility* of every possible act.

This means that the *only* difference between analysis of a problem in which expected monetary value is a valid guide to action and analysis of a problem in which it is not is that in the latter case we must replace the monetary payoff table by a table showing conditional utilities. Once this has been done, probabilities

are assigned to the events in the utility table exactly as they would be if the table showed monetary values rather than utilities, and the expected utility of each act is computed from the conditional utilities in exactly the same way that expected monetary value is computed from conditional monetary values. For this reason we shall talk exclusively in terms of the more familiar monetary values in all future chapters, leaving it to the student to remember that in any real problem he must apply the test [of pp. 252–255] and substitute utilities for monetary values if necessary. It follows that the remaining sections of the present chapter can be read just as well at the end of this course as at the present time.

OUTLINE OF THE METHOD OF ANALYSIS

Suppose that the businessman with limited working capital who refused the contracts described in Tables 2 and 4 is offered two other contracts to whose possible consequences he assigns the probabilities shown in Table 5. It is easy to calculate the expected *monetary* value of contract M as +$3825 and that of contract N as +$2025, and the expected monetary value of taking neither contract is obviously $0; but we assume that the businessman tells us that he would certainly *not* be willing to accept any deal in which there was an even chance of making or losing $9000, and this, as we have seen, means that expected monetary value is of no help to him in choosing among the three acts actually open to him.

If the two contracts offered to the businessman had been those described in Table 6 rather than those described in Table 5, his decision problem would obviously have been much easier. Each of these contracts has only two possible consequences and these consequences are the same for both contracts; the *only* difference between the two contracts is in the probabilities attached to the consequences, and it is obvious that the more desirable contract is the one with the higher probability of obtaining the $10,000 profit. All that the businessman has to do to make a completely

Table 5

| | Contract M | | | Contract N | |
Event	Probability	Consequence	Event	Probability	Consequence
A	.30	+ $9000	Q	.25	+ $7500
B	.45	+ 7500	R	.60	+ 2000
C	.25	− 9000	S	.15	− 7000
	1.00			1.00	

Table 6

| Contract X | | Contract Y | |
Consequence	Probability	Consequence	Probability
+ $10,000	.8	+ $10,000	.7
− 10,000	.2	− 10,000	.3
	1.0		1.0

reasoned analysis of this problem and reach a decision is to make up his mind whether or not he prefers a certainty of $0 to the combination of a .8 chance of + $10,000 and a .2 chance of − $10,000 which he will obtain if he accepts contract X.

We shall now show that the problem of deciding whether to take contract M, contract N, or neither can be reduced to a number of problems every one of which is just as simple as the problem of choosing between contract X and $0 cash certain. To do this we proceed as follows.

1. Simply to make the reasoning concrete, we *represent* each real contract by an *equivalent lottery* which in the businessman's own judgment has exactly the same value as the real contract, whatever that value may be.

2. We select two "reference consequences," one of which is at least as bad as the worst possible consequence in the real decision problem and one of which is at least as good as the best, and we show that each of the lotteries representing real contracts must have the same value in the businessman's own judgment as a ticket with a certain probability of winning in a *reference lottery* in which these two "reference consequences" are the *only* prizes.

Once this has been done, all that is left is to select the real contract which corresponds

to the *highest probability of winning* in the reference lottery.

THE EQUIVALENT LOTTERIES

As our first step in the procedure we have just outlined we represent the real contract M by the following equivalent lottery. An urn contains 1000 balls of which 300 are marked A, 450 are marked B, and 250 are marked C. A single ball is to be drawn from this urn; and *if* the businessman chooses to participate in the lottery he will *receive* $9000 if the ball is marked A or $7500 if it is marked B but will be obliged to *pay the bank* $9000 if the ball is marked C. The businessman is to imagine that this imaginary drawing will be made in such a way that every ball has an equal chance of being drawn, whereupon he will see that the probability of winning any one of the three prizes in the lottery is exactly the same as the probability which *he himself has assigned* to obtaining the same prize by signing contract M. We may therefore say that *this imaginary lottery M has exactly the same value as the real contract M in the businessman's own opinion*.

We next proceed to represent contract N by an equivalent lottery N involving an urn of appropriate composition—*not* the same urn that represents contract M. The two urns are both described in Table 7, and the student will see that we have completed the first step in our procedure: we have reduced the businessman's problem of choosing between contracts M and N to a completely equivalent problem of choosing between lotteries M and N.

EVALUATION OF CONSEQUENCES IN TERMS OF TICKETS IN A REFERENCE LOTTERY

We must next select two "reference consequences," one at least as good as the best consequence in the decision problem and one at least as bad as the worst. The best and worst of the real consequences are respectively $+ \$9000$ and $- \$9000$, and these could be taken as the reference consequences; but just to emphasize that we are not bound to this choice we shall actually take $+ \$10,000$ and $- \$10,000$ as our reference consequences.

We next set up our *reference lottery* by imagining an urn containing a number of balls some of which are marked "win," the remainder "lose." A ticket in *this* lottery entitles the holder to receive $\$10,000$ if a ball marked "win" is drawn from this urn, but obliges him to pay the bank $\$10,000$ if the ball is marked "lose."

We are now able to *evaluate each possible consequence* in the decision problem by equating it to a ticket in a reference lottery in which the mix of balls is such as to give the "right" probability of winning in the *businessman's own opinion*. Starting with the consequence $\$0$ of the act "sign *neither* contract" or the equivalent act "accept *neither* lottery M nor lottery N," we address the businessman as follows.

"Imagine that you have refused both lottery M and lottery N but that you are now offered, at a price of exactly $\$0$, a ticket in a *reference lottery* in which you will either win $\$10,000$ or lose $\$10,000$. Just how good would the chances of winning have to be to make you *just indifferent* whether you took this free ticket or not?"

The businessman will see at once that the *expected monetary value* of this ticket will be equal to its $\$0$ price if the chances of winning are 50 in 100; but we shall imagine that he would by no means accept the ticket if these were in fact the chances of winning. He feels that losing $\$10,000$ is a very good deal worse than winning $\$10,000$ is good; and we shall therefore suppose that after careful reflection he decides that he would barely be willing to accept the ticket if the chances of winning were 85 in 100—he *really* dislikes the idea of losing $\$10,000$. Given this answer, we can say that *the consequence $\$0$ has exactly the same value in this particular businessman's own personal opinion as a ticket in a reference lottery with probability $\pi = .85$ of winning.*

We next make a similar evaluation of the consequence $+ \$9000$, which may occur if the businessman chooses act M, by asking him: "Imagine that you have already accepted lottery M in Table 2, that a ball marked A has already been drawn from the urn, and that you have accordingly received the $\$9000$ prize. Imagine further that you are now offered a chance to exchange this $\$9000$ for a ticket in a reference lottery in which you will either win $\$10,000$ or lose $\$10,000$. How good would the chances of winning in this reference lottery have to be to make you *just indifferent*

Table 7. Equivalent lottery tickets

| | Lottery M | | | Lottery N | |
Label on balls	Number of balls	Prize	Label on balls	Number of balls	Prize
A	300	+ $9000	Q	250	+ $7500
B	450	+ 7500	R	600	+ 2000
C	250	− 9000	S	150	− 7000
	1000			1000	

about trading your $9000 cash for the lottery ticket?"

We can imagine the businessman starting to think out his answer by quickly computing that the *expected monetary value* of the ticket in the reference lottery would be exactly $9000 if the chances of winning were 95 in 100, since

$$.95\ (+\$10{,}000) + .05\ (-\$10{,}000) = \$9000;$$

but we already know that this particular businessman is very averse to risk, and we shall therefore suppose that he finally answers that he would be barely willing to pay $9000 for the ticket if the chances of winning were 99 in 100.

We have thus established that *the consequence* + $9000 *has exactly the same value in this particular businessman's own personal opinion as a ticket in a reference lottery with probability* $\pi = .99$ *of winning;* and without repeating the details of the questioning procedure we shall suppose that we can similarly establish that + $7500 is equivalent to a reference lottery with $\pi = .98$, while + $2000 is equivalent to $\pi = .90$. Our man is *very* averse to risk.

We must now evaluate the *negative* consequences which may occur if the businessman chooses act *M* or *N*, and to do so we start with the following question.

"Imagine that you have already accepted a ticket in lottery *M*, that the ball has already been drawn from the urn, and that you have unfortunately found yourself with an *obligation to pay* $9000 to the bank. Imagine further that someone offers to relieve you of this obligation provided that you will accept in its stead a lottery ticket which may win you

$10,000 but may oblige you to pay out $10,000 instead of $9000. How good would the chances of winning have to be to make you just indifferent between 1) actually paying the $9000 you now owe and 2) accepting the ticket?"

The businessman may calculate that the expected monetary value of the ticket would be − $9000 if the chances of winning were 5 in 100, since

$$.05(+\$10{,}000) + .95(-\$10{,}000) = \$9000,$$

but if losing the extra $1000 would put him in a really tight position, he will not be at all willing to accept the ticket in the reference lottery with the chances of winning being actually .05. We shall suppose that he finally says he would be barely willing to trade if the chances of winning were .24. We have thus established that for *this* businessman the consequence − $9000 is equivalent to a reference lottery with $\pi = .24$, and we shall suppose that we similarly establish that − $7000 is equivalent to $\pi = .50$.

All of our results to date are summarized in Table 8, where we replace the monetary *consequences* of Table 7 by the π's of the equivalent *reference* lottery.

REDUCTION OF LOTTERIES TO REFERENCE LOTTERIES

We now come to the last stage of the procedure outlined [on pp. 255–56]: we must reduce the "complicated" and incomparable lotteries *M* and *N* to *reference* lotteries which *can* be

Table 8

| | Lottery M | | | Lottery N | |
Label on ball	Number of balls	Reference π	Label on ball	Number of balls	Reference π
A	300	.99	Q	250	.98
B	450	.98	R	600	.90
C	250	.24	S	150	.50
	1000			1000	

Act "do nothing": $\pi = .85$

directly compared in terms of the probability of winning.

Starting with act *M* and event *A* in Table 8, we argue as follows. *If* the businessman takes lottery *M* and if the ball which is drawn from the urn is one of the 300 marked *A*, he has already told us that he would value the consequence of *A* neither more nor less than a ticket in a reference lottery with probability $\pi = .99$ of winning. Such a lottery can be constructed by drawing one ball from among 300 balls 297 of which are marked win and 3 marked lose, and we now come to the crucial step in our reasoning. We assume that

Since *this* businessman is just indifferent between the actual consequence of drawing a ball marked *A* and a ticket in a reference lottery with 297 balls marked "win" and 3 marked "lose," the value of lottery *M* will be completely unchanged for *this* businessman if we remove the 300 balls which are marked *A* from the urn for lottery *M* and replace them with 300 balls of which 297 are marked "win $10,000" and 3 are marked "lose $10,000."

By similar reasoning we will leave the value of lottery *M* unchanged if we replace the 450 balls marked *B* by 450 balls of which .98 × 450 =441 are marked "win $10,000" and 9 are marked "lose $10,000"; and the value of *M* will still be unchanged if we replace the 250 balls marked *C* by .24 × 250 = 60 balls marked "win $10,000" and 190 marked "lose $10,000."

Without in any way changing the value of lottery M for this particular businessman, we have now reduced it to a form in which *it will result, not in any of its three original consequences, but in one or the other of our two reference consequences.* If we count up the number of winning balls, we find there are 297 + 441 + 60 = 798 out of the 1000 total; and one conclusion emerges immediately. Since the probability of winning in lottery *M* is only $\pi = 798/1000 = .798$, whereas this businessman has already told us that he would be barely willing to accept a ticket at a price of $0

if the probability of winning were $\pi = .85$, we can say that $0 cash certain *should* logically be worth more to this businessman than lottery *M*. Then since lottery *M* has the same value as contract *M* in the real problem and the real act "do nothing" is certain to have the consequence $0, it follows that the businessman *should not* sign contract *M* if he wants to behave in a way which is *logically consistent with his own basic judgments and preferences.*

It is still possible, of course, that the *other* contract is *better* than "do nothing," and it turns out that it actually is, although not by much. We leave it to the student to show that lottery *N* can be reduced to a reference lottery in which the probability of winning is

$$\pi = 860/1000 = .86,$$

which is just slightly better than the $\pi = .85$ which is equivalent to "do nothing."

UTILITY

At the beginning of this section we said that when expected monetary value was not a valid guide to action the person responsible for a decision could always find a valid guide by assigning utility values to the various possible consequences of his acts and then choosing the act with the highest expected utility. We shall now see that this is simply another way of describing the calculation of the π's of the several reference lotteries to which the several real-world acts can be reduced.

In Table 9 we show the *same* calculation of the reference π corresponding to lottery *M* which we carried out in the text of the preceding section, the only difference being that we have written the number of *A* balls in the form $1000 \times .30$ rather than in the form 300, and similarly for other numbers of balls. It is completely obvious at once that the fact that we had *N* = 1000 balls in the urn is irrelevant to the final probability of winning $\pi = .798$; it is only the *proportions P* and π which count. Now *P* is simply the original *probability* of each *event* and π is simply the *break-even probability* which makes a reference lottery

Table 9. Evaluation of act M

Label	Number		Reference	Number marked "win $10,000"				
	N	P	π	N	P	π	N	$P\pi$
A	$1000 \times$	$.30$	$.99$	$1000 \times .30 \times .99 =$			$1000 \times$	$.297$
B	$1000 \times$	$.45$	$.98$	$1000 \times .45 \times .98 =$			$1000 \times$	$.441$
C	$1000 \times$	$.25$	$.24$	$1000 \times .25 \times .24 =$			$1000 \times$	$.060$
	1000×1.00						$1000 \times$	$.798$

just equivalent to each *consequence*. Since it is customary in technical subjects to assign curious names to things, we may if we like give the name "utility" to these "break-even probabilities" π and say, for example, that the *utility* of the consequence $+\$9000$ corresponding to act M and event A is .99.

Now the utility π attached to any act-event combination can if we like be called the *conditional* "value" of that act if that event occurs; and then, following the definition of expected value [on pp. 250–51], we can say that the expected value or *expected utility* of any act is the number found by multiplying each conditional utility by the corresponding probability and adding the products. The last column of Table 9 shows that the result $\pi = .798$, which gives the probability of winning in a reference lottery that is just equivalent to act M, is exactly such a sum of products—i.e., *the expected utility of act M is* .798; and since we have already seen that, to be logically self-consistent, the businessman *should* choose the act which corresponds to the *highest* probability of winning in a reference lottery, we can say that

Any decision maker who wishes to choose among acts in a logically self-consistent manner must choose the act which has the greatest expected utility.

ESTABLISHMENT OF UTILITY CURVES

The way in which we have hitherto questioned the businessman of our example has served the purpose of making clear the reason why an intelligent businessman will *want* to choose the

act with the highest expected utility, but is actually a very poor way of proceeding in practice because it forces the businessman to evaluate lotteries with extreme probabilities such as $\pi = .99$ and it is very difficult for most people to do this. A much better quantification of a businessman's really basic attitudes toward risk and uncertainty can be obtained by proceeding as follows.

1. We start exactly as before by asking what the π of a reference lottery would have to be to make the businessman just willing to accept a free ticket.

2. We then ask a series of questions about gambles in all of which there is an *even* chance of winning either some prize or *nothing*, since such gambles are in general the easiest kind to evaluate.

Thus suppose that our businessman has answered our first question as before and told us that the utility of the consequence $0 is $\pi = .85$. We know automatically that the utility of the consequence $+\$10,000$ is $\pi = 1$, since *anyone* would be willing to pay $10,000 for a lottery ticket which is sure to win $10,000; and similarly we know that the utility of $-\$10,000$ is 0. We can now proceed as follows.

We first ask the businessman how large a premium he would pay for insurance against a $10,000 loss if he felt that there was an *even* chance that this loss would occur. From his previous answers that the utility of $-\$10,000$ is 0 and that the utility of $0 is .85, we know that the expected utility of *not* insuring is $1/2(0) + 1/2(.85) = .425$; and if he now answers this new question by saying that a loss of $10,000 would put him in so tight a position

Table 10

Question number	Gamble between		Utility π	Equivalent consequence
	− $10,000 and	+ $10,000	0	− $10,000
	− 10,000	+ 10,000	1	+ 10,000
1	− 10,000	+ 10,000	.85	0
2	− 10,000	0	.425	− 7,700
3	− 7,700	0	.6375	− 5,200
4	− 5,200	0	.74375	− 3,100
5	0	+ 10,000	.925	+ 3,300
6	0	+ 3,300	.8875	+ 1,600
7	0	+ 1,600	.86875	+ 600

that he would be willing to pay up to, say, $7700 for insurance against it, then we have established that the utility of − $7700 is .425.

Now that we know the utility of − $7700, we can calculate the expected utility of *not* insuring against an even chance of losing $7700; it is $1/2(.425) + 1/2(.85) = .6375$. We therefore next ask the businessman how much he would just be willing to pay for insurance against *this* risk; and if he answers that he would be just willing to pay $5200, we have established that the utility of − $5200 is .6375.

By next asking about insurance against a 50–50 chance of losing $5200, and continuing in this way to build on each previous answer, we can end up by establishing the utilities of a

large number of *negative* consequences or losses.

We then turn to *positive* consequences or profits and proceed similarly. The utility of a deal in which the businessman feels that he has an even chance of *winning* either $10,000 or $0 can be calculated as $1/2(.85) + 1/2(1) = .925$; and if the businessman tells us that he would be just willing to exchange such a deal for receipt of $3300 certain, we have established that the utility of + $3300 is .925. We next ask about the cash value of a 50–50 chance of winning $3300 or $0, which has a utility of $1/2(.85) + 1/2(.925) = .8875$; and we then make use of this answer to obtain the utility of another consequence, and so forth.

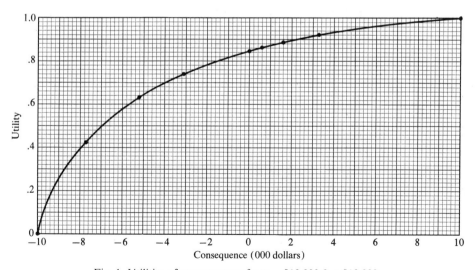

Fig. 1. Utilities of consequences from − $10,000 0 + $10,000

Suppose then that our successive questions have established the utilities shown in Table 10. If now we plot each utility against the corresponding consequence, we obtain the points shows as heavy dots in Figure 1, and we can then fair in a smooth curve and read from it *this* businessman's utility for *any* monetary consequence between − $10,000 and + $10,000.

Such a procedure makes it easy to evaluate utilities in problems where there are hundreds of possible consequences and where it would therefore be completely impossible for the businessman to take the time to assign a utility π to each consequence individually.

DIFFERING ATTITUDES TOWARD RISK

In Figure 2 we reproduce with the label *A* the utility curve of the businessman whose preferences in risky situations we have been examining thus far, and we also show utility curves which we might have obtained from two *other* businessmen with quite *different* preferences in risky situations. Utility as we have defined it above is to be read from the *left*-hand vertical scale in this figure; the use of the *right*-hand scale will be explained later on.

From the curves in Figure 2 we now read off and show in Table 11 the amount of cash which each of the three men would be willing to pay for tickets in reference lotteries with three different probabilities of winning rather than losing $10,000. The differing evaluations of the various lotteries can then be explained as follows.

Because a loss of $10,000 would put Mr. A's business in an extremely critical position, he feels that he would rather pay $3000 out of pocket than run a risk of a $10,000 loss even though he thinks that there is only one chance in four that the loss will actually occur against three chances in four that there will be a $10,000 profit. As the chance of the loss becomes larger and the chance of the profit smaller, Mr. A naturally becomes willing to pay even more to avoid the risk: he will pay

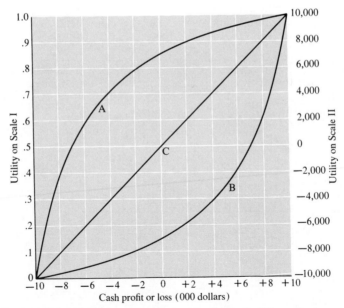

Fig. 2. Utilities of various cash consequences for three different businessmen

Table 11. Cash values of reference lotteries for three different
businessmen

Probability of $10,000 profit	Cash equivalent for Mr.		
π	A	B	C
3/4	− 3000	+ 9000	+ 5000
1/2	− 7000	+ 7000	0
1/4	− 9000	+ 3000	− 5000

$7000 for a release when the probability of the loss is 1/2, and when it is 3/4 he will even pay $9000 certain rather than run the risk of losing the extra $1000 which might put him in bankruptcy.

Mr. B has attitudes diametrically opposed to those of the very cautious and conservative Mr. A; he represents the player of long shots, the man who feels that even a large loss could not make things much worse than they are now whereas a large profit would very substantially improve his whole situation. This attitude is more commonly found among players of numbers pools and the like than it is among business executives, but it is perhaps worth pointing out that even the extremely conservative Mr. A might take this attitude if his misfortunes continued to the point where he would not be able to meet his next payroll unless something extremely fortunate happened between now and Friday. Whatever his motives, Mr. B wants an additional $10,000 so badly that he would consider a $\pi = 1/4$ chance of making it to be worth as much to him as $3000 cash certain even though this chance was accompanied by a 3/4 chance of taking a $10,000 loss; by the time $\pi = 3/4$ and $(1 - \pi)$ is only 1/4, he would not sell his chance at $10,000 for less than $9000.

The attitudes of Mr. C will serve as a kind of standard of comparison. Mr. C represents a businessman well supplied with working capital who believes in self-insurance against moderate risks, considers $10,000 to be in fact a very moderate risk, and is therefore willing to use expected monetary value as his guide to action in any problem where the stakes do not exceed plus or minus $10,000. When the

chances of a $10,000 profit and a $10,000 loss are equal, Mr. C does not care whether he takes the gamble or not. When the probability of winning is 3/4, he would be willing, but not eager, to trade the gamble for its expected monetary value of $5000; if the probabilities of winning and losing were reversed, he would be willing, but not eager, to pay $5000 to avoid the gamble.

THE INTERPRETATION OF UTILITY

In a certain sense analysis of a problem in terms of conditional and expected utilities rather than in terms of reference lotteries enables us to gain a better feeling for the reasons behind a given person's preferences, but unless we are very careful this feeling will do our real understanding more harm than good.

Let us look first at the advantages to be gained from the use of the concept of utility. Looking at curve A in Figure 2 we can "explain" Mr. A's extremely cautious attitude toward all risky contracts by observing that moving any given distance to the right of 0 on the horizontal axis increases his utility by much less than moving a corresponding distance to the left decreases it—a profit of any specified amount increases his utility by less than a loss of the same amount decreases it. For Mr. B, on the contrary, the situation is just the reverse: a profit of any given amount increases his utility by more than a loss of the same amount decreases it; while for Mr. C a dollar lost is worth neither more nor less than a dollar gained.

Now it is true that most people will actually

think in terms much like these when they are deciding how to evaluate risky acts. A person is likely to say that he would prefer $1 million certain to a 50–50 chance of $2 million or nothing because he would be almost as well off with $1 million as with $2 million and "therefore" the chance at the extra million is not worth the risk of losing the first one. Similarly a person who buys life insurance despite the fact that the premium is always larger than the expected monetary value of the benefits by the amount of the insurance company's costs and profits will explain his action by saying that the dollars he now uses to pay the premium are worth much less to his family than the dollars which would be paid as benefits in case of his death.

We must be very careful, however, not to lose sight of the fact that all utilities are and must be evaluated by looking at *particular types* of risky acts or reference contracts and that a person may well have one attitude toward risk in one situation and a quite different attitude in a different situation. The businessman who decided to submit the proposal under the conditions described in Table 2 is in effect betting $10,000 against $25,000 in a situation where he thinks that he has an even chance of winning his bet; but the same businessman might flatly refuse to make the same bet on the toss of a coin even though he was absolutely convinced that the coin was fair and therefore that he had an even chance of winning the bet.

> Curves like those shown in Figure 2 do *not* purport to represent the "value of money" as such; they reflect an indecomposable mixture of attitude towards risk, profit, and loss in a particular kind of situation.

Finally we warn the student emphatically against two common interpretations of the meaning of utility which are totally false.

First, the utilities of two separate consequences cannot be added to obtain the utility of both consequences together—the utility of an apple plus an orange is usually *not* equal to the utility of an apple plus the utility of an orange. All that is required to understand this assertion is to look at curve *A* or *B* in Figure 2, observe that the utility of a $10,000 profit is not equal to twice the utility of a $5000 profit, and remember the reason why.

Second, we cannot use curves like those in Figure 2 as the basis for an assertion that any given consequence is worth less or more to one man than to another if by this we mean that one of the two men "really needs" the money more than the other or that the money will do more "real good" to one man than to another; nor can we say for example that because a loss of $10,000 would reduce Mr. C's utility by only .5 utile while a profit of $10,000 would increase Mr. B's utility by .85 utile, therefore there would be a net social gain if Mr. C were taxed $10,000 and the proceeds handed over to Mr. B. *All* that we can say on the basis of curves like those of Figure 2 is that one man will *want to behave* differently from another when faced with choices under uncertainty. Ethical and social issues cannot be handled by the methods we shall use in this course.

The Justification for the Use of Expected Monetary Value
ALTERNATIVE SCALES FOR MEASURING UTILITY

Suppose now that we were to *rescale* the numerical values of the utilities in Figure 2 by first multiplying every number on the left-hand scale to 20,000 and then subtracting 10,000. The result of such a change of scale is shown on the right-hand side of the figure.

If now we were to evaluate act *M* for our old friend Mr. A by reading the "value" of each consequence from the right-hand rather than the left-hand scale and then taking the expectation of these values, we would obtain the result shown in the last column of Table 12 in place of that obtained in Table 9 and shown again in the next to the last column of Table 12. Comparing the sums of these two columns we see that the only element which depends on *either* the probabilities or the consequences of this particular act *M* is the factor .798

Table 12. Expected utility of contract M to Mr. A

Event	Probability	Expected utility on scale I	Expected utility on scale II
A	.30	.30 × .99	$-10,000(.30) + 20,000(.30 \times .99)$
B	.45	.45 × .98	$-10,000(.45) + 20,000(.45 \times .98)$
C	.25	.25 × .24	$-10,000(.25) + 20,000(.25 \times .24)$
	1.00	.798	$-10,000(1)\quad +20,000(.798)$

which appears in *both* column sums; it is obvious that if we were to reevaluate act N in this way we would get the same factor .86, instead of .798, in *both* column sums; and finally, the utility of the consequence $0 of the act "do nothing" is .85 on the left-hand scale and $-10,000 + 20,000(.85)$ on the right-hand scale.

Clearly, then, use of the right-hand scale for evaluation of acts will lead to exactly the same *results* as use of the left-hand scale, and therefore we can if we like say that the right-hand scale measures "utilities" of consequences just as well as the left-hand scale. The whole problem is exactly like the problem of scaling a thermometer: no matter what numerical values we give to the top and bottom of the scale, the thermometer will give just as good *comparisons* of the temperatures of various objects. To sum up:

A utility scale can always be transformed by *multiplying or dividing* every value by the *same* constant, or by adding the *same* constant (positive or negative) to every value, or by both these operations together.

EXPECTED UTILITY WHEN CONDITIONAL UTILITY
IS LINEAR IN MONEY

We are now able to prove the correctness of the rule which we gave [on pages 252–54] for testing whether expected *monetary* value would be a correct guide to action in a given complex decision problem. What we shall show is that a person who chooses the act with the highest expected monetary value when this rule tells him to do so will necessarily choose the act with the highest expected

utility; the student will follow the argument more easily if he first observes that the utility which Mr. C assigns to any consequence on scale II is numerically equal to the monetary value of the consequence and therefore that the expected monetary value of any act involving these consequences will be numerically equal to its expected utility on scale II.

Letting $W denote the monetary value of the worst possible consequence of any complex decision problem and $B that of the best, the rule said in effect that expected monetary value would be a valid guide to action if and only if the person responsible for the decision would use this guide in simple problems involving a choice between 1) a specified amount of cash certain and 2) a reference lottery which would result with probability π in $B and with probability $(1-\pi)$ in $W. Such a person is saying that for him the cash equivalent of the reference lottery is given by the formula

$$\$W(1-\pi) + \$B\pi.$$

Since the choice of the end points of a utility scale is always arbitrary, this person can always choose a scale in which the number W without the dollar sign represents the *utility* of the consequence whose monetary value is $W and in which the number B represents the utility of the consequence whose monetary value is $B. On this scale the utility of the reference lottery and therefore of its cash equivalent is *by definition*

$$W(1-\pi) + B\pi,$$

and we conclude that *a person who values all reference lotteries at their expected monetary value* can always find a utility scale such that the utility of every consequence between the reference consequences is numerically equal to the monetary value of the consequence and therefore such that *the expected utility of any act involving consequences within this range*

is numerically equal to the expected monetary value of the act. By choosing the act with the highest expected monetary value, such a person automatically chooses the act with the highest expected utility.

GORDON F. PITZ

31 An Example of Bayesian Hypothesis Testing: The Perception of Rotary Motion in Depth

The Bayesian method of employing likelihood ratios is illustrated in an analysis of an experiment reported by Hershberger, supposedly disconfirming a theory proposed by Day and Power. The original experiment produced results significant at the .02 level when using a 1-tailed test; it is shown that, by interpreting these results as evidence against the null hypothesis, one is making certain strong assumptions that should be recognized. In fact, the Bayesian analysis suggests that the null hypothesis is not discredited nearly as much as is suggested by the classical significance level.

The present note deals with an experiment reported by Hershberger (3) and reviews the interpretation of Hershberger's results in order to illustrate the approach which a Bayesian statistician might take towards the testing of hypotheses. The details of the Bayesian approach have been described by Edwards, Lindman, and Savage (2), and the present note follows these procedures closely. Whether or not one agrees with the fundamentals of this approach, the present analysis may illustrate the incompleteness of the traditional significance level approach. It may also help to clarify some misunderstandings of Bayesian procedures that have recently been published.

In a discussion of the apparent reversal of rotary motion in depth, an experiment was de-

scribed by Hershberger which, it was claimed, supported his own interpretation of the perception of rotary motion, and disconfirmed a theory proposed by Day and Power (1). Briefly, subjects were required to identify the direction of rotation of a stimulus based only upon the horizontal movement of components of the stimulus. Of 48 subjects, 32 apparently perceived the direction of rotation as that being simulated. Applying a two-tailed binomial test, Hershberger rejected the null hypothesis at the .05 level. Since Day and Power would predict an inability to identify the direction of rotation, their theory would be associated with the null hypothesis.

It is difficult to see why Hershberger used a two-tailed rather than a one-tailed test. Advocates of any theoretical position would

From *Psychological Bulletin*, Vol. 70, No. 4, pp. 252–55, 1968. Copyright © 1968 by the American Psychological Association, and reprinted by permission.

presumably feel unhappy if the proportion of subjects identifying correctly the direction of rotation were markedly less than expected by chance. If one is concerned with significance levels, a one-tailed test would seem to be appropriate. The one-tailed significance level of Hershberger's results is approximately .02, a value that has been reported only for comparison with later analyses. More important for a Bayesian is the value of the likelihood ratio, which may be thought of as a measure of the impact of the experimental results upon the personal opinions of some ideally rational individual. It is the ratio of two conditional probabilities, $P(D|H_1)/P(D|H_2)$, where D is the experimental data, and H_1 and H_2 are alternative hypotheses. In further discussion, it will be assumed that H_1 is the Day and Power hypothesis, and H_2 the Hershberger hypothesis; then a likelihood ratio greater than 1.0 may be interpreted as favoring Day and Power.

The critical parameter in interpreting Hershberger's study is the probability that the subject correctly detects the direction of rotation. Let Q be this parameter; it may be thought of as a measure of the effectiveness of the stimulus cue used by Hershberger, and its value determines the appropriateness of the two conflicting theories. From the Day and Power theory it is reasonable to hypothesize that $Q = .5$; consequently it is easy to see that $P(D|H_1)$, H_1 being the hypothesis that $Q = .5$, is found directly from a binomial distribution with parameter .5. The significance level is, in fact, derived from this probability distribution. Unfortunately, Hershberger's theory does not allow one to specify an exact value for Q under H_2. Ideally, Q would be 1.0; however, if this were the case, the only data that would not refute Hershberger would be correct reports by all subjects. Presumably it is reasonable to suppose that some subjects would not give correct reports even if Hershberger's theory was correct.

In general, suppose n independent observations were taken, of which s were successes, in that the subject correctly reported the di-

rection of rotation. If Hershberger is correct, suppose the value of Q to be q^*, with $q^* > .5$. Assuming then, that Q is known to equal q^*, the likelihood ratio from Hershberger's data is as follows:

$$L = \frac{(.5)^n}{q^{*s}(1-q^*)^{n-s}} = \frac{(.5)^{48}}{q^{*32}(1-q^*)^{16}} \quad \text{Eq. 1}$$

From Equation 1 we can determine the value of q^* that would make L equal to 1.0, that is, for which the data would be equivocal. Solving the equation

$$q^{*32}(1 - q^*)^{16} = (.5)^{48}$$

we find $q^* \cong .8$. In other words, if Hershberger's theory implies that the probability of the stimulus cue being effective is greater than .8, Hershberger's data actually favor the hypothesis derived from Day and Power's theory.

The preceding argument was based on the assumption that q^* was a known constant. A more appropriate procedure is to reflect one's opinion concerning the unknown Q by means of a probability distribution. Let $g(Q = q)$, or, more simply, $g(q)$, be the probability that $Q = q$, given that Hershberger is correct. This distribution is a set of personal opinions, not necessarily based upon objective frequencies. It may be referred to as a conditional prior distribution, being conditional upon the correctness of Hershberger's theory. Methods for arriving at this distribution have been discussed by Edwards et al. (2) and by Raiffa and Schlaifer (4), and some reasonable examples will be suggested below. With the incorporation of a conditional prior distribution, the likelihood ratio for Hershberger's data is

$$L = \frac{(.5)^{48}}{\int_{.5}^{1.0} q^{32}(1-q)^{16}g(q)dq} \quad \text{Eq. 2}$$

Notice that the denominator is the probability of the data given any alternative to the null hypothesis. Some misunderstanding concerning this denominator may be found in an article by Wilson, Miller, and Lower (5), in which they have apparently confused the two factors involved in the integration. The term $q^8(1-q)^{n-8}$ is the distribution of the data given some alternative hypothesis concerning Q, and $g(q)$ is the prior probability distribution defined over all possible alternatives. Comments such as, "The calculation of a likelihood ratio requires at least one specifiable alternative distribution [5, p. 194]," suggest that the authors have confused $g(q)$, which must be specified, with the distribution of the data given Q, which is a whole family of distributions. What is meant by "alternative distribution" is not clear, but Wilson et al. made some very misleading statements about the applicability of likelihood ratios, predicated on the assumption that it is frequently impossible to find an "alternative distribution."

It may not be necessary to know $g(q)$ in detail. Since the number of observations was fairly large, one may normally use the procedure known as stable estimation. The distribution $g(q)$ may in most cases be replaced by a constant $g(\hat{q})$, where $\hat{q}$ is the value of Q most favored by the data, provided that $g(\hat{q})$ is reasonably linear in the region of $\hat{q}$. In general, $\hat{q} = s/n$, and in this case $\hat{q} = 32/48 = 2/3$. Since the lower limit of the integral in Equation 2 may be changed to zero with very little difference in the result, Equation 2 simplifies to the following

$$L \cong (.5)^{48} C_{32}^{48} \frac{49}{g(2/3)} = \frac{.394}{g(2/3)}$$

In order to evaluate Hershberger's data, we need some estimate for $g(2/3)$. This estimate must ultimately be an expression of opinion by a person evaluating the data, but it is still possible to show the consequences of certain assumptions concerning $g(q)$. Suppose we make the assumption that, given that Hershberger is correct, any value of Q between .5 and 1.0 is equally likely. In this case, $g(q)$ is a uniform distribution, shown in Figure 1 as $g_1(q)$. Since the integral of $g(q)$ between

$Q = .5$ and $Q = 1.0$ must be 1, $g_1(q) = 2.0$, and $L = .197$.

The assumption of a uniform prior implies that the stimulus cues that form the basis for Hershberger's theory may not be very effective determinants of perception. A strong belief in the effectiveness of these cues might be represented by a probability distribution defined over Q such as that shown as $g_2(q)$ in Figure 1. This distribution has its maximum

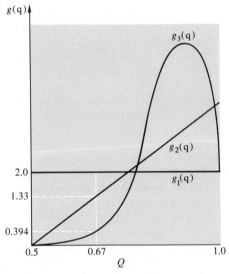

Fig. 1. Three possible prior probability distributions defined for values of Q, given the correctness of Hershberger's theory. (It is assumed that values of Q less than 0.5 are impossible.)

at $Q = 1.0$, is zero at $Q = .5$, and is linear between these two values. Thus $g(2/3) = 1.33$, and $L = .296$. A third distribution, $g_3(q)$, illustrates a still more firm commitment to the idea that Q must be large, while maintaining approximate linearity around $Q = 2/3$. This distribution implies, for example, that the probability prior to the experiment that Q is less than 2/3 is approximately .03 (the area to the left of $Q = 2/3$). The value of $g_3(2/3)$ was deliberately chosen to be .394, since for this value L would be 1.0. In other words, if

$g_3(q)$, or some similar distribution for which $g(2/3) = .394$, reflects one's prior opinions concerning the value of Q, given that Hershberger is correct, the data speak just as strongly for the null hypothesis as they do against.

An alternative to the use of stable estimation is provided by the method of conjugate prior distributions; the integral in Equation 2 may be solved analytically if $g(q)$ is a distribution of a certain form. Specifically, a beta distribution is "conjugate" to observations that are generated by a Bernoulli process, as in this example, and it may be convenient to approximate $g(q)$ by one member of the family of beta distributions. This alternative will not be pursued, but details may be found in Raiffa and Schlaifer (4). One advantage of using this approximation to the conditional prior is that it is possible to interpret one's belief concerning Q as reflecting prior experience with the Bernoulli process. Suppose one assumes Hershberger's theory to be true, and is willing to behave as if a certain number of observations, n_0, had already been made, of which s_0 were successes. Then the conditional prior would be a beta distribution with parameters n_0 and s_0, and the likelihood ratio would be a function of n_0, s_0, n, and s. In this case we have

$$L = \frac{(s_0-1)!\,(n_0-s_0-1)!\,(n_0+47)!}{(s_0+31)!\,(n_0-s_0+15)!\,(n_0-1)!}\,(.5)^{48}$$

If one's opinions prior to the experiment give equal credence to the null hypothesis derived from the theory of Day and Power's, and to Hershberger's theory, then the odds against the null hypothesis is equal to the likelihood ratio. Otherwise, posterior odds is obtained by multiplying prior odds by the likelihood ratio. It is in this sense that L is a measure of the impact of the data upon one's opinions. As has been shown, the odds will depend quite strongly upon certain assumptions concerning values of the parameter Q, a parameter that summarizes either theoretical position. However, given any reasonable assumption concerning the form of the prior distribution, it is clear that the data do not argue as strongly against Day and Power as is implied by the test of significance. Under the conditions that neither hypothesis is initially favored, the posterior probability that the null hypothesis is correct is the ratio $L(1.0+L)$. This probability for $g_1(q)$ is .16 and is .23 for $g_2(q)$, both values being larger than the significance level of .02. For $g_3(q)$ the probability is, of course, .5.

That the interpretation of data must depend upon one's initial beliefs is not necessarily a flaw in the Bayesian approach. It may be argued that it is a characteristic of any form of data analysis. Rather than leave this interpretation to the unaided intuition of the scientist, the Bayesian statistician attempts to formalize the inferential process by making clear the implications of any interpretation. This note has attempted to show that, by interpreting Hershberger's data as evidence against the Day and Power's theory, one is making certain strong assumptions concerning the value of a hypothetical parameter Q. If these assumptions can be justified, the interpretation is valid; otherwise, one must conclude that the issue is still open to debate.

References

1. Day, R. H., & Power, R. P. Apparent reversal (oscillation) of rotary motion in depth: An investigation and a general theory. *Psychological Review*, 1965, 72, 117–127.
2. Edwards, W., Lindman, H., & Savage, L. J. Bayesian statistical inference for psychological research. *Psychological Review*, 1963, 70, 193–242.
3. Hershberger, W. A. Comment on "Apparent reversal (oscillation) of rotary motion in depth." *Psychological Review*, 1967, 74, 235–238.
4. Raiffa, H., & Schlaifer, R. *Applied statistical decision theory*. Boston: Harvard University Graduate School of Business Administration, 1961.
5. Wilson, W., Miller, H. L., & Lower, J. S. Much ado about the null hypothesis. *Psychological Bulletin*, 1967, 67, 188–196.

JOHN E. OVERALL

32 Classical Statistical Hypothesis Testing Within the Context of Bayesian Theory

A portion of results that are judged significant on the basis of classical statistical tests will be due, in fact, to chance. The conditional probability of error in the presence of statistical significance depends upon the significance level employed, the power of the test, and the prior probability that a valid null hypothesis was chosen for testing. Bayesian theory provides a logical model for the design of experiments in which classical hypothesis testing is to be used. In this manner, Bayesian objectives can be realized while the safeguards of classical statistical hypothesis testing are retained.

Certain concepts from Bayesian theory appear to have logical implications for the design of experiments, as distinct from decisions concerning implications of experimental results. Choice of sample size and specification of the significance level to be used in testing hypotheses are matters of experimental design which traditionally have been left, within broad limits, to the discretion of the experimenter who employs classical statistical models. No logical basis exists in traditional statistical theory for determining *which* significance level and *what* power are required under particular experimental conditions. In the present article, a logical model for use in simultaneous determination of both sample size and significance level consistent with desired probable validity of conclusions is discussed.

This is not an article concerned with Bayesian likelihood methods for reaching decisions based on experimental outcome. Bayesian likelihood principles have been proposed as an alternative to classical hypothesis testing (1); however, most psychologists feel uncomfortable with an approach to statistical inference in which conclusions depend so frankly upon subjective probability estimates. It is proposed that subjective probability estimates should be employed in a logically consistent manner to reach preliminary decisions which have traditionally been left to the experimenter, and that hypothesis testing subsequently proceed along classical lines. In this way, Bayesian objectives can be achieved without sacrificing the safeguards of classical hypothesis testing.

The central problem with which this article is concerned is invalid conclusions which appear to be supported by statistical significance as the result of application of classical statistical decision procedures. With reference to this problem, Bayes theorem provides a formal statement of the probability that null hypothesis H_0 is valid, in fact, given that a statistically significant result has been obtained. In the notation of Edward, Lindman, and Savage (1), Bayes theorem can be stated as follows.

$$P(H_0 \mid D) = \frac{P(D \mid H_0)P(H_0)}{P(D)}$$

where $P(H_0 \mid D)$ is the probability of valid H_0 given significant result D; $P(D \mid H_0)$ is the probability of significant result D given that H_0 is valid; $P(H_0)$ is the probability that a valid null hypothesis has been chosen for testing, and $P(D)$ is the probability of a

From *Psychological Bulletin*, Vol. 71, No. 4, pp. 285–95, 1969. Copyright © 1969 by the American Psychological Association, and reprinted by permission.

statistically significant result when either H_0 or H_1 is valid.

Thus, Bayes theorem states that the probability of a statistically significant result representing chance rejection of a valid null hypothesis is a joint function of significance level, power of the test, and the a priori probability that a valid null hypothesis has been chosen for testing. The controversies surrounding Bayesian theory have not arisen from denial of the validity of this model, which is a simple consequence of the multiplicative law of probability. The principal difficulty lies in determining, or even defining, the prior probabilities (3). It is for this reason that the author proposes to use Bayesian theory only for preliminary decisions concerning experimental design, which decisions customarily have been made without benefit of logic or theory. It seems far better to employ an elegant model, in which parameters are subject to crude estimation, than to employ no logic at all in the selection of significance level and determination of sample sizes.

Conditional alpha probability is the central concept in the present discussion. It is the probability that a result *which is judged statistically significant* has occurred by chance rejection of a valid null hypothesis. In a scientific community in which only statistically significant results are published, the conditional alpha probability determines the frequency with which invalid conclusions are presented in the literature. *The conditional alpha probability ($P_{\alpha 1s}$) is the ratio of probability of invalid rejection of the null hypothesis to the total probability of both valid and invalid rejection of the null hypothesis.* As defined in the Bayes theorem, it depends upon (*a*) the simple alpha probability or significance level specified by the investigator, (*b*) the power of the test of significance, and (*c*) the a priori probability that the null hypothesis is valid.

Disregarding the problem of a priori probabilities for a moment, if the power of a test is low, the probability of rejecting the null hypothesis when it is really true may be only slightly smaller than the probability of reject-

ing the null hypothesis when the alternative is really true. As a consequence, false rejections of valid null hypotheses may constitute a large proportion of all significant results. If, in addition, the a priori probability of validity for the null hypothesis is substantial, an even larger proportion of significant results may be due to chance. Consider the case of an investigator who works entirely within an area where the null hypothesis is always true. If he consistently employs the proper classical statistical model with $\alpha = .05$ or $\alpha = .01$, the probability will be only .05 or .01 that he will reject a null hypothesis when it is in fact valid; however, of the statistically significant results reported by this hapless investigator, 100% will be due to chance. This ad absurdum example illustrates the difference between simple alpha probabilities and conditional alpha probabilities as the terms are employed in this article.

The probability that a test will lead to *invalid* rejection of the null hypothesis is the joint probability that H_0 is true (P_0) and that the test will lead to rejection of H_0 when it is true (P_α). In the notation to be used throughout the remainder of the present article, this probability of erroneous rejection of a valid null hypothesis is given in Equation 1.

$$P_\epsilon = P_\alpha \cdot P_0 \qquad \text{Eq. 1}$$

where P_ϵ is the probability of invalid rejection of the null hypothesis; P_α is the simple alpha level representing probability of rejecting null hypothesis H_0 when it is really true, and P_0 is the a priori probability that a valid null hypothesis has been chosen for testing.

The probability that a test will lead to *valid* rejection of H_0 is the joint probability that alternative hypothesis H_1 is really true (P_1) and that the test will lead to rejection of H_0 when H_1 is true [$P_{(1-\beta)}$]. The probability that a test will lead to rejection of H_0 when H_1 is true is the power of the test against alternative H_1.

$$P_v = P_{(1-\beta)} \cdot P_1$$

where P_v is the probability of valid rejection

of H_0; $P_{(1-\beta)}$ is the probability that the test will lead to rejection of null hypothesis H_0 when H_1 is true (power), and P_1 is the a priori probability that a valid alternative hypothesis has been chosen for testing ($P_1 = 1.0 - P_0$).

The conditional alpha probability is the ratio of probability of invalid rejection of H_0 to the sum of probability of valid plus invalid rejections of H_0.

$$P_{\alpha 1 s} = \frac{P_\epsilon}{P_\epsilon + P_v} = \frac{P_\alpha \cdot P_0}{P_\alpha \cdot P_0 + P_{(1-\beta)} \cdot P_1} \quad \text{Eq. 3}$$

The simple alpha probability P_α is the probability that a test will result in rejection of the null hypothesis when it is really true. Even where the null hypothesis is true, certain sampling variability is to be expected in values of the test statistic. In Figure 1, the sampling distribution of an F statistic under the condition of valid null hypothesis is shown in the distribution labeled F. The point F_α is the critical value of the test statistic beyond which the null hypothesis will be rejected. The simple alpha probability P_α is the integral of the central F distribution from F_α to ∞ represented by the area under F to the right of F_α.

$$P = F_\alpha \int^{\infty} P(F) df$$

The power of an F test against a specified alternative hypothesis H_1 is the probability $P_{(1-\beta)}$ that the test will lead to rejection of H_0 when H_1 is actually true. In Figure 1, the probability distribution F' is the theoretical

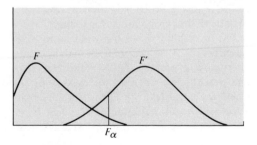

Fig. 1. Schematic diagram of central and non-central F distribution.

(noncentral) distribution of the test statistic under the condition that the alternative hypothesis H_1 is actually true—that is, a true treatment difference exists. When F_α is the critical value of the test statistic used in rejecting H_0, the probability that the test will result in rejection of H_0 when H_1 is really true is represented by the area under F' to the right of F_α. The power of the test is the integral of the F' distribution from F_α to ∞.

$$P_{(1-\beta)} = F_\alpha \int^{\infty} P(F') df.$$

It is important to note in Figure 1 that the critical value F_α represents the lower limit of integration for both F and F' in determining simple alpha probability P_α and power $P_{(1-\beta)}$. By shifting F_α to the right, the area under F representing simple alpha probability P_α is decreased, and the area under F' representing power $P_{(1-\beta)}$ is also decreased. By shifting F_α to the left, both simple alpha probability and power are increased. The *relative* change in P_α and $P_{(1-\beta)}$ produced by varying the critical value F_α is complexly determined by parameters of the two distributions. For the present, it is sufficient to note that the relationship between P_α and $P_{(1-\beta)}$ can be systematically varied by shifting the critical value of the test statistic F_α.

The a priori probability P_0 is the probability that the null hypothesis is true apart from evidence provided by the particular experimental results. The hypothetical experimenter, who works entirely within an area in which the null hypothesis is always true, is confronted with $P_0 = 1.0$. Although the concept of a priori probability is a difficult one, the presence and effect of such probabilities in experimental research can hardly be questioned. Some experiments are much more likely to involve false null hypotheses than are others, and in many instances this likelihood can be agreed upon by independent judges prior to the experiment. The likelihood that a test will result in rejection of null hypothesis H_0 depends upon the probability that true treatment differences exist in the experimental situation.

The definition and estimation of a priori probabilities have been most controversial problems in application of Bayesian concepts to statistical decision making. In large measure, the seriousness of these problems for the proposed use of the Bayesian model is minimized by the fact that decisions to accept or to reject the null hypothesis continue to be made on the basis of classical statistical tests. Bayes theorem simply provides a logical model for decisions concerning sample size and simple alpha level.

Estimation of Conditional Alpha Probabilities

One is frequently faced with a situation in which an estimate of conditional alpha probabilities would be valuable. Perhaps an experiment is being designed, or perhaps published research results are being evaluated.

To illustrate in a practical way the dangers inherent in small sample, low power tests in research areas where true treatment differences are unlikely, an example from psychiatric drug research will be used. Reliable estimates of power of tests of significance for commonly employed research designs in this area have been published (4). The usual clinical drug study has involved fewer than 20 patients per group. In the face of rather extreme variability in response to treatment, the power of analysis of variance F tests in detecting even large differences is as low as .25 for such small samples, $P_{(1-\beta)} = .25$. If we consider that as high as 90% of the new drugs tested actually will not be meaningfully different from an effective standard drug employed as control ($P_0 = .90$), the high risk of invalid conclusions becomes apparent.

Consider the simple hypothesis testing situation in which null hypothesis H_0 is tested against alternative hypothesis H_1. With usual oversimplification, it is assumed that either H_0 or H_1 is true ($P_0 + P_1 = 1.0$), and that when H_1 is true, the test has power $P_{(1-\beta)} = .25$. The a priori probability that H_0 is valid

is $P_0 = .90$, and the a priori probability that H_1 is valid is $P_1 = .10$.

The conditional alpha probability is the probability that if a statistically significant result is obtained, it will be due to chance and, in fact, not reflect true superiority of a new drug. It is the ratio of probability of incorrectly rejecting H_0 to the total probability of rejecting H_0, as defined in Equations 1, 2, and 3.

$$P_{\alpha 1 s} = \frac{P_\epsilon}{P_\epsilon + P_v} = \frac{.05 \times .90}{.05 \times .90 + .25 \times .10} = .643$$

The analysis leads us to estimate that almost two-thirds of statistically significant results derived from studies in which a new drug is compared with an effective standard may represent invalid rejections of the null hypothesis.

Controlling Conditional Alpha Probabilities

It is possible to plan research in such manner that any specified safe conditional alpha probability will be (approximately) maintained. Equation 3 reveals that the conditional alpha probability depends upon a priori probabilities, simple alpha level, and power of test. Given that one estimates the a priori probabilities and specifies a required conditional alpha probability, a particular ratio of simple alpha level to power is defined.

$$\Delta = \frac{P_1 P_{\alpha 1 s}}{P_0(1 - P_{\alpha 1 s})}, \text{ where } \Delta = \frac{P_\alpha}{P_{(1-\beta)}} \quad \text{Eq. 4}$$

The Δ ratio required to satisfy specified conditional alpha and a priori probabilities can be obtained by adopting a conventional simple alpha level and then choosing sample size adequate to yield power determined by Equation 5.

$$P_{(1-\beta)} = \frac{P_\alpha P_0(1 - P_{\alpha 1 s})}{P_1 P_{\alpha 1 s}} \quad \text{Eq. 5}$$

Sample size required to yield specified power can be estimated using procedures described in numerous texts (5). In practice, it will not always be feasible to increase sample size enough to obtain power determined from Equation 5 for an arbitrarily chosen significance level. An additional problem is that previously published constant power curves represent only a few widely separated significance levels—for example, $P_\alpha = .5$, $.7$, and $.9$ (2). One is always conservative in using power greater than that required by Equation 5. Also, simple alpha level can be adjusted by trial and error among alternative conventional values ($P_\alpha = .05$, $.01$, $.005$, and $.001$) to arrive at a feasible combination of power and significance level under conditions of the experiment. Constant power charts offering a wider range of simple alpha probabilities are included as Figure 2.

An alternative approach to ensuring specified conditional alpha probability involves selection of an acceptable value for power, $P_{(1-\beta)}$, and solving of Equation 6 for required simple alpha level.

$$P_\alpha = \frac{P_{(1-\beta)}P_1 P_{\alpha 1 s}}{P_0(1-P_{\alpha 1 s})} \qquad \text{Eq. 6}$$

The conventional simple alpha level which is next smaller than the value obtained from Equation 6 can be employed with sample size chosen to provide power $P_{(1-\beta)}$.

To use the charts included in this article, one must first calculate ϕ.

$$\phi = \frac{1/k\Sigma\beta_i^2}{\sigma_0^2} \qquad \text{Eq. 7}$$

where β_i^2 is the square of the (hypothesized) deviation of the ith treatment mean about the grand mean; k is the number of treatments, and σ_0^2 is the anticipated experimental error variance.

Next, identify the chart appropriate for number of degrees of freedom for treatments ($N_1 = 1$, 2, 3, or 4) and the desired power $P_{(1-\beta)} = .50$, $.75$, or $.90$. Solve Equation 6 to determine required simple alpha level in light of desired power and estimated a priori probabilities. Enter the appropriate chart with

calculated ϕ value and go up to the curve representing required significance level P_α. (Any P_α value which is smaller than that calculated from Equation 6 will be acceptable.) Finally, read total degrees of freedom for error from vertical scale. The required number of subjects per group will be $(N_2+k)/k$, where N_2 is df for error.

As an example of use of the charts to ensure a specified conditional alpha probability, consider a researcher who is conducting an investigation of effectiveness of tranquilizing drugs for retarding stress-induced rise in serum-free fatty acids. It is decided that a mean difference between drug and placebo of 100 units would be clinically significant; thus, $B_i = 100/2$ or one-half the distance between drug and placebo means. On the basis of prior experience, the investigator feels "fairly confident" that a true difference of 100 units will be found to exist, and he, accordingly, specifies $P_1 = .67$ and $P_0 = .33$. He sees no excessive loss involved in failing to find a significant difference if a true difference actually does exist; so he specifies required power $P_{(1-\beta)} = .50$. He is concerned about the danger of publishing invalid conclusions and desires to maintain an overall conditional alpha probability $P_{\alpha 1 s} = .05$. Previous data and laboratory norms suggest a within-groups sampling variability $\sigma_0^2 = 6,000$. In summary, $P_{\alpha 1 s} = .05$, $P_1 = .67$, $P_0 = .33$,

$$B_i^2 = \left(\frac{100}{2}\right)^2 = 2,500, \quad \sigma_0^2 = 6,000, \quad N_1 = 1.$$

From these parameters and estimates, the value of ϕ is calculated using Equation 7.

$$\phi = \frac{(2,500+2,500)/2}{6,000} = .417$$

Using the desired value for power, required simple alpha probability is obtained from Equation 6.

$$P_\alpha = \frac{.50 \times .67 \times .50}{.33 \times .95} = .017$$

From these calculations, it appears that a simple alpha level $P_\alpha = .01$ will satisfy con-

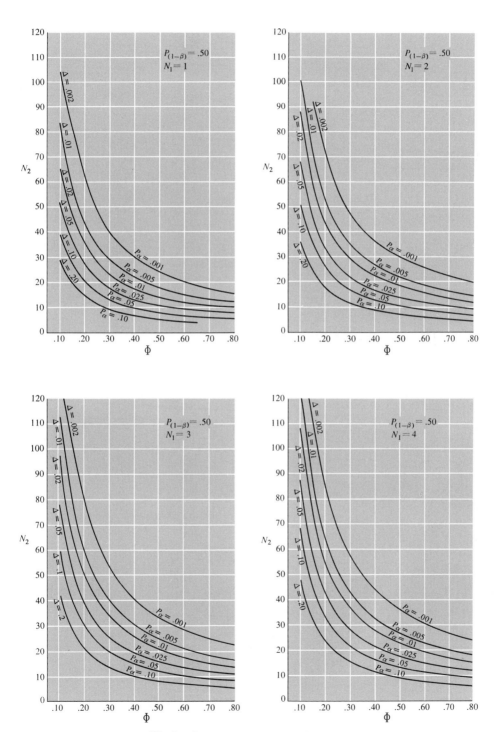

Fig. 2a. Constant power curves for $P_{(1-\beta)} = .50$.

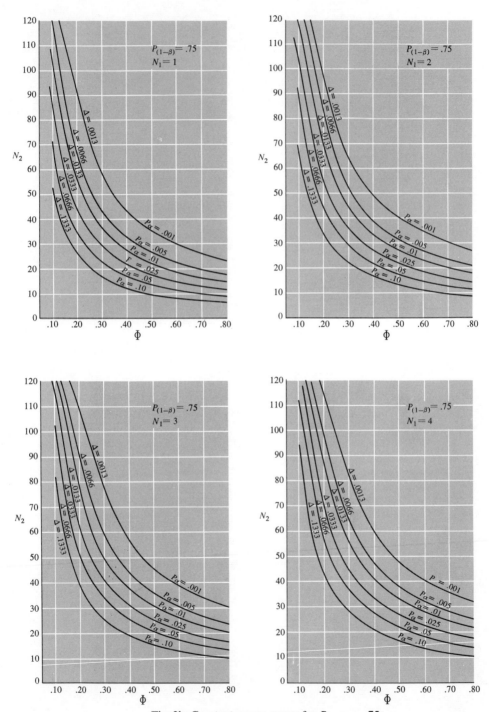

Fig. 2b. Constant power curves for $P_{(1-\beta)} = .75$.

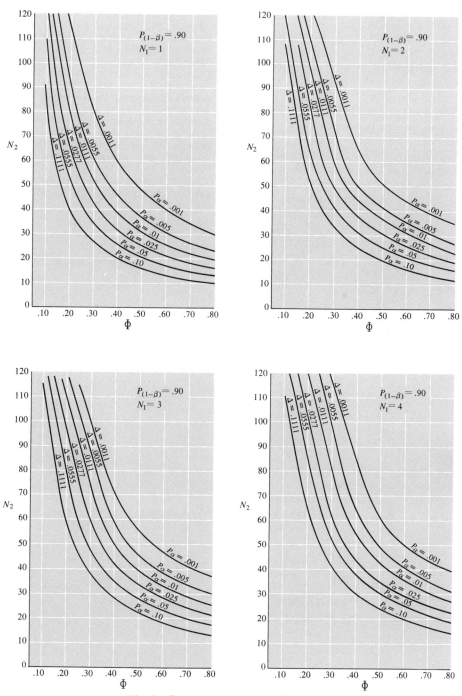

Fig. 2c. Constant power curves for $P_{(1-\beta)}, = .90$.

ditions of the experiment and provide a conditional alpha probability $P_{\alpha 1s} = .05$.

The chart for power $P_{(1-\beta)} = .50$ and $N_1 = 1$ is identified. Entering the chart with $\phi = .417$, the curve for significance level $P_\alpha = .01$ is used to estimate appropriate degrees of freedom for error. The value $N_2 = 20$ appears adequate. The number of subjects per treatment group should be approximately $(N_2 + k)/k$ or $(20 + 2)/2 = 11$. The procedure led to an experimental design involving 11 subjects per group and power of .50 against a true mean difference between drug and placebo of 100 units. Using this design, the investigator can feel confident that *if a statistically significant result is obtained*, it can be relied upon to represent a true treatment difference with probability $1 - P_{\alpha 1s} = .95$.

References

1. Edwards, W., Lindman, H., & Savage, L. J. Bayesian statistical inference for psychological research. *Psychological Review*, 1963, 70, 193–242.
2. Feldt, L. S., & Mahmoud, M. W. Power function charts for specification of sample size in analysis of variance. *Psychometrika*, 1958, 23, 201–210.
3. Kendall, M. D., & Buckland, W. R. *A dictionary of statistical terms.* New York: Hafner, 1960.
4. Overall, J. E., Hollister, L. E., & Dalal, S. N. Psychiatric drug research. *Archives of General Psychiatry*, 1967, 16, 152–161.
5. Winer, B. J. *Statistical principles in experimental design.* New York: McGraw-Hill, 1962.

The Use and Misuse of Chi-Square

If it did not exist before, a controversy about the proper use of the chi-square test was initiated in November, 1949, when D. Lewis and C. Burke published their article, "The Use and Misuse of the Chi-Square Test." In the article the authors reported the results of a study in which they reviewed the uses of the chi-square test in the *Journal of Experimental Pyschology* in the years 1944, 1945, and 1946. They found what they believed to be numerous incorrect uses of the test. Their paper is a lengthy one and is reproduced in its entirety. C. C. Peters, one of the investigators accused of misusing the chi-square test, promptly defended his work and the controversy followed. Other articles discussing the Lewis and Burke, and the Peters articles were published and a number of them are reproduced here. The student will benefit from this debate; his knowledge of the characteristics of the chi-square test will be deepened.

DON LEWIS   C. J. BURKE

33 The Use and Misuse of the Chi-Square Test

It has become increasingly apparent over a period of several years that psychologists, taken in the aggregate, employ the chi-square test incorrectly. The number of applications of the test does not seem to be increasing, but the number of misapplications does. This paper has been prepared in hopes of counteracting the trend. Its specific aims are to show the weaknesses in various applications that have been made and to set forth clearly the circumstances under which χ^2 can be legitimately applied in testing different hypotheses.

To confirm a general impression that the number of misuses of χ^2 has become surprisingly large, a careful survey was made of all papers published in the *Journal of Experimental Psychology*[1] during the three years 1944,

1. The choice of this particular journal resulted from a belief that the psychologists who publish in it are probably better versed, on the average, in statistical

1945, and 1946. Fourteen papers were found which contained one or more applications of the chi-square test. The applications in only three of these papers (1, 15, 18) were judged to be acceptable. In one other paper (21), the several applications could be called "correct in principle" but they involved extremely small theoretical frequencies. In nine of the fourteen papers (2, 4, 10, 16, 17, 20, 28, 29, 30) the applications were clearly unwarranted. In the remaining case,[2] it was

methodologies than are those publishing in other journals. No criticism of the journal nor of individual authors nor of experimental findings is intended. The sole purpose is to illustrate correct and incorrect applications of the chi-square test.
2. This paper, by Pronko (27), fails to provide the reader with any basis whatever for forming an independent judgment relative to the correctness or incorrectness of the two applications of χ^2 which were made. In this respect it is a good example of the current trend in papers published in psychological

From *Psychological Bulletin*, Vol. 46, No. 6, pp. 433–89, 1949. Copyright © 1949 by the American Psychological Association and reprinted by permission.

not possible to determine what had been done; and the author, when questioned twice by letter, did not choose to reply.

The principal sources of error (or inaccuracy) in the fourteen papers just referred to, as well as in papers published in other journals, are as follows:

1. Lack of independence among the single events or measures[3]
2. Small theoretical frequencies
3. Neglect of frequencies of non-occurrence
4. Failure to equalize ΣF_o (the sum of the observed frequencies) and ΣF_t (the sum of the theoretical frequencies)
5. Indeterminate theoretical frequencies
6. Incorrect or questionable categorizing
7. Use of non-frequency data
8. Incorrect determination of the number of degrees of freedom
9. Incorrect computations (including a failure to weight by N when proportions instead of frequencies are used in the calculations)

These errors will be explained in detail and illustrated with examples taken for the most part from books and published papers.

It is not surprising that errors of the types listed are frequently made; several of the standard texts to which psychologists turn for statistical guidance contain faulty illustrations. For example, Peters and Van Voorhis (26) make four applications of χ^2, only one of which is without flaws; and in one of the applications made by Guilford (13, p. 91), there is a failure to equalize ΣF_0 and ΣF_t and to calculate the number of degrees of freedom correctly.

A single application made by Peters and Van Voorhis contains the first four errors in the above list. Table 1 is based on their Table XXXV (26, p. 411). Twelve dice were thrown fourteen times, and a record was kept of the number of aces appearing at each throw. The observed frequencies F_o are entered in the second column of the table. A value of χ^2, given in the last column, was calculated for each of the fourteen throws. A composite value of χ^2 was obtained by summing the separate values. The first of the four errors in this application is that the observed frequencies lack independence. They lack independence because the same twelve dice were thrown each time. This means that, when the frequencies are grouped, it is impossible to take into account the effects of individual differences in the dice and possible compensating effects from one die to another. As a consequence, no statements can be made about the behavior of an individual die, nor is it possible to generalize the findings to any population of dice from which the twelve can be considered a sample. Therefore, only hypotheses which relate specifically to the twelve dice as a group can be tested. More will be said later about this kind of error.

The second flaw in the application comes from using theoretical frequencies of 2. These values are too low to yield a quantity whose distribution approximates the χ^2 distribution. The third mistake is the failure to equalize ΣF_o and ΣF_t, which are shown in the table as 30 and 28 respectively. This mistake is related to a fourth one—a failure to take account of the frequencies of non-occurrence of aces. Any of the four errors is sufficient to invalidate this use of the χ^2 test.[4]

---

journals to reduce explanations of methods of analyzing data to a point where they are quite unintelligible.

3. The term independence, as here used, has reference to individual or single events. In contrast, the hypothesis of independence that is tested by means of χ^2 specifies a lack of relationship (that is, an absence of interaction) between the variates represented in a contingency table. The events that occur to yield the frequencies of a contingency table must be mutually independent even though the variates are related.

4. If the observed and theoretical frequencies of non-occurrence of aces had been used in the calculations, the composite value of χ^2 would have been 12 instead of 10. This difference happens not to be large. But in another illustration used by Peters and Van Voorhis (26, Table XXXVI, p. 414), the difference is large. The value of 14.52 is given in the text. When χ^2 is correctly computed by taking account of the frequencies of non-occurrence, the resulting value is 29.72. The number of degrees of freedom remains the same, but the calculated value of χ^2 is more than doubled.

Table 1. Application of the chi-square test by Peters
and Van Voorhis (26)

Throw	F_o	F_t	$(F_o - F_t)^2$	$\dfrac{(F_o - F_t)^2}{F_t}$
1	1	2	1	0.5
2	3	2	1	0.5
3	2	2	0	0.0
4	3	2	1	0.5
5	1	2	1	0.5
6	4	2	4	2.0
7	2	2	0	0.0
8	4	2	4	2.0
9	1	2	1	0.5
10	0	2	4	2.0
11	3	2	1	0.5
12	2	2	0	0.0
13	3	2	1	0.5
14	1	2	1	0.5
Σ	30	28		10

Fundamental Theory

The two most basic requirements in any application of the chi-square test are (a) independence among the separate measures and (b) theoretical frequencies of reasonable size. These requirements can be shown in an elementary way by examining a two-category distribution of measures. But first, an unequivocal definition of χ^2 is needed.

If z is a normal deviate in standard form defined in relation to population parameters m and σ, then

$$z = \frac{X - m}{\sigma}$$

and

$$\chi^2 = z^2 = \frac{(X - m)^2}{\sigma^2} \quad \text{with } df = 1. \quad \text{Eq. } 1^5$$

Chi-square with 1 degree of freedom is thus defined as the square of a deviation from the population mean divided by the population variance.

If there are r independent measures of the variate X, there will be r independent values of z, and the resulting formula for χ^2 is

5. Equation 1 verifies the statement that the square root of χ^2 with $df = 1$ is distributed as z (or Student's t) with $df = \infty$.

$$\chi^2 = \sum_{i=1}^{r} z_i^2 = \sum \frac{(X_i - m)^2}{\sigma^2}, \text{ with } df = r.$$

$$\text{Eq. } 2$$

Values of χ^2 may range from 0 to ∞, and they have frequency distributions which depend upon the value of r. The distribution function of χ^2, in general form, will be given later. It will then be made clear that the chi-square tests of independence and goodness of fit can be applied unequivocally only to frequency data (or to proportions derived from frequency data). For the present, the plausibility of the two basic requirements stated above will be shown through an examination of the two-category case.

The Two-Category Case. Consider a population of N independent events (things; measures), each of which may fall either into category A or into category B. It is assumed that these categories are clearly defined before samples are drawn, and that the category in which a given event falls can be unequivocally determined. A sample is drawn from the population and the sample data to be employed in determining whether or not a certain hypothesis regarding the proportion of cases in each category is tenable. If p is the expected (theoretical) proportion for category A and q

the expected proportion for category B, it follows that

$$p+q = 1.$$

The probability $P(n)$ that n of the N events will fall into category A is given by the binomial distribution function

$$P(n) = \frac{N!}{n!(N-n)!} \, p^n q^{N-n}, \qquad \text{Eq. 3}$$

which is the general expression for obtaining the successive terms arising from the expansion of the binomial $(p+q)^N$. The limiting form of equation 3, as N becomes indefinitely large, is a normal distribution function having a mean of Np and a variance of Npq. In symbols,

$$\lim_{N \to \infty} P(n) = \frac{1}{\sqrt{2\pi}\sqrt{Npq}} e^{-(n-Np)^2/2Npq}.$$

$$\text{Eq. 4}[6]$$

Np is the *population* mean of category A. It is the expected value of n, that is, the theoretical frequency to be associated with category A. Nq is the corresponding theoretical frequency to be associated with category B. Npq is the *population* variance. As stated in equation 1, the square of a deviation from the population mean divided by the population variance is distributed as χ^2 with 1 df. Thus, from equation 4, it is seen that the quantity

$$\chi^2 = \frac{(n-Np)^2}{Npq} \qquad \text{Eq. 5}$$

would be distributed exactly as χ^2 with 1 df, provided that N is indefinitely large. In the two-category case, equation 5 may be employed to calculate an approximate value of χ^2. It should be noted that both p and q appear in the denominator of the right-hand term. No restriction is placed during the calcu-

6. If the investigator is concerned with the probability $P(N-n)$ that $(N-n)$ events will fall into category B, the limiting form of equation 3 would be written

$$\lim_{N \to \infty} P(N-n) = \frac{1}{\sqrt{2\pi}\sqrt{Npq}} e^{-(N-n-Nq)^2/2Npq}$$

$$\text{Eq. 4a}$$

lation; the equation gives an approximate solution for any value of N.

The formula that is commonly used in the two-category case to obtain a value of χ^2 is

$$\chi'^2 = \frac{(n-Np)^2}{Np} + \frac{(N-n-Nq)^2}{Nq}, \qquad \text{Eq. 6}$$

where Np and Nq are theoretical frequencies and n and $(N-n)$ are the corresponding observed frequencies. The prime symbol is placed on χ^2 in formula 6 to distinguish between χ^2 as *defined* by equation 5 and χ^2 as ordinarily *calculated* with formula 6. When 6 is used, the number of df is 1 less than the number of categories because one restriction ($\Sigma F_t = N$) is imposed on the theoretical frequencies. Therefore, the number of df for 6 is 1, just as it is for equation 5.

It can readily be shown that χ^2 and χ'^2 are identical quantities. It is for this reason, and this reason alone, that formula 6 may be used in obtaining an estimate of χ^2 in the two-category case.[7]

The foregoing discussion reveals the two limitations that hold in any application of the chi-square test. The first limitation is that χ^2 is correctly used only if the N events or measures are independent. Equations 3 and 4 are valid statements only when independence exists. The second basic limitation relates to the size of the theoretical frequencies. If Np (or Nq) remains small as N becomes large,

7. If observed and theoretical proportions are used in calculating values of χ^2, equations 5 and 6 become

$$\chi^2 = N \frac{(p_o - p_t)^2}{p_t q_t} \qquad \text{Eq. 5a}$$

or

$$\chi^2 = N \frac{(q_o - q_t)^2}{p_t q_t}; \qquad \text{Eq. 5b}$$

and

$$\chi^2 = N \frac{(p_o - p_t)^2}{p_t} + \frac{N(q_o - q_t)^2}{q_t}. \qquad \text{Eq. 6a}$$

In these equations, N is the total number of cases while p_o and q_o are the observed proportions and p_t and q_t are the theoretical proportions for categories A and B, respectively. The equations may be derived from 5 and 6, and they reveal that if proportions are used instead of frequencies, the values calculated from the proportions must be multiplied by N.

the limiting form of the binomial distribution function is not a normal distribution, as was assumed in writing equation 4. If, for any reason, either Np or Nq is small, the limiting form of equation 3 is the Poisson distribution function. Under such circumstances, the quantity on the right of equation 5 would not be the square of a normal deviate divided by the population variance and, consequently, would not be distributed as χ^2 with 1 df.

It should be emphasized that the categories are assumed to be designated in the population before the individual sample is drawn. It should also be emphasized that the equating of the sums of observed and theoretical frequencies *and* the use of the frequency of non-occurrence (in this case, the frequency with which measures fall in category B) are necessary to establish the identity between the quantities defined in equation 5 and equation 6.

The more general case. It is common to have frequency data that fall into several categories instead of just two. This fact requires an extension of the ideas discussed in the two-category case to encompass any number of categories. The basic features of this extension will now be presented. Actually, no new ideas enter into the development. The proof is mathematically more complex, but the under-lying ideas are the same.

Consider a population of N *independent* events, with k possible outcomes, $v_1, v_2, \ldots v_k$. Assume that, in the population

v_1 occurs with a probability of p_1
v_2 occurs with a probability of p_2
v_3 occurs with a probability of p_3

. . . .

v_k occurs with a probability of p_k

The *joint* probability $P(n_i)$ that out of N events exactly n_1 will fall in category v_1, n_2 will fall in category v_2, n_3 in v_3, *and* . . . n_k in v_k, is given by the multinomial distribution function

$$P(n_i) = \frac{N!}{n_1!n_2!n_3!\ldots n_k!} p_1{}^{n_1} p_2{}^{n_2} p_3{}^{n_3} \ldots p_k{}^{n_k},$$

Eq. 7

where

$$\sum_{i=1}^{k} n_i = N.$$

This is the fundamental expression from which the distribution function of χ^2 is derived. It confirms the statement that the measures (frequencies) in the various cells (categories, classes, etc.) of a multidimensional table must be mutually independent to enable a legitimate application of χ^2 in testing any hypothesis concerning the table. And because equation 7 is written in terms of the frequencies n_1, n_2, $n_3 \ldots n_k$, the chi-square tests of independence and goodness of fit, based as they are on a distribution function derived from 7, may be used unequivocally only in relation to frequency data.[8]

The distribution function of χ^2, here symbolized by $g_r(\chi^2)$, may be written

$$g_r(\chi^2) = C_r(\chi^2)^{(r+2)/2} e^{-(\chi^2/2)},$$

where C_r, a coefficient which changes with r, is given by

$$C_r = \frac{1}{2^{(r/2)} \Gamma(r/2)}. \qquad \text{Eq. 9}[9]$$

It should be emphasized that equation 8 is an exact distribution function for the quantity defined in equations 2 and 5 but only an approximation of the distribution of the quantity defined by equation 7. Its use in relation to equation 7 requires three separate approxima-

8. This statement limiting the use of χ^2 to frequency data is not meant to exclude certain special applications such as finding confidence limits for a population variance from a known sample variance or testing several sample variances for homogeneity. These special applications are mentioned again toward the end of the paper.

9. This expression for C_r contains the gamma function $\Gamma(r/2)$. A gamma function is a function which reduces to a factorial whenever the argument is an integer. In the general case, $(n-1)! = \Gamma(n)$. Equation 9 may be written

$$C_r = \frac{1}{2^{r/2}\left(\dfrac{r-2}{2}\right)!}. \qquad \text{Eq. 9a}$$

Whenever r is an even number, the factorial in 9a is an integral number, and its value along with the value of C_r, can be determined in a straight forward manner. On the other hand, if r is an odd number, the "factorial" is fractional, and its value must be determined

tions, each of which assumes a theoretical frequency of reasonable size. The three approximations are:

1. Replacing each of the factorials in equation 7 by its Stirling approximation.
2. Taking a step similar to the one whereby $(1 + [X/n])^n$ is replaced by e^X when n is large.
3. Substituting a continuous integral for a summation of discrete quantities.

All of these approximations are quite acceptable and lead to inconsequential errors so long as Np is reasonably large. This reaffirms the fundamental requirement that *the theoretical frequencies must not be small*, if any calculated value of χ^2 is to be distributed as χ^2.[10]

General Computational Formula. The formula that is commonly employed in calculating values of χ^2 is

$$\chi^2 = \sum \frac{(F_o - F_t)^2}{F_t}, \qquad \text{Eq. 10}$$

where F_o and F_t, as usual, are observed and theoretical frequencies and the summation extends over all cells (categories) of the table. The equation holds for any number of categories and reduces to the form of 6 when the number of categories is 2. It serves as a constant reminder that the chi-square tests of independence and goodness of fit can be applied unequivocally only to frequency data.

either by referring to a table of the gamma function or by using the equation

$$\left(\frac{r-2}{2}\right)! = \left(\frac{r-2}{2}\right)\left(\frac{r-4}{2}\right)\left(\frac{r-6}{2}\right)\cdots\left(\frac{r-[r-1]}{2}\right)(\sqrt{\pi}).$$

A reader who is interested in plots of the χ^2 distribution function for various values of r is referred to Lewis (19).
10. A derivation of equation 8 from equation 7 is presented in considerable detail by Greenhood (11) and can be followed by persons familiar with advanced calculus. Greenhood's development, which is more complete but similar to one given by Fry (8), indicates clearly the limitations which hold in applications of the chi-square test to frequency data. It is not necessary, of course, to derive equation 8 from the multinomial distribution function; it may be derived directly from the joint normal distribution function in n variables.

Applications: I. The Goodness of Fit of Distribution Functions

One of the commonest applications of the chi-square tests is in evaluating the hypothesis that a set of frequency data can be satisfactorily represented by some specified distribution function. It makes little difference what the function is, so long as its fundamental properties are known. The goodness of fit of binomial, Poisson, and normal distribution functions is often tested.

Two-Category Case. The correct use of χ^2 in connection with a symmetrical binomial distribution function (where $p = q$) can be illustrated with data obtained in a coin-guessing "experiment." A coin was tossed, and 96 students of elementary psychology each guessed whether the coin came up "heads" or "tails." The hypothesis to be tested is that the guess of each student, like the fall of the coin itself, was a purely chance occurrence and that each student was as likely to say heads as to say tails. The results are shown in Table 2.

Table 2. Data from a
Coin-Guessing Experiment

H_o (= F_o for heads)	68
H_t (= F_t for heads)	48
T_o (= F_o for tails)	28
T_t (= F_t for tails)	48

As seen in the first and third rows, 68 students guessed heads and 28 guessed tails. The theoretical frequencies are 48 and 48. The value of χ^2 is obtained as follows:

$$\chi^2 = \frac{(H_o - H_t)^2}{H_t} + \frac{(T_o - T_t)^2}{T_i} =$$
$$= \frac{(68-48)^2}{48} + \frac{(28-48)^2}{48} = 16.67.[11]$$

11. Two alternative formulas that may be used in the two-category case when $p = q$ are as follows:

$$\chi^2 = (H_o - H_t)^2(2/H_t);$$
$$\chi^2 = \frac{(H_o - T_o)^2}{H_o + T_o}.$$

These formulas are the exact equivalents of the one used above.

With 1 df, this value is significant at better than the 0.1% level of confidence; so it must be concluded that the guesses of the 96 students were somehow biased in favor of heads.

Additive Property of χ^2, Illustrated with Two-Category Data. A fundamental property of χ^2 is indicated by the rule which states that the sum of any number of separate and independent values of χ^2 is distributed as χ^2, the number of df being the sum of the separate df's. The rule will now be applied in relation to coin-guessing data. Two applications will be made, the first of which is incorrect. *This incorrect application is purposely included* as a means of showing how it differs from a correct application and also of revealing the source of many of the errors made by investigators when employing the chi-square test.

Ninety-six students of elementary psychology were given five successive "trials" in coin guessing. A single coin was tossed five times. After each toss, the 96 students each guessed whether the coin came up "heads" or "tails." Each student wrote his five guesses in order on a sheet of paper. The turn of the coin was never revealed. The results are summarized in Table 3. The frequencies for toss 1 are the same as those given in Table 2.

With the ten pairs of observed and theoretical frequencies in Table 3 (two pairs for each toss), it is possible to test five separate hypotheses—that the guesses of the 96 students on *any one* of the five tosses were chance occurrences and were as apt to be heads as tails. Five values of χ^2 are given in the bottom row of the table. Each of the values was computed with the formula employed with the data of Table 2. The number of degrees of freedom is 1 in each case. For 1 df, the value of χ^2 at the

5% level of confidence is 3.841. Four of the five calculated values are less than this and provide no satisfactory basis for rejecting the hypothesis of chance occurrence.

To secure an estimate of χ^2 which makes the probability of rejecting a false hypothesis large, it is desirable, when conditions warrant, to summate separate estimates of χ^2 and obtain a composite estimate. The number of df for the composite estimate is always the sum of the separate df's. The sum of the five values in Table 3 is 23.08. The number of df is 5. The hypothesis under test is that the guesses of students *on five successive tosses* of a coin are purely chance occurrences, with the probability of a guess of heads (by any student on any toss) equal to the probability of a guess of tails. The composite value of 23.08 is significant at better than the 0.1% level of confidence, and would warrant a rejection of the hypothesis if the application of the test were correct.

But it is not correct to summate the five values of χ^2 in Table 3. The reason is that the responses of the 96 students from one toss to the next cannot be assumed to have been independent. In other words, the tabulated values of H_o and T_o from toss to toss are interdependent. Consequently, there is no way of obtaining an unbiased estimate of the theoretical frequency for any toss beyond the first (unless previous guesses are completely ignored). It is unreasonable to assume that a student's knowledge of his guess on one toss did not influence his guess on succeeding tosses. (It will be shown from the data that such an assumption is unsound.) The χ^2 test should never be based on an assumption that is already known to be false. On a single toss,

Table 3. Data from a second coin-guessing experiment

	\multicolumn{5}{c}{*Tosses*}	
	1	2	3	4	5	
H_o	68	49	39	54	54	
H_t	48	48	48	48	48	
T_o	28	47	57	42	42	
T_t	48	48	48	48	48	
χ^2	16.67	.04	3.37	1.50	1.50	$\Sigma = 23.08$

the guess of each student was independent of the guess of the other students; but between tosses, the five guesses of each student were undoubtedly interrelated.

A lack of independence between separate events (measures) is the commonest flaw in the applications of χ^2 that are made by psychologists. Six of the fourteen papers (2, 10, 17, 28, 29, 30) referred to in the opening paragraphs contain applications having this shortcoming.

There are two ways in which the responses of subjects may be interdependent. They may be related from trial to trial, as they were in the coin-guessing illustration, or they may be internally linked within a single trial. Whenever individual subjects each make more than one response per trial, linkages among the measures within the trial must result unless there are no individual differences. Many investigators ignore this restriction and apply the χ^2 test even though the same subjects are used from trial to trial and make several responses on each trial.

The Correct Use of the Additive Principle with Two-Category Data. The conditions under which separate values of χ^2 may be legitimately summed can be illustrated with two-category data. Five non-overlapping groups of subjects made a single guess on each of five successive tosses of a coin. The number of subjects per group was 86. Each subject wrote down his guesses in order on a sheet of paper, the sequence of his guesses remaining on the sheet before him. The results for the five groups are summarized in Tables 4 (A to E, inclusive). Twenty-five separate values of χ^2 appear in the bottom rows of the five sections of the table. The question to be answered is: *Which of these 25 values may be legitimately summated and which may not be?* The five values in any one of the sections cannot be meaningfully added for reasons already given in the discussion of the data in Table 3. However, the five values in the five sections for *any single toss* may be summated to yield a single composite value having 5 *df*. For example, a composite value may be obtained for the third toss and may

be used to test the hypothesis that, on the third toss of the coin, the guesses of the members of the five groups were random occurrences with the probability of a heads guess equalling that of a tails guess. Neither the presence nor the absence of individual biases would nullify a meaningful test of this hypothesis. If the hypothesis could not be retained, it would be correct to conclude that the guesses were not chance occurrences and were perhaps influenced by what had gone before. The difference between this case and the one illustrated in Table 3 is clear-cut. The data in Table 3 are for five successive guesses by one group, and the successive theoretical probabilities cannot be established without making specific assumptions concerning prior events. In contrast, when the five χ^2 values for a single toss are taken from the five sections of Table 4 and summated, the only assumption that is made is that the guesses on that particular toss were in accordance with a theoretical probability for heads of .50.

Composite values of χ^2 for the five tosses are given in Part A, Table 5. The number of *df* in each case is 5. Except for toss 5, the composite values are all significant at far better than the 1% level of confidence. The value for toss 5 falls near the 80% level and lends support for the belief that on a fifth successive toss of a coin, the probability of a heads guess is .50. The values for tosses 1 and 2 show that, on these tosses, the guesses were strongly biased toward heads. Conclusions regarding tosses 3 and 4 should be made in the light of the large contributions made to the composite values for these tosses by the guesses of group 5 alone. As seen in Table 4 E, the χ^2 values for tosses 3 and 4 are 7.86 and 16.79, respectively. With 1 *df* in each case, both values are significant at better than the 1% level. The corresponding values in the other four parts of the table all fall below the 5% level. However, the deviations on tosses 3 and 4 are in the same direction for all five groups, and this fact indicates a definite departure from chance expectations.

It is legitimate to combine for each toss separately the empirical and theoretical fre-

Table 4. Data from a third coin-guessing experiment

			Tosses		
	1	2	3	4	5
A. Group 1					
H_o	63	56	36	45	41
H_t	43	43	43	43	43
T_o	23	30	50	41	45
T_t	43	43	43	43	43
χ^2	18.60	7.86	2.28	0.19	0.19
B. Group 2					
H_o	63	56	42	48	45
H_t	43	43	43	43	43
T_o	23	30	44	38	41
T_t	43	43	43	43	43
χ^2	18.60	7.86	0.05	1.16	0.19
C. Group 3					
H_o	65	55	40	48	46
H_t	43	43	43	43	43
T_o	21	31	46	38	40
T_t	43	43	43	43	43
χ^2	22.51	6.70	0.42	1.16	0.42
D. Group 4					
H_o	68	54	38	52	41
H_t	43	43	43	43	43
T_o	18	32	48	34	45
T_t	43	43	43	43	43
χ^2	29.07	5.62	1.16	3.77	0.19
E. Group 5					
H_o	72	57	30	62	38
H_t	43	43	43	43	43
T_o	14	29	56	24	48
T_t	43	43	43	43	43
χ^2	39.12	9.12	7.86	16.79	1.16

Table 5. Values of chi-square based upon data from Table 4

Part A. Composite Values of χ^2

Toss	χ^2	df
1	127.90	5
2	37.16	5
3	11.77	5
4	23.07	5
5	2.15	5

Part B. Values of χ^2 for Combined Frequencies

Toss	χ^2	df
1	125.17	1
2	36.92	1
3	7.82	1
4	14.88	1
5	.149	1

quencies listed in Table 4-A-B-C-D-E, and use the resulting sums to compute values of χ^2, each with 1 *df*. Values of χ^2 obtained in this way are given in Part B of Table 5. As in the case of the composite values, all of the values except the one for toss 5 are significant at better than the 1% level of confidence. Nevertheless, the procedure of combining frequencies is not recommended except where the theoretical frequencies for each of several duplicated experiments are too small to yield satisfactory individual estimates of χ^2. Other things equal, the greater the number of degrees of freedom is, the more stable is a value of χ^2 and the greater is the probability of rejecting a false hypothesis.

Table 6. Composite value of chi-square, based on data in
Table 4

	Tosses				
	1	2	3	4	5
H_o	63	54	30	48	46
H_t	43	43	43	43	43
T_o	23	32	56	38	40
T_t	43	43	43	43	43
χ^2	18.60	5.62	7.86	1.16	0.42

Composite $\chi^2 = 33.66$

Five values of χ^2 may be selected from Table 4-A-B-C-D-E and used compositely to test the hypothesis that the guesses of persons on *five successive tosses* of a coin are chance occurrences, with the probability of a heads guess equalling that of a tails guess. The hypothesis is inclusive enough to cover the entire population from which the groups of subjects were randomly selected. To provide for independence between tosses, it is necessary to choose the five values of χ^2 so that there is one value for each toss and so that no two values are based on the guesses of a single group. To this end, numbers from 1 to 5 were assigned to the five sections of the table. The χ^2 value for toss 1 was taken from the section whose number first appeared in a table of random numbers; the χ^2 value for toss 2 from the section whose number next appeared, and so on. The values thus chosen are shown in Table 6. The composite value is 33.66, with 5 df. It is highly significant and leaves no grounds for believing that the hypothesis is true.

The discussion in the preceding pages on the necessity for independence between measures can perhaps be further clarified through a consideration of coin-tossing. Three different situations will be described to reveal unmistakable differences in hypotheses to be tested and methods of handling data. Suppose, first, that a single penny is selected at random from a large collection of pennies. This penny is tossed successively, say 100 times, and a record is kept of the way it turns. The probability of a head (or a tail) is .50. The χ^2 test may be applied to determine whether or not the

empirical results conform to this theoretical probability. If they do conform, it may justifiably be concluded that the penny is "unbiased." The test is an unequivocal one. The extent to which the investigator should generalize to the collection of pennies from which the single penny was chosen is a matter for personal judgment. The χ^2 test, as made, reveals nothing concerning the probability that the selected penny either represents or misrepresents the collection of pennies.

Suppose next that *two* pennies are randomly selected from a collection of pennies and that each penny is tossed 50 times to give a total of 100 tosses. The frequencies of occurrence of heads and of tails are combined (pooled) for the two coins. It may be assumed that the probability of a head is .50, but the χ^2 test cannot be *meaningfully* applied to test this theoretical probability.[12] The reason is that each penny makes its own unique contribution to the results. If one of them is biased while the other is unbiased, the obtained value of χ^2 could easily be significant and lead to a rejection of the hypothetical probability, even though it is correct for one of the pennies. Furthermore, one penny could be strongly biased for heads and the other equally strongly biased for tails, and the obtained value of χ^2 would turn out to be insignificant. The possible presence of individual idiosyncrasies precludes an unequivocal application of χ^2. The same

12. The pooling of two or more sets of frequencies to obtain a single value of χ^2 is warranted if the aim is to study the "heterogeneity" or "interaction" aspects of the data. In this connection, see Snedecor's discussion (31, pp. 191–192) of "pooled" and "total" chi-squares.

thing would be true if five pennies were randomly selected, each one tossed, say 20 times, and the results pooled; or if 10 pennies were selected and each tossed 10 times, or 20 selected and each tossed five times.

Suppose, finally, that 100 pennies are randomly selected from a collection of pennies, that each penny is tossed a single time, and that the number of heads is recorded. It may be assumed that the probability of a turn of heads, in the population from which the pennies are selected, is .50. The fall of each coin is clearly independent of the fall of every other coin. The χ^2 test may be legitimately applied to determine whether or not the observed frequency of heads conforms to the hypothetical frequency. The results of the test can be generalized to the entire collection of pennies. This would hold even though less than 100 pennies were selected, so long as a sufficient number was chosen to provide theoretical frequencies of the occurrence of heads and the occurrence of tails of sufficient magnitude to warrant an application of the χ^2 test. No statements can be made, of course, regarding the tendencies of any individual penny.

The crucial point is that frequencies obtained from individuals, whether pennies or subjects in psychological experiments, should not be pooled if the χ^2 test is to be used, except when it can be shown that there is an absence of biases or idiosyncrasies among them[13] or when "interaction" effects are specifically under scrutiny. Results on individuals may be combined, but the combining should be done *after* the χ^2 test has been applied to the data on individuals separately. For example, if two pennies are each tossed 50 times, the χ^2 test may be applied to the results for each penny separately, and then the two values of χ^2 may be added to provide a composite value.

13. If an investigator firmly intends to restrict all generalizations to the group of persons studied—the group considered *in toto*, as a sort of amorphous mass —then the pooling of individual frequencies may be logically defended. In such a situation, the group is analogous to a single individual and must be treated as such.

Similarly, separate values of χ^2 may be obtained from the guesses made by two individuals. The separate values may then be combined to furnish a single composite value. As in the well-known analysis of variance techniques where each source of variability contributes to the total variability, each source of variability should be allowed to make its contribution to the value of χ^2. Unfortunately, χ^2 procedures provide no way, as analysis of variance techniques do, of introducing *statistical* controls over individual subjects as a source of variability. Therefore, in the use of χ^2, the control over individuals must be introduced as an intrinsic part of the sampling process.

Table 7. Data obtained in die throwing

Face	F_o	F_t	$\dfrac{(F_o - F_t)^2}{F_t}$
1	23	20	.45
2	20	20	.00
3	22	20	.20
4	15	20	1.25
5	18	20	.20
6	22	20	.20
Σ	120	120	2.30

Multi-Category Case (Single Dimension). Frequency data sometimes fall into several categories along a single dimension. If the frequencies from category to category are independent and if some hypothesis regarding their distribution can be meaningfully set up, then the chi-square test may be used to evaluate the hypothesis, provided that the theoretical frequencies for the various categories are of reasonable magnitude. The correct application of the test in such a situation will be illustrated with data obtained in die throwing. A single die was thrown 120 times. There was no reason for believing that any throw was influenced by any other. The results are given in Table 7, where the first column lists the six faces of the die and the second column gives the number of times that each face turned up. The theoretical probability, on each throw, that any specified face of the die would turn up was 1/6. Consequently, the theoretical frequency of occurrence of each of the six faces was 20, as shown in the third column of the table. A single restriction, the sum of the observed frequencies, was placed in calculating the theoretical frequencies. Consequently, there are 5 df. With 5 df, the obtained value of χ^2 falls near the 80% level of confidence, and there is no basis for rejecting the hypothesis that the fall of the die was, on each throw, a strictly chance occurrence.[14]

Another illustration of a multi-category frequency distribution (along a single dimension) comes from results on the coin-guessing experiment. A total of 439 subjects each guessed heads or tails on each of five successive tosses of a coin. All but 9 of the subjects were the ones whose guesses were tabulated in Table 4. The χ^2 test will be applied to evaluate the hypothesis that chance factors operated in determining the frequencies of occurrence of the various possible "patterns" of guesses. With five successive tosses and five successive guesses, there were 32 possible patterns, as shown in the first column of Table 8. If there was no biasing of the guesses (that is, if the guess of every subject on every trial was as likely to be heads as to be tails), then each of the 32 patterns was as probable as any other;

14. It would be possible to use the data in Table 7 to test six separate hypotheses—that the appearance of *each* of the six faces was a chance occurrence, with a probability of 1/6. For example, to test the hypothesis that the appearance of the ace (one-spot) was a chance occurrence, a value of χ^2 would be computed as follows:

$$\chi^2 = \frac{(23-20)^2}{20} + \frac{(97-100)^2}{100} = .45 + .09 = .54.$$

The number of df is 1. Observe that in the calculation, the frequency of non-occurrence of the ace was taken into account. (The probability of occurrence of the ace was 1/6 (= p) while the probability of its non-occurrence was 5/6 (= q). This is an example of an asymmetrical binomial.) It is clear that six separate values of χ^2 could be computed in the way just indicated. But these values could not then be legitimately summated to yield a composite value of χ^2 with 6 df. They could not be combined because they would lack independence; the frequency of non-occurrence in each calculation would include the frequency of occurrence of the other five faces.

and with $N = 439$, the theoretical frequency for each pattern was $1/32 \times 439 = 13.7$, rounded to the first decimal place. This is the value shown in the third column of the table, except where parentheses appear. Note that 32×13.7 does not equal 439 exactly, but equals 438.4. One of the requirements in the

Table 8. Analysis of coin-guessing responses of 439 subjects

Patterns	F_o	F_t	$\dfrac{(F_o - F_t)^2}{F_t}$
H H H H H	25	(13.8)	9.089
H H H H T	12	13.7	0.211
H H H T H	22	13.7	5.028
H H H T T	18	13.7	1.350
H H T H H	29	(13.8)	16.742
H H T H T	96	(13.8)	489.626
H H T T H	22	(13.8)	4.872
H H T T T	14	13.7	0.007
H T H H H	5	13.7	5.525
H T H H T	15	13.7	0.123
H T H T H	12	13.7	0.211
H T H T T	4	13.7	6.868
H T T H H	33	(13.8)	26.713
H T T H T	17	13.7	0.795
H T T T H	12	13.7	0.211
H T T T T	3	13.7	8.357
T H H H H	3	13.7	8.357
T H H H T	7	13.7	3.277
T H H T H	10	13.7	0.999
T H H T T	14	13.7	0.007
T H T H H	5	13.7	5.525
T H T H T	1	13.7	11.773
T H T T H	6	13.7	4.328
T H T T T	0	13.7	13.700
T T H H H	4	13.7	6.868
T T H H T	6	13.7	4.328
T T H T H	25	(13.8)	9.089
T T H T T	7	13.7	3.277
T T T H H	2	13.7	9.992
T T T H T	5	13.7	5.525
T T T T H	2	13.7	9.992
T T T T T	3	13.7	8.357
Σ	439	439.0	$\chi^2 = 681.122$

* All but nine of the subjects are the same as those whose guesses are analyzed in Table 4.

application of χ^2 is that $\Sigma F_o = \Sigma F_t$. Therefore, six of the theoretical frequencies are given as 13.8. These are the theoretical frequencies corresponding to the six largest observed frequencies. This insures that any slight error that may result from equalizing ΣF_o and ΣF_t operates to make the test more conservative.

In the calculation of χ^2 for Table 8, a value of $(F_o - F_t)^2/F_t$ was secured for each row. These values are given in the fourth column, and their sum ($= 681.122$) is the desired estimate. The number of df is $(32-1) = 31$. The only restriction placed in figuring the theoretical frequencies was ΣF_o, and this meant the loss of a single degree of freedom. Even with 31 df, the value of χ^2 is so large as to leave no basis whatever for retaining the hypothesis that the guesses were chance occurrences.

Normal Distribution Function. The chi-square test is often used in evaluating the fit of a normal curve to a set of frequency data. Applications of this type are usually correct except for an occasional failure to equalize ΣF_o and ΣF_t, a tendency to use some theoretical frequencies that are too small, and, most importantly, an incorrect specification of the number of degrees of freedom. The correct procedure will now be illustrated.

The distribution of the midterm scores of 486 students in a course in elementary psychology is shown in Table 9. The mid-points of class intervals of ten score units are given in the X-column, frequencies in the F_o-column. The mean M of the distribution of scores is 104.0, while the standard deviation is 16.1. There are two methods that can be used in fitting a normal curve to the data (that is, in calculating the theoretical frequencies that correspond to the observed frequencies). One method involves the estimation of areas under segments of the normal curve through the process of multiplying ordinate values by the class interval.[15] This is an approximation procedure. A more exact method (and the one used here) is to obtain the values for the areas from proportions taken from a table of the probability integral.

The column in Table 9 labeled X' gives the upper limits of the various score categories. Deviate scores and z scores based on the values of X' are shown in the fourth and fifth columns. Proportions of the total area under the normal curve from $-\infty$ to z are given in

the P column. Proportions of the area in the segments corresponding to the various score intervals are shown in column P' and were obtained by taking the differences between the successive values of P. The theoretical frequencies came from multiplying the values of P' by N which is 486 in this case.

Because the first and the last two values of F_t are less than 10, they were combined with the adjacent values, as were the corresponding values of F_o. The sum of the last column in the table ($= 5.538$) is the value of χ^2. Seven differences between F_o and F_t entered into the calculations. The number of degrees of freedom is $7-3 = 4$. Three degrees were lost because three restrictions were placed in determining the theoretical frequencies.[16] The restrictions were the computed values of ΣF_o, M, and σ. The hypothesis being tested is that the frequency data arose from a normal population. With 4 df, the probability of obtaining, by chance, a value of χ^2 greater than 5.538 is around .25; so the hypothesis is tenable.

The Poisson distribution function. If the probability of the occurrence of an event is quite small, so that Np remains small even though N is relatively large, the distribution of observed frequencies in samples of size N may be of the Poisson type. The equation for the Poisson distribution may be written

$$P(n) = \frac{m^n}{n!} e^{-m} \qquad \text{Eq. 11}[17]$$

where $m = Np$ and e has its conventional meaning. As in equations 3 and 4, the symbol

---

15. For an example of this method, see Guilford (13, p. 91).

16. Some statistics texts (6, 25, 26) perpetuate the view, erroneously attributed to Pearson (24), that the number of restrictions imposed in fitting a normal curve is *1* or *3*, depending upon the hypothesis that the investigator wishes to test. There is only one hypothesis open to test—that the frequency data arose from a normal population. If the mean and standard deviation of the fitted function are estimated from the data, three restrictions are imposed and 3 df are lost. The same texts give a similar misinterpretation of the number of restrictions imposed when χ^2 is applied in testing independence.

17. A derivation of this formula is given by Lewis (19, pp. 168–169).

Table 9. Application of the chi-square test in evaluating the fit of a normal curve to a set of frequency data

X	F_o	X'	x $(= X' - M)$	z $(= x/\sigma)$	P	P'	F_t $(= P'N)$	$\dfrac{(F_o - F_t)^2}{F_t}$
			$(+\infty)$		(1.0000)			
144.5	1 ⎫					.0141	6.9 ⎫	
	⎬	139.5	35.5	2.195	.9859		⎬	.926
134.5	22 ⎭					.0437	21.2 ⎭	
		129.5	25.5	1.574	.9422			
124.5	56					.1125	54.7	.031
		119.5	15.5	0.953	.8297			
114.5	112					.1960	95.3	2.926
		109.5	5.5	0.342	.6337			
104.5	111					.2440	118.5	.475
		99.5	− 4.5	−0.280	.3897			
94.5	94					.2032	98.8	.233
		89.5	− 14.5	−0.891	.1865			
84.5	54					.1211	58.8	.392
		79.5	− 24.5	−1.512	.0654			
74.5	27 ⎫					.0489	23.8 ⎫	
	⎪	69.5	− 34.5	−2.133	.0165		⎪	
64.5	7 ⎬					.0135	6.6 ⎬	.555
	⎪	59.5	− 44.5	−2.754	.0030		⎪	
54.5	2 ⎭					.0030	1.4 ⎭	
			$(-\infty)$		$(.0000)$			
Σ	486					1.0000	486.0	5.538

$P(n)$ represents the probability of n occurrences out of N possible occurrences. The symbol $\doteq$ is used in place of the equal sign to indicate that 11 is an approximation formula. The errors introduced by the approximation are negligible, provided that N is quite large and provided also that N is very much larger than the largest value of n that may reasonably be expected in random sampling.

The χ^2 test may be applied in relation to the data of Table 10. The column labeled F_o gives the number of samples, in a total of 120 short samples of American speech, that contained n occurrences of the consonant "th" (as in thin). Each of the 120 samples was 400 sounds in length. As seen from the table, 31 of the samples did not contain any "th" sounds; 31 samples contained one "th" sound each; and

Table 10. Analysis of Frequencies of occurrence of the consonant "TH" in samples of American speech

n	F_o	$P(n)$	F_t	$(F_o - F_t)^2$	$\dfrac{(F_o - F_t)^2}{F_t}$
0	31	.1868	22.42	73.61	3.283
1	31	.3138	37.66	44.35	1.178
2	30	.2636	31.63	2.66	.084
3	11	.1476	17.71	45.02	2.542
4	11 ⎫	.0620	7.44 ⎫		
5	3 ⎬	.0209	2.51 ⎬	41.22	3.896
6	3 ⎭	.0050	.60 ⎬		
>6	· · · ·	.0003	.03 ⎭	· ·	
Σ	120	1.0000	120.00		$\chi^2 = 10.983$

so on. As a first step, the data in Table 10 will be compared with some results obtained by Voelker (33). In a study of over 600,000 sounds occurring in almost 6,000 announcements over the radio, Voelker found the proportion of "th" sounds to be .0065. Each of the 120 samples represented in Table 10 contained 400 sounds. This made a total of 48,000 sounds. The use of the proportion obtained by Voelker leads to 260 as the predicted, or theoretical, number of "th" sounds among the 48,000. The observed number was 201.[18] The χ^2 test may be applied in evaluating the hypothesis that the sounds in the present over-all sample, were drawn from a general population of American speech sounds which is assumed to be characterized exactly by the value of m obtained by Voelker. The value of χ^2 is computed as follows:

$$\chi^2 = \frac{(201-260)^2}{260} + \frac{(47,799-47,740)^2}{47,740} =$$
$$= 13.388 + 0.073 = 13.461.$$

Note that the observed and theoretical frequencies of non-occurrence of the "th" enter into the calculation. With 1 df, the obtained value of χ^2 is significant at better than the 0.1% level of confidence; so there is a firm basis for rejecting the hypothesis.

The observed proportion of .0042 ($= 201/48,000$) may be used in testing the hypothesis that the 120 samples were all drawn from the same Poisson distribution. If $p_o = .0042$ and $N = 400$, then $m = Np = 1.68$, and the equation for the hypothetical distribution function may be written

$$P(n) = \frac{(1.68)^n}{n!} e^{-1.68}.$$

Values of $P(n)$ computed with this formula are given in the third column of Table 10, and the corresponding values of F_t are given in the fourth column. As shown in the last column of the table, the value of χ^2 was computed in accordance with equation 10. The last 4 values

18. $\Sigma n F_o$ = $0(31) + 1(31) + 2(30) + 3(11) + 4(11) + 5(3) + 6(3) = 201.$

of F_t and the last 3 values of F_o were combined to avoid the use of theoretical frequencies of less than 10. The computed value of χ^2 is 10.982. Five differences between F_o and F_t were used in the computations. Two restrictions (N and m)[19] were imposed in calculating values of F_t. This leaves 3 df. With this number of df, the obtained value χ^2 falls at about the 3% level of confidence. The hypothesis may, therefore, be tentatively retained or may be rejected, depending upon the level of confidence that has been prescribed.

Applications: II. The Chi-Square Test of Independence

A common application of the χ^2 test enables an examination of the frequencies of a contingency table to determine whether or not the two variables or attributes represented in the table are independent. The number of cells in the table may range from four (as in a 2×2 table) to an indefinitely large value. The χ^2 test is perhaps most commonly applied by psychologists in relation to 2×2 tables. The chief weaknesses in such applications are (a) a strong tendency to use excessively small theoretical frequencies and (b) an occasional failure to categorize adequately. The same two weaknesses are apt to occur when the number of categories in either, or both, of the "dimensions" of the table is greater than two.

ILLUSTRATIONS OF THE CHI-SQUARE TEST OF INDEPENDENCE

Comparison of Coin- and Die-Coin Guessing. To obtain data for illustrating the χ^2 test of independence, 384 students of psychology were each asked to guess heads or tails on five successive tosses of a coin, where the tosses were interspersed among five throws of a die.

19. If the value of p had not been estimated from the empirical data, but had been taken from the Voelker study or from some other completely independent source, the only restriction that would have been placed would have been N, and there would have. been 4 df instead of 3 df.

The die was thrown; a guess was made as to the face that turned up. This guess was written on the edge of a sheet of paper. The edge of the paper was then folded under, to hide the guess. The coin was then tossed, the guess being written down. Again the paper was folded under, to hide the guess. The die was thrown a second time, the guess made, the paper folded under. The coin was then thrown a second time, the guess made, the paper folded under. Each of the five guesses on the coin was preceded by a throw of the die and a guess on its fall. The paper was folded under after each guess on the die and each guess on the coin. Thus, the guesses on the coin were not only separated by guesses on the die, but the sequence of guesses was hidden from view. The subjects were never informed as to how the coin or the die actually fell.

The frequencies of occurrence of the 32 possible patterns of guesses on the five successive tosses of the coin (with guesses on the die ignored) are given in the third column of Table 11. The frequencies in the second column of this table were copied directly from Table 8 and are based on guesses on five successive tosses of a coin alone.[20] The subjects for the two conditions of guessing were completely different.

The first 16 patterns listed in Table 11 begin with a guess of heads, the last 16 with a guess of tails. A 2×2 contingency table, shown in Table 12 was set up, the division along one "dimension" being between first-guess-heads and first-guess-tails and along the other "dimension" between the two conditions of guessing. The four sub-totals in Table 11 constitute the observed frequencies appearing in the four cells of the 2×2 table.

The hypothesis to be tested in this case is that the occurrence of a first guess of heads

was independent of the condition under which the guessing was done. If the observed frequencies in Table 12 were independent of the conditions of guessing, the probability of a guess of heads was 586/823. The probability of a subject's being in the coin guessing group was 439/823. The joint probability that a subject would be in the coin guessing group and would also guess heads was $439/823 \times 586/823$. The theoretical frequency for the upper left-hand cell of the table was obtained by mutiplying this joint probability by 823. The other three theoretical frequencies were automatically determined by this single calculated frequency and by the restrictions of the border sums. The four values of F_t are shown in parentheses in the table. The value of χ^2 was computed as follows:

$$
\begin{aligned}
\chi^2 &= \frac{(339-312.6)^2}{312.6} + \frac{(100-126.4)^2}{126.4} + \\
&\quad \frac{(247-273.4)^2}{273.4} + \frac{(137-110.6)^2}{110.6} \\
&= (26.4)^2 \left(\frac{1}{312.6} + \frac{1}{126.4} + \frac{1}{273.4} + \frac{1}{110.6} \right) \\
&= 696.96 \,(.02381) = 165.946.
\end{aligned}
$$

The number of df is 1. This follows because there are four cells and because three restrictions were placed in determining the theoretical frequencies. The three restrictions were the total number of subjects ($= 823$) and two border sums, one for a row and one for a column.[21] The calculated value of χ^2 is highly significant and leads immediately to a rejection of the hypothesis that the conditions of guessing had no influence on the tendency to guess heads on the first guess.

Table 11 may be regarded as a 32×2 contingency table, 32 "patterns" by 2 "conditions of guessing." In order to use the χ^2 test in evaluating the hypothesis that the patterns were independent of the conditions of guessing, the border sums would be used in calcu-

20. As will be seen, the 32 patterns in Table 11 have been divided into groups of four patterns each. The basis for the division will be discussed later. Short horizontal lines divide the corresponding observed frequencies. A numeral is placed to the right of each of these lines. Each numeral is the sum of the observed frequencies for the corresponding group of four patterns. Each is a sub-sum and will be used in Table 13.

21. The sums 439 and 237 (or 384 and 237, or 384 and 586) could have been used instead of 586 and 439. The values of F_t for all but one cell may be obtained by subtraction.

Table 11. Results from coin- and die-coin guessing experiments

Patterns	F_o Coin Guessing	Die-Coin Guessing	Totals	F_t Coin Guessing	Die-Coin Guessing
H H H H H	25	29	54	28.8	25.2
H H H H T	12	9	21	11.2	9.8
H H H T H	22	9	31	16.5	14.5
H H H T T	18	5	23	12.3	10.7
	77	52			
H H T H H	29	38	67	35.7	31.3
H H T H T	96	59	155	82.7	72.3
H H T T H	22	24	46	24.5	21.5
H H T T T	14	8	22	11.7	10.3
	161	129			
H T H H H	5	7	12	6.4	5.6
H T H H T	15	9	24	12.8	11.2
H T H T H	12	2	14	7.5	6.5
H T H T T	4	9	13	6.9	6.1
	36	27			
H T T H H	33	12	45	24.0	21.0
H T T H T	17	20	37	19.7	17.3
H T T T H	12	3	15	8.0	7.0
H T T T T	3	4	7	3.7	3.3
	65	39			
Sub-totals	(339)	(247)			
T H H H H	3	3	6	3.2	2.8
T H H H T	7	5	12	6.4	5.6
T H H T H	10	9	19	10.1	8.9
T H H T T	14	3	17	9.1	7.9
	34	20			
T H T H H	5	4	9	4.8	4.2
T H T H T	1	8	9	4.8	4.2
T H T T H	6	4	10	5.3	4.7
T H T T T	0	1	1	0.5	0.5
	12	17			
T T H H H	4	13	17	9.1	7.9
T T H H T	6	19	25	13.3	11.7
T T H T H	25	37	62	33.1	28.9
T T H T T	7	13	20	10.7	9.3
	42	82			
T T T H H	2	4	6	3.2	2.8
T T T H T	5	5	10	5.3	4.7
T T T T H	2	1	3	1.6	1.4
T T T T T	3	8	11	5.9	5.1
	12	18			
Sub-totals	(100)	(137)			
Totals	439	384	823	438.8	384.2

Table 12. 2×2 contingency table based upon the coin- and die-coin guessing experiments

	First Guess		
	H	T	
Coin Guessing	339	100	439
	(312.6)	(126.4)	
Die-Coin Guessing	247	137	384
	(273.4)	(110.6)	
	586	237	823

lating theoretical frequencies. For example, the two theoretical frequencies for the pattern $H\ H\ H\ H\ H$ are given by the relations: $F_t = (54 \times 439)/823 = 28.8$; and $F_t = 54 - 28.8 = 25.2 = (54 \times 384)/823$. These two values of F_t are shown in the top row of the last two columns of Table 11. The theoretical frequencies for the other 31 patterns were obtained in a similar way and are listed in the table. These frequencies are included to emphasize the fact that the χ^2 test cannot be legitimately applied to this table as it stands. The reason is that 37 of the 64 theoretical frequencies are less than 10 (some of them very much less than 10) and cannot be depended upon to yield quantities distributed as χ^2. To make a legitimate application of χ^2 in this particular case, it would be necessary to increase the number of subjects to ·a point where the smallest of the theoretical frequencies was close to 10.

It must now be decided whether or not the observed frequencies in Table 11 can be combined so as to permit the use of the χ^2 test in evaluating the hypothesis of non-relationship between the patterning of the guesses and the conditions of guessing. The frequencies have already been combined in a gross way to yield the observed frequencies in Table 12. This division was on the basis of the first guess. Divisions might be made on the basis of the first two guesses or the first three guesses or the first four guesses. It is not possible to use the patterning on all five guesses because the theoretical frequencies become too small, as already seen. It turns out that a division on the basis of the first four guesses also leads to several theoretical frequencies that are less

than 10. Consequently, a division based on the patterning of the first three guesses will be illustrated. In the division that was made, the following rule held: there would be a decreasing number of heads in the pattern and, contrariwise, there would be an increasing number of tails, from the first guess on. The resulting division of the patterns is shown in Table 11 and also in Table 13, the one to be used in applying the χ^2 test.

Table 13. Combination of the frequencies shown in Table 11, based on the first three guesses

Pattern on 1st Three Guesses	Coin Guessing	Die-Coin Guessing	Totals
H H H	77	52	129
	(68.8)	(60.2)	
H H T	161	129	290
	(154.7)	(135.3)	
H T H	36	27	63
	(33.6)	(29.4)	
H T T	65	39	104
	(55.5)	(48.5)	
T H H	34	20	54
	(28.8)	(25.2)	
T H T	12	17	29
	(15.5)	(13.5)	
T T H	42	82	124
	(66.1)	(57.9)	
T T T	12	18	30
	(16.0)	(14.0)	
Totals	439	384	823

As seen, there are eight different patterns listed in Table 13. The observed frequencies for the two conditions of guessing are shown (together with parenthesized theoretical frequencies) in the second and third columns. The hypothesis to be tested is that the patterns of guessing on the first three of five consecutive guesses were independent of the conditions of guessing. The theoretical frequencies were secured in the usual way by employing border sums and the value of $N(= 823)$. The value of χ^2 was computed as follows:

$$\chi^2 = \frac{(77-68.8)^2}{68.8} + \frac{(161-154.7)^2}{154.7} + \ldots$$
$$\ldots + \frac{(82-57.9)^2}{57.9} + \frac{(18-14.0)^2}{14.0} = 31.162.$$

The number of df is 7. The computed value of χ^2 is significant at far better than the 1% level of confidence and leads to a rejection of the hypothesis. It may be confidently concluded that the patterning of the guesses through the first three guesses was somehow influenced by the conditions under which the guessing was done.

The number of df for a value of χ^2 obtained from a contingency table is always the number of cells in the table minus the number of restrictions imposed during the calculation of the theoretical frequencies. In Table 13, for example, there are 16 cells. Nine restrictions must be imposed in obtaining values of F_t. These restrictions are: 7 of the row sums, 1 of the column sums, and the total number of cases. Thus, $df = 16 - 9 = 7$.

A convenient formula for determining the number of df for a contingency table when the χ^2 test is applied is

$$df = (n_c - 1)(n_r - 1), \qquad \text{Eq. 12}$$

where n_c and n_r are the number of columns and the number of rows, respectively. There is only one hypothesis to be tested—that the variables are independent in the population from which the samples arise; so the number of df is always given by 12. (See footnote 16.)

Contingency Table with more than Two Categories in Each Direction. For the sake of completeness, a contingency table having five categories in one direction and four in the other will be included. A total of 2,274 eighth-grade pupils, enrolled in 91 different schools, took an English Correctness Test. A summary of the scores obtained by these pupils has been taken from a report by Lindquist (23). The scores were divided into five categories and symbolized by numbers from 1 to 5, as seen in Table 14. The schools were divided into four enrollment groups, labeled A to D in the table. The observed frequencies in the 20 cells of the table range from 3 to 342. These frequencies would obviously have been different if the enrollment groups had been differently established, and if the scores had been divided into different categories. The enrollment grouping

of the schools was that commonly used in the Iowa Every-Pupil Testing Program.[22] The division of the scores was made by starting at the bottom and "stepping off" successive standard deviation "distances" (approximately). The distribution of scores was positively skewed; so it was necessary to combine the two upper score categories to provide satisfactorily large frequencies in the top row of cells.

Table 14. 5×4 contingency table based upon Lindquist's data (23)

| Scores | Enrollment Groups* | | | | Totals |
	A	B	C	D	
1	36	40	20	3	99
	(23.5)	(38.4)	(28.2)	(8.9)	
2	76	108	59	11	254
	(60.2)	(96.8)	(72.3)	(22.9)	
3	150	181	111	28	470
	(111.4)	(182.5)	(133.7)	(42.4)	
4	211	342	285	88	926
	(219.5)	(359.6)	(263.5)	(83.5)	
5	66	212	172	75	525
	(124.4)	(203.8)	(149.4)	(47.3)	
Totals	539	883	647	205	2274

* See footnote 22.

The theoretical frequencies for Table 14 were computed in the usual way when the hypothesis of independence is under test. The computations required the use of three column sums and four row sums, as well as the value of $N(= 2274)$. This made a total of 8 restrictions; so the number of $df = 20 - 8 = 12 = (5 - 1)(4 - 1)$. The value of χ^2 was computed as follows:

$$\chi^2 = \frac{(36 - 23.5)^2}{23.5} + \frac{(76 - 60.2)^2}{60.2} + \cdots$$
$$\cdots + \frac{(88 - 83.5)^2}{83.5} + \frac{(75 - 47.3)^2}{47.3} = 99.038.$$

With $df = 12$, this value is highly significant and leads to a rejection of the hypothesis that the scores obtained on the test were independent of school size.

22. The enrollment categories were: A, greater than 400; B, 126–400; C, 66–125; D, less than 66.

Table 15. Data upon the "Zeigarnik Effect" Presented by Lewis (20), and Lewis and Franklin (21)

							Subjects							
Ration of Recall Scores	1	2	3	4	5	6	7	8	9	10	11	12	13	14
RI/RC—Group I (Indiv. Work Condition)	1.00	.80	.80	.80	.75	.71	.63	.57	.57	.44	.40	.25		
RI/RC—Group II (Coop. Work Condition)	1.67	1.25	1.00	1.00	1.00	1.00	1.00	1.00	1.00	1.00	.80	.75	.60	.14

A comment should be made concerning the theoretical frequency in the upper right-hand cell of the table. Its value is 8.9. Ordinarily, a value this small should not be used in obtaining an estimate of χ^2. In this case, however, the other 19 values of F_t are satisfactorily large, and the inclusion of one theoretical frequency that is less than 10 is permissible since an error in a single category will have slight effect on the resulting value of χ^2. The obtained value of χ^2 is so large that it makes no difference whether or not the small theoretical frequency is included in the calculations. It is only in situations of this general kind that one or two small theoretical frequencies may be retained. When the number of df is less than 4 or 5, and especially when $df = 1$, the use of theoretical frequencies of less than 10 should be strictly avoided.

USE OF THE CHI-SQUARE TEST WITH TOO SMALL
THEORETICAL FREQUENCIES

The Studies of Lewis and Franklin (21) and Lewis (20). The commonest weakness in applications of the χ^2 test to contingency tables is the use of extremely small theoretical frequencies. This weakness is clearly present in most of the applications made in a paper by Lewis and Franklin (21). The paper is concerned with the Zeigarnik effect (that is, with the relative amounts of recall of interrupted and completed tasks). In one experiment, 12 subjects were each presented with 18 problems, 9 of which were interrupted by the experimenter, the other 9 being completed without interruption. The ratio (RI/RC) of the number of interrupted tasks recalled to the number of completed tasks recalled is given for each

subject in the top row of Table 15. In a previous study, Lewis (20) had employed a cooperative work situation in which a co-worker completed the tasks on which the subject was interrupted. The conditions were otherwise the same as in the later experiment by her and Franklin. Fourteen subjects were used. The RI/RC ratio for each subject is shown in the second row of Table 15. The median ratio for Group I was .67. The ratios for the two groups were divided (dichotomized) at this point. The 2×2 contingency table shown as Table 16 was the

Table 16. Contingency table based upon data in Table 15

	Group		
RI/RC	I	II	
Greater than 0.67	6	12	18
	(8.3)	(9.7)	
Less than 0.67	6	2	8
	(3.7)	(4.3)	
	12	14	26

result. The hypothesis to be tested was that the conditions of the two experiments had no differential effects on the recall of interrupted and completed tasks. The theoretical frequencies are shown in parentheses in the table. The investigators calculated a value of χ^2 in the usual way. Finding it to be approximately 3.8 and to fall near the 5% level of confidence, they were inclined to reject the hypothesis.

Entirely aside from any of the conclusions reached by Lewis and Franklin, it must be firmly stated that all four of the theoretical frequencies in Table 16, and especially the two that are less than 5, are too small to warrant an application of the χ^2 test. Furthermore, the other applications made in their paper, with one or two possible exceptions, involved theoretical frequencies that should be avoided (theoretical frequencies, for example, of 4.4, 6.0, 7.0, 7.6, etc.).

Kuenne's Study of Transposition Behavior. An application, which is correct in principle but which must be regarded somewhat unfavorably because of the size of the F_t's, comes from a paper by Kuenne (18). Kuenne made a study of transposition behavior in four groups of young children, the ages for the groups being 3, 4, 5, and 6 years. Some of the children displayed size transposition, others of them did not. Kuenne realized that, because of the small number of cases in each age group, she could not apply the χ^2 test to the data for the four groups considered separately. Consequently, she combined the results for ages 3 and 4, and those for ages 5 and 6. The children were divided into two categories—those who did and those who did not meet the transposition criterion. The resulting 2×2 contingency table is shown as Table 17. The hypothesis to

Table 17. Contingency table based upon Kuenne's (18) transposition data

Age-Groups	Transposition	Non-Transposition	Total
3–4 years	3 (9.4)	15 (8.6)	18
5–6 years	20 (13.6)	6 (12.4)	26
	23	21	44

be tested is that the occurrence of transposition behavior was independent of age. Theoretical frequencies were determined by using two of the border sums and the value of N. It will be seen that two of these frequencies are less than 10. Because they are fairly close to 10, many investigators would proceed as Kuenne did, and make a χ^2 test of the hypothesis of independence. In fact, there are textbooks in statistics which place 5 as the minimum value for theoretical frequencies. A value of 5 is believed to be too low. In any event, it is the smallest value that should be used even when there are several other theoretical frequencies that are far greater than 10.

The value of χ^2 computed from Table 17 is 15.434. With 1 *df*, this value falls close to the 0.1% level. It is only because the value is so large that confidence can be placed in the conclusion that transposition behavior was related to age. In view of the smallness of all four of the theoretical frequencies, very great doubt would have remained if the χ^2 value had fallen at a border-line level of confidence. Whenever small theoretical frequencies enter into calculations of χ^2, the experimenter has no sound basis either for accepting or rejecting a hypothesis except when the value is quite extreme.

Yates' Correction for Continuity. No mention has as yet been made of a correction proposed by Yates (30) which reduces the value of χ^2 to compensate for errors which may arise as a result of one of the approximations made in deriving the formula for the χ^2 distribution. It will be recalled that three approximations are made in this derivation. One of the three involves the substitution of an integral for a summation of discrete quantities. This approximation introduces an error (an error of overestimation) that is of consequence when values of F_t are small. The correction is justified only when the number of *df* is 1.[23] It provides for the reduction of all differences between observed and theoretical frequencies by 0.5. For example, all of the differences between observed and theoretical frequencies in Table 17 are 6.4. These are reduced to 5.9 if Yates' correction is applied. The calculation, using the correction, would be as follows:

$$\chi^2 = (5.9)^2 \left(\frac{1}{9.4} + \frac{1}{8.6} + \frac{1}{13.6} + \frac{1}{12.4} \right) =$$
$$= (34.81)(.3768) = 13.1.$$

With 1 *df*, this value is still highly significant and leads to a rejection of the hypothesis. But the use of Yates' correction does not remove the objection to theoretical frequencies that are less than 10.

23. The correction should not be made if several values of χ^2 are to be summated. The additive principle does not apply to corrected values.

Lewis' (20) *Study of Recall of Interrupted and Completed Tasks.* Another weakness which is sometimes present in applications of the χ^2 test to contingency tables is that the categorizing is done on either a questionable or a clearly incorrect basis. An illustration of incorrect categorizing is found in the paper by Lewis (20) discussed above. The *RI/RC* ratios for 14 subjects were obtained in a "cooperative work experiment." The ratios are the ones given in the second row of Table 15. On the assumption that the recall of interrupted and completed tasks should have been the same, Lewis writes: " . . . we should have an equal number of ratios above 1.00 and below 1.00. . . . The expected distribution of ratios should, therefore, be 7 below 1.00 and 7 at 1.00 or above. The obtained distribution of ratios is 4 below 1.00 and 10 at 1.00 or above." The categorizing is plainly wrong; there is no more reason for placing an obtained ratio of 1.00 in the upper category than for placing it in the lower category. A better procedure would have been to divide the 8 ratios of 1.00 equally between the two categories. This flaw in Lewis' division of the ratios is remindful of the belief of many graduate students in psychology that it is quite permissible to set up several different sets of dichotomy lines, compute a value of χ^2 for each set, and finally select the dichotomies that yield a χ^2 value to support the experimenter's own point of view. In any investigation where the χ^2 test is to be applied, the categories must be established in a logically defensible and reliable manner—before the data are collected, if possible.

Anastasi and Foley's (1) *Study of Drawings of Normal and Abnormal Subjects.* The whole problem of categorizing may be brought clearly before the reader by taking an illustrative case from a study by Anastasi and Foley (1). These two investigators had each of 340 normal subjects and 340 abnormal subjects draw a picture which depicted danger. The pictures were then divided into the 20 subject-matter categories listed in Table 18. The

Table 18. Data from Anastasi and Foley's (1) study of drawings
of normal and abnormal subjects

Subject-Matter Categories	F_o (Abnormal)	F_o (Normal)	F_t	χ^2
1. Traffic	105	124	114.5	1.576
2. Conventional sign or signal	36	37	36.5	.014
3. Skating, ice	5	10	7.5	1.667
4. Falling	21	17	19.0	.421
5. Drowning, sinking, flood	8	10	9.0	.222
6. Falling objects, explosion	6	6	6.0	.000
7. Arms and explosives	10	22	16.0	4.500
8. War	3	7	5.0	1.600
9. Fire	26	37	31.5	1.921
10. Lightning, electricity	6	15	10.5	3.857
11. Animals	3	16	9.5	8.895
12. Abstract or conventionalized symbolism	3	8	5.5	2.273
13. Fantastic compositions	26	0	13.0	26.000
14. Several discrete objects	9	2	5.5	4.454
15. Scribbling or scrawl	6	0	3.0	6.000
16. Writing only	12	1	6.5	9.308
17. Miscellaneous	23	26	24.5	.184
18. Recognizable object not representing danger	8	1	4.5	5.444
19. Refusal to draw	14	1	7.5	11.267
20. No data for other reasons	10	0	5.0	10.000
	340	340		99.603

application of the χ^2 test yields a value of 99.603 which, with 19 df, falls far beyond the 0.1% level of confidence. This leads to a rejection of the hypothesis that the subject matter of the drawings was independent of the two "kinds" of subjects.

Let it again be emphasized that the criticism here, as elsewhere in the paper, is not directed at any of the conclusions reached by the investigators. But the illustration provides a very satisfactory basis for discussing the fundamental problem of categorizing. In the published article, the principles adopted in classifying the pictures are not explicitly stated. Furthermore, evidence is not presented regarding the reliability of the categories. Two generalizations may be offered. The first is that, *whenever possible, categories for frequency data should be established on the basis of completely external criteria* (for example, criteria that have been used or proposed by some other investigator) and should be set up independently of the data under study. Such a procedure frees a person from any charge of bias and guards against tendencies to juggle data. A second generalization is that *information on the reliability of categories should be offered*, and this is the case whether or not the categories have stemmed from an independent source.

A study of Table 18 shows rather quickly that the value of χ^2 for the drawings depicting danger would have been quite different if the categorizing had been different. For example, the amount 26.000 was contributed to the value of χ^2 by the frequencies of category 13 alone. As seen, this is the category "fantastic compositions." The decision which established this category and the judgments which placed 26 of the drawings of the abnormal subjects in the category and none of the drawings of the normal subjects in it, should have been explicitly justified and a precise statement concerning reliability should have been included. The discrepancy between the frequencies in category 13 (along with the discrepancies in such categories as "refusal to draw" and "no data for other reasons") required that there be

discrepancies in one or more of the other categories. Unreliability at one point in a multicelled table automatically produces unreliability elsewhere.

It is well to emphasize, by reiteration, that when the χ^2 test is to be applied to a collection of data, the categories should be established independently of the data and, once established, should never be modified on the basis of the way the data happen to fall. Categories should usually, if not always, be established before the data have been scrutinized.

Applications: III. The Goodness of Fit of Functions in which Frequency is the Dependent Variable

The frequency (or relative frequency) of occurrence of a response is sometimes used as the dependent variable in psychological experiments. For example, in psychophysical investigations based on the method of constant stimuli, the number or proportion of judgments in a given direction serves as the dependent variable, while in studies of the conditioned response, the frequency of occurrence of the CR is often taken as the dependent variable. If a mathematical function is fitted to data of this type, it is sometimes possible to apply the χ^2 test in evaluating the goodness of the fit. However, care must be taken to insure a correct application.

Goodness of Fit of the Phi-Gamma Function. It is a fairly common practice among psychophysicists to apply the χ^2 test to the differences between observed and theoretical proportions in order to evaluate the phi-gamma hypothesis—the hypothesis that the observed proportions can be represented satisfactorily by the phi-gamma function.[24] The usual procedure in making the test will be illustrated with some weight-lifting data.

As part of a laboratory exercise, a graduate student in an advanced experimental course

24. The use of the phi-gamma function in psychophysical research is explained by Guilford (13, Chap. VI).

Table 19. Test of goodness of fit of the phi-gamma function to weight-lifting data

X	p_o	γ	$X\gamma$	X^2	γ'_t	p_t	(A) $(p_o-p_t)^2$	(A) $(p_o-p_t)^2\dfrac{}{p_tq_t}$	(B) p_o	(B) p_t	(B) $n_k\dfrac{(p_o-p_t)^2}{p_tq_t}$
104	.97 ⎱	1.3299	138.31	10,816	1.246	.960 ⎱	.000100	.002600	⎰ .935	⎰ .934	.0032
102	.90 ⎰	0.9062	92.43	10,404	.942	.908 ⎰	.000064	.000768			
100	.79	0.5702	57.02	10,000	.638	.816	.000676	.004516	.79	.816	.4516
98	.65	0.2724	26.70	9,604	.334	.681	.000961	.004421	.65	.681	.4421
96	.53	0.0532	5.11	9,216	.030	.517	.000169	.000676	.53	.517	.0676
94	.37	−0.2347	− 22.06	8,836	− .274	.350	.000400	.001760	.37	.350	.1760
92	.20	−0.5951	− 54.75	8,464	− .578	.208	.000064	.000384	.20	.208	.0384
90	.13 ⎱	−0.7965	− 71.68	8,100	− .882	.107 ⎱	.000529	.005539	⎰ .085	⎰ .077	.1804
88	.04 ⎰	−1.2379	−108.94	7,744	−1.186	.047 ⎰	.000049	.001103			
Σ864		0.2677	62.14	83,184				.021767			1.3593

made 100 judgments on each of nine pairs of weights. The weights, in grams, are listed in the X column of Table 19. The method of constant stimuli was employed. The 100-gram weight was the standard and was paired 100 times, not only with itself, but with *each* of the other eight ("variable") weights. The standard weight was always lifted first, the variable weight second. Each of the 900 judgments was made in terms of the question: Which weight is the heavier, the first or the second? The second column of the table, labelled p_o, gives the proportion of times (in 100) that each weight was judged heavier than the standard weight.[25]

A phi-gamma function may be fitted to the proportions in Table 19, and the χ^2 test may then be applied (with a reservation to be specified later) to evaluate the goodness of fit. The phi-gamma function is basically the same as the equation for the normal ogive, which may be written

$$p = \int_{-\infty}^{x} \frac{1}{\sigma\sqrt{2\pi}}\, e^{-x^2/2\sigma^2}\, dx, \qquad \text{Eq. 13}$$

with p standing for proportion of area under

25. The reason that the value of p_o for the 100-gram weight is significantly greater than .50 is that a negative time error was operating. This means that there was a consistent tendency for the subject to over-estimate the weight of the second member of a pair. The tendency was present in all comparisons, but was most immediately apparent from the value of p_o when the standard weight was compared with itself.

the normal curve from $-\infty$ to x. As usual, x represents a deviation of the variate X from the mean of X. The substitution in equation 13 of the symbol h for the quantity $1/\sigma\sqrt{2}$ yields

$$p = \int_{-\infty}^{x} \frac{h}{\sqrt{\pi}}\, e^{-h^2x^2}\, dx. \qquad \text{Eq. 14}$$

In this expression, $x = X-L$, where L is the value of X corresponding to a proportion of .50. The constant h is an index of the steepness or "precision" of the ogive curve. The phi-gamma function, written directly from 14, takes the form

$$p = \int_{-\infty}^{\gamma} \frac{1}{\sqrt{\pi}}\, e^{-\gamma^2}\, d\gamma \qquad \text{Eq. 15}$$

where γ has been substituted for hx.

In fitting the phi-gamma function to a set of observed proportions, it is necessary to obtain estimates of the constants h and L. Since $\gamma = hx$ and $x = X-L$, it follows that

$$\gamma = hX - hL. \qquad \text{Eq. 16}$$

This equation is linear in γ and X. The principle of least-squares is invoked in deriving the following two equations with which estimates of h and L may be computed:

$$h = \frac{N\sum X_\gamma - \sum\gamma\sum X}{N\sum X^2 - (\sum X)^2}; \qquad \text{Eq. 17}$$

$$L = \frac{\sum Xh - \sum\gamma}{Nh}. \qquad \text{Eq. 18}$$

In the derivation of these equations, the quantity that is minimized is

$$\sum (\gamma_o - \gamma_t)^2 = \sum (\gamma - hX + hL)^2.$$

Before equations 17 and 18 can be solved, values of γ must be obtained. They may be found in a table of the phi-gamma function (that is, in a table based on solutions of equation 15 for values of p).[26] The table is entered with values of p_o.

Values of γ corresponding to the nine values of p_o in Table 19 are given in the third column of the table. The fourth column gives values of $X\gamma$, the fifth column values of X^2. The four sums needed for solving equations 17 and 18 appear at the bottom of the table. Estimates of constants h and L are computed as follows:

$$h = \frac{9(62.14) - (.2677)(864)}{9(83,184) - (864)^2} = 0.152;$$

$$L = \frac{(864)(.152) - (.2677)}{9(.152)} = 95.8.$$

The insertion of these estimates into equation 16 gives

$$\gamma_t = 0.152X - 14.562.$$

This equation was used to calculate the values of γ_t shown in Table 19. The corresponding values of p_t were read from a table of the phi-gamma function.

The χ^2 test may be applied (with a reservation) to test the goodness of fit, that is, to test the hypothesis that the difference between the observed and theoretical proportions arose from sampling fluctuations and, consequently, that the observed proportions may be satisfactorily represented by the phi-gamma function. The procedure for calculating the value of χ^2 based on all nine theoretical proportions is illustrated in the two columns of Table 19 denoted by (A). Values of $(p_o - p_t)^2$ were first

26. Tables of the phi-gamma function (which give paired values of p and γ) are not usually included in statistics books published in the United States. However, it is easy to obtain value of γ indirectly from an ordinary table of the probability integral. Since $z = x \, \sigma$; $\gamma = hx$, and $h = 1 \, \sigma \sqrt{2}$, it follows that $\gamma = .7071z$ and $z = 1.4142\gamma$.

obtained and were then divided by the product $p_t q_t$. This single division by $p_t q_t$ took account of differences between p_o and p_t as well as differences between q_o and q_t (where, as usual, $q_o = 1 - p_o$ and $q_t = 1 - p_t$). It can easily be shown that

$$\frac{(p_o - p_t)^2}{p_t} + \frac{(q_o - q_t)^2}{q_t} = \frac{(p_o - p_t)^2}{p_t q_t}.$$

Emphasis is here given again to the fact that in the calculation of χ^2, account must be taken of the frequency of occurrence *and* the frequency of non-occurrence of an event.

The sum of the second column under (A) is .021767. This is not the value of χ^2. However, it becomes the value of χ^2 after it has been weighted by 100, the number of judgments upon which each value of p_o was based. In other words,

$$\chi^2 = n_k \sum \frac{(p_o - p_t)^2}{p_t q_t} =$$
$$= 100(.021767) = 2.1767$$

where n_k is the number of judgments per proportion. The number of df is $7 = 9 - 2$. It is two less than the number of rows in the table.[27] The computed value of χ^2 falls near the 95% level of confidence; so the phi-gamma hypothesis cannot be rejected.

The applicability of the last statement rests upon the validity of applying the χ^2 test in the manner illustrated. There are two weaknesses in the application, one relating to the size of two of the theoretical frequencies and the other relating to the restrictions imposed during curve fitting. Before the frequencies are considered, a few comments will be made on the

27. The number of degrees of freedom for a table such as 19 is readily determined by starting with the number of rows. Each row contributes 2 df before any restrictions are imposed. (This is because each row actually covers two pairs of proportions. The pair which is omitted in the formula is q_o and q_t). The restriction that $(p_t + q_t) = 1.00$ is imposed on *each* row; so 1 df is lost for each. Further, 1 df is lost for each constant estimated from the data during the curve fitting process. Since two constants (h and L) must be estimated, the number of df is 2 less than the number of rows (or the number of pairs of p_o and p_t) that enter into the calculations.

nature of the restrictions that were imposed, although it must be said that a meaningful explanation of restrictions is mathematically rather complex and lies beyond the scope of this paper. Whenever a curve is fitted to a set of empirical data, there are usually several acceptable methods of determining values for the constants to be inserted in the equation. It is relatively easy to show that some of these methods lead to values of "χ^2," as computed by the familiar formula, which tend to be consistently larger or smaller than the values obtained when other curve fitting methods are employed. Therefore, when a value of χ^2 is computed to test the goodness of fit of such functions as the phi-gamma function, the method used to estimate the constants becomes a matter of importance. The computed quantity is distributed as χ^2 only when the restrictions imposed during curve fitting are both *linear* and *homogeneous*. (The meaning of these terms is explained more fully in a later section.) In many instances of curve fitting, and the present one is a case in point, the restrictions that are imposed do not have the requisite properties. When this is true, the investigator must be especially cautious in interpreting his results.

Some consideration must now be given to the theoretical frequencies represented by the theoretical proportions in Table 19. The proportion .960 in the first row corresponds to two theoretical frequencies: 96.0 and 4.0. These values are estimates of the number of judgments "heavier" and the number of judgments "lighter" that the subject should have made when comparing the 104-gram weight with the standard weight. The proportion .047 in the bottom row also corresponds to theoretical frequencies of 4.7 and 95.3. These frequencies indicate that, according to the fitted function, the subject should have said "heavier" 4.7 times and "lighter" 95.3 times when comparing the 88-gram weight with the standard. The two frequencies of 4.0 and 4.7 are too small to yield quantities distributed as χ^2 and should not have been used in the calculations. They were included in

the illustration as a means of contrasting the correct with the incorrect procedure. The two extreme proportions should have been combined with adjacent proportions. Table 19 shows the results after the combining has been done. New values of p_o, based on .97 and .90, and also on .13 and .04, are shown in the column labeled p_o under the general heading (*B*). Corresponding theoretical proportions are given in the column labeled p_t. The two combined values of p_o (.935 and .085) are averages based on 200 judgments each and the quantity $(p_o - p_t)^2/p_t q_t$ calculated for each must be weighted by 200 instead of 100. Because of this differential weighting, it is better to multiply by n_k, as shown in the last column of the table, before the sum of the column is taken. When this is done, the sum is the estimate of χ^2. In other words,

$$\chi^2 = \sum n_k \frac{(p_o - p_t)^2}{p_t q_t} = 1.3593.$$

The number of *df* is now 5, and the calculated value of χ^2 falls between the 98% and 99% levels. The phi-gamma hypothesis is still highly tenable.

This last calculation included two theoretical frequencies which are less than 10. They are 7.7 and 6.6. Further combining has not been carried out because such a step would, in effect, eliminate values of p which are critical in making a test of the phi-gamma function. There is perhaps some justification for retaining two theoretical frequencies as small as 7.7 and 6.6 when there are 12 other theoretical frequencies ranging from 18.4 to 93.4. An investigator may choose to be somewhat lenient in this regard, but leniency should never lead to the inclusion of frequencies of less than 5 or 6, and under no circumstances to a frequency as low as 0.5, one that is retained in an example in a widely used text (13, p. 181).

It is deemed advisable, except under unusual circumstances, to adhere to the policy of never using theoretical frequencies of less than 10. This means that if the χ^2 test is to be suitably applied in testing the phi-gamma hypothesis, the number of judgments at extreme values of the variable stimulus must be several hundred.

It is sometimes a temptation to pool the separate proportions obtained for several subjects in a psychophysical experiment. This practice should never be followed. The reason is clear; individual differences in judgements would yield interdependent proportions. It is permissible to apply the χ^2 test in relation to frequencies (or proportions) obtained from the judgments of a group of observers provided that each subject makes a single judgment. For example, a series of proportions for several different values of a variable stimulus, where no person makes more than a single judgment in the entire experiment, may be fitted with a phi-gamma function to obtain theoretical proportions; and the χ^2 test may be used to test the goodness of fit of the function. It is obvious, however, that this situation is entirely different from one where the proportions are the averages of several sets of individual proportions.

Evaluation of an Extended Application of the χ^2 *Test To Psychophysical Data Made by Stevens, Morgan and Volkmann.* An interesting and instructive application of the χ^2 test of goodness of fit was made by Stevens, Morgan, and Volkmann (32) in their theoretical study of pitch and loudness discrimination. A representative segment of their data will be discussed. In one part of the investigation, they presented each of six subjects with an auditory stimulus which continued over a prolonged period but which was quickly changed in frequency, every three seconds, by a predetermined number of cycles. The duration of each altered segment was 0.3 sec. A subject was instructed to press a button every time a change in pitch was detected. The frequency increments that were used (in cycles per sec.) are listed in the first column of Table 20 (except as explained in the note at the bottom of the table). Each subject made 100 judgments in relation to each of the increments which fell within his discrimination range. The observed proportions for the six

subjects are shown in the table. (These proportions were furnished through the courtesy of Dr. Morgan.)

The study was designed to evaluate the theory of the neural quantum in auditory discrimination. The theory required, among other things, that the observed proportions for a subject could not be adequately represented by the phi-gamma function.[28] Consequently, phi-gamma function were fitted to each of the six sets of proportion in Table 20. All proportions greater than .97 and less than .03 were omitted during the curve fitting process. A few of these proportions later played a part in the calculations of χ^2. This is one of the pitfalls to be carefully avoided. Another important aspect of the curve-fitting procedure was that the Müller-Urban weights were utilized. The nature of these weights and the detailed procedures for treating weighted data are adequately explained by Guilford (13) and need not be discussed here. It is enough to say that the weights are designed to diminish the influence of extreme proportions in the computations of the constants h and L.

The values of h and L for the six fitted functions are shown in Table 21. These constants were used in the manner illustrated in Table 19 to obtain theoretical proportions

28. The theory also required that the proportions for the several subjects could be fitted satisfactorily with straight-line functions. The results for the straight-line fits will be omitted here. It is obvious, however, that a straight line can be fitted to each set of proportions in Table 20 as a means of obtaining theoretical (calculated) proportions. The χ^2 test could then be applied to the differences between the observed and theoretical proportions, in a manner exactly analogous to that employed when theoretical proportions are obtained with phi-gamma functions. Whenever a comparison is to be made between the goodness of fit of two different functions, the same quantity should be minimized in the process of obtaining the constants for the functions. In their study, Stevens, Morgan, and Volkmann minimized the sum of squared differences between observed and theoretical values of gamma in fitting phi-gamma functions but minimized the sum of squared differences between observed and theoretical proportions in fitting straight-line functions. According to a theorem given by Cramér (5, pp. 426 ff.), the values of χ^2 obtained with the phi-gamma functions would be expected to be larger than those obtained with the straight lines.

Table 20. Data from the pitch discrimination study by Stevens, Morgan and Volkmann (32)

							Subjects						
X	JV		GS		RR		JM		DM			$MJ*$	
	p_o	p_t	p_o	p_t	p_o	p_t	p_o	p_t	p_o	p_t		p_o	p_t
1.0							.00	—			(0.75)	.00	—
1.5	.00	—	.01	—			.00	—	.00	—	(1.00)	.00	—
2.0	.00	—	.00	.036	.01	—	.10	.088	.00	—	(1.25)	.13	.143
2.5	.03	.044	.18	.172	.01	—	.29	.273	.06	.089	(1.50)	.40	.365
3.0	.18	.136	.45	.464	.02	.093	.49	.560	.30	.233	(1.75)	.62	.647
3.5	.31	.310	.78	.778	.21	.234	.84	.816	.44	.457	(2.00)	.87	.864
4.0	.49	.542	.95	.947	.52	.450	.96	.950	.64	.695	(2.25)	.99	.966
4.5	.74	.761	1.00	—	.64	.682	.98	—	.90	.870	(2.50)	1.00	—
5.0	.94	.905	1.00	—	.84	.858	.99	—	1.00	—			
5.5	1.00	.972			.97	.953	1.00	—	1.00	—			
6.0	1.00	—			.99	—							
6.5					1.00	—							

* The frequency increments presented to subject MJ are given in parenthesis at the left of the values of p_o in the last column. This subject was unusually acute and had to be tested with smaller increments than those used with the other five subjects.

for each set of observed proportions. The theoretical proportions used by the investigators in calculating values of χ^2 are shown in Table 20. The six calculated values of χ^2 are given in the first row of Table 22, along with the number of df for each. (The other two rows of values in this table will be explained later.) Only one of the values in the

Table 21. Values of h and L secured by Stevens, Morgan and Volkmann (32)

Subject	h	L
JV	0.8520	3.9120
GS	1.2098	3.0525
RR	0.8476	4.1051
JM	1.0640	2.9001
DM	0.8754	3.5885
MJ	2.0432	1.6194

first row (the value for subject RR) is sufficiently large to justify the rejection of the phi-gamma hypothesis at better than the 5% level of confidence. However, the six separate values of χ^2 are completely independent estimates and, therefore, may be summated to provide a single composite value of χ^2, the number of df for which is the sum of the six separate df's. The composite value appears in the last column of the table and is 33.80, with 21 df. This value falls at about the 3% level of confidence and indicates that the fits of the phi-gamma curves were generally poor.

A serious flaw in this application was that four of the extreme observed proportions, no one of which played any part in determining constants h and L, were included during the calculations of the values of χ^2. A specific

Table 22. Values of chi-square based upon the data of Stevens, Morgan and Volkmann (32)

				Subjects			
	JV	GS	RR	JM	DM	MJ	Composite
χ^2	7.64	4.02	10.35	2.97	5.90	2.92	33.80
df	5	3	4	3	3	3	21
χ^2	4.94	0.13	4.06	2.97	5.90	1.02	19.02
df	4	2	3	3	3	2	17
χ^2	1.70	0.13	3.14	2.87	2.90	1.02	11.76
df	2	1	2	1	2	2	10

example will clarify the point. The observed and theoretical proportions for subject *RR* are listed in the second and third columns of Table 23. The observed proportion .02, shown in parentheses, was purposely excluded by the investigators when making least-squares solutions for *h* and *L*. Once obtained, these constants were crucial in determining the theoretical proportions. The investigators decided to include all observed proportions whose corresponding theoretical proportions were neither greater than .97 nor less than .03. This meant including the observed proportion .02 in the calculations for Table 23. It also meant the inclusion of observed proportions 1.00, .00, and .99 in the calculations for subjects JV, GS, and MJ, respectively.

As shown in Table 23, the estimated value of χ^2 was 10.35 when $p_o = .02$ and $p_t = .093$ were included in the calculation. If this pair of proportions is not included, the estimated value is 4.06. The number of *df* for the first estimate is 4, for the second, 3. There can be no doubt that the second estimate is the better of the two. In the calculation of χ^2, it is incorrect to use observed proportions which have not been allowed to influence the magnitude of the theoretical proportions.

The values of χ^2 shown in the second row of Table 22 were obtained by excluding the observed proportions which played no role in the curve-fitting process. There are still six

independent values, each with its own number of *df*. It is entirely legitimate to add these values to obtain the composite value of 19.02 (with 17 *df*) given in the last column of the table. This new composite value falls at about the 30% level and provides no basis for rejecting the phi-gamma hypothesis for the six sets of proportions.

Still another flaw in the calculations of the values in Table 22 was that theoretical proportions representing theoretical frequencies of less than 10 were not first combined with adjacent theoretical proportions. For example, the theoretical proportion .953 (in Table 23) represents theoretical frequencies of 95.3 and 4.7. A theoretical frequency of 4.7 is too small to yield a quantity distributed as χ^2. Therefore, theoretical proportion .953 should have been combined, as shown in Table 23, with the theoretical proportion .858 to give $p_o = .905$. The modified value of χ^2 is 3.14, with 2 *df*. This value appears for subject *RR* in the third row of Table 22. Similarly modified values for three other subjects are included in the same row. Again there are six independent estimates of χ^2, and these may be added to obtain the single composite value of 11.76, listed in the last column of the table. With 10 *df*, this estimate falls around the 30% level.

It will be realized that the elimination of the small and large proportions makes im-

Table 23. Showing the effects upon chi-square values of using observed proportions which were excluded in the derivation of theoretical proportions (data from Table 20)

X	p_o	p_t	$(p_o - p_t)^2$	(A) $\dfrac{(p_o-p_t)^2}{p_t q_t}$	(B) $\dfrac{(p_o-p_t)^2}{{}^1 b^1 d}$	p_o	P_t	(C) $\dfrac{(p_o-p_t)^2}{n_k \ p_t q_t}$
3.0	(.02)	.093	.005329	.0629	—	—	—	—
3.5	.21	.234	.000576	.0032	.0032	.21	.234	.32
4.0	.52	.450	.004900	.0201	.0201	.52	.450	2.01
4.5	.64	.682	.001764	.0081	.0081	.64	.682	.81
5.0	.84	.858	.000324	.0027	.0027 ⎱	.905	.905	.00
5.5	.97	.953	.000289	.0065	.0065 ⎰			
				.1035	.0406			3.14

From Column A: $\chi^2 = 100\,(.1035) = 10.35$, with 4 *df*
From Column B: $\chi^2 = 100\,(.0406) = 4.06$, with 3 *df*
From Column C: $\chi^2 = 3.14$, with 2 *df*.

possible a really critical evaluation of the phi-gamma hypothesis through the use of the χ^2 test. But this is not a fault of χ^2; it is a weakness in the experimental data. Whenever χ^2 is to be employed, the experimenter must take precautions to insure theoretical frequencies of adequate size.

The principal pitfalls in the use of χ^2 with proportions have been designated. Two others should be mentioned—the tendency to divide $(p_o - p_t)^2$ by p_t alone instead of by the product $p_t q_t$ without including frequencies of non-occurrence, and the tendency to neglect to weight by the number of judgments upon which the proportions are based.

An Application of χ^2 to Percentages (Grant and Norris, 10). A recent application of the χ^2 test to percentages (or relative frequencies) is taken from a paper by Grant and Norris (10). These investigators were concerned with the influence of different amounts of dark-adaptation on the sensitization of the beta-response of the human eyelid to light.[29] One of their measures of degree of sensitization was the frequency of occurrence of the response. A subject looked straight ahead into a small box-like enclosure which was painted flat black inside and out. The stimulus was a small circle of light emitted from a circular milk-glass plate, 10 cm. in diameter, located at the back of the enclosure. When illuminated, the plate had a surface brightness of 241 millilamberts. The duration of the stimulus was about 750 milliseconds.

Four experimental conditions were employed, all subjects serving in each condition. The conditions differed in the amount of dark-adaptation present in the subjects. The amount of dark-adaptation depended upon the total length of time the subjects spent in darkness. The measure of amount of adapta-tion was the product It, where I was the surface brightness of the stimulus plate and t was the number of seconds spent in darkness. The It products for the four conditions were 28,920; 187,980; 347,040; and 506,100. The

29. The beta-response is one of two reflexes displayed by the eyelid when the eye is light-stimulated.

corresponding values of t were 120, 780, 1414, and 2100 seconds.

Thirty-three subjects participated in the experiment. A subject was first dark-adapted for 120 seconds. The stimulus light was then presented four times, with a "control" trial between the first two and last two presenta-tions. The control trial served as a check on possible conditioning. The four stimulus trials were separated by dark intervals of 35 sec. on the average. The first four stimulus trials (coming after 120 secs. in darkness) were the trials for condition 1. Condition 2, in which the stimulus light was again presented four times along with a control trial, came after the subject had spent a total of 780 secs. in darkness. Conditions 3 and 4, with the stimuli presented in the same general fashion, came after 1414 and 2100 secs. in darkness.

Table 24. Data from the experiment of Grant and Norris (10)

	Conditions			
	1	2	3	4
P_o	13.2	30.0	45.6	51.5
P_t	11.05	36.10	44.30	49.35

It should be noted that each of the thirty-three subjects was given four stimulus trials in each of the four dark-adapted conditions. A count was made of the number of beta-responses occurring in each subject in each condition. The results were then combined to provide frequencies of occurrence of the response for each condition. These frequencies were used in computing percentages. The four observed percentages are shown in the first row of Table 24. They indicate the *relative* frequency of occurrence of the beta-response in each of the experimental conditions. In condition 1, for example, 13.2% of the 132 possible responses of the eyelid displayed the beta-response. The other three percentages may be similarly interpreted.

A logarithmic function was fitted to the data. The two variables were It, the amount of dark-adaptation, and P_o, the relative frequency of occurrence of the beta-response. The fitted function was: $P_t = 13.38 \log_e It - 126.39$.[30] Its solution for the empirical values of It yielded the values of P_t given in the bottom row of Table 24.

A value of χ^2 was calculated as follows:

$$\chi^2 = \frac{(13.2 - 11.05)^2}{11.05} + \frac{(30.0 - 36.10)^2}{36.10} + \dots$$
$$\dots + \frac{(51.5 - 49.35)^2}{49.35} = 1.579.$$

Two constants were estimated from the data, leaving 2 df. With this number of df, the obtained value of χ^2 falls near the 40% level of confidence. This led the investigators to conclude that the data could be satisfactorily represented by a logarithmic function.

There are four mistakes in this application of the χ^2 test: two computational mistakes and two "theoretical" mistakes. The computational mistakes will be discussed first. The calculated value of χ^2 was not corrected to take account of the use of percentages instead of frequencies. It should have been multiplied by the ratio 132/100. The second computational mistake was a failure to take account of the frequency of non-occurrence of the beta-response in each of the four conditions. In condition 1, for example, the beta-response occurred 13.2% of the time and failed to occur 86.8% of the time. This latter percentage played no part in the calculation of χ^2. All four percentages of non-occurrence should have been employed. The value of χ^2 for Table 24, when correctly computed, is 3.081. The number of df is still 2.

The other two mistakes were more basic. The use of χ^2 to test goodness of fit was not warranted, for two reasons. In the first place, there were linkages within conditions. Each of the subjects was given four trials in each of the four conditions of dark-adaptation. The results for the subjects were pooled. There were undoubtedly individual differences in capacity to display the beta-response; so there must have been linkages within condi-

30. With common logarithms, the function becomes: $P_t = 30.81 \log_{10} It - 126.39$.

tions. In applying the χ^2 test, the investigators assumed, in effect, that the 132 trials per condition were given to 132 instead of 33 subjects. The test was inapplicable because the assumption could not justifiably be made.

The second reason that the χ^2 test should not have been used arises from the lack of independence from condition to condition. As already stated, a fundamental requirement for the use of the χ^2 test in independence between individual measures. The differences between individual subjects that manifested themselves in any condition were certain to be maintained in the other conditions; so it cannot be assumed that the values of P_o in Table 24 are unrelated.

Applications of the χ^2 Test to Non-Frequency Data

Some investigators are prone to use a χ^2 test of goodness of fit whenever a set of observed and theoretical values of any kind is available for comparison. This mistake apparently grows from a misinterpretation of the well-known formula for computing χ^2:

$$\chi^2 = \sum \frac{(F_o - F_t)^2}{F_t}. \qquad \text{Eq. 10}$$

Because this equation involves differences between observed and theoretical values, the conclusion is reached that the summation of the weighted squares of differences between observed and theoretical quantities yields a meaningful estimate of χ^2. Formulas superficially resembling equation 10 have been applied to non-frequency data, where theoretical values have been obtained from fitted curves.

Suppose that a study has been made of the amount of activity displayed by several groups of white rats deprived of food for differing lengths of time. Enough rats have been included in each deprivation group to provide means that are quite stable. These means, when plotted against time of food deprivation, show a systematic trend; so a curve is fitted to them. The equation for the curve permits the calculation of theoretical means which may be compared with the observed means. To test goodness of fit, differences between the observed and theoretical means are obtained. Each difference is squared and then divided by the appropriate theoretical mean. The sum of these weighted squared differences is taken as a meaningful estimate of χ^2.

Two of the fourteen papers (4, 16) referred to in the opening paragraphs contain applications of this type. The fallaciousness of such applications becomes obvious when it is realized that values of χ^2 computed from non-frequency data vary in magnitude with the size of the units employed in measurement. Assume that two investigators have a common aim: To determine how the height of human males varies with age. They make measurements of the same individuals in various age groups, fit equations of the same form to their data, use these equations to compute theoretical values of height, and then obtain estimates of χ^2 in a manner similar to the one described above. One of the investigators has measured height in centimeters, the other in inches. Except for incidental discrepancies, the value of χ^2 calculated from the centimeter data will turn out to be 2.54 times the value calculated from the inch data.

The χ^2 Test of Linearity of Regression. A χ^2 test is recommended in certain textbooks (26, p. 319; 12, p. 237) as suitable for use, with non-frequency data, in evaluating linearity of regression. The formula, as usually presented, is as follows:

$$\chi^2 = \frac{\eta^2 - r^2}{1 - \eta^2}(N - k). \qquad \text{Eq. 19}$$

In this formula, η stands for correlation ratio; r for product-moment coefficient of correlation; N for the total number of measures; and k for the number of columns (groups) into which the measures have been divided. The number of df is $k - 2$. The formula yields a variable, the distribution of which approximates the χ^2 distribution, under certain con-

ditions. It can be used with some degree of confidence provided that N is quite large and k is quite small, and provided also that the measures from column to column are independent and homoscedatic as well as normally distributed.

An exact test of linearity of regression, which is applicable whenever equation 19 is, can be made by computing an F-ratio. The formula is

$$F = \frac{(\eta^2 - r^2)(N - k)}{(1 - \eta^2)(k - 2)}. \qquad \text{Eq. 20}$$

The df's for this F are $(k - 2)$ and $(N - k)$. The reason that the χ^2 test, as defined by equation 19, can be substituted under any circumstances for the F test, as defined by equation 20, is that the distribution of F approximates the distribution of χ^2 when one of the df's for F is very small and the other is very large. The particular χ^2 distribution that is approximated is the one for the smaller df (that is, for $df = k - 2$). To state the point in another way: The sampling distribution of estimates of F, obtained with equation 20, approximates the sampling distribution of estimates of χ^2 obtained with equation 19, provided that k is very small relative to N.

Inasmuch as the χ^2 test, as represented by equation 19, is inexact, while the F test, as represented by equation 20, is exact, nothing is gained by using the χ^2 test.[31]

Special Problems: I. Indeterminate Theoretical Frequencies

It sometimes happens, despite superficial indications to the contrary, that meaningful theoretical frequencies cannot be determined for a set of observed frequencies. This situation commonly arises from a lack of independence between measures. Two illustrations will be presented to reveal some of the chief sources of difficulty.

First Illustration. The first illustration is concerned with coin-guessing data. Two

31. A fuller explanation of equation 20, together with a detailed discussion of other F tests of goodness of fit, is given by Lewis (19).

hundred and forty university students each made a guess of heads or tails on four successive tosses of a coin. They recorded their guesses on individual record sheets. They were not told in advance the number of tosses that would be made, nor were they told how the coin turned up on the four tosses until the record sheets had been collected. The turns, on order of occurrence, were $H\,T\,T\,H$. The succession of guesses of each student could easily be compared with this succession of turns and the number of correct guesses for each could be tabulated. As expected, the number of correct guesses ranged from none to 4. The results are summarized in the first two columns of Table 25. As shown, 15 students made no correct guesses; 47 made one correct guess; 60 made two correct guesses, etc. With frequency distributions of this type, it is common practice to apply the chi-square test after a binomial distribution function has been employed to calculate the required theoretical frequencies. The function for the present case, modelled after equation 3, would have the form

$$P(n) = \frac{4!}{n!\,(4-n)!} \left(\frac{1}{2}\right)^n \left(\frac{1}{2}\right)^{4-n} =$$
$$= \frac{4!}{n!\,(4-n)!} \left(\frac{1}{2}\right)^4, \quad \text{Eq. 31}$$

and would yield theoretical probabilities of obtaining n correct guesses in 4.

Values of $P(n)$ calculated with equation 3′ are given in the third column of Table 25 with corresponding theoretical frequencies appearing in the fourth column. If these values

of F_t were legitimate estimates, a value of χ^2 could be computed as illustrated in the fifth column of the table and used to test the hypothesis that the observed frequencies are distributed in accordance with equation 3′. In effect, this would be testing the hypothesis that each guess of every student was a purely chance occurrence, completely independent of every other guess, the probability of a guess of heads always being .50. The number of df is 4. If the hypothesis were true, the obtained value of χ^2, 43.351, would not be expected to arise in random sampling once in a million times.

The use of a binomial distribution function in calculating theoretical probabilities cannot be justified in this case. There is good reason for believing that the guess of a student on any of the last three tosses was not independent of previous guesses. The binomial distribution function is applicable only when there is a sound basis for assuming that every event under consideration is completely independent of every other event.

Theoretical frequencies for the empirical data in Table 25 are indeterminate—except as they might be estimated for probabilities yielded by extraneous empirical data. When hypothetical probabilities do stem from other empirical results, the hypothesis that can be tested may be quite different from the one that would be tested if a binomial distribution function yielded the theoretical values. For example, the data of Table 25 may be compared with somewhat similar findings published several years ago by Goodfellow (9), who analyzed the patterning of the guesses

Table 25. Analysis of coin-guessing data

Number Correct	F_o	$P(n)$	F_t	$\dfrac{(F_o-F_t)^2}{F_t}$	$P(n)'$	F_t'	$\dfrac{(F_o-F_t')^2}{F_t'}$
0	15	.0625	15	.000	.0490	11.76	.893
1	47	.2500	60	2.817	.1680	40.32	1.107
2	60	.3750	90	10.000	.3129	75.10	3.036
3	86	.2500	60	11.267	.3289	78.93	.633
4	32	.0625	15	19.267	.1412	33.89	.105
Σ	240	1.0000	240	43.351	1.0000	240.00	5.774

on five successive tosses of a coin by a large number of radio listeners. These listeners participated in the "telepathic experiments" conducted in 1937–38 by the Zenith Foundation. The coin was tossed in the broadcasting studio in Chicago. A total of 5,687 members of the radio audience wrote down their guesses in order and mailed in their answer sheets. They were told in advance that they were to make five guesses, but were not told until two or three weeks after the broadcast how the coin had actually turned up each time. The conditions of guessing were not identical with those holding when the data in Table 25 were secured, but were similar enough to permit a comparison of the results.

Goodfellow (9, Table 2) tabulated the results on the radio listeners in a way closely approximating that used in Table 8. In fact, the only difference of any consequence is that he tabulated percentages instead of frequencies. The "correct" pattern of $HTTH$ was checked against the 32 patterns in Goodfellow's table to obtain the proportions of individuals in the total group of 5,687 that hypothetically made 0, 1, 2, 3, and 4 correct guesses. These proportions are given in Table 25, in the column headed F_t'. The resulting value of χ^2, as shown in the last column of the table, is 5.774 with $df = 4$. The hypothesis that may now be tested is that the patterning of the guesses by the 240 students was the same as the patterning of the first four or five guesses by the large group of Zenith Foundation listeners. The obtained value of χ^2 falls near the 20% level of confidence and provides no basis for rejecting this hypothesis. If the value of χ^2 *had been* large enough to justify a rejection of the hypothesis, it would not be possible to decide whether the patterning tendencies were basically different in the two groups or whether the differences in the conditions of guessing produced an apparent difference in patterning. Nevertheless, the test of the hypothesis, as stated, is an exact one. This is in sharp contrast to the indefiniteness which was present when a value of χ^2 was based on theoretical frequencies obtained with

a binomial distribution function. Because of the strong likelihood of interdependence between the guesses of individual guessers, the highly significant value of χ^2 in the fifth column of Table 25 could be interpreted to mean that all guessers were biased, that some of the guessers were strongly biased while others were unbiased, that the probability of a guess of heads was not .50, that the probability of a guess of heads was .50 on some tosses but not on others, etc. The absence of independence and the consequent inability to obtain unequivocal theoretical (chance) frequencies made this application of the chi-square test a meaningless procedure.

Second Illustration. Another illustration of the indeterminateness of theoretical frequencies comes from a paper by Seward, Dill and Holland (28). These investigators were concerned with an aspect of learning theory which need not be explained in order to describe their application of χ^2. The experimental procedure was relatively simple. A subject sat at a table facing a panel. On the table in front of him was a row of twelve push buttons. Ten colored cards were used as stimuli. They were exposed, one at a time, in a small rectangular window in the panel.

In the "learning" series, the colors (except blue-green) were exposed once each in a predetermined order and the subject pressed the buttons until one was found which turned on a light. Nine of the ten colors were each paired with one of the buttons. The blue-green color was associated with two buttons, the fifth and eighth. The ninth button was a blank. The blue-green color was presented twice in the "learning" series. When first presented, the light was connected with the fifth button for half of the subjects and with the eighth button for the other half. On the second presentation, the connections were reversed. Thus each subject had an opportunity to develop associative connections between blue-green and button 5, and also between blue-green and button 8.

In the "test" series, the ten colors were again presented in a predetermined order and each subject was given six chances to push the correct button for each color. In this series, blue-green was exposed last and the connection was such that the pressing of button 5 *or* button 8 would turn on the light. The testing on any color was terminated as soon as the subject pushed the button that turned on the light or had pushed six buttons.

The investigators applied the chi-square test to the results on blue-green in an attempt to determine whether or not learning had occurred. Values of F_o and F_t, taken directly from their Table I (28, p. 231), are shown in the first two rows of Table 26. As seen, 24 of the 110 subjects pressed either button 5 or button 8 on the first trial. Twenty-five subjects pressed one of these two buttons on Trial 2, 22 on Trial 3, etc. Ten of the subjects failed to find either of the correct buttons in six trials.

The values of F_t in the second row of Table 26 were obtained by assuming that the probabilities of success on the six trials were those given in the third row. In other words, p was assumed to be 2/12 on trial 1, 2/11 on trial 2, 2/10 on trial 3, etc. A value of χ^2 was computed as follows:

$$\chi^2 = \frac{(24-18.3)^2}{18.3} + \frac{(25-16.7)^2}{16.7} + \cdots$$
$$\cdots + \frac{(10-25.0)^2}{25.0} = 31.3.$$

The only restriction imposed during the calculations was that $\Sigma F_o = \Sigma F_t = 110$. This left 6 degrees of freedom. With this number of *df*, the computed value of χ^2 is highly significant. It led the investigators to reject the hypothesis that the button pushing occurred by chance and to conclude that the subjects had, in fact,

learned to associate blue-green with button 5 and/or button 8.

This application of the chi-square test was unwarranted because unequivocal theoretical frequencies for all trials, except possibly for trial 1, were indeterminate. The reason is that the events on trials 2 to 6 were related to previous events. The investigators seemed to be partially aware of this fact, as is shown by their choice of values of *p*. For example, consider the probability of success on trial 4; it was put at 2/9. This probability arose from the assumption that each subject remembered and avoided the three buttons that had already been pushed, completely forgetting, meanwhile, all choices that had previously been made when other colors were presented. Just prior to the blue-green test series, the subjects had each pushed up to six buttons in relation to each of the other nine colors. It is inconceivable that the subjects could have remembered perfectly the buttons that had been "used up" either during the blue-green series or before on other series, unless they adopted "systems" of pressing—a system, for example, of pressing from either end toward the center, or from the center toward either end, or from the third button toward the right, or from the tenth button toward the left, etc. The adoption of any system or systems of pressing by any subject would mean that any hypothesis concerning chance proportions was open to rejection prior to the calculation of a value of χ^2.

When a decision concerning the legitimacy of theoretical probabilities is difficult to reach, it is sometimes helpful to see what happens if different probabilities are secured on the basis of new and non-unreasonable assumptions.

Table 26. Data from the learning experiments of Seward, Dill and Holland (28)

| | Trials Required to Find Correct Button | | | | | | | |
	1	*2*	*3*	*4*	*5*	*6*	*<6*	*Total*
F_o	24	25	22	21	4	4	10	110
F_t	18.3	16.7	15.0	13.3	11.7	10.0	25.0	110
p	2/12	2/11	2/10	2/9	2/8	2/7	?	
n	110	91.7	75.0	60.0	46.7	35.0	25.0	

Table 27. Alternative analysis of the data of Seward, Dill and Holland (28)

| | Trials Taken to Find Correct Button | | | | | | | |
	1	2	3	4	5	6	6	Total
F_o	24	25	22	21	4	4	10	110
F_t	24.4	21.4	18.3	15.3	12.2	9.2	9.2	110
p	2/9	2/8	2/7	2/6	2/5	3/4	?	
n	110	85.6	64.2	45.9	30.6	18.4		

It could be assumed, for example, that the 110 subjects used by Seward, Dill and Holland had, during the learning and early test series, discovered (on the average) that three of the twelve buttons (the two at the ends perhaps, and one in the middle) "belonged" to three colors other than blue-green, and thus by inference *did not belong* to blue-green. When blue-green was finally exposed, three of the buttons were already "used up" and were not likely to be pressed. The theoretical frequencies might be the ones given in the second row of Table 27. A value of χ^2 for this table is calculated as follows:

$$\chi^2 = \frac{(24-24.4)^2}{24.4} + \frac{(25-21.4)^2}{21.4} + \cdots$$
$$\cdots + \frac{(10-9.2)^2}{9.2} = 12.005.$$

With 6 *df*, this value falls slightly below the 5% level of confidence. It rests on dubious assumptions and, regardless of its confidence level, provides no grounds for meaningful conclusions; but the fact that it differs so greatly from the χ^2 value of 31.3 computed for Table 26 strongly suggests that unequivocal theoretical frequencies are indeterminate in both cases.

It is not possible to provide rules-of-thumb for deciding whether theoretical frequencies are calculable or incalculable in particular situations. Decisions must ordinarily be based on careful logical analysis. However, *it is usually true that theoretical frequencies are incalculable if the observed frequencies are in any way related, and also if mutually contradictory assumptions can be made, with about*

equal justification, concerning the likelihood of occurrence or non-occurrence of the events (responses) that yielded the observed frequencies.

Special Problems: II. The Nature of Imposed Restrictions

All restrictions that are imposed during the determination of theoretical frequencies should be both linear and homogeneous. This limitation is seldom mentioned in either theoretical or practical treatments of the chi-square test, and even when mentioned is usually left unexplained. The main reason for the omission is that anything beyond a very superficial explanation cannot be given in other than mathematical terms.[32] It follows that only a few very general ideas can profitably be included here.

It is probably quite obvious to most readers why restrictions must be imposed—why the sums of the observed and theoretical frequencies, for example, must always be equalized. The value of ΣF_o is fixed for any set of empirical data. The value of ΣF_t cannot "wander around any place" without at times yielding entirely impossible cell frequencies. Any hypothesis must be tied down at some point to the sample data. There should be as much freedom as possible (for example, as much freedom as possible for fluctuations in the individual cell frequencies) and yet there must be enough restrictions to bring the over-all values within the same general area.

32. The excellent attempt at elementary explanation offered by Greenhood (11, Chap. 3) is about as non-mathematical as it could conceivably be made, and yet requires a considerable amount of mathematical sophistication.

The one restriction that must always hold may be symbolized as follows:

$$\sum F_o = \sum F_t, \qquad \text{Eq. 21}$$

or

$$\sum (F_o - F_t) = 0. \qquad \text{Eq. 21a}$$

This restriction is clearly linear.

Some of the other restrictions that must be imposed in familiar applications of the chi-square test may be shown to be linear—and to be homogeneous also. Suppose, for example, that a normal curve is to be fitted to an array of observed frequencies. It is not enough to impose the single restriction specified by equation 21. The reason is that a multitude of different combinations of values of F_t, all arising from normal distributions, will each, when summated, equal ΣF_o. A second restriction must obviously be placed. It may be written

$$\sum F_o X = \sum F_t X, \qquad \text{Eq. 22}$$

or

$$\sum X(F_o - F_t) = 0, \qquad \text{Eq. 22a}$$

where X is the measure associated with the cell. Stated in more familiar verbal terms, the restriction is that the means of the observed and hypothetical arrays of measures shall be equal.

There is still too much freedom for values of F_t, if a normal curve is being fitted. The "scatter" of the hypothetical measures must also be restricted. In symbols,

$$\sum F_o X^2 = \sum F_t X^2, \qquad \text{Eq. 23}$$

or

$$\sum X^2 (F_o - F_t) = 0. \qquad \text{Eq. 23a}$$

These equations, in effect, state that the variances of the observed and hypothetical arrays shall be the same.

The three restrictions represented by equations 21, 22, and 23 are imposed when a normal curve is fitted to a set of observed frequencies.[33] The equations are all linear *and*

homogeneous in $(F_o - F_t)$. This is best seen from a comparison of equations 21a, 22a, and 23a.

Examples of Non-Linear Restrictions. As a general rule, the restrictions imposed in applications of the chi-square test meet the linearity requirement. However, there are a few situations where non-linear restrictions are made. One of these has already been mentioned in the discussion of the phi-gamma function. In the phi-gamma case, theoretical frequencies are commonly obtained through a process that involves the minimizing of the sum of the square of the differences between empirical and theoretical value of γ, where γ and p are non-linearly related. This non-linear relationship is clearly indicated by equation 15. Despite the lack of linearity, the chi-square test is often applied. It must be realized that this test is not a rigid one; any estimate of χ^2 obtained from the differences between observed and theoretical values of p is not necessarily distributed as χ^2. Consequently, whenever χ^2 is used in evaluating the goodness of fit of the phi-gamma function, conclusions regarding the fit must be made with caution.

Another situation where a non-linear restriction is imposed in calculating theoretical proportions is in the use of Thurstone's Case V in treating data obtained by the method of paired comparisons (13, Chap. VII). The observed proportions are based on comparative judgments, the various stimuli being compared with each other. The proportions are translated into normal deviates (that is, into z-scores). Several z-scores typically enter the calculation of each scale separation (distance). A scale separation based on several z-scores may be reconverted into a single "theoretical" z-score, the z-score then being used to obtain a theoretical proportion. A chi-square value computed from the differences between observed and theoretical proportions would not necessarily be distributed as χ^2. Ordinarily, of course, the chi-square test

33. One exception to this generalization should be mentioned. If values of the hypothetical mean and hypothetical variance are not estimated from the empirical data but come from some extraneous source, the only restriction is that $\Sigma F_o = \Sigma F_t$.

is not applicable to paired comparisons data because of a lack of independence between the observed proportions.

Non-linear restrictions are always imposed in obtaining theoretical frequencies or proportions if the reduction (transformation) process is used in curve fitting. (Almost any method of estimating parameters for complex functions may involve non-linear restrictions.) To illustrate: Grant and Norris (10) fitted a logarithmic function to the percentages in Table 24. In doing this, they probably transformed values of the independent variable (that is, values of It) into their logarithmic equivalents and used these in estimating the parameters for the logarithmic function. If they followed such a procedure, the calculated theoretical percentages were dependent upon a non-linear restriction.

Unfortunately, there is no way of determining the exact influence of non-linear restrictions on estimated values of χ^2. Therefore, if the chi-square test is applied, despite the imposition of non-linear restrictions, the investigator must be extremely cautious in interpreting the results,[34] bearing in mind that, as Cramér shows (5, Ch. 30), the calculated value of χ^2 is probably somewhat larger than it would be if the restrictions were linear.

Conclusions

Most readers will by now have correctly concluded that the chi-square test has a restricted usefulness. However, it usually cannot be replaced in those situations where it is applicable and it thus stands as a valuable research tool. Perhaps the chief trouble is that the test is too often applied without adequate prior planning; it is frequently "hit upon" and adopted after data have been collected and sometimes after other techniques of statistical analysis have been found

unproductive. The aim of every investigator should be to plan, in advance, not only every detail of every experiment but every step in the analysis of the anticipated data. All contingencies cannot be foreseen; but if the chi-square test is to be employed, there is no good reason for failing to provide for independence among the measures and for frequencies of adequate size.

There should seldom if ever be any compromising on the requirement of independence.[35] There should usually be no compromising on the size of frequencies. There are occasions, of course, when it is very time-consuming and perhaps very expensive to add more cases to a mere handful. The best procedure under such circumstances is to try for an experimental design which utilizes each subject to the limit and leads to an analysis of data on an individual rather than a group basis. If it turns out that only a few subjects can be studied and the data on each one cannot be analyzed separately, it may still be possible to find a method of analysis which is more exact than the chi-square test. For example, if the data can be arranged into a 2×2 table and the individual cell frequencies are less than 10, the *exact treatment* proposed by Fisher (7, pp. 96–97) is to be preferred to the chi-square test. The treatment is rather tedious to apply, but in view of its exactness there is no adequate excuse for avoiding it.

Many users and would-be users of the chi-square test gain erroneous impressions from what they read about limitations on the size of theoretical frequencies. A textbook says that frequencies of less than 10 are to be avoided. This statement is often interpreted to mean not that 10 is a limiting value to be exceeded whenever possible, but that 10 is a value around which the various theoretical frequencies may fall; and if an occasional frequency happens to be as low as 4 or 5, that is all right because other frequencies will be larger than

---

34. These statements hold also when the F statistic, based as it is on two independent estimates of χ^2, is applied in testing goodness of fit. For example, several of the F-tests proposed by Lindquist (22) depend for their exactness on the type of restrictions placed in estimating the parameters of the fitted functions.

35. Any investigator who applies the chi-square test to interdependent frequency data should always feel obligated to include, in published accounts of his findings, a full explanation of the procedures employed and a justification of them.

10 and everything will average out in the end. A textbook that gives 5 as the suggested minimum tends to encourage the retention of impossibly small theoretical frequencies. And so does a text which states, in effect, that Yates' correction for continuity should be applied if the cell frequencies are 5 or less and precision is desired. This implies not only that frequencies of less than 5 are quite acceptable but also that Yates' correction is an antidote for small frequencies. Both implications are fallacious.

The following excerpts from Yule and Kendall (35, p. 422) may help to dispel false notions concerning the size of theoretical frequencies and also concerning the size of N:

In the first place, N must be reasonably large. ... It is difficult to say exactly what constitutes largeness, but as an arbitrary figure we may say that N should be at least 50, however few the number of cells.

No theoretical cell frequency should be small. Here again it is hard to say what constitutes smallness, but 5 should be regarded as the very minimum, and 10 is better.

Hoel (14, p. 191), while giving 5 instead of 10 as the recommended minimal value of F_t, nevertheless emphasizes the importance of having a fairly large value of N by stating that if the number of cells or categories is less than 5, the individual theoretical frequencies should be larger than 5. Cramér (5, p. 420 f.) firmly recommends a minimal value of 10 and says that if the number of observations is so few that the theoretical frequencies, even after grouping, are not greater than 10, the chi-square test should not be applied. In all but one of the illustrations used by Cramér, the theoretical frequencies are considerably larger than 10, and in the exceptional case, he admits (p. 440) that the frequencies are smaller "than is usually advisable." An investigator handicaps himself whenever he applies the chi-square test in relation to small theoretical frequencies.

There are a few applications of the χ^2 test which have not been described and illustrated in the present survey, either because they are quite specialized in character or because they

provide only approximate solutions One of the specialized applications which may be of interest to some readers is Bartlett's test of the homogeneity of variance (3). Those who do not have access to Bartlett's original discussion will find a description of the test in Snedecor (31, pp. 249–251). Another specialized application of interest is the use of χ^2 in setting the confidence limits for a population variance from a known sample variance. The procedure is explained by Hoel (14, pp. 138–140) and need not be included here.

In general, any suggested applications of χ^2 which deviate from the well-established tests should be avoided except by those qualified to evaluate their full import or upon the advice of an expert.

References

1. Anastasi, Anne, & Foley, J. P., Jr. An experimental study of the drawing behavior of adult psychotics in comparison with that of a normal control group. *J. exp. Psychol.*, 1944, 34, 169–194.
2. Arnold, Magda B. Emotional factors in experimental neuroses. *J. exp. Psychol.*, 1944, 34, 257–281.
3. Bartlett, M. S. Properties of sufficiency and statistical tests. *Proceed. Royal Soc.*, 1937, A 160, 268–282.
4. Chen, H. P., & Irwin, O. C. Development of speech during infancy: Curve of differential percentage indices. *J. exp. Psychol.*, 1946, 36, 522–525.
5. Cramér, H. *Mathematical methods of statistics.* Princeton: Princeton Univ. Press, 1946.
6. Edwards, A. L. *Statistical analysis for students in psychology and education.* New York: Rinehart, 1946.
7. Fisher, R. A. *Statistical methods for research workers* (10th Ed.). Edinburgh: Oliver and Boyd, 1946.
8. Fry, T. C. The chi-square test of significance. *J. Amer. stat. Ass.*, 1938, 33, 513–525.
9. Goodfellow, L. D. A psychological interpretation of the results of the Zenith Radio experiments in telepathy. *J. exp. Psychol.*, 1938, 23, 601–632.
10. Grant, D. A., & Norris, Eugenia B. Dark adaptation as a factor in the sensitization of the beta response of the eyelid to light. *J. exp. Psychol.*, 1946, 36, 390–397.

11. Greenhood, E. R., Jr. *A detailed proof of the chi-square test of goodness of fit.* Cambridge: Harvard Univ. Press, 1940.
12. Guilford, J. P. *Fundamental statistics in psychology and education.* New York: McGraw-Hill, 1942.
13. Guilford, J. P. *Psychometric methods.* New York: McGraw-Hill, 1936.
14. Hoel, P. G. *Introduction to mathematical statistics.* New York: Wiley, 1947.
15. Holt, R. B. Level of aspiration: Ambition or defense? *J. exp. Psychol.*, 1946, 36, 398–416.
16. Irwin, O. C., & Chen, H. P. Development of speech during infancy: Curve of phonemic types. *J. exp. Psychol.*, 1946, 36, 431–436.
17. King, H. E., Landis, C., & Zubin, J. Visual subliminal perception where a figure is obscured by the illumination of the ground. *J. exp. Psychol.*, 1944, 34, 60–69.
18. Kuenne, Margaret R. Experimental investigation of the relation of language to transposition behavior in young children. *J. exp. Psychol.*, 1946, 36, 471–490.
19. Lewis, D. *Quantitative methods in psychology.* Ann Arbor: Edwards Bros., 1948.
20. Lewis, Helen B. An experimental study of the role of the ego in work. I. The role of the ego in cooperative work. *J. exp. Psychol.*, 1944, 34, 113–126.
21. Lewis, Helen B., & Franklin, Muriel. An experimental study of the role of the ego in work. II. The significance of task-orientation in work. *J. exp. Psychol.*, 1944, 34, 195–215.
22. Lindquist, E. F. Goodness of fit of trend curves and significance of trend differences. *Psychometrika*, 1947, 12, 65–78.
23. Lindquist, E. F. *Summary report of results.* Iowa City: Sixth Annual Every-Pupil Testing Program, 1934.
24. Pearson, K. Experimental discussion of the (χ^2, p) test for goodness of fit. *Biometrika*, 1932, 24, 351–381.
25. Peatman, J. G. *Descriptive and sampling statistics.* New York: Harpers, 1947.
26. Peters, C. C., & Van Voorhis, W. R. *Statistical procedures and their mathematical bases.* New York: McGraw-Hill, 1940.
27. Pronko, N. H. An exploratory investigation of language by means of oscillographic and reaction time techniques. *J. exp. Psychol.*, 1945, 35, 433–458.
28. Seward, J. P., Dill, Jane B., & Holland, Mildred A. Guthrie's theory of learning: A second experiment. *J. exp. Psychol.*, 1944, 34, 227–238.
29. Shaw, F. J., & Spooner, Alice. Selective forgetting when the subject is not "ego-involved." *J. exp. Psychol.*, 1945, 35, 242–247.
30. Smith, S. The essential stimuli in stereoscopic depth perception. *J. exp. Psychol.*, 1946, 36, 518–521.
31. Snedecor, G. W. *Statistical methods* (4th Ed.). Ames, Ia.: Iowa State College Press, 1946.
32. Stevens, S. S., Morgan, C. T., & Volkmann, J. Theory of the neural quantum in the discrimination of loudness and pitch. *Amer. J. Psychol.*, 1941, 54, 315–335.
33. Voelker, C. H. Phonetic distribution in formal American pronunciation. *J. acous. Soc. Amer.*, 1934, 5, 242–246.
34. Yates, F. Contingency tables involving small numbers and the χ^2 test. *Suppl. J. Royal stat. Soc.*, 1934, 1, 217–235.
35. Yule, G. U., & Kendall, M. G. *An introduction to the theory of statistics* (12th Ed.). London: Griffin, 1940.

CHARLES C. PETERS

34 The Misuse of Chi-Square—A Reply to Lewis and Burke

In the preceding article Lewis and Burke discuss at length "The Use and Misuse of the Chi-square Test." They allege misuses in all but three out of 14 articles, and charge the Peters and Van Voorhis textbook with six misses out of seven tries. In our case every

From *Psychological Bulletin*, Vol. 47, pp. 331–37, 1950. Copyright © 1950 by the American Psychological Association, and reprinted by permission.

one of these six criticisms is invalid, although they could have made, but did not, a seventh criticism which would have been valid. If the same distribution of validities holds for the other writers (a possibility that I have not investigated), the situation may not be so bad as they make out. Lewis and Burke play up only some partial applications of chi-square at the expense of more fundamental and general considerations, thus frequently overshooting the mark in their generalizations. They make no mention of Karl Pearson's 1900 article in the London–Edinburgh–Dublin *Philosophical Magazine* (Vol. 50, pages 157–175), in which chi-square was first announced; yet no one can expect to have a basic understanding of this statistic without a thorough reading of this article and of Pearson's follow-up articles in volumes 14, 24 and 26 of *Biometrika*. We shall take up in turn some wrong allegations in the Lewis and Burke article.

1. *That chi-square applies fundamentally only to frequencies.* It is more general than that. The starting point for the derivation of the distribution function of chi and chi-square, which is always assumed for the "makings" of these statistics, is the normal distribution function for standard scores:

$$df = \frac{1}{\sqrt{2\pi}} e^{-z^2/2} dz \qquad \text{Eq. 1}$$

By methods recently available, the distribution function for chi and for chi-square come rather easily from this normal distribution function. They are:

$$df(\chi) = \frac{1}{\frac{n-2}{2}! \, 2^{(n-2)/2}} \chi^{n-1} e^{-x^2/2} d(\chi) \qquad \text{Eq. 2}$$

$$df(\chi^2) = \frac{1}{\frac{n-2}{2}! \, 2^{n/2}} (\chi^2)^{(n-2)/2} e^{-x^2/2} d(\chi^2) \qquad \text{Eq. 3}$$

where *n* is the number of degrees of freedom.[1]

1. Lewis and Burke do not give quite correctly the distribution function for chi-square. In their terminology, the exponent of chi-square should be $(r-2)/2$ instead of $(r+2)/2$.

In this derivation no conditions whatever are imposed about the nature of *z* except that it shall be a deviation from a true value, that the *z*'s shall be normally distributed about this central value in the population, and that the deviations of which they are composed be divided by the true variance. The deviations may be individual variates or frequencies or means or any other statistics, provided only that they are normally distributed in the population, are from a true central value, and are divided by the true variance. However, aside from the case of frequencies, we can not often know the true variance and (somewhat less rarely) the true central value; but sometimes we can.

2. *That the sum of the theoretical frequencies must always equal the sum of the observed frequencies, and that our example reproduced in Table 1 of their article violates this principle.* The generalized definition of chi-square is:

$$\chi^2 = \sum \frac{(\mu - x)^2}{\tilde{\sigma}^2} \qquad \text{Eq. 4}$$

where μ is the true central value and the tilde over the σ means that it is the true standard deviation. The true variance for the frequency in a cell is $N\tilde{p}\tilde{q}$, where $\tilde{p}$ is the true proportion belonging in the cell and $\tilde{q}$ equals $(1 - \tilde{p})$. So the generalized formula in the case of frequencies would be:

$$\chi^2 = \sum \frac{(f_t - f_o)^2}{N\tilde{p}\tilde{q}}. \qquad \text{Eq. 5}$$

This involves nothing whatever about what the frequencies shall sum to. In a setup such as ours of Table 1 in the Lewis and Burke article the f_o could be made to sum to equality with the f_t only by artificial doctoring, except in very rare cases. Yet, so long as the "cramping" features about to be discussed are not present, 5 is the basic formula to apply to get the correct chi-square.

But Pearson showed, in the original article referred to above, that *if* the condition is imposed upon a universe of samples that the total *N* shall always be the same, and the same for theoretical and observed frequencies so that the sum of the errors is zero, then a system of intercorrelations is introduced of which account must be taken in getting the values for chi-square. For under these restrictions, an excess of frequencies in one cell must necessarily be accompanied by a deficiency in others. He set up the system of intercorrelations for this condition along with the squared deviations, worked them through an elaborate and highly technical solution by determinants, and emerged with the now well-known formula:

$$\chi^2 = \sum \frac{(f_t - f_o)^2}{\tilde{p}N} = \sum \frac{(f_t - f_o)^2}{f_t}. \quad \text{Eq. 6}$$

This is the formula that *must* be used when the limitation is imposed that the frequencies in a set shall always sum to N so that intercorrelations are involved; but, just as unequivocally, it must *not* be used otherwise.[2]

3. *That the frequencies of "non-occurrence" must always be present.* There is by no means always such necessity; it depends upon the nature of one's problem. One of the studies to which violation of this is charged is that by Grant and Norris, in which these investigators fitted a logarithmic curve and tested the agreement of the theoretical frequencies distributed to categories under it with the same aggregate of frequencies distributed according to observation. They applied the chi-square test in the customary manner for such frequency distribution testing. In such a procedure it would be entirely meaningless to set up for each category the number *not* in the category and compute chi-square elements for this second set of deviations to add to the ones conventionally used.

In their footnote 4, Lewis and Burke also charge us with violation of this principle. In our example, statistics were given for the

number of Italians, Russians, Poles, and Others who had been naturalized out of totals for those nationals in a community. The p was inferred from the sample, and the distribution tested for possible nationality differences. The chi-square was computed from only the row of "successes" by formula 6. We made the customary assumption that the total for the row is to be constant from sample to sample, and our generalization was about a universe of samples of which that description would hold. For our assumption of a fixed marginal total for the row, our procedure was in exact conformity with the conditions for which Pearson developed formula 6: a fixed N (the total number of naturalized) in a series of samples, f_t equal to f_o so that the sum of the errors in each sample is zero, a shifting incidence of the fixed number of naturalizations to the different nationalities in successive samples with the inevitable intercorrelations that would result, deviations of the frequencies in each cell from a theoretical number, and a test whether the deviations in this sample exceed those which could fall within the credible limits of sampling fluctuation. The degrees of freedom for this universe of samples are 3 and the p is .0024.

To install in this table a row of "non-occurrences" (the non-naturalized) would be essentially to establish a series of ratios, one for each nationality group, apply formula 6 to each with N being the number in that nationality group to get a chi-square for it, then sum across these two-cell columns for a composite chi-square for testing the homogeneity of these ratios. Karl Pearson says (*Biometrika*, Vol. 14, p. 418, and Vol. 24, p. 353) that a table thus set up is not a true contingency table to which the chi-square test is appropriate. At any rate, it automatically freezes the N_c's for the universe of samples, which is sometimes a natural and therefore desirable feature and sometimes is not. Instead of following blindly a rule regarding the nature of the universe about which one shall generalize, the researcher should make a choice of such universe accord-

---

2. We made a slip in using the customary formula, 6, in connection with our dice throwing example when we should have used formula 5. If formula 5 is used, chi-square is 12 with the same number of degrees of freedom. If Lewis and Burke had pointed this out, it would have been a valid criticism—the only one I acknowledge as legitimate.

ing to what is most meaningful in his particular problem, then say what his universe is. In our naturalization problem, for example, we can state what the probability is that as great discrepancies in ratio as we found in our sample would arise merely by sampling fluctuation in a universe of samples of size N taken at random from the same or similar total communities; that $P(df = 7)$ would be .000138. Or we could state what would be the probability of the obtained discrepancies in a sub-universe of samples with always exactly the same numbers of Poles, Russians, etc. and exactly the same aggregate number of naturalizations and non-naturalizations; that $P(df = 3)$ is .000002. There is a whale of a difference, although here both, of course, are statistically highly significant refutations of the null hypothesis. In cases like this one the former generalization would seem to be much the more natural and meaningful. It requires, of course, that the values obtained from the sample be taken as acceptable estimates of the true values; but Pearson argued, very persistently and to this writer very convincingly, that these estimates are quite satisfactory and that the gain from using them is greater than the loss; and he supports his arguments with experimental evidence. An awkward and stilted generalization is too great a price to pay for excessive finicalness about true values. However, the fourfold-table (if used) is an exception, if one wishes outcomes that are comparable with those of differences between proportions or of tetrachoric correlations; for the standard error formulas of both of these statistics assume fixed marginal totals.

4. *That chi-squares may not be summed where the same set of individuals is used in the series, because the sets are not independent; and that this principle is violated in our dice throwing example of their Table 1.* That idea rests upon a misunderstanding of the nature of independence. When you throw a set of dice, they fall according to some law actually *within* them, within the limits of sampling fluctuation involved in that law. You also know the credible limits in the distribution of

samples according to some *external* law which you suspect may be the law operating within the sample. You apply a chi-square test to see whether the behavior of the sample lies within the credible limits according to the external law. If it does not, you reject the hypothesis that your external law may be the law operating in the sample. You have made this test for one cell. Then you make a second throw and in it the dice behave again according to the law within them, quite independently of their behavior during the first throw. And so on with successive throws. The reason for summing these is merely to increase the reliability of the test and thus get a more dependable generalization for *these* dice. To do anything else than use the same dice, or the same subjects, would rob your investigation of all meaning for testing that hypothesis. But if on a second throw you picked up only *some* of the dice while allowing the others to lie and be counted in the next throw as they lay in the former throw, the sets would not then be independent. So if you are intending to generalize about the bias of *these* dice, or *these* subjects in a guess-heads or a choice-of-values experiment, it is correct to sum successive throws of the same dice, or successive responses of the same subjects. But if your purpose is to generalize about a wider universe of dice or of subjects, then a new sample of that wider universe must be chosen on each successive trial. Then you can generalize about the wider universe from which the samples have been randomly drawn. Our generalization was specifically about *these* dice.

With dice this procedure could scarcely go awry. But, with human or animal subjects, if something happened between trials that might affect the next ones (as information about success), the chi-squares could not be meaningfully summed because we would have on the different trials not further samples from the same universe but each time a sample from a different universe. To study thus in a series of summed trials the bias if just *these* dice or *these* students may not be a very useful form of research, because the universe is too narrow to be, ordinarily, of much social importance. But it is sound statistically if one's purpose requires it.[3]

5. *That the view that the number of degrees of freedom appropriate in testing the fit of a normal curve depends upon the hypothesis to be tested is erroneously attributed to Karl Pearson.* It is not erroneously attributed to Pearson: it is correctly attributed to him, as a reading of *Biometrika*, Vol. 24, pp. 359 and 361 will show.

6. *That certain writers, including us, recommend a chi-square test of goodness of fit of regression lines which is a rather poor one.* This should have been attributed to R. A. Fisher, not to either of the two writers to whom reference is made. We merely passed on Fisher's scheme, though unfortunately with our blessing. But in a footnote on the same page we referred the reader to "a better test of the goodness of fit of regression lines" in a section of our book where a test is developed in terms of the unbiassed correlation ratio, which is a statistic closely related to F.

Much of the difficulty with chi-square arises from a frenzy to extend its use into areas where it is not needed, because we have for them better statistics. All applications of chi-square with one degree of freedom should be cleared out with one sweep of the broom. For with one degree of freedom the distribution of chi is normal, so that nothing remains at that level that is distinctive for chi-square. Lewis and Burke say that for one *df* the square-root of chi-square (which is chi) is distributed as Student's *t* with N equal infinity. That is true because the distribution of Student's *t* with N equal to infinity *is* normal; but that fact does not follow from the stated distribution function of Student's *t*, because that contains no χ. But it does follow easily from

our formula 2; by substituting 1 for *n* and remembering that χ^0 equals 1 and that $(-\frac{1}{2})!$ (which equals gamma $\frac{1}{2}$) equals $\sqrt{\pi}$, formula 2 reduces to formula 1 (with, however, 2 in the numerator instead of 1, which does not affect the *shape* of the distribution and which compensates for the fact that chi's run only from zero to plus infinity instead of from minus infinity to plus infinity). If one applies in a four-fold table the well-known technique of a difference of proportions divided by the conventional standard error of a difference of proportions and goes to the normal curve for the interpretation of the probability, he will get the same result as by the chi-square technique to the hundredth decimal place—provided he is testing the same hypothesis and remembers that there belong in the standard error formula the "true" values of *p* and *q*. Even amateur statisticians know that you may not carry ratios from proportion to the normal curve and claim exactness for your probability in researches with such N's as we ever get in practice. But these same persons will go blithely and confidently ahead with chi-square, not knowing that none of the chi-square table entries hold strictly for N's short of infinity, and that this principle is violated just as badly in chi-square as it is in proportion.[4]

Tetrachoric correlation, which can be applied to any four-fold table where the

---

3. The example in our dice throwing of Table 1 was not, of course, the report of a research. It was intended merely as a schematic example for illustrating the meaning of deviations from a true value, worked up in the conventional manner, excessively simplified for pedagogical purposes. The objection that it would be a poor research, and that the frequencies are too small, seems under the circumstances to be picayune.

4. There is much talk about what minimum number of frequencies is required in a cell before using it in a chi-square calculation: whether five or ten or twenty, or what. The number required for *exactness* in fulfilling the assumptions is infinite; for *any* number short of infinity the determination is only rough, but good enough. In the binomial $(p+q)^N$, where $p+q$ equals 1, it is only as N (the frequency in the sample) approaches infinity that the distribution approaches the normality assumed for chi-square. When *p* (the proportion of the total N of the whole sample that belongs in the cell) and *q* are unequal, the distribution remains markedly skew far beyond the number usually mentioned as the minimum; but for any *definite p* it always approaches normality (around *p*) as the N of its exponent approaches infinity (and hence as the *f* in each cell approaches infinity). The damaging fact is not so much the intrinsic smallness of the f_t of the cell as it is the smallness of the *p* representing the proportion of the total number in the sample that belongs in the cell.

variates make a continuous distribution, also has a constructive meaning which shows the nature and the strength of the law that is present (while chi-square shows only whether *some* law is present without indicating either its nature or its strength). Tetrachoric *r* is, by the cosine-pi formula, as easily computed as chi-square; it assumes a normal distribution only over the table as a whole, not in the separate cells; and it has a good and reasonably simple test of reliability.

There are also available now more convenient tests than chi-square for testing the goodness of fit of the normal curve (because simpler), and for testing the goodness of fit of all regression lines. There remains little

more for chi-square than the test of multiple contingency tables with greater complexity than four-fold. If research workers would not, in a mad rush to use chi-square, raise an unnecessary dust, they would not need to complain that they can not see.

This note has involved criticism of six allegations made by Lewis and Burke in their article. But, in spite of these particular criticisms and possibly some others that might have been made, their article contains many sound and useful ideas, and serves a good purpose. But it should be read with critical alertness, not taken offhand as gospel.

NICHOLAS PASTORE

35 Some Comments on "The Use and Misuse of the Chi-Square Test"

Lewis and Burke [Ch. 33 of this book] rightly call attention to the necessity for familiarity and understanding of the assumptions underlying the chi-square test. It is unfortunate, however, that some of the crucial points in this rather lengthy article are either incorrect or confusing. The purpose of this comment is to indicate some of these incorrect or confusing statements.

1. There is a typographical error in the statement of the equation of the distribution function of chi-square (equation 8). The numerator of the exponent of χ^2 should be $(r - 2)$ instead of $(r + 2)$.

2. [On pp. 281 f.] Lewis and Burke discuss a number of errors which were made by Peters and Van Voorhis in illustrating a chi-square problem. In this discussion Lewis and

Burke fail to present or indicate a possibly superior method for dealing with the problem. Such a method would involve the determination of the proportion of the fourteen throws which yield exactly 0, 1, 2, ..., 12 aces. The proportions are the successive terms of the expansion of $14(q + p)^{12}$, where $p = 1/6$ and $q = 5/6$. The number of degree of freedom would then be 11. (In the Peters and Van Voorhis example, however, the chi-square test is not applicable, as Lewis and Burke themselves point out, because the theoretical frequencies are too small.)

3. In connection with the previous example, Lewis and Burke raise another objection to the procedure followed by Peters and Van Voorhis: "... the observed frequencies lack independence. They lack independence be-

From *Psychological Bulletin*, Vol. 47, pp. 338–340, 1950. Copyright © 1950 by the American Psychological Association and reprinted by permission.

cause the same twelve dice were thrown each time" [p. 281]. This is an irrelevant objection. The usual assumption is that the wear and tear on a set of twelve dice are unrelated to the probability of the specified event. Furthermore, if the purpose is to determine whether a particular set of dice is biased, the thing to do is to experiment with the given set of dice. Lewis and Burke imply that the set of dice should be changed with each successive throw.

4. [On p. 286] the authors present and discuss a presumably "incorrect" application of the additive property of chi-square. Actually the application of the additive property of chi-square to this example is correct.

Ninety-six students were each asked to guess the fall of a coin five times. The actual turn of the coin was never revealed. "The hypothesis under test is that the guesses of students *on five successive tosses* of a coin are purely chance occurrences, with the probability of a guess of heads (by any student on any toss) equal to the probability of a guess of tails" [p. 286].[1] In other words, the authors propose to study the response-tendencies of students in order to determine whether such response-tendencies represent the same type of occurrence as tossing a set of five unbiased coins 96 times. It is assumed that each set of coins is properly shuffled before each toss. On the basis of the hypothesis, and the assumed independence of each toss, it is possible to calculate the expected number of heads for each set of 96 tosses. Since the coin is assumed to be unbiased the expected number of heads is 48. On the basis of this theoretical picture it is possible to calculate the probability of obtaining either a set of observed frequencies, or a set of more divergent frequencies. This probability can be calculated for each of the five coins. The authors calculate the chi-square value for each coin and then determine the appropriate probability with one degree of freedom. (See Table 3 [p. 286]. The relevant question is whether the

1. Author's italics.

five values of chi-square can be added, as well as the degrees of freedom, in order to determine the over-all probability for the set of five chi-squares. The authors claim that this addition is incorrect because "between tosses, the five guesses of each student were undoubtedly interrelated" [p. 287]. Actually, however, the addition is quite permissible. It is correct that the additive property of chi-square assumes that the individual chi-squares are independent. This assumption correctly characterizes the theoretical model against which the observed frequencies are compared. If the probability corresponding to the sum of the chi-squares is small (less than five per cent or less than one per cent) then we may infer either that an unusual event has occurred or that the hypothesis underlying the theoretical model is incorrect, or that some condition underlying the chi-square test was violated.

Although the authors deny the applicability of the additive property of chi-square to the particular example, they do affirm the applicability of chi-square to the first toss of the coin because "on a single toss, the guess of each student was independent of the guess of the other students" [p. 286]. Following the thinking of the authors, the chi-square text should not be even applicable to the first toss because the guess of one student is not necessarily independent of the guesses of the other students. There could be a general cultural bias in favor of heads on the first toss. In addition, in the same sense in which the second guess of a student may be related to his first, the first guess may be related to some psychological tendency of the student.

5. [On pp. 311–313] the authors present an example in detail in order to clarify the meaning of "independence between measures." The discussion of this example is quite confusing.

Each of 240 students was asked to guess the fall of four successive tosses of a coin. The authors use the binomial formula in order to determine the probability distribution of the number of hits. It is assumed that the response of a subject is just as likely to be "head" as "tail." Since the probability of a hit is $1/2$ the theoretical number of 0, 1, 2, 3, 4 hits can be calculated. This distribution is then compared with the observed distribution of hits. The value of chi-square in this problem is equal to 43.351, with four degrees of freedom [see Table 25, p. 440]. Since the probability associated with this value of chi-square indicates the occurrence of a very unusual event, one would expect that the authors would reject the hypothesis. Since the original hypothesis was that the probability of a hit was equal to $1/2$, an alternative hypothesis would be one for which the probability of a hit is greater than $1/2$. The practical inference is that either the individuals responded with some knowledge of the actual fall of the coin or that the average response patterns of the subjects happened to coincide with the fixed pattern of the four coins ($H\,T\,T\,H$).

Rather than reject the hypothesis or question the associated conditions, the authors come to the remarkable conclusion that "The absence of independence and the consequent inability to obtain unequivocal theoretical (chance) frequencies made this application of the chi-square test a meaningless procedure" [p. 313]. By the phrase "absence of independence" the authors mean that there is some psychological linkage between the responses of a subject to the four successive tosses of a coin. Thus it is that the authors reject the application of the binomial formula in this particular problem [p. 440]. It should be noted, however, that the application of the binomial formula assumes independence in a statistical sense, viz., that the joint probability of two random events is equal to the product of the respective probabilities of the two events. The binomial formula can be correctly applied to the problem on hand because the probability of getting a hit is not affected by the psychological tendencies of the subject. Of course, since the pattern of the four coins was fixed, $H\,T\,T\,H$, it could happen that psychological tendencies of the subject may produce a disproportionate number of hits. To obviate this factor it is necessary to toss the four coins for each trial. The thing which is at fault, if there is any fault, in this application is not the binomial formula but the structure of the experiment.

6. In a criticism of a problem cited from the literature, Lewis and Burke fail to mention the significant point that the sum of the probabilities is greater than unity (viz., 1.7), whereas the sum of the probabilities must be equal to unity [Table 26, p. 314]. Moreover, the authors' own alternative analysis of the same problem contains the same error, the sum of the probabilities being somewhat larger than 1.8 [Table 27, p. 315].

ALLEN L. EDWARDS

36 On "The Use and Misuse of the Chi-Square Test"—The Case of the 2 x 2 Contingency Table

In [Chapter 33], Lewis and Burke (7) provide an excellent guide for the research worker in psychology in terms of what to do and what not to do in applying the χ^2 test of significance. It is, of course, obvious that there are conditions which will invalidate any test of significance. In the case of the χ^2 test, authorities tend to agree that one of these conditions is the presence of small theoretical frequencies. That Lewis and Burke are seriously concerned about what they believe to be violations of this principle by psychologists is indicated by the fact that warnings against the use of small theoretical frequencies appear through their paper. For example:

The use of "small theoretical frequencies" is listed as one of the "principal sources of error" in applications of the χ^2 test by psychologists in articles published in the *Journal of Experimental Psychology* over a three-year period [p. 280],

"The commonest weakness in applications of the χ^2 test to contingency tables is the use of extremely small theoretical frequencies" [p. 299].

If we have but a single *df*, as in the case of the 2×2 contingency table, "the use of theoretical frequencies of less than 10 should be strictly avoided" [p. 299].

"Whenever small theoretical frequencies enter into calculations of χ^2, the experimenter has no sound basis either for accepting or rejecting a hypothesis except when the value (of χ^2) is quite extreme" [p. 300].

Several applications of the χ^2 test by Lewis and Franklin (9) are judged not acceptable because "they involved extremely small theoretical frequencies" [p. 299].

In this paper we shall be concerned only with applications of the χ^2 test to the 2×2 contingency table. More specifically, we shall be concerned with what constitutes a small theoretical frequency in this application.

1. There is no quarrel with the idea that a large number of well-controlled observations is more satisfying than a small number of well-controlled observations. However, if only a limited number of well-controlled observations can be made, this may be more satisfying than a large number of poorly-controlled observations. At the same time, with other conditions remaining constant, a small number of observations will yield smaller theoretical frequencies than a large number of observations. Let us grant, then, that a large N is a good thing, if observations are well-controlled, and that we like to have it when possible. This, in turn, means that we like to avoid small theoretical frequencies. There is no disagreement on this point.

Disagreement does occur when we ask the pertinent question: How large must a theoretical frequency be before it is considered not small? Or, to turn the question around: How small may a theoretical frequency be before it is considered not large? The problem of adequately defining smallness, in the case of the χ^2 test, is, as Yule and Kendall (12, p. 422) have pointed out, not a simple one.

Cramér (1), according to   vis and Burke, "firmly recommends a minin. d value of 10" [p. 318], and Lewis and Burke are quite explicit in stating that in their opinion: "A value of 5 is believed to be too low" [p. 300]. Yule and Kendall (12, p. 422) take a more moderate view. They regard 5 as a minimal value, but add that 10 is better. Hoel (5, p. 191)

From *Psychological Bulletin*, Vol. 47, pp. 341–46, 1950. Copyright © 1950 by the American Psychological Association, and reprinted by permission.

suggests that 5 is satisfactory if the number of
cells or categories is equal to or greater than 5.
But this is not the case with the 2×2 contingency table and, in this instance, Hoel suggests
that it is better to have theoretical frequencies
"somewhat greater than 5" (5, p. 191). Fisher
(3, p. 87, 97), on the other hand, seems content
with the rule of 5.

The position taken in this paper is that
psychologists (and other research workers) are
not necessarily "misusing" the χ^2 test when
they apply it to the 2×2 contingency table
when a theoretical cell frequency is as low as 5.

2. The exact probability for any set of
frequencies in a 2×2 table can be obtained by
direct methods of calculation as given by
Fisher (3, pp. 100–102). At the same time, it is
important to emphasize, as Fisher has, that
the χ^2 test applied to the same data "can only
be of approximate accuracy" (3, p. 97), and
that its usefulness lies in "the comparative
simplicity of the calculations" (3, p. 100).

The "approximate accuracy" of the χ^2 test
can be judged by the extent to which the
probability associated with the obtained value
of χ^2 is in accord with that obtained by the
direct method. Agreement between the two
values of P is likely to be best when theoretical
frequencies are not small. The reasons for this
are well stated by Lewis and Burke [p. 282].
This does not mean, however, that χ^2 is
not useful for its "approximate accuracy" in
estimating the exact probabilities in 2×2
tables involving theoretical frequencies as
small as 5. Nor is the application of the χ^2
test in this instance a "misuse" of χ^2.

Consistently rejecting a null hypothesis when
P is .05 or less and accepting the hypothesis
when P is greater than .05 is a practice followed
by many research workers. It is suggested here
that the research worker will not be led badly
astray in evaluating the 2×2 contingency table
with theoretical frequencies as small as 5 1) if
he consistently follows the P equal to or less
than .05 standard (or some other standard
which is acceptable); 2) if his attitude toward
the null hypothesis is based upon the value of
χ^2 corrected for continuity; and 3) if he calcu-

lates the exact probabilities for those cases
where the probability value obtained by the χ^2
test is of borderline significance.

In practice, as Fisher (3, p. 83) states with
his usual common sense attitude, our interest
is not primarily in the exact value of P for any
given hypothesis, but rather in whether or not
the hypothesis is open to suspicion.

3. Let us examine the two sets of data given
by Lewis and Burke involving a 2×2 table
with small theoretical frequencies. Table 1,

Table 1. Classification of subjects working under
different conditions on the basis of the ratio
(RI/RC) of the number of interrupted tasks
recalled to the number of completed tasks recalled*

RI/RC	Individual Work Condition	Cooperative Work Condition	Total
Greater than 0.67	6	12	18
Less than 0.67	6	2	8
Total	12	14	26

* This table corresponds to Table 16 in the Lewis
and Burke article (p. 299). The data presented are
based upon experiments by Lewis (8) and Lewis
and Franklin (9).

given below, is their Table 16, and is based
upon the data of Lewis (8) and Lewis and
Franklin (9). With respect to this table, Lewis
and Burke state that "all four of the theoretical
frequencies . . . are too small to warrant an
application of the χ^2 test (p. 299).

Introducing Yates' correction for continuity
in one of the standard computational formulas
for χ^2, we have

$$\chi^2 = \frac{N\left(\left|bc - ad\right| - \dfrac{N}{2}\right)^2}{(a+b)(a+c)(b+d)(c+d)}, \quad \text{Eq. 1}$$

where the letters a, b, c, and d correspond to
the cell frequencies and N represents the total
number of observations. Calculating χ^2 for the
data of Table 1, we obtain a value of 2.374.
And since χ, the square root of χ^2 with 1 df,
is distributed as a normal deviate z, we find
from the table of the normal curve that when
$z = 1.54$, P is .0618. The corresponding value

of P for χ^2 will be (2) (.0618) = .1236.[1] What is the "approximate accuracy" of this value in terms of the probability obtained by direct methods?

Assuming the constancy of the marginal totals, as is assumed in calculating χ^2 also, the probability of any observed set of frequencies is given by the product of the factorials of the four marginal totals, divided by the product of the factorials of the grand total and the four cell entries (3, pp. 100–102). In terms of a formula[2]

$$P = \left(\frac{(a+b)!\,(a+c)!\,(b+d)!\,(c+d)!}{N!}\right)\left(\frac{1}{a!\,b!\,c!\,d!}\right). \quad \text{Eq. 2}$$

The desired probability, however, involves not only the arrangement of frequencies as given in Table 1, but all other possible arrangements (deviations) which are more extreme. Thus we need the probabilities for the following arrangements:

6	12		5	13		4	14
6	2		7	1		8	0

The probability desired will then be the sum of the probabilities for the three arrangements. Direct calculation shows this to be .0612, a value which may be compared with the probability of 0.618 for χ. We also have (2) (.0162) = .1224 with which we may compare the probability of .1236 for χ^2. Not only would no conclusions concerning significance be changed, if χ^2 is calculated with the correction for continuity, but the "approximate accuracy" of the χ^2 test seems quite good in this particular instance.

Table 2 reproduces Kuenne's (6) data as given by Lewis and Burke in their Table 17 and for which they are also concerned about

1. The reason why we take $2P$ for the probability associated with χ^2 is discussed in Edwards (2) and Goulden (4).
2. A table of the logarithms of factorials such as may be found in Pearson's tables (10) or the *Mathematical Tables from Handbook of Chemistry and Physics* (13) facilitates the necessary calculations.

the application of the χ^2 test because of small theoretical frequencies. From formula 1 we find χ^2 to be 13.1585, and χ to be equal to 3.627. From the table of the normal curve, in the manner previously described, we find that the value of P corresponding to χ is .0001433, and for χ^2 we have (2) (.0001433) = .0002866. Direct calculation, in the manner described earlier, shows that the corresponding values of P are .0000985 and (2) (.0000985) = .0001970, respectively. Again no conclusions concerning significance would be changed, regardless of whether the data are evaluated by means of χ^2 or by the direct method. As to the "approximate accuracy" of the χ^2 test, it may be observed that the discrepancy between the two values of P for χ^2 and for the direct method is .0000896.

Table 2. Classification of subjects in two age groups on the basis of those showing transposition and non-transposition*

Age Groups	Trans-position	Non-Trans-position	Total
3–4 years	3	15	18
5–6 years	20	6	26
Total	23	21	44

* This table corresponds to Table 17 in the Lewis and Burke article [p. 423]. The data are based upon an experiment by Kuenne (6).

A few additional examples taken from Goulden (4) and Yates (11) illustrate the degree of "approximate accuracy" which χ^2 may give, even when theoretical frequencies are smaller than the value of 5. In these examples the probability obtained by the direct method has been given by the source from which the data are taken. χ^2 has in all cases been corrected for continuity. For simplicity, the value of P is given for χ and as obtained by the direct method. The value P for χ^2 and the corresponding value for the direct method may be obtained by doubling the reported values. Examples 1, 2, and 3 are real in that they are based upon actual data, and Example 4 is simply an exercise taken from Goulden.

As will be apparent, each of the examples

Example 1—Hellman's data cited by Yates (11).

	Normal Teeth	Malocclusion	Total
Breast-fed	4	16	20
Bottle-fed	1	21	22
Total	5	37	42

$\chi = 1.068$: $P = .1427$
Direct method: $P = .1435$

Example 2—Grant's data cited by Goulden (4).

	Blood Group 0	Blood Group Not 0	Total
Fond du lac Indians	18	11	29
Chipewyan Indians	13	1	14
Total	31	12	43

$\chi = 1.75$: $P = .0401$
Direct method: $P = .0349$

Example 3—Mainland's data on the position of polar bodies in the ova of the ferret cited by Goulden (4).

	Similar	Different	Total
10μ apart	5	1	6
More than 10μ apart	1	6	7
Total	6	7	13

$\chi = 1.93$: $P = .0268$
Direct method: $P = .025$

Example 4—Exercise given in Goulden (4).

	Recovered	Died	Total
Animals inoculated	7	3	10
Animals not inoculated	3	9	12
Total	10	12	22

$\chi = 1.68$: $P = .0465$
Direct method: $P = .0456$

cited involves theoretical frequencies of less than 5, yet the degree of "approximate accuracy" of the χ^2 test seems satisfactory. We should not expect, however, that all 2×2 tables with theoretical frequencies as small as these will yield P's, when tested by means of the χ^2 test, which are as close to those obtained by the direct method.

4. It is to be emphasized that there is no magic involved in the rule of 5 as a minimal theoretical frequency—any more than there is in the rule of 10. It will be true, however, that if we calculate the value of P directly whenever the theoretical frequency is under 10, we shall be involved in roughly about twice as much labor as would be the case if we accept 5 as the minimal theoretical frequency.

The procedure suggested here is to apply the rule of 5 and to calculate χ^2, keeping in mind the correction for continuity. If the obtained value of χ^2, in such cases, is of borderline significance, then calculate the value of P by the direct method. If theoretical frequencies of less than 5 are involved, the desired probability may be found, not too inconveniently, by the direct method.

References

1. Cramér, H. *Mathematical methods of statistics.* Princeton: Princeton Univ. Press, 1946.
2. Edwards, A. L. *Experimental design in psychological research.* New York: Rinehart, 1950.
3. Fisher, R. A. *Statistical methods for research workers* (6th Ed.). Edinburgh: Oliver and Boyd, 1936.
4. Goulden, C. H. *Methods of statistical analysis.* New York: Wiley, 1939.
5. Hoel, P. G. *Introduction to mathematical statistics.* New York: Wiley, 1947.

6. Kuenne, M. R. Experimental investigation of the relation of language to transposition behavior in young children. *J. exp. Psychol.*, 1946, 36, 471–490.

7. Lewis, D., & Burke, C. J. The use and misuse of the chi-square test. *Psychol. Bull.*, 1949, 46, 433–489.

8. Lewis, H. B. An experimental study of the role of the ego in work. I. The role of the ego in cooperative work. *J. exp. Psychol.*, 1944, 34, 113–126.

9. Lewis, H. B., & Franklin, M. An experimental study of the role of the ego in work. II. The significance of task-orientation in work. *J. exp. Psychol.*, 1944, 34, 195–215.

10. Pearson, K. *Tables for statisticians and biometricians.* Cambridge: Cambridge Univ. Press, 1914.

11. Yates, F. Contingency tables involving small numbers and the χ^2 test. *Suppl. J. Royal stat. Soc.*, 1934, 1, 217–235.

12. Yule, G. U., & Kendall, M. G. *An introduction to the theory of statistics.* (13th Ed.). London: Griffin, 1947.

13. *Mathematicals tables from handbook of chemistry and physics* (7th Ed.). Cleveland: Chemical Rubber Publishing Co., 1941.

DON LEWIS   C. J. BURKE

37 Further Discussion of the Use and Misuse of the Chi-Square Test

The articles by Peters (5 [Ch. 34 of this book)], Pastore (4 [Ch. 35]), and Edwards (2 [Ch. 36]) objecting in one way or another to our paper on chi-square (3 [Ch. 33]), indicate either that the paper was not carefully studied or that our exposition was less clear than we had supposed. Since Peters and Pastore raise several points in common, we are forced to conclude that the fault was ours to a considerable extent. A clarification of the points in question will be attempted.

We should perhaps say, parenthetically, that we are confident we could have written a clear, concise paper in mathematical language which would have left little or no room for disagreement between Peters, Pastore, and Edwards, on the one hand, and ourselves, on the other. Because the paper was aimed at the average user of statistics among psychologists, we rejected a mathematical type of exposition in favor of proceeding largely by example. We are disappointed but not surprised to discover

that our treatment has been found obscure in a few places.

Reply to Peters

Before the writing of the paper was begun, we carefully surveyed the basic literature on chi-square, including several papers by Pearson, but could see no good reason for basing our discussion on the earliest proofs. Full credit is due Pearson for originating the chi-square test. His proofs are adequate for establishing the general validity of the statistic. However, advancements have been made in the mathematical methods applied to statistical problems; mathematicians have been able to improve upon many of the early proofs. Such recent treatises as Cramér's *Mathematical Methods of Statistics* (1) provide a more complete background for the χ^2 distribution function and for the tests associated with it, and they serve as a suitable point of departure for

From *Psychological Bulletin*, Vol. 47, pp. 347–55, 1950. Copyright © 1950 by the American Psychological Association, and reprinted by permission.

any discussion of χ^2. In making this statement we intend no disparagement of Pearson. He falls easily among the four or five most eminent statisticians. It is a commonplace in science that later investigators, often persons of lesser ability, using the insights of a great innovator, frequently improve upon his work.

The specific points made by Peters will be discussed in the order in which he presents them.

1. *That we claim chi-square applies fundamentally only to frequencies.* An examination of our equations 1, 2, and 8 and of the comments in footnote 8, page 284, and on page 318 will show that we do no such thing. Our equation 8 is the exact equivalent of Peter's equation 3, except for the error in the exponent of χ^2 which Peters and Pastore both mention. Several persons have written since November calling our attention to this error, and we discovered it ourselves soon after it appeared in cold ineradicable print. We will be greatly indebted to anyone who can provide a foolproof method of avoiding errors of this kind.

What we do claim is that the formula

$$\chi^2 = \sum \frac{(F_o - F_t)^2}{F_t} \qquad \text{Eq. 10}^1$$

can be legitimately applied only to raw frequency data. Applications involving frequencies are the ones of greatest interest to most psychologists, so it seemed appropriate to emphasize these applications and to enumerate certain fundamental assumptions and restrictions through a discussion of the binomial and multinomial distribution functions. We are well aware of the fact (stated in our footnote 10) [Ch. 33] that the chi-square distribution function may be derived from the joint normal distribution function in n variables, and aware of the additional fact (stated several times in the paper) that the chi-square statistic plays an important role in the study of variances.

2 *and* 3. *That the sum of the theoretical frequencies need not equal the sum of the observed*

frequencies, *and that the frequencies of non-occurrence need not always enter into the calculations.* These two points can best be discussed together, as they are intimately related.

Cramér (1, pp. 426 ff.) rigorously proves an underlying theorem on chi-square and indicates how the proof of a generalization of the theorem would be handled. The generalized theorem is broad enough to include as special cases all applications of chi-square which are based on formula 10. It encompasses the tests of fixed probabilities, tests of goodness of fit, and tests of independence, and shows clearly the conditions which must prevail for other tests of the same general kind. It includes the case covered by Pearson as well as the new derivation requested by Peters in his third footnote, and establishes the fact that *the number of degrees of freedom is the same in both cases.* In Cramér's proof, it is necessary to assume that the frequency associated with every possible outcome of the experiment is used and that the sum of the theoretical frequencies is made equal to the sum of the observed frequencies. It should be emphasized that these restricting assumptions hold only for applications of chi-square based on formula 10.

Peters states that he and Van Voorhis erred in one of their examples (6, Table XXXV) by using his formula 6 instead of 5. This is simply an alternative way of wording one of our objections. We show in our paper [pp. 283–84] that using his formula 5 is exactly equivalent to using our formula 10 and taking account of frequencies of non-occurrence after the sums of the observed and theoretical frequencies have been equated.[2] What Peters does, in effect, is to accept our criticism but insist that it be stated in another way.

Peters maintains that the application of chi-square which he and Van Voorhis made in

---

1. The formula carries this number in the original paper.

2. In this particular case, by using equation 5 Peters obtains a correct value of 12, as he reports in his second footnote (5, p. 452). Using equation 10, we obtained the correct value of 12 and so stated in our fourth footnote [p. 396]. This agreement is not a coincidence.

Table 1. Observed and theoretical frequencies from Table XXVI in Peters and Van Voorhis (6, p. 414)

A. Observed Frequencies

	Italians	Russians	Polish	Others	Totals
Number Naturalized	161	82	20	32	295
Remainder	205	34	32	22	293
Totals	366	116	52	54	588

B. Theoretical Frequencies

	Italians	Russians	Polish	Others	Totals
Number Naturalized	183	58	26	28	295
Remainder	183	58	26	26	293
Totals	366	116	52	54	588

relation to numbers of naturalized citizens among several nationality groups is a correct one. Since a careful examination of this application is instructive, we give in Table I, Part A, observed frequencies (of occurrence and non-occurrence of naturalization) adapted from Peters and Van Voorhis' Table XXXVI. In Part B of the table are the theoretical frequencies as calculated by Peters and Van Voorhis on the assumption of homogeneity of nationality groups with respect to the proportion naturalized. Note that the marginal totals in the two parts of the table are identical. The theorem given by Cramér provides unimpeachable proof that the quantity obtained by using formula 10 and summing over all eight categories will have a distribution approximating the χ^2 distribution with 3 df provided that the hypothesis of homogeneity is true. In this example, as can be readily verified, the value of χ^2 based on the eight categories is 29.72. Peters and Van Voorhis used formula 10 also, but excluded the "remainder" categories and summed over only the top four categories, to obtain a value of 14.52. Since their computations included only half of the categories, they would obtain for any similar sample a value considerably smaller than we would obtain, regardless of the truth or falsity of the hypothesis. The value computed from all eight categories is known to have, approximately, the χ^2 distribution with 3 df, when the hypothesis is true. It follows, of course, that the quantity they computed cannot have the

distribution they attribute to it because it is systematically too small.[3] Thus, there is no logic for interpreting their statistic by means of the χ^2 distribution with 3 df. The fact that the decision reached in this particular case would be the same for both computational methods is completely beside the point.

Peters seems to imply that there are no differences between an application of this kind and the tests of goodness of fit for ordinary distribution functions. Where, we ask, in testing the goodness of fit of a normal curve, do categories of "success" and "failure" ever exist over the same class interval? The difference between the applications is really quite profound.

4. *That no difficulties arise in applying chi-square in situations where the presence of individual differences may bring about a lack of independence.* Here Peters misunderstands what we mean by *independence*, a misunderstanding that often arises because the term is used with at least four distinct meanings in connection with chi-square tests. We have in mind the well-known distinction between the Bernoulli-De Moivre theorems on the large sample binomial distribution (based on constant probabilities) and the Poisson generalization of these theorems (including variable and linked probabilities). A somewhat extreme, but simple, example will clarify our objection to

3. On the same grounds, we reaffirm our statement that Grant and Norris erred in omitting frequencies of non-occurrence.

the dice-throwing illustration used by Peters and Van Voorhis.

Suppose that we have 20 coins which are of three kinds. With two of them, the probability of obtaining either a head or a tail is 1/2; but nine of the coins have heads on both sides while the remaining nine have tails on both sides. If we toss the 20 coins together we will observe either 9, 10 or 11 heads, the remainder being tails. From such a toss, the value of χ^2 computed with formula 10 with theoretical frequencies of 10 must be either 0.0 or 0.2, with a probability of 1/2 associated with each. If we were to toss the coins five times and combine the results as Peters and Van-Voorhis did in their dice-throwing illustration, we would obtain for the computed quantity the following exact distribution:

$\chi^2 -$	0.0	0.2	0.4	0.6	0.8	1.0
$P -$	1/32	5/32	10/32	10/32	5/32	1/32

If a quantity having this distribution were interpreted in accordance with the χ^2 distribution, the hypothesis that the coins are unbiased would never be rejected since, with 5 df, a χ^2 value larger than 1.0 has a probability of occurrence of over 0.95. And yet, we know that the coins are biased.

Too much emphasis should not be placed on the incorrectness of adding χ^2 values in a situation of this kind. The results would not be much better if the hundred turns (20 coins each tossed 5 times) were treated as a unit. The use of formula 10 with the pooled results, the theoretical frequencies now being 50, would yield a quantity having the following exact distribution:

$\chi^2 -$	0.0	0.04	0.16	0.36	0.64	1.0
$P -$	126/512	210/512	120/512	45/512	10/512	1/512

Again, the hypothesis that the coins are unbiased would never be rejected through the use of the χ^2 distribution because, with 1 df, the probability of obtaining a value of χ^2 larger than 1.0 by chance is over 0.3.

In order to make a meaningful study of the coins, we would be obliged to specify (if we could) some event which had a uniform and not a varying probability of occurrence. With a population of coins of the three specified types, we might test the hypothesis that the probability of selecting a coin at random, tossing it, and observing a head is 1/2. To do this, we would need to select different coins for each repetition of the experiment (a procedure which apparently surprises Pastore).

We would not object quite so strongly to the dice-throwing illustration of Peters and Van Voorhis if there were not a simple modification in procedure which eliminates the difficulty. If each die were tossed a sufficient number of times to permit the computation of separate values of χ^2 to represent the "behavior" of the separate dice and the χ^2 values were then summed over the set of dice, the deviations due to individual differences would appear. In this design, there could be no compensating effects from one die to another. The same general procedure could be used for generalizing to a larger collection of coins.

The objection may be raised that our coin example is too bizarre to be taken seriously. (Who ever heard of a coin with heads or tails on both sides?) Our answer is that, in any situation where individual differences in the underlying probabilities exist, the same effect is present although usually not so conspicuously. We are inclined to believe that individual differences among coins and dice may actually contribute to their ways of turning. We insist that with subjects in psychological experiments, individual differences cannot be ignored.

Peters finds us picayune in our discussion of one of his examples, and his attitude is not entirely unwarranted. However, for better or worse, we are forced to judge his book partly by the uses our students and colleagues make of it. Some psychologists are prone to take any example in an authoritative text as a model of experimental design and to copy it in their own work. The text by Peters and Van Voorhis is widely used, and justifiably so; in many respects, most notably in its exposition of mathematical backgrounds, it is an admirable book. This wide use imposes certain obligations on the authors. We suspect that they may be partly responsible for experimental designs which they would certainly not sanction. This is admittedly a poor way to judge books, but in the field of statistics we have no other recourse. Because of the unexpected uses to which examples may be put, we believe that correctness should never be sacrificed to pedagogical simplicity.

5. *That we erred in not attributing to Karl Pearson the notion that a quantity computed according to fixed rules can have two different distributions depending on the choice of the experimenter.* We readily concede that Pearson discusses this point in almost the same way that Peters and Van Voorhis do. And yet, we find a certain ambivalence in his position. At times, he writes as if he regarded his recommendations as approximations which are acceptable only on empirical grounds. It comes down to a matter of interpretation, and we doubt that anything can be proved one way or the other. We retract the statement to which Peters objects as being too firmly worded and admit that his interpretation of Pearson's views may be the correct one. However, the retraction does not alter the fact that the number of degrees of freedom for χ^2 in situations of the type discussed by Pearson and Peters is unaffected by the way the investigator phrases the hypothesis under test.

6. *That the χ^2 test of linearity of regression is adequate in some circumstances, but can be replaced by a better test.* This is precisely the view taken in our paper. We might have attributed the χ^2 linearity test to Fisher, as Peters says we should have done, but it was not our aim to designate the originator of every technique we mentioned. For our purposes, the best points of departure were the formulas and recommendations in the texts and reference works most widely used by psychologists.

We share many of the views expressed by Peters in his closing paragraphs but are less sanguine than he concerning the likelihood of finding suitable replacements for χ^2.

Reply to Pastore

Several of Pastore's criticisms have been answered either directly or indirectly in our reply to Peters. Those which remain will now be discussed, with the numbering kept the same as his.

2. He contends that we fail to offer a better method for handling the dice-throwing problem of Peters and Van Voorhis. We actually present a correct method [pp. 287–90] indicating that separate values of χ^2 should be obtained for the individual dice and that these values could then be summed. This procedure is without flaws. The method proposed by Pastore is also a correct one and would avoid the difficulties posed by the possibility of individual differences, but a large number of throws (much larger than 14) would be required. Also, because there are 13 categories, there would be 12 *df* instead of 11, as stated by Pastore—provided, of course, that enough throws were made to yield theoretical frequencies of acceptable size in all categories.[4] With the technique we suggest, the particular dice (if any) which were biased could be spotted; with Pastore's technique, this would not be possible.

4. Pastore maintains that values of χ^2 can be combined even when they are known to be interdependent, provided that there is independence in the underlying model. It is made quite clear in our paper [p. 403 ff] that we are discussing a case in which linkages between guesses on separate trials are empirically known to be present. Frankly, we are rather surprised at being asked to defend the thesis that a test should not be based on a demonstrably false assumption, and wonder why anyone would wish to use a model which is already known to be inappropriate. However, we shall present an artificial example of a rather extreme type to clarify the major issue.

Suppose that we run a coin-guessing experiment of the kind described in our original

4. The probability of 12 aces on a single throw would be about .000000000459, so it would take around 20 billion throws to give a theoretical frequency of 10 in that category.

paper, but someone instructs the subjects to alternate their guesses throughout the experiment. We happen to select a group of 100 subjects such that, on the first guess, 55 responses are heads and 45 are tails. The resulting value of χ^2 is 1. On the second guess, the responses are 45 heads and 55 tails, and the value of χ^2 is again 1. After 20 guesses, we would have a composite χ^2 value of 20, with 20 df. Since a value larger than this would have a probability greater than 0.4 of occurring by chance, we would retain the hypothesis that each guess was mediated entirely by chance factors. But in this situation, the only random event is the first guess. We wonder if Pastore would wish to consider this set of guesses as a purely chance affair throughout.

If the experiment were repeated under the same conditions, 43 guesses of heads and 57 guesses of tails might be obtained on the first trial. The resulting value of χ^2 would be 1.89. Larger values than this have a probability roughly equal to 0.15 associated with them. The difference between 1.89 and 1.00 is not large and little importance would be attached to it. After 20 guesses, however, we would have a composite value of 37.8, significant at the 1% level. Thus, under these conditions, first-trial differences which are unimportant can lead, after summation, to rather extreme differences in interpretation.

Whenever interdependencies exist, effects of the type just illustrated will be present. Pastore's extension of our argument to the first guess is clearly illegitimate. Any deviation of the frequencies from the theoretical values to be tested can be unambiguously interpreted and no difficulties arise. Also, if a different sample of subjects is used on each guess in obtaining a composite value of χ^2, there are no interdependencies to complicate the result.

5. It is asserted that, in one of our examples illustrating indeterminate theoretical frequencies, the test which we reject is a correct one. Since a detailed discussion of this point turns upon interdependencies of the kind already treated in detail and would merely be a repetition of an argument previously given, we shall confine ourselves to a few general remarks. (If one considers what would happen with a group of subjects who were systematically alternating their guesses, the difficulties become quite clear.)

Pastore may be justified in saying that the obtained value of χ^2 ($= 43.351$, with 4 df) is large enough to warrant a rejection of the hypothesis without further question. But here again, he shows a willingness to use a model that is known to be inapplicable. What can be gained from such a procedure? If the hypothesis is rejected, nothing is gained because it was already known to be false. If it is not rejected, it still cannot be retained in view of its known falseness.

Pastore writes as if a statistic can be correct for an experiment even though the structure of the experiment is faulty. As far as we are concerned, the experimental design and the statistical treatment constitute a unit and must be treated as such. Incidentally, we should like to learn Pastore's technique for testing the hypothesis that a probability is greater than 1/2.

6. Pastore objects because we include [p. 314] two sets of probabilities which sum to more than unity. Considered in their proper setting, they are obviously conditional probabilities. The sum of the corrected probabilities is unity in each case, since the sum of the observed frequencies is equal to the sum of the theoretical frequencies. Perhaps this point can be made clear by an example which is a close parallel to the case under consideration.

Suppose that someone offers us a gift which is hidden under one of three upturned cups. The gift is to be ours if we can guess the cup under which it lies. The probability is 1/3 that we will guess right. Our first guess is wrong, but we are invited to try again. The cups and gift remain as they were. The probability of a correct guess is now 1/2. Following our second incorrect guess, a third one is proffered. Our memory is sufficiently good—under ordinary circumstances—to make the third probability 1.0. The sum of this set of probabilities is 1.83.

Reply to Edwards

Edwards' paper (2) [Chap. 36] seems less a criticism of ours than an attempted advance based on a new collection of evidence; and we doubt that there are any serious disagreements between him and us. Our paper, although strongly recommending a minimal value of 10 for theoretical frequencies, allows for smaller values in the 2×2 table and proposes the use of Fisher's exact treatment whenever they occur. Edwards argues for frequencies as low as five and for the use of χ^2 as a sort of screening device and the use of the exact treatment as a check. The difference in viewpoint is not very great.

We may have overstated our case. At least Edwards' examples are quite convincing as far as they go, and his recommendations seem reasonable.[5] Nevertheless, we are inclined to take a position of "wait-and-see." In many cases, as shown by Edwards' examples, chi-square tests based on small theoretical frequencies are not far off, and there appears to be the possibility of proving that such tests will never

5. With reference to his reworking of the frequency data obtained by Lewis, Lewis and Franklin, and Kuenne, we disavow in our paper any criticism of the experimental conclusions reached by these investigators.

be far off. Until such proof is forthcoming, however, the possibility must be accepted that combinations of numbers in fourfold tables may exist for which the divergences could not be neglected. In this connection, we will be quite happy to see final proof that we are wrong.

As a final word, we wish to express the sincere hope that everything we have written on chi-square will (to borrow a phrase from Peters). "be read with critical alertness, not taken offhand as gospel."

References

1. Cramér, H. *Mathematical methods of statistics.* Princeton: Princeton Univ. Press, 1946.
2. Edwards, A. L. On "The use and misuse of the chi-square test"—The case of the 2×2 contingency table. *Psychol. Bull.*, 1950, 47, 341–346.
3. Lewis, D., & Burke, C. J. The use and misuse of the chi-square test. *Psychol. Bull.*, 1949, 46, 433–489.
4. Pastore, N. Some comments on "The use and misuse of the chi-square test." *Psychol. Bull.*, 1950, 47, 338–340.
5. Peters, C. C. The misuse of chi-square—A reply to Lewis and Burke. *Psychol. Bull.*, 1950, 47, 331–337.
6. Peters, C. C., & Van Voorhis, W. R. *Statistical procedures and their mathematical bases.* New York: McGraw-Hill, 1940.

C. J. BURKE

38 Letter to the Editor on Peters' Reply to Lewis and Burke*

In connection with the discussion of chi-square in the July 1950 issue of the *Psychological Bulletin* [Ch. 34] the paper submitted by Peters differs in an important respect from the copy to which Dr. Lewis and I wrote our reply [Ch. 37]. In our discussion [on p. 304] we have a reference to Peters' third footnote. In his published criticism of our original paper, the footnote in question was omitted, with the consequence that our remark is left dangling. Further consequences are that our reply to Peters' point 3 [on p. 332] is inadequate, since this reply was based upon the missing footnote. The omitted footnote is crucial for our reply and serves better than anything we could write to illustrate Peters' confusions with respect to the chi-square test. The omitted footnote, numbered 3 in Peters' original manuscript, reads as follows:

There may be needed a re-examination of the

applicability of Pearson's formula 6 to the new conditions for which he did not intend it. He developed the formula on the assumption of freely floating marginal totals, only the total N being fixed. When R. A. Fisher, for the sake of using true values for a narrower universe rather than estimated ones for a broader universe, proposed constant marginal totals with a consequent change in the number of degrees of freedom, he does not appear to have re-examined Pearson's fundamental derivation under these new conditions. With freely floating marginal totals and only a limitation on the total N, a certain system of intercorrelations among the cells arose of which he took account. Under the new conditions a new system of inter-correlations would arise which might very well not be the same. A new derivation with the new assumptions might not come through with the same simple formula 6. I am not myself able to carry this through; but invite the attention of expert mathematicians to it.

Our comment [on p. 304] indicates that the derivation Peters requests is already available in one of the best known statistical sources and that he is mistaken in his notion that the degrees of freedom are changed.

Peters' comments on his point 3 are part of the same confusion. Without the footnote just quoted our reply does not cover the points he raises and adequate clarification would require considerable discussion. With the footnote, the discussion as given in our reply is easy and adequate.

* *Psychological Bulletin Editor's Note:* The editor is entirely responsible for the error which caused Drs. Lewis and Burke to criticize a footnote in Dr. Peters' original manuscript which he subsequently deleted from the galley proof of the article. Dr. Peters wrote to the editor before his paper was sent to Drs. Lewis and Burke for comment, and asked that the footnote in question be deleted. He stated that if the paper had gone to press he would take the note out of the galley proof. Through an oversight, the editor did not delete the footnote from the manuscript, nor did he read the galley proof of the article. Galley proofs and subsequent editorial work are now handled in the central office of the American Psychological Association.

SAMUEL T. MAYO

39 Towards Strengthening the Contingency Table as a Statistical Method[1]

Few statistical methods are better known to research workers in the behavioral sciences than the simple, or two-way, contingency table with its corresponding chi square test for association between the two classifications. It has served and will serve a unique function in research by facilitating the analysis of data, either when we have little knowledge of the underlying quantitative properties or rather when we deliberately choose the method for a cursory analysis. Also, there are, perhaps, instances when it provides the only method of analysis. Kelley (23, p. 311) has listed the conditions under which data are placed in categories: "1) when a quantitative relationship in classes is not known to exist; 2) when the quantitative relationship is only vaguely surmisable; and 3) when the known quantitative relationship between classes is neglected because the more primitive and simple qualitative methods would seem to suffice."

Despite the widespread use of contingency analysis during its first four decades, the method until recently was applicable only to limited kinds of research problems and data. Since World War II many contingency techniques have been developed. It is the purpose of the present paper to describe some of these techniques briefly and to show how they overcame problems which have limited the usefulness of the contingency method. Problems to be considered are concerned with such aspects as small samples, indices of relationship, specification of hypotheses, higher-order interactions, and computational procedures.

1. A preliminary version of this paper was read before the Division on Evaluation and Measurement (Div. 5) of APA in New York, September 1957.

Small Samples

One problem arises in analysis of contingency tables when the data constitute a "small sample." The statistical theory presupposes "large samples" which are not always conveniently available. The definition of "small sample" has been arbitrary. Karl Pearson suggested that any expected cell frequency below 10 is small, while Fisher set 5 as the limit. The typical solution to this problem has been to pool rows or columns so as to eliminate small expected frequencies or to use Yates' correction (44) for a 2×2 table.

Cochran (9) believes that no rule of thumb is entirely adequate, and he indicated that, in a 2×2 table, the magnitude of all four expected frequencies affect the quality of the approximation. His paper clarifies the choice of tests when one has small samples or small cell frequencies. Since his rules shed new light on proper decisions to be made in analyzing small sample data and since they have not been readily available to behavioral researchers, they are given here in full.

SUMMARY RECOMMENDATIONS FOR THE USE OF X^2

I. *Attribute data.* The data comes to us in grouped form. Pooling of classes is considered undesirable because of loss of power.

1. The 2×2 table. Use Fisher's exact test (*a*) if $n < 20$, (*b*) if $20 < n < 40$ and the smallest expectation is less than 5. Mainland's tables ... are helpful in all such cases. If $n > 40$, use X^2, corrected for continuity if the smallest expectation is less than 5.

2. Tables with degrees of freedom between 2 and 60 and all expectations less than 5. If n

From *Psychological Bulletin*, Vol. 56, No. 6, pp. 461–70, 1959. Copyright © 1959 by the American Psychological Association, and reprinted by permission.

is so small that Fisher's exact test can be computed without excessive labor, use this. Otherwise use X^2, considering whether this needs correction for continuity by finding the next largest value of X^2.

3. Tables with degrees of freedom greater than 60 and all expectations less than 5. Try to obtain the exact mean and variance of X^2 and use the normal approximation to the exact distribution.

4. Tables with more than 1 df and some expectations greater than 5. Use χ^2 without correction for continuity.

II. *Continuous data.* The data must first be grouped. Use enough cells to keep the expectations down to the levels recommended by Williams (12 per cell for $n = 200$, 20 per cell for $n = 400$, 30 per cell for $n = 1,000$). At the tails, pool (if necessary) so that the minimum expectation is 1.

It should be noted that Cochran's n is the total number of cases in the contingency table. The symbol X^2 is what Cochran has suggested for the value of chi square obtained by substituting empirical data in the formula. The Greek symbol "χ" is reserved for the tabled values given by the theoretical distribution.

Fisher (12) has shown how a test of significance using the exact probability of an observed table and certain other configurations of cell frequencies can be applied to a 2×2 table with small or zero frequencies. Freeman and Halton (13) have extended the principle to any number of attributes and any number of categories per attribute. In general, both methods consist of assuming the border totals fixed, considering only relationships internal to the contingency table, considering every possible array of cell frequencies with the given border totals, and applying a test of significance as follows: (*a*) all arrays subject to the same general conditions as observed (i.e., the same border totals); (*b*) the corresponding a priori probabilities are calculated by means of the appropriate probability expression; (*c*) the values of the a priori probabilities smaller than or equal to the probabilities of all arrays which are a priori as probable as, or less probable than, the observed array; (*d*) all probabilities satisfying the conditions in (*c*) are summed to yield the probability of obtaining an array as probable as or less probable than the observed array.

Fisher's technique has appeared in a number of textbooks to date, but the technique of Freeman and Halton seems not to have caught on. The computational labor in either technique is tedious, since it involves the quotient of the products of sets of factorials. However, by using appropriate tables which are based upon Fisher's formula and which yield the approximate significance level for 2×2 data of various sample sizes and marginal totals, one may save much of the labor. Such tables ranging collectively up to sample sizes of 50 have been published by Armsen (1), Finney (11), Latscha (26), and Mainland (29).

Indices of Relationship

We sometimes wish to express the *degree* of association in a two-way contingency table with a significant chi square. We would prefer a coefficient similar to that for product-moment correlation. Some problems have arisen in attempts to develop such indices. Some that have been devised are the coefficient of means square contingency, the phi coefficient, tetrachoric correlation, the point-biserial coefficient, the coefficient of association, and the coefficient of colligation.

Inferences about the degree of association based upon the numerical size of a coefficient can be misleading. A number of authors (17, 21, 24) have called attention to the fallacies of such inferences. In general, the coefficients often fail to satisfy the desiderata of Kendall (24, p. 310), namely, that "(a) it shall vanish when the associations are independent; (b) it shall be $+1$ when there is complete positive association and -1 when there is complete negative association; (c) it should increase as the frequencies proceed from dissociation to association." In using these indices, one does not have the same intuitive feeling for strength of relationship as in the case of product-moment correlation. The latter has a stable, comprehensive frame of reference to aid in the interpretation. Also, the sampling distribution of the statistic is well known.

Kendall (24) pointed out that there is a distinction between the concepts of *association* and *correlation*. For example, it is possible to have strong association between two variables, when the correlation between them is zero. The discrepancy comes from the fact that the two types of conclusions arise from two types of hypotheses. In testing for association, we consider all types of departures from independence; in testing for correlation we consider a much more limited kind of alternative hypothesis.

All of the indices previously mentioned, other than product-moment correlation, are subject to criticism. Let us single out one of them to illustrate some weaknesses of such devices. The coefficient of mean-square contingency, C, is purported to be comparable to the Pearson product-moment correlation coefficient, r, under some conditions. Guilford (17, p. 357) has pointed out that C becomes identical with r under the following conditions: "(a) The variables are of the continuous type; (b) N is large; (c) the number of classes is sufficient to overcome errors of grouping; and (d) the distributions are normal." A number of weaknesses can be pointed out in attempts to meet these assumptions. Regarding (a), some data are either incapable of expression in terms of continuous scales or are difficult to quantify. Indeed, some data are inherently qualitative and by definition are nonquantifiable. Regarding (b), it is not always feasible to collect a large sample. Regarding (c), the number of classes used in practice will rarely be large enough so that C approaches 1.00 (the upper limit of the product-moment correlation coefficient). One formula yields the value of the upper limit of C for a $t \times t$ table. For example, it has been shown that in a 2×2 table, C cannot exceed .707; in a 4×4 table, C cannot exceed .866; in a 5×5 table, C cannot exceed .894; and in a 10×10 table, C cannot exceed .949. Regarding (d), it is not always

convenient or even possible to have both the distributions normal.

Rather than computing the mean-square contingency, one could consolidate rows and columns of a larger table into a 2×2 table and compute any of several indices for a fourfold table. However, information is thus wasted, and the indices themselves leave something to be desired.

One new solution for the problem is the use of scores for rows and columns and the calculation of regression coefficients and correlation coefficients from such scores (10, 45, 43). Such techniques result in more sensitive tests for alternative hypotheses. The general procedure is to first test the hypothesis of independence by the over-all chi square test. If the hypothesis is rejected, and one concludes that association does, in fact, exist, he may use scoring methods to partition out the portion of the association which may be explained by correlation or regression. It is easiest to explain association as being due to the linear correlation of two underlying variates. In some cases, it may be necessary to resort to one or more additional pairs of variates as manifested by new sets of row and column scores.

Two kinds of scores are feasible for contingency tables, arbitrary, or a priori, scores, and empirical scores. Arbitrary scores are chosen along some convenient scale according to a knowledge of the kind of data itself. The use of such scores serves to make some persons uncomfortable. However, Cochran (10, p. 436) defends the use of arbitrary scores when they have embodied "the best insight available about the way in which the classification was constructed and used." Furthermore, he pointed out that "any set of scores give a *valid* test, provided that they are constructed without consulting the results of the experiment." He goes on to say that "If the set of scores is poor, in that it badly distorts a numerical scale that really does underlie the ordered classification, the test will not be sensitive."

Empirical scores are derived from the data themselves by statistical computation so that the correlation between row and column scores is a maximum. Such scores are optimal in the sense that they yield the highest value possible for any set of scores that could be chosen. Thus, they are an improvement over arbitrary scores. The procedures for calculating empirical scores grew out of work begun by Fisher (12) who considered contingency tables from the point of view of discriminant analysis. Suppose that we wish to assign scores to rows and columns. What are the best scores to assign so that a linear function of row and column scores will best differentiate the classes determined by the columns, and vice versa? This turns out to be a problem in maximizing the correlations between the scores, and the required correlations are those known as "canonical" in the sense of Hotelling (19). Work in this area was continued by Maung (30). The methods were applied to a practical problem of quantifying letter grades of college students by Johnson (20). Bock (5) showed that the empricial scoring scheme of Williams is similar theoretically to the techniques of Maung (30), Johnson (20), and Guttman (18). He gives the name "optimum scaling" to the general theory and shows relatively simple computational procedures for solving the necessary matrices. His approach to scaling is particularly appropriate if the data are to be used in analysis of variance or multivariate analysis.

Several of the above references (4, 5, 10, 12, 20, 43) have described ways of testing concordance of scores. In testing concordance, one asks two questions: First, of the total departures from expectation, how much can be explained by a set of scores, and second, how much is not explained by the set of scores? Thus, we may discover whether any given set of scores is sufficient to explain a significant amount of the association between two classifications and whether only one set of scores is sufficient. In answering these questions, we have access to partitioning of chi square or analysis of variance techniques.

In summary, arbitrary scores can be useful in instances in which one is familiar with the underlying quantitative basis of the classifica-

tions and when one wishes to save computational labor at some loss in accuracy; on the other hand, empirical scores might be used when one is unfamiliar with the underlying quantitative basis or wishes a more accurate set of scores.

Illustrations of scoring techniques as applied to data in the behavioral sciences have been given by Mayo (31, 32).

Stuart (40) devised a correlation coefficient for two-way tables which is a variety of Kendall's tau. His formulas, however, do not require scores for rows and columns as do those of Cochran, Yates, and Williams. Rather, his coefficient depends only on ordinal properties and was offered as a device to measure strength of association. He showed how the existing theory of the coefficient may be used to estimate the population association, to set confidence limits for it, and also to test the differences in the coefficients calculated for two contingency tables.

A general review of the methodology of measures of association for contingency tables with two or more attributes, together with a clarification and discussion of some of the underlying concepts was given by Goodman and Kruskal (15, 16).

Specification of Hypotheses under Test

The usual chi square test of independence between two classifications can be very useful in the exploratory, or pilot, stages of research, when one does not or cannot specify the alternative hypotheses. For nonsignificant results, one probably would not inquire further; however, once significance is demonstrated, it is well to inquire as to what alternative hypotheses might be plausible and to test these empirically. For example, if one were interested in explaining association by assuming linear correlation between two underlying quantitative variates, the coefficient of mean-square contingency would be misleading. This coefficient is based upon obtained chi square which subsumes *all* forms of departure from expectation, rather than departures due to linear correlation which are only one kind of departure. The scoring techniques previously mentioned constitute one solution to the problem of testing more specific alternative hypotheses. In addition to testing for significant regression coefficients and for correlation, one may also test for homogeneity of row or column means, and for differences between pairs of row or column means. The analogy to the *t* test and analysis of variance is apparent here.

Distinction among three different kinds of sampling processes which might have yielded the same 2 ×2 table of data was made by Barnard (2) and Pearson (36). These authors maintained that the abstract configuration of a given 2 ×2 table could have meaning for at least three different classes of empirical data, depending upon the sampling process and the assumptions. Barnard used three kinds of "urn experiments" as models and called the three classes the (*a*) 2 ×2 Independence Trial, (*b*) 2 ×2 Comparative Trial, and (*c*) Double Dichotomy. He also maintained that Fisher's exact formula applied only to the 2 ×2 Independence Trial and presented different formulas for the two classes. Pearson designated the first two classes of Barnard as Problem I and Problem II, respectively. It was pointed out, however, that for large samples, the results tend to approach each other asymptotically. A discussion of the theory of the power function, computational formulas for the function and some illustrative tables of the function were presented for Problem I by Pearson and Merrington (37) and for Problem II by Patnaik (35).

Cochran (8) has given the theory and application of a test of significance for a 2 ×2 contingency table in which there is correlation between the observations themselves in the cells. Such a situation occurs in practice when the same individuals are observed under different treatments.

Snedecor (39) has described and illustrated a technique of testing the discrepancies of several 2 ×2 samples which represent replications of the same experiment in regard to the evidence which they furnish regarding the hypothesis under test. His illustration was for a single attribute with expected frequencies given a priori.

Higher-Order Interactions

Interactions among three or more classifications are often of intrinsic interest in contingency analysis. However, most of the development of concepts for understanding and techniques for analyzing higher-order interactions has come about rather recently.

Simpson (38) pointed out the possibilities for fallacious conclusions that might be drawn from data in two-way form where certain effects are obscured, while if the data had been classified in a three-way form, the covert relationships would have shown up. The same effect applied to test item interactions has been called "Meehl's Paradox" by Fricke (14). The effect also appeared in a description of latent structure analysis by Lazarsfeld (27). The analogue for continuous variables is the well known argument against doing separate *t* tests rather than a single factorial experiment.

At present, there are available three approaches toward the assessment of higher-order interaction. It is not clear just how these three are related, or whether they are independent approaches to the same problem. There appears to be much to be done by both mathematical statisticians and by the applied researcher in clarifying the distinctions among these three techniques.

The simplest case of higher-order interaction is that given in the 2 ×2 ×2 table. A test for this case was first described by Bartlett (3), who wrote the general formula for a cubic equation in which the independent variable *x* is the deviation of each observation in the 2 ×2 ×2 table from the corresponding expected values. Having solved the cubic equation for *x*, it was easy to compute chi square by means of a formula which he gave. Bartlett also treated more complex tables of more than three dichotomized attributes. Norton (34) maintained that the calculation of chi square for the complex table of dichotomized attributes is purely a computational difficulty. He presented the algebraic model and an approximate method of computing chi square for such a table. However, Norton's method is computationally tedious. Kastenbaum and Lamphiear (22) demonstrated an iterative technique for solving the general three-way table which, while practical for a desk calculator, is particularly well suited for modern high-speed computers. It is of interest to note that a general computer program covering certain selected cases of a three-way table up to size $5 \times 5 \times 16$ is available at Oak Ridge National Laboratory. Illustrations of $2 \times 2 \times 2$ problems have been given from biometrics by Snedecor (39) and from the behavioral sciences by Mayo (31).

Another technique for testing higher-order interactions utilizes approximation by means of the likelihood ratio criterion and has been described and illustrated by Mayo (31). In this technique, one can test a number of different kinds of higher-order interactions. For example, in a single four-way table, in addition to the six simple interactions of pairs of attributes, one may test 24 different null hypotheses about higher-order interactions, or a total of 30 null hypotheses for the table. Thus, one may test (a) mutual independence among all four attributes; (b) mutual independence among any three attributes; (c) independence between any two attributes; (d) independence between one attribute and a combination of the remaining three; (e) independence between one attribute and a combination of the remaining two; and (f) independence between a combination of any two attributes with a combination of the other two.

A third technique for testing higher-order interactions was given by Lancaster (25). His estimate of higher-order interaction is based upon the partition of the chi square. It is applicable whether the parameters used are given a priori or are estimated from the data. It is also general for any number of attributes and any number of categories. Although Lancaster's component for inter-

action is different from Bartlett's, he shows that they are asymptotically the same. Lancaster's method has the advantage of being computationally simpler, although it is not made clear just what hypotheses are being tested.

Simpson (38) has clarified the interpretation of interaction in contingency tables to some extent; he has compared the specific interpretations of Bartlett and Lancaster; he has also pointed out some pitfalls to be avoided in the interpretation of interactions. Illustrations of higher order interactions from the behavioral sciences have been given by Mayo (31) and by Sutcliffe and Haberman (41).

Computational Procedures

The computational labor involved in applying some analyses to contingency data has been prohibitive; examples are data involving a large number of cells, higher-order interactions, exact tests, and iterative procedures for a series of like data such as item analysis or large scale questionnaire interpretation. The problem of computational labor has been attacked in a number of ways. For Fisher's exact test, the tabled probabilities for a great many 2×2 configurations and sample sizes by Armsen, Finney, Latscha, and Mainland have already been mentioned. Also, for the usual chi-square test there are number of formulas which do not require the computation of expected frequencies as an intermediate step. Such a formula for the 2×2 case is well known and has appeared in a number of textbooks; the formula for the $r \times 2$ case is also well known; it sometimes goes under the name of the "Brandt-Snedecor" formula and has also appeared in a number of textbooks. A similar formula for the $r \times s$ case is less well known. To the author's knowledge, it has not appeared in a textbook, although it was published in two rather specialized journals (7, 28). It has been known by some research workers at universities and in military research; however, it does not seem to be as generally known as the other formulas for chi square. A computing routine for the $r \times s$ formula was described by Mayo (33). In one case, use of the formula reduced the number of machine and pencil operations by one half.

An approximate graphical technique for determining significance level for the 2×2 table by the simple addition and subtraction of cell frequencies was described by Trites (42). The sample sizes tabled have a lower limit of 40, which is approximately equal to the upper limit for the exact functions previously referred to, while the upper limit is 200. To use this test, one must draw independent samples; for maximum usefulness, the two samples should be of equal size, although the author does show how some cases can be handled in a more approximate fashion. Another approximate, graphical technique was devised by Bross and Kasten (6); it does not require equal samples and is amenable for cases in which one column total is as large as 49.

With the advent of electronic computers, one should find that some older, formerly prohibitive techniques will become feasible and probably newer computing programs will become available.

Summary

The contingency principle for classifying, analyzing, and interpreting categorical data has been well known by research workers for several decades. Not until the last decade, however, has it realized more of its potential usefulness as it has been applied to a wider range of data. Some problems inherent in the furtherance of its usefulness were discussed as well as solutions for these problems.

The analytical techniques treated here and those additional ones sure to come in the near future promise: (a) improved interpretation of contingency data of the usual kinds; (b) means of quantifying qualitative data so as to provide additional variables for research investigations; and (c) contributions to both theory and practice in configural scoring and pattern analysis problems, when one is interested in higher-order interactions.

References

1. Armsen, P. Tables for significance tests of 2×2 contingency tables. *Biometrika*, 1955, 42, 494–511.
2. Barnard, G. A. Significance tests for 2×2 tables. *Biometrika*, 1947, 34, 123–138.
3. Bartlett, M. S. Contingency table interactions. *J. Roy. Statist. Soc. Suppl.*, 1935, 2, 248–252.
4. Bock, R. D. The selection of judges for preference testing. *Psychometrika*, 1956, 21, 349–366.
5. Bock, R. D. Methods and application of optimal scaling. Paper read at APA, New York, September, 1957.
6. Bross, I. D. J., & Kasten, E. L. Rapid analysis of 2×2 tables. *J. Amer. Statis. Ass.*, 1957, 52, 18–28.
7. Carroll, J. B., & Bennett, C. C. Machine short-cuts in the computation of chi-square and contingency coefficient. *Psychometrika*, 1950, 15, 441–447.
8. Cochran, W. G. The comparison of percentages in matched samples. *Biometrika*, 1950, 37, 256–266.
9. Cochran, W. G. The χ^2 test of goodness of fit. *Ann. math. Statis.*, 1952, 23, 315–345.
10. Cochran, W. G. Some methods for strengthening the common χ^2 tests. *Biometrics*, 1954, 10, 417–451.
11. Finney, D. J. The Fisher-Yates test of significance in 2×2 tables. *Biometrika*, 1948, 35, 145–156.
12. Fisher, R. A. *Statistical methods for research workers*. New York: Hafner, 1946.
13. Freeman, G. H., & Halton, J. H. Note on an exact treatment of contingency, goodness of fit and other problems of significance. *Biometrika*, 1951, 38, 141–149.
14. Fricke, B. G. A configural-content-intensity item for personality measurement. *Educ. psychol. Measmt.*, 1956, 16, 54–62.
15. Goodman, L. A., & Kruskal, W. H. Measures of association for cross-classifications. *J. Amer. Statis. Ass.*, 1954, 49 732–764.
16. Goodman, L. A., & Kruskal, W. H. Measures of association for cross-classifications. II: Further discussion and references. *J. Amer. Statis. Ass.*, 1959, 54, 123–163.
17. Guilford, J. P. *Psychometric methods*. New York: McGraw-Hill, 1936.
18. Guttman, L. The quantification of a class of attributes: A theory and method of scale construction. In P. Horst et al., *The prediction of*

personal adjustment. New York: Soc. Sci. Res. Coun., 1941. Pp. 319–348.

19. Hotelling, H. Simplified calculation of principal components. *Psychometrika*, 1936, 1, 27–35.

20. Johnson, P. O. The quantification of data in discriminant analysis. *J. Amer. statis. Ass.*, 1950, 45, 65–76.

21. Johnson, P. O., & Jackson, R. W. B. *Introduction to statistical methods.* New York: Prentice-Hall, 1953.

22. Kastenbaum, M. A., & Lamphiear, D. E. Calculation of chi-square to test the no three-factor interaction hypothesis. *Biometrics*, 1959, 15, 107–115.

23. Kelley, T. L. *Fundamentals of statistics.* Cambridge: Harvard Univer. Press, 1947.

24. Kendall, M. G. *The advanced theory of statistics.* Vol. I. London: Griffin, 1947.

25. Lancaster, H. O. Complex contingency tables treated by the partition of χ^2. *J. Roy. Statist. Soc., Series B*, 1951, 13, 242–249.

26. Latscha, R. Tests of significance in a 2×2 contingency table: Expression of Finney's table. *Biometrika*, 1953, 40, 74–86.

27. Lazarsfeld, P. F. A conceptual introduction to latent structure analysis. In P. F. Lazarsfeld (Ed.), *Mathematical thinking in the social science.* Glencoe: Free Press, 1954. Pp. 349–387.

28. Leslie, P. H. The calculation of χ^2 for $r \times c$ contingency table. *Biometrics*, 1951, 7, 283–286.

29. Mainland, D. Statistical methods in research. I. Qualitative statistics (Enumeration data). *Canad. J. Res.*, 1948, 26, 1–166.

30. Maung, K. Discriminant analysis of Tocher's eye-color data for Scottish school children. *Ann. Eugen.*, 1941, 11, 64–76.

31. Mayo, S. T. Recent techniques for analyzing association in contingency tables as applied to an analytical follow-up survey of education graduates. *J. exp. Educ.*, 1957, 25, 213–232.

32. Mayo, S. T. The use of scores in analyzing association between attributes. *Yearb. Nat. Coun. on Measmt. used in Educ.*, 1958, 15, 39–49.

33. Mayo, S. T. A computing routine for chi-square without expected frequencies in a two-way contingency table. *Psychol. Newsltr., NYU*, 1959, 10, 286–288.

34. Norton, H. W. Calculation of chi-square for complex contingency tables. *J. Amer. Statis. Ass.*, 1945, 40, 251–258.

35. Patnaik, P. B. The power function of the test for the difference between two proportions in a 2×2 table. *Biometrika*, 1948, 35, 157–174.

36. Pearson, E. S. The choice of statistical tests illustrated on the interpretation of data classed in a 2×2 table. *Biometrika*, 1947, 34, 139–167.

37. Pearson, E. S., & Merrington, M. 2×2 tables: The power function of the test on a randomized experiment. *Biometrika*, 1948, 35, 331–345.

38. Simpson, E. H. The interpretation of interaction in contingency tables. *J. Roy. Statist. Soc., Series B*, 1951, 13, 238–241.

39. Snedecor, G. W. *Statistical methods.* Ames: Iowa State Coll. Press, 1946.

40. Stuart, A. The estimation and comparison of strengths of association in contingency tables. *Biometrika*, 1953, 40, 105–110.

41. Sutcliffe, J. P., & Haberman, M. Factors influencing choice in role conflict situations. *Amer. sociol. Rev.*, 1956, 21, 695–703.

42. Trites, D. K. Graphic determination of significance of 2×2 contingency tables. *Psychol. Bull.*, 1957, 54, 140–144.

43. Williams, E. J. Use of scores for the analysis of association in contingency tables. *Biometrika*, 1952, 39, 274–289.

44. Yates, F. Contingency tables involving small numbers and the χ^2 test. *J. Roy. Statist. Soc. Suppl.*, 1934, 1, 217–235.

45. Yates, F. The analysis of contingency tables with groupings based on quantitative characters. *Biometrika*, 1948, 35, 176–181.

6

Violations of Assumptions

The proper use of a statistical test or model depends, in part, upon the assumptions required for the use of the model and the corresponding characteristics of the data. Sometimes our data do not fit the model; not every assumption of the model is satisfied by the data. Some critics have argued that if not all the assumptions of a model are satisfied by the data the use of the model is inappropriate. Others argued that it is permissible to use models whose assumptions are violated by the data, but this should be done with appropriate care and caveat.

Recently a number of studies have been published that show the effects of violating the assumptions of statistical models. A summary of one such study by D. Norton entitled, "An Empirical Investigation of Some Effects of Non-Normality and Heterogeneity of the F-Distribution," was published in E. Lindquist's *Design and Analysis of Experiments in Psychology and Education*. This discussion, which is reproduced in this section, examined the actual effects of violating the assumptions required for the use of the F test. C. Boneau studied the effects of violating the assumptions of the t-test; and B. Baker, C. Hardyck, and L. Petrinovich extended Boneau's study of the t-test. From these studies the student should learn that violating the assumptions of a statistical model, while not a desirable procedure—it is always best to use a test whose assumptions our data satisfy—can at times be done, and at other times should not be done. Sometimes, depending on the specific characteristics of the model and the data, the violation of the assumptions is unlikely to lead to erroneous or misleading statements, while at other times erroneous or invalid statements are far more likely.

E. F. LINDQUIST

40 The Norton Study of the Effects of Non-normality and Heterogeneity of Variance

To investigate the effects of non-normality and of heterogeneity of variance upon the F-distribution, D. W. Norton[1] constructed "card populations" of 10,000 cases each, from which samples could be conveniently drawn by means of electric tabulating equipment (International Business Machines). The first phase of this study was concerned with the situation in which the distribution of criterion measures is identical for all treatment populations, but in which each differs from the normal population. Six different forms of distributions, selected as representatives of the range of forms of distributions most fre-

1. This study was first reported in an unpublished Ph.D. dissertation, "An Empirical Investigation of Some Effects of Non-normality and Heterogeneity on the F-distribution," Ph.D. Thesis in Education, State University of Iowa, 1952.

quently met in educational and psychological research, were investigated. Figure 1 presents histograms representing the distributions of criterion measures for these populations. Population I, except for a finite range and lack of complete continuity, is essentially a normal distribution, and was included as a check upon the sampling procedures employed. These distributions has been plotted with approximately the same variance and the same area, so that they may be readily compared.

From each of these populations independently, Norton selected 3,000 *sets* of k random samples of n cases each (k and n taking different values for different F-distributions). Each set thus corresponded to a hypothetical simple-randomized experiment with k treat-

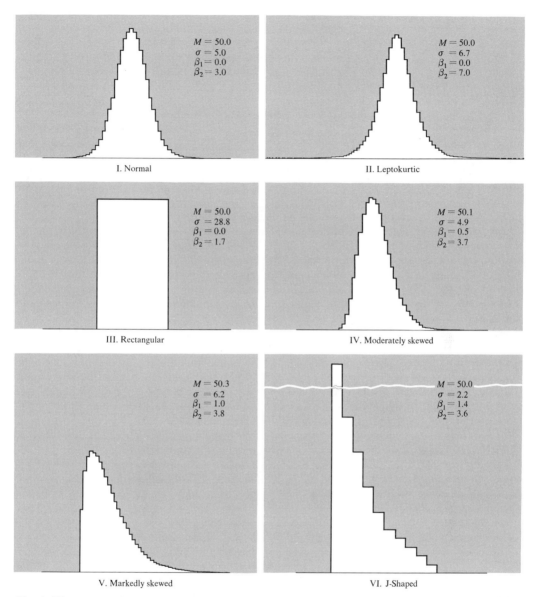

Fig. 1. Histograms of populations for which empirical *F*-distributions were obtained in Phase 1 of the Norton Study

ments and *n* cases in each treatment group. For each set (or experiment) the ratio of the mean squares for "between-treatments" and "within-treatments" was computed, and a distribution of these ratios was tabulated for the 3,000 experiments. An empirical distribution of 3,000 *F*'s was thus obtained for either one or two combinations of *k* and *n* for each of the six populations.

The discrepancies, in the critical upper-tail

VIOLATIONS OF ASSUMPTIONS

Table 1. Phase 1 of the Norton study. Percents of mean square ratios in empirical distributions exceeding given per cent points in the normal theory F-distribution

				Per cent:	50.00	25.00	20.00	10.00	5.00	2.50	1.00	0.50	0.10
Number of Population	*Type of Population*	*k*	*n*	*df*	*Points: df* = 2,6	.780	1.76	2.13	3.46	5.14	7.26	10.92	14.54	27.00
					df = 3,16	.823	1.51	1.74	2.46	3.24	4.08	5.29	6.30	9.00
I	Normal	4	5	3,16		50.88	25.13	19.95	9.98	5.61	2.94	1.44	0.74	0.17
II	Leptokurtic	3	3	2,6		53.00	28.07	23.40	12.93	7.83	4.63	2.76	1.53	0.80
II	Leptokurtic	4	5	3,16		54.02	28.53	22.43	11.26	6.56	3.76	1.63	1.00	0.37
III	Rectangular	3	3	2,6		47.78	25.03	20.44	11.54	6.07	3.24	1.77	0.90	0.13
IV	Mod. Skew	4	5	3,16		51.08	25.30	20.21	10.28	5.15	2.75	1.32	0.69	0.13
V	Ext. Skew	3	3	2,6		49.97	24.23	19.47	9.67	4.77	2.07	0.80	0.40	0.13
V	Ext. Skew	4	5	3,16		51.19	25.63	20.39	10.16	4.76	2.33	1.00	0.70	0.10
VI	J-Shape	3	3	2,6		50.96	23.83	19.43	9.43	4.80	2.57	1.00	0.53	0.20

region, between the empirical distributions thus obtained and the normal-theory F-distribution are described by the data in Table 1. The entry in a given row and column of this table represents the percent of mean square ratios in the empirical distribution (for sets drawn from the population identified at the left in the same row) which exceeds the percent level in the theoretical F-distribution identified at the top of the same column. For example, the entry 12.93 in the second row and fourth column of the body of the table indicates that in the empirical F-distribution for sets of 3 samples of 3 cases each ($df = 2.6$) drawn from the leptokurtic distribution, 12.93 percent of the obtained F's exceeded the value 3.46, which is the 10% point in the F-distribution for the same degrees of freedom. At this point, then, the discrepancy is $12.93 - 10.00 = 2.93\%$.

The data in the first row of Table 1 provide a check on the sampling procedures employed in this study. The method of sampling[2] used

2. The 10,000 cards (containing the criterion measures) were arranged in random order, and were then tabulated by fives to provide means and sums of squares for 2,000 samples of 5 cases each, these data being punched in a summary card for each sample of 5. The 10,000 cards were then arranged in a new random order, and again tabulated by fives to produce another 2,000 summary cards. The 4,000 summary cards were then arranged in a random order and tabulated by fours to provide the necessary data for computing the F's for 1,000 sets of 4 samples of 5 cases each. The 4,000 summary cards were then arranged in a new random order and again tabulated by fours to provide another

may be described as one of continuous sampling without replacement from a finite, but very large, population ($N = 10,000$). As will be noted in the first row of Table 1, the empirical sampling distribution of F for samples drawn from Population I contained a larger proportion of large F's than the theoretical, but the discrepancies are not significant at the 10% level. They are, however, large enough to suggest that this kind of sampling may tend to produce slightly more large F's than would be found in simple random sampling from an infinite normal population. There is no apparent logical basis for this suggestion, but if the suggestion is true, the discrepancies reported in the remainder of Table 1 are due in part to the method of sampling, rather than to lack of normality or heterogeneity of variance alone, or the effects of the latter factors are somewhat smaller than those reported.

It is evident from Table 1 that the F-distribution is amazingly insensitive to the form of the distribution of criterion measures in the parent population, granting that the same form is common to all treatment populations. Discrepancies significant at the 5% level are found only for the leptokurtic and rectangular distributions, and even then the absolute discrepancies are quite small. Apparently,

1,000 F's, and then finally arranged in a third and independent random order to provide still another 1,000 F's.

the F-distribution is practially unaffected by lack of symmetry, *per se*, in the distributions of criterion measures, but is slightly affected if the distribution of criterion measures is roughly symmetrical but either very flat or very peaked. In the latter cases, the probabilities read from the normal-theory F-table are too small to represent the true risk of a Type I error, and due allowances should be made for this in the interpretation of results. In such cases, judging by the results reported in Table 1, when the "apparent" risk (as read from the F-table) of a Type I error is 5%, the true risk may be as large as 8%, and when the apparent level of significance of an F-test is the 1% level, the actual level of significance may be the 2% level (approximately).

In the second phase of his study Norton investigated the effect of heterogeneity of variance alone upon the F-distribution. For this purpose he constructed three card populations, all of which were like Population I (normal), with the same mean, but with markedly different variances. Specifically, the population variances were approximately 25, 100, and 225, or the standard deviations 5, 10, and 15, respectively.

The instances would be rare, of course, in which the effect of the treatments in an experiment would be to bring about large differences among the variances without also affecting the means. Generally, both mean and variance would be affected together, so that if the mean of one treatment population were higher than that of the others, the variance of this population would tend to be larger also. In many such experiments, the purpose of the experimenter is not to test the hypothesis that the treatment population means are identical, but rather that they lie along some specified line, either straight or curved. If this hypothesis is true, the form of the distribution of the F employed in testing the hypothesis is independent of the form of the line, and the distribution would be the same if the means lie along a straight horizontal line (the usual null-hypothesis), or along any other line. In the second phase of his study, then,

Norton really investigated the form of the F-distribution in the general case in which a *true* hypothesis concerning the populations means is being tested under the condition that the population variances differ as described.

As in the first phase of his study, Norton selected 3,000 sets of 3 samples of 3 cases each, but this time each set consisted of 3 samples drawn one from each of the three different populations (differing variances). The F-ratio was again computed for each set (or hypothetical experiment), and the distribution of F-ratios obtained for all sets. This procedure was repeated with 3,000 sets of 3 samples of 10 cases each, yielding a second empirical F-distribution with 2 and 27 degrees of freedom. The discrepancies between these two empirical F-distributions and the corresponding normal-theory F-distributions may be inferred from the data reported in the first two lines of Table 2 in the same manner as in Table 1.

It is apparent from these results that marked heterogeneity of variance has a small but real effect on the form of the F-distribution. If one used the probabilities read from the normal-theory F-table in interpreting the results of an experiment with this degree of heterogeneity, he might think he was making a test at the 5% level when actually he was making it at the 7% level, or might think he was testing at the 1% level, when actually he was doing so at the $2+$% level of significance, etc. Accordingly, where marked (but not extreme) heterogeneity is expected, it is desirable to allow for the discrepancy by setting a slightly higher "apparent" level of significance for this test than one would otherwise employ (the "apparent" level being that indicated by the F-table). For example, if one wished the risk of a Type I error to be less than 5%, he might require that the obtained F exceed the 2.5% point in the normal-theory F-distribution. The "apparent" level of significance would then be the 2.5%, but the actual level would be the 5% level.

In a third phase of his study, Norton investigated the effect of heterogeneity in

Table 2. Phases 2, 3, and 4 of the Norton study. Per cents of mean square ratios in empirical distributions exceeding given per cent points in the normal theory F-distribution

No. Sets	Description	k	n	df	Per cent: Points:	50.00	25.00	20.00	10.00	5.00	2.50	1.00	0.50	0.10
					$df = 2,6$	.780	1.76	2.13	3.46	5.14	7.26	10.92	14.54	27.00
					$df = 2,15$	.726	1.52	1.79	2.70	3.68	4.76	6.36	7.70	11.34
					$df = 2,27$	.710	1.46	1.71	2.51	3.35	4.24	5.49	6.49	9.02
					$df = 3,8$	.860	1.67	1.95	2.92	4.07	5.43	7.59	9.60	15.83
					$df = 3,36$	.803	1.43	1.62	2.24	2.87	3.51	4.38	5.07	6.77
3333	Heterogeneous Variances	3	3	2,6		50.42	27.48	23.01	13.47	7.26	4.29	2.13	1.23	0.36
3000			3	10	2,27		49.46	26.83	21.56	11.73	6.56	3.83	2.00	1.20	0.37
3333	Heterogeneous Forms	3	3	2,6		49.89	26.85	22.56	13.23	6.72	3.84	1.65	1.02	0.15
3333			3	6	2,15		49.78	26.25	21.69	11.37	6.81	3.93	1.98	1.29	0.39
3333	Heterogeneous Forms and Variances	4	3	3,8		48.84	28.53	24.63	15.88	10.02	6.33	3.57	2.16	0.84
3000			4	10	3,36		47.35	26.90	23.13	13.37	8.10	5.30	2.93	1.90	0.87

form of distribution (accompanied by only a slight degree of heterogeneity of variance). In each "experiment" of this phase, one sample was drawn from each of three populations. The first population was the same as Population V in Figure 4, with a σ of 5.0. The second population was approximately normal, but with a limited range (5 σ's) and a σ of 7.4. The third population was exactly like Population V, except that the skew was in the opposite direction. Experimental situations of his kind are quite frequently met in educational and psychological research, when, due to the limited range of the criterion test (that is, to the effect of a low test "ceiling" or a high "floor"), the distribution of test scores is skewed in one direction for the "low" treatment group, and in the opposite direction for the "high" treatment group.

As previously noted, variations in form and variance of the type just described would usually also be accompanied by variations in the population means. That is, such variations in form and variance would most often be found in "trend" studies where the hypothesis to be tested is that the treatment-population means lie along some specified line, other than a straight horizontal line. So long as the hypo-thesis being tested is true, however, the form of the distribution of the F used to test the hypothesis is independent of the nature of the line. Accordingly, in the third phase of his study, Norton investigated the general case in which *any* true hypothesis concerning the population means is being tested, but in which the forms and variances of the populations differ in the manner described.

In this third phase of his study, Norton selected 3,333 sets of 3 samples of 3 cases each ($df = 2,6$) and also 3,333 sets of 3 samples of 6 cases each ($df = 2,15$). The discrepancies between each of the empirical F-distributions and the corresponding normal-theory F-distributions may be inferred from the data in lines 3 and 4 of Table 2. As in the case of heterogeneous variance only, the discrepancies in the extreme upper-tail region are significant, but small, and due allowances should be made for these discrepancies in interpreting the results of an F-test. Again it is remarkable how slightly this degree of heterogeneity of form and variance affects the F-distribution.

In the fourth phase of the study, Norton investigated the type of situation graphically portrayed [on p. 348]—a situation frequently met in learning experiments and trend studies in psychological research. In this phase of the study, each "experiment" involved 4 samples, drawn one from each of four different populations. The first population was the same as Population VI in Figure 4, with a σ of 2.2. The second was the same as Population V in Figure 4, with a σ of 6.2. The third population was like Population IV, except that the σ was 10.0, rather than 4.9, and the fourth population was like Population I, except that the σ was 14.9, rather than 5.0. Thus the variance of one of the populations was almost 45 times that of another, so that the heterogeneity both of form and of variance was extreme.

As in previous instances, Norton investigated the specific case in which the population means are identical, but as before, this is equivalent to investigating the general case in which any *true* hypothesis concerning the population means is being tested, the forms and variances of the populations being as described.

In this final phase of the study, Norton drew 3,333 sets of 4 samples of 3 cases each, and 3,000 sets of 4 samples of 10 cases each. The discrepancies between the two empirical F-distributions thus obtained and the corresponding normal-theory F-distributions may be determined from the data in the last two rows of Table 2.

Even with the violent departure from the theoretical requirements represented in this fourth phase of the study, the F-distributions still represent a fairly good fit to the normal-theory distribution. The discrepancy between the distributions is highly significant at nearly all points, but the absolute discrepancy is still not large enough to render the ordinary F-table valueless in such situations. True, the actual risk of a Type I error may be larger than that indicated by the ordinary F-table (about twice as large at the 1% point), but if one knows that this is the case and makes due allowance for it, one may still use the normal-theory table to good advantage.

The results of the Norton study should be extremely gratifying to anyone who has used or who contemplates using the F-test of analysis of variance in experimental situations in which there is serious doubt about the underlying assumptions of normality and homogeneity of variance. Apparently, in the great majority of situations, one need be concerned hardly at all about lack of symmetry in the distribution of criterion measures, so long as this distribution is *homogeneous* in both form and variance for the various treatment populations, and so long as it is neither markedly peaked nor markedly flat. Most non-normal distributions met in practice are probably non-normal primarily because of lack of symmetry rather than because of lack of the "normal" degree of peakedness. In general, the F-distribution seems so insensitive to the form of the distribution of criterion measure that it hardly seems worthwhile to apply any statistical test to the data to detect non-normality, even though such tests are available. Unless the departure from normality is so extreme that it can be easily detected by mere inspection of the data, the departure from normality will probably have no appreciable effect on the validity of the F-test, and the probabilities read from the F-table may be used as close approximations to the true probabilities.

The findings of the Norton study are not quite so encouraging with reference to situations in which the treatment populations are *heterogeneous*, either in form, or in variance, or in both. However, the heterogeneity must be quite extreme to be of any serious consequence. While statistical tests of heterogeneity of variance are available (one is presented in the following section), there will be relatively few situations in which any such test is required. In general, unless the heterogeneity of either form or variance is so extreme as to be readily apparent upon inspection of the data, the effect upon the F-distribution will probably be negligible. In general, when the heterogeneity in form or variance is "marked" but not "extreme", allowance may be made for this fact by setting a higher "apparent" level of significance for the tests of treatment effects than would otherwise be employed. In cases of very marked heterogeneity, for example, if one wishes the risk of a Type I error not to exceed 5%, he might require the effect to be "significant" at the 2.5% level, or if he wants the risk of a Type I error not to exceed 1%, he might set the "apparent" level of significance of the test at 0.1%.

The preceding is not meant to imply, of course, that allowance may *always* be made for heterogeneity of form or variance by "corrections" of the type suggested. On the contrary, there undoubtedly are some situation in psychological research in which the heterogeneity in either form or variance, or both, may be considerably more extreme than in any of the hypothetical situations investigated by Norton. In these situations it is not know what "corrections" should be applied to the ordinary *F*-test, and special procedures to be considered in a later section (the use of transformations) must be employed in analyzing and interpreting the results.

The Test of Homogeneity of Variance. Several tests[3] of homogeneity of variance have been suggested, of which the most useful and convenient is perhaps that devised by M. S. Bartlett. Before considering this test, we may note that an estimate of the population variance (σ^2) can be derived from each of the *a*

3. A modification of the Bartlett test which is slightly more accurate when the n_j's are very small has been provided by H. O. Hartley, "Testing the Homogeneity of a Set of Variances," *Biometrika*, vol. 31 (1940), pp. 249–255.

treatments groups by

$$\text{est'd } \sigma^2 = \sum^{n_j}(X - M_j)^2/n_j - 1.$$

We have noted also that a better estimate of σ^2 is provided by the mean square for within-groups (ms_w), which is essentially an "average" of the estimates obtained from the *a* groups.

Bartlett's test is based upon the difference between the logarithm of this "average" estimate and the sum of the logarithms of the individual estimates. More precisely, Bartlett has shown that the expression

$$\frac{2.3026}{C}\left[(N - a)\log(ms_w) - \sum_{j=1}^{a}(n_j - 1)\log\left(\frac{\sum^{n_j}(X - M_j)^2}{n_j - 1}\right)\right]$$

is distributed approximately as χ^2 with $a - 1$ *df*, the notation being precisely what we have used earlier.

The *C* is a constant $=$

$$= 1 + \frac{1}{3(a - 1)}\left[\sum_{j=1}^{a}\frac{1}{(n_j - 1)} - \frac{1}{\sum_{j=1}^{a}(n_j - 1)}\right]$$

but need not be computed if the χ^2 for the expression before division by *C* is not significant, since *C* is always larger than 1.00. The value of 2.3026 is the ratio between a natural and a common logarithm.

In one example, the application of this test is as follows:

Treatments

	A_1	A_2	A_3	A_4
$n_j =$	5	4	6	4
$\sum^{n_j}(X - M_j)^2 = \sum X^2 - \dfrac{T_j^2}{n_j} =$	13.20	14.75	6.00	2.00
$\sum^{n_j}(X - M_j)^2/(n_j - 1) =$	3.30	4.92	1.20	0.67
$\log\left[\sum^{n_j}(X - M_j)^2/(n_j - 1)\right] =$	0.51851	0.69197	0.07918	9.82607 − 10
$n_j - 1)\log\left[\sum^{n_j}(X - M_j)^2/(n_j - 1)\right] =$	2.07404	2.07591	0.39590	9.47821 − 10

$$\sum_{j}^{a}(n_j-1)\log\left[\sum^{n_j}(X-M_j)^2/(n_j-1)\right] = 4.02406$$

$$(N-a)\log ms_w = 15\times.38021 = 5.70315$$

$$\chi^2 = \frac{2.3026}{C}(5.70315-4.02406) = \frac{3.87}{C}$$

20% value of χ^2 for 3 $df = 4.642$

Hence, $\dfrac{3.87}{C}$ is not significant.

As previously noted, the usefulness of this test is quite limited. In view of the results of the Norton study, it is apparent that the test is needed at all only when the treatment groups are quite small. When the treatment groups are large, one has only to tally the distributions of criterion measures for the various treatments groups to tell by inspection if the heterogeneity is sufficiently marked to be likely to have any appreciable effect on the F-distribution. When the treatment groups are small, the Bartlett test may be needed to determine whether or not *any* heterogeneity of variance characterizes the treatment populations, but the Bartlett test will not indicate how marked the heterogeneity really is, nor how seriously it affects the validity of the usual F-test.

The Use of Transformations. The assumptions of homogeneity of variance and of normality of distribution are often intimately related, so that a serious failure to satisfy one condition is accompanied by a failure to satisfy the other. For example, in any instance in which there is a definite relationship between the means and variances of the treatment groups, there is likely also to be a tendency for some of the distributions to be sharply skewed to the right. Sometimes it is possible to overcome such difficulties by *transforming* the criterion measures into derived measures whose variances are more homogeneous and whose distributions are also more nearly normal. For example, the standard deviations of the treatment groups may tend to be linearly related to their means, as could be true in the

type of situation considered [on pp. 348–56]. In this case, if the logarithm of X or of $(1+X)$ is substituted for X as a criterion measure, it may be found that the variances of the transformed measures are much more homogeneous than those of the original measures and that the transformed distributions are much more nearly normal as well. In that case, the F-test of significance applied to the transformed measures will, of course, be more valid than that applied to the original measures. Other functions of X that have been frequently employed in transformations are its square and square root. Transformations of the type $Y = f(X)$ are appropriate only when there is a relationship between the means and variances of the treatment groups; or, if the means of the treatment groups do not differ markedly, only when the distribution of the criterion measures is of the same *form* for all treatments. If the treatments cause the variances of the criterion measures to differ but do not create differences among the means, or if they cause the variances to differ independently of the differences among the means, then no valid transformation is possible. Again, if the distributions are homogeneous in variance but differ in form of distribution, no valid transformation is possible. Sometimes the variances are homogeneous and all distributions are of the same form, but this form is one that cannot be normalized by a transformation of the type $Y = f(X)$. In this case, it may be possible to normalize the distribution by means of an "area transformation" based on a large independent sample from one of the treatment populations, or from a population known to be closely similar to this population. If the treatments have identical effects, the distribution will then, of course, be normalized for all treatment populations. This is done by transforming each value of the original measure into a derived measure whose percentile rank in a normal distribution of selected mean and variance is the same as the percentile rank of the original measure in the independent sample. Students of educational and psychological measurement will recognize the McCall "*T*-score" as a transformation of this type. Scores on educational and psychological tests are frequently normalized in this fashion, and when thus normalized may more appropriately be used in analysis of variance tests than could the original measures. There are many important types of psychological data which require transformation before the test of analysis of variance may be validly applied, and the subject of transformations is therefore of considerable importance to many psychological research workers. A thoroughgoing treatment of this subject is beyond the scope of this text but helpful discussions of this problem are readily available elsewhere.[4]

Difficulties due to the non-normality of the criterion measures may sometimes be avoided by employing a different criterion variable than that originally contemplated. Very frequently, in educational and psychological research, the choice of a criterion is quite arbitrary, and several alternate criteria may be available,

4. Students particularly interested in this subject should see C. G. Mueller, "Numerical Transformations in the Analysis of Experimental Data," *Psychological Bulletin*, vol. 46, no. 3 (May, 1949), pp. 198–223. This is perhaps the most comprehensive of available discussions of the use of transformations in psychological research and contains an excellent bibliography of forty-nine references. A useful discussion of transformations is also found in Oscar Kempthorne, *The Design and Analysis of Experiments* (New York: John Wiley and Sons, Inc., 1952), pp. 153–158.

all of which are about equally appropriate to the general purpose of the experiment, but some of which are more nearly normally distributed than others or some of which can more readily be transformed to normally distributed measures. Research workers in psychology have often caused themselves needless trouble by failing to give consideration to this possibility in the early stages of planning their experiments.

There are some experimental situations in which the data show extreme deviations from normality of distribution, and which are not amenable to transformation. This is particularly likely to be true when the criterion measures represent *frequencies of occurrence* of a certain type of behavior, such as frequency of aggressive behavior, frequency of stuttering, number of trials needed to run a maze, number of trials required to learn to perform a task, etc. With such data, the distribution is sometimes J-shaped, with a large number of undistributed cases at the zero point on the scale. Such non-continuous or discrete distributions are frequently not amenable to successful transformation, and the tests of analysis of variance may therefore not be applicable to the data. Fortunately, considerable interest has been shown recently in the development of non-parametric tests, that is, tests that make no assumptions about population parameters, and some effective work has been done in the development of such tests. Non-parametric tests will undoubtedly soon occupy a very important place in psychological research. However, all of these tests are less powerful than those assuming normality and homogeneity of variance. It is highly probable, therefore, that the more powerful tests of analysis of variance will continue indefinitely to be employed in the majority of experiments performed in education and psychology, or in all situations in which the necessary assumptions seem satisfied.

C. ALAN BONEAU

41 The Effects of Violations of Assumptions Underlying the *t* Test[1]

As psychologists who perform in a research capacity are well aware, psychological data too frequently have an exasperating tendency to manifest themselves in a form which violates one or more of the assumptions underlying the usual statistical tests of significance. Faced with the problem of analyzing such data, the researcher usually attempts to transform them in such a way that the assumptions are tenable, or he may look elsewhere for a statistical test. The latter alternative has become popular because of the proliferation of the so-called nonparametric or distribution-free methods. These techniques quite generally, however, couple their freedom from restricting assumptions with a disdain for much of the information contained within the data. For example, by classifying scores into groups above and below the median one ignores the fact that there are intracategory differences between the individual scores. As a result, tests which make no assumptions about the distribution from which one is sampling will tend not to reject the null hypothesis when it is actually false as often as will those tests which do make assumptions. This lack of power of the nonparametric tests is a decided handicap when, as is frequently the case in psychological research, a modicum of reinforcement in the form of an occasional significant result is required to maintain the research response.

Confronted with this discouraging prospect and a perhaps equally discouraging one of laboriously transforming data, performing related tests, and then perhaps having diffi-

culty in interpreting results, the researcher is often tempted simply to ignore such considerations and go ahead and run a *t* test or analysis of variance. In most cases, he is deterred by the feeling that such a procedure will not solve the problem. If a significant result is forthcoming, is it due to differences between means, or is to due to the violation of assumptions? The latter possibility is usually sufficient to preclude the use of the *t* or *F* test.

It might be suspected that one could finesse the whole problem of untenable assumptions by better planning of the experiment or by a more judicious choice of variables, but this may not always be the case. Let us examine the assumptions more closely. It will be recalled that both the *t* test and the closely related *F* test of analysis of variance are predicated on sampling from a normal distribution. A second assumption required by the deviations is that the variances of the distributions from which the samples have been taken is the same (assumption of homogeneity of variance). Thirdly, it is necessary that scores used in the test exhibit independent errors. The third assumption is usually not restrictive since the researcher can readily conduct most psychological research so that this requirement is satisfied. The first two assumptions depend for their reasonableness in part upon the vagaries inherent in empirical data and the chance shape of the sampling distribution. Certain situations also arise frequently which tend to produce results having intrinsic non-normality or heterogeneity of variance. For example, early in a paired-associate learning task, before much learning has taken place, the modal number of responses for a

1. The author wishes to express his appreciation to Thomas M. Gallie for his cooperation and assistance.

From *Psychological Bulletin*, Vol. 57, No. 1, pp. 49–64, 1960. Copyright © 1960 by the American Psychological Association, and reprinted by permission.

group will be close to zero and any deviations will be in an upward direction. The distribution of responses will be skewed and will have a small variance. With a medium number of trials, scores will tend to be spread over the whole possible range with a mode at the center, a more nearly normal distribution than before, but with greater variance. When the task has been learned by most of the group, the distribution will be skewed downward and with smaller variance. In this particular case, one would probably more closely approximate normality and homogeneity in the data by using some other measure, perhaps number of trials for mastery. In many situations this option may not be present.

There is, however, evidence that the ordinary t and F tests are nearly immune to violation of assumptions or can easily be made so if precautions are taken (17, 4, 20, 10, 18, 12, 13, 11, 14, 6, 7, 8). Journeyman psychologists have been apprised of this possibility by Lindquist (5) who summarizes the results of a study by Norton (16). Norton's technique was to obtain samples of Fs by means of a random sampling procedure from distributions having the same mean but which violated the assumptions of normality and homogeneity of variance in predetermined fashions. As a measure of the effect of the violations, Norton determined the obtained percentage of sample Fs which exceeded the theoretical 5% and 1% values from the F tables for various conditions. If the null hypothesis is true, and if the assumptions are met, the theoretical values are F values which would be exceeded by chance exactly 5% or 1% of the time. The discrepancy between these expected percentages and the obtained percentages is one useful measure of the effects of the violations.

Norton's results may be summarized briefly as follows: (a) When the samples all came from the same population, the shape of the distribution had very little effect on the percentage of F ratios exceeding the theoretical limits. For example, for the 5% level, the percentages exceeding the theoretical limits were 7.83% for a leptokurtic population

as one extreme discrepancy and 4.76% for an extremely skewed distribution as another. (b) For sampling from populations having the same shape but different variances, or having different shapes but the same variance, there was little effect on the empirical percentage exceeding theoretical limits, the average being between 6.5% and 7.0%. (c) For sampling from populations with different shapes and heterogeneous variances, a serious discrepancy between theoretical and obtained percentages occurred in some instances. On the basis of these results, Lindquist (15, p. 86) concluded that "unless the heterogeneity of either form or variance is so extreme as to be readily apparent upon inspection of the data, the effect upon the F distribution will probably be negligible."

This conclusion has apparently had surprisingly little effect upon the statistical habits of research workers (or perhaps editors) as is evident from the increasing reliance upon the less powerful nonparametric techniques in published reports. The purpose of this paper is to expound further the invulnerability of the t test and its next of kin the F test to ordinary onslaughts stemming from violation of the assumptions of normality and homogeneity. In part, this will be done by reporting results of a study conducted by the author dealing with the effect on the t test of violation of assumptions. In addition, supporting evidence from a mathematical framework will be used to bolster the argument.

To temper any imputed dogmatism in the foregoing, it should be emphasized that there are certain restrictions which preclude an automatic utilization of the t and F tests without regard for assumptions even when these tests are otherwise applicable. It is apparent, for example, that the violation of the homogeneity of variance assumption is drastically disturbing to the distribution of t's and Fs if the sample sizes are not the same for all groups, a possibility which was not considered in the Norton study. It also seems clear that in cases of extreme violations, one must have a sample size large enough to allow the statistical effects of averaging to come into play. The need for such considerations will be made apparent in the ensuing discussion. There is abundant evidence, however, that both the t and the F tests are much less affected by extreme violations of the assumptions than has been generally realized.

A Sampling Experiment

At this point we will concern ourselves with the statement of the results of a random sampling study. The procedure is one of computing a large number of t values, each based upon samples drawn at random from distributions having specified characteristics, and constructing a frequency distribution of the obtained t's. The present study was performed on the IBM 650 Electronic Computer programmed to perform the necessary operations which can be summarized as follows: (a) the generation of a random number, (b) the transformation of the random number into a random deviate from the appropriate distribution, (c) the successive accumulation of the sums and sums of squares of the random deviates until the appropriate sample size is reached, (d) the computation of a t based upon the sums and sums of sqaures of the two samples, (e) the sorting of the t's on the basis of size and sign and the construction of a frequency distribution based upon the sorting operation. The complete sequence of operations was performed internally, the end result, the frequency distribution of 1000 t's, being punched out on IBM cards.

Comments on many of the above operations are relevant and will be made according to their order above.

(a) The random numbers consisted of 10 digits, the middle 10 digits of the product of the previously generated random number and of one of a sequence of 10 permutations of the 10 digits (0, 1, 2, . . . , 9) placed as multipliers in the machine. To start the process it was necessary to place in the machine a 10 digit random number selected from a table of random numbers. The randomness of numbers

generated in such a fashion was checked by sorting 5000 of them into 50 categories on the basis of the first 2 digits. A χ^2 was computed to determine the fit of the obtained distribution to a theoretical one consisting of 100 scores in each of the 50 categories. The obtained χ^2 of 47.83 is extremely close to the 49.332 value, which is the theoretical median of the χ^2 distribution with 50 degrees of freedom.

(b) In order to obtain the random deviates (the individual random scores from the appropriate population), the random numbers obtained in the above fashion were considered to be numbers between 0 and 1 and interpreted as the cumulative probability for a particular score from the prescribed population. From a table entered in the machine, a random deviate having that probability was selected. This is identical with the procedure one uses in entering the ordinary z table to determine the score below which, say, 97.5% of the scores in the distribution lie. The obtained value, 1.96, is the deviate corresponding to that cumulative percentage. The distribution of such deviates from a normal population obtained by using a large random sample of probabilities is normally distributed. Similar tables can be constructed for other populations. The populations selected for this study were the normal, the exponential (J-shaped with a skew to the right) having a density function of $y = e^{-x}$, and the rectangular or uniform distribution. These distributions represent extremes of skewness and flatness to compare with the normal. The tables of deviates corresponding to each of the selected distributions were contained internally in the computer and were so arranged that the mean of each distribution was 0 and the variance 1. To verify these values, population means and variances based on samples of 5000 deviates from each of the three populations were estimated by the usual formulas. The results were for the normal distribution a sample mean of .0024 and a variance of 1.0118, for the exponential a mean of .0128 and a variance of 1.0475, and for the rectangular a mean of

−.0115 and a variance of .9812. All of these results could quite easily have arisen from random sampling from distributions having the assumed characteristics. To change the size of the variance of the population, all deviates were multiplied when necessary by a constant, in this case, the number 2. The resulting distribution has a mean of 0 and variance of 4. The only variances used in this study were 1 and 4.

(c) The sample sizes selected were 5 and 15.

(d) The formula used for the computation of t was the following:

$$t = \frac{M_1 - M_2}{\sqrt{\dfrac{\Sigma X_1{}^2 - N_1 M_1{}^2 + \Sigma X_2{}^2 - N_2 M_2{}^2}{N_2 + N_2 - 2}\left(\dfrac{1}{N_1} + \dfrac{1}{N_2}\right)}}$$

where M_1 and M_2 are the means of the first and second samples and N_1 and N_2 are the respective sample sizes. This expression, or an equivalent statement of it, is found in any statistics book and is undoubtedly employed in a preponderance of the research in which a t test involving nonrelated means is used. As pointed out in most statistic texts, this test is not appropriate when variances are different. Tests are available which are more or less legitimate under these conditions, but a certain amount of approximation is involved in them. It was felt, however, that the ordinary t test might under some conditions be as good an approximation as the more complex forms of t tests and that a verification of this notion was desirable. In addition, the above formula makes use of a pooled estimate of variance for the error term and in this respect is similar to the F test of analysis of variance. Because of this fact, certain results can be generalized from the t to the F test.

To summarize, random samples were drawn from populations which were either normal, rectangular, or exponential with means equal to 0 and variances of 1 or 4. For several combinations of forms and variances, t tests of the significance of the difference between sample means were computed using combinations of the sample sizes 5 and 15. For each of these

combinations, frequency distributions of sample t's were obtained on the IBM 650 Electronic Computer.

Results

The results of the sampling study will be presented in part as a series of frequency distributions in the form of bar graphs of the obtained distribution of t's for a particular condition. Upon these have been superimposed the theoretical t distribution curve for the appropriate degrees of freedom. This furnishes a rapid comparison of the extent to which the empirical distribution conforms to the theoretical.

First we shall consider these combinations possible when both of the samples are from normal distributions but variances and sample sizes may vary. Next will be considered the results of sampling from non-normal distributions, but both samples are from the same type of distribution. Finally we deal with the results of sampling from two different kinds of populations, for example, one sample from the normal distribution, and another from the exponential.

Potentially, a very large number of such combinations are possible. Limitations of the time available on the computer necessitated a paring down to a reasonable number. Although the computer is relatively fast when optimally programmed, it nevertheless required almost an hour, on the average, to complete a frequency distribution of 1000 t's. The combinations presented here are those which seemed most important at the time the study was made.

As a measure of the effect of violation of assumptions, the percentage of obtained t's which exceed the theoretical values delineating the middle 95% of the t distribution is used. For 8, 18, and 28 df which arise in the present study, the corresponding values are respectively ±2.262, ±2.101, and ±2.048. If the assumptions are met, and if the null hypothesis of equality of means is true, 5% of the obtained *t*'s should fall outside these limits. The difference between this nominal value and the actual value obtained by sampling should be a useful measure of the degree to which violation of assumptions changes the distribution of *t* scores. There is, of course, a random quality to the obtained percentage of *t*'s falling outside the theoretical limits. Hence, the obtained value should be looked upon as an approximation to the true value which should lie nearby.

In the figures and in the text, the various combinations of population, variance, and sample size will be represented symbolically in the following form: $E(0, 1)5$-$N(0, 4)15$. Here the letters E, N, and R refer to the population from which the sample was drawn, E for exponential, N for normal, and R for rectangular. The first number in the parenthesis is the mean of the population distribution, in all cases zero, while the second number is the variance. The number following the parenthesis is the sample size for that particular sample. In the example above, the first sample of Size 5 from an exponential distribution having a variance of 1. The second sample is from a normal distribution with variance of 4 and the sample size is 15.

SAMPLING FROM NORMAL DISTRIBUTIONS

In order to justify the random sampling approach utilized in this study, and partly to confirm the faith placed in the tabled values of the mathematical statisticians, the initial comparisons are between the theoretical distributions and the obtained distributions with assumptions inviolate. Figures 1 and 2 exhibit the empirical distributions of *t*'s when both samples are taken from the same normal distribution with zero mean and unit variance —designated $N(0, 1)$. In Fig. 1 both samples are of Size 5, while both are 15 in Fig. 2. The theoretical curves, one for 8 *df*, the other for 28, represent quite well the obtained dis-

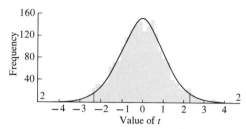
Fig. 1. Empirical distribution of *t*'s from $N(0, 1)5$-$N(0, 1)5$ and theoretical distribution with 8 *df*.

tributions. Ordinates approximately two units from the mean of the theoretical distributions mark off the respective 5% limits for rejecting the null hypothesis. In Fig. 1,[2] 5.3% of the obtained *t*'s fall outside these bounds, while in Fig. 2 only 4.0% of the sample *t*'s are in excess. Since in both cases the expected value is exactly 5%, we must attribute the discrepancy to random sampling fluctuations. The size of these discrepancies should be useful measures in evaluating the discrepancies which will be encountered under other conditions of sampling. For examples of 2000 *t*'s a discrepancy as large as 1% from the nominal 5% value evidently occurs frequently, and for this reason should not be considered as evidence to reject the theoretical distribution as an approximation to the empirical one.

As an initial departure from the simplest cases just presented, Fig. 3 compares theoretical and empirical distributions when sam-

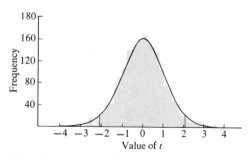
Fig. 2. Empirical distribution of *t*'s from $N(0, 1)15$-$N(0, 1)15$ and theoretical distribution with 28 *df*.

2. The numbers in the tails of some of the figures report the number of obtained *t*'s falling outside the boundaries.

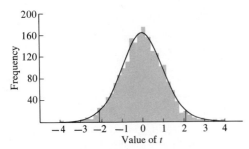

Fig. 3. Empirical distribution of t's from $N(0, 1)5$-$N(0, 1)15$ and theoretical distribution with 18 df.

ples are taken from the same $N(0, 1)$ population, but the first sample size is 5, the second is 15—that is, $N(0, 1)5$-$N(0, 1)15$. While this in no sense is a violation of the assumptions of the t test, it is interesting to note that again sampling fluctuations have produced an empirical distribution with 4.0% of the t's falling outside the nominal 5% limits.

The violation of the assumption of homogeneity of variance has effects as depicted in Fig. 4. Here the obtained distribution is based upon two samples of Size 5, one from $N(0, 1)$ and the other from $N(0, 4)$. The fit is again seen to be close between theoretical and empirical distributions, and 6.4% of the obtained t's exceed the theoretical 5% limits. By increasing the sample size to 15, a distribution results (not shown here) for which only 4.9% of the t's fall outside the nominal limits. It would seem that increasing the sample size produces a distribution which conforms rather closely to the t distribution. As will be seen later, this is a quite general result based upon mathematical considerations, the im-

plications of which are important to the argument. For the moment it is evident that differences in variance at least in the ratio of 1 to 4 do not seriously affect the accuracy of probability statements made on the basis of the t test.

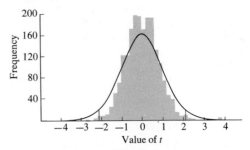

Fig. 5. Empirical distribution of t's from N-$(0,1)5$-$N(0, 4)15$ and theoretical distribution with 18 df.

The last conclusion is true only so long as the size of both samples is the same. If the variances are different, with the present set of conditions there are two combinations of variance and sample size possible. In one case the first sample may be of Size 5 and drawn from the population with the smaller variance, while the second sample of Size 15 is drawn from the population having the larger variance—$N(0, 1)5$-$N(0, 4)15$. In the second case the small sample size is coupled with the larger variance, the larger sample size with the smaller variance—$N(0, 4)5$-$N(0, 1)15$. The respective results of such sampling are presented in Fig. 5 and 6. The empirical distributions are clearly not approximated by the t distribution. For the distribution of Fig. 5, only 1% of the obtained t's exceed the nominal 5% values,

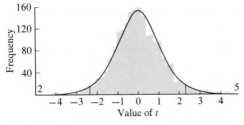

Fig. 4. Empirical distribution of t's from $N(0, 1)5$-$N(0, 4)5$ and theoretical distribution with 8 df.

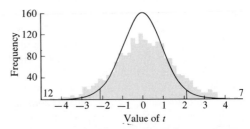

Fig. 6. Empirical distribution of t's from $N(0, 4)5$-$N(0, 1)15$ and theoretical distribution with 18 df.

while in Fig. 6, 16% of the t's fall outside those limits.

There are good mathematical reasons why a difference in sample size should produce such decided discrepancies when the variances are unequal. Recall that $\Sigma(X-M)^2/(N-1)$ is an estimate of the variance of the population from which the sample is drawn. Hence, $\Sigma(X-M)^2$ will in the long run be equal to $(N-1)\sigma^2$. The formula used in this study for computing t makes use of this fact and, in addition, under the assumption that the variances of the populations from which the two samples are drawn are equal, pools the sum of the squared deviations from the respective sample means to get a better estimate. That is $\Sigma(X_1-M_1)^2 + \Sigma(X_2-M_2)^2$ is an estimate of $(N_1-1)\sigma_1^2$ $(N_2-1)\sigma_2^2$. If $\sigma_1^2 = \sigma_2^2 = \sigma^2$ (homogeneity of variance), then the sums estimate $(N_1+N_2-2)\sigma^2$. Hence,

$$\frac{\Sigma(X_1-M_1)^2+\Sigma(X_2-M_2)^2}{N_1+N_2-2} \quad \text{Eq. 1}$$

is an estimate of σ^2. If $\sigma_1^2 \neq \sigma_2^2$ the estimating procedure is patently illegitimate, the resulting value depending in a large measure upon the combination of sample size and variance used. For example, the case $N(0, 1)5$-$N(0, 4)$ has $N_1 = 5$, $N_2 = 15$, $\sigma_1^2 = 1$, $\sigma_2^2 = 4$, and $N_1+N_2-2 = 18$. With these values, Formula 1 has an expected value of $[(4\cdot1)+(14\cdot4)]/18 = 3.33$. Using the appropriate values for the other situation, $N(0, 4)5$-$N(0, 1)15$, the result of formula 1 is $[(4\cdot4)+(14\cdot1)]/18 = 1.67$. This means that on the average, the denominator for the t test will be larger for the first case than for the second. If the sample differences between means were of the same magnitude for the two cases, obviously more "significant" t's would emerge when the denominator is smaller. It so happens that when this latter condition exists, the variance of the numerator also tends to be greater than in the other condition, a fact which accentuates the differences between the two empirical distributions.

Welch (20) has shown mathematically that in the case of sample sizes of 5 and 15, a state which prevails here, the percentage of t's

exceeding the nominal 5% value varies as a function of the ratio of the two population variances and can be as low as 0% and as high as 31.3%. If $N_1 = N_2$ there is never much bias, except perhaps in the case in which the sample sizes are both 2. For $N_1 = N_2 = 10$, the expected value of the percentage of t's exceeding the nominal 5% limits varies between 5% and 6.5% regardless of the difference between the variances. For larger sample sizes, the discrepancy tends to be even less.

Since the pooling procedure for estimating the population variance is used in ordinary analysis of variance techniques, it would seem that the combination of unequal variances and unequal sample sizes might play havoc with F test probability statements. That is, a combination of large variance and large sample size should tend to make the F test more conservative than the nominal value would lead one to expect, and, as with the t test, small variance and large sample size should produce a higher percentage of "significant" Fs than expected. These conclusions are based upon a very simple extension to more than two samples of the explanation for the behavior of the t test probabilities with unequal sample sizes.

A more sophisticated mathematical handling of the problem by Box (6) reaches much the same conclusions for the simple-randomized analysis of variance. In a table in his article are given exact (i.e., mathematically determined) probabilities of exceeding the 5% point when variances are unequal. In this case, sampling is assumed to be from normal distributions. If the sample sizes are the same, the probability given for equal sample sizes ranges from 5.55% to 7.42%, for several combinations of variances, and numbers of samples. If, when variances are different, the samples are of different sizes, large discrepancies from the nominal values result. Combining large sample and large variance lessens the probability of obtaining a "significant" result to much less than 5%, just as we have seen for the t test. In a subsequent article, Box (7) presents some results from two-way analysis of variance. Since these designs generally have equal cell frequencies the results are not too far from expected. His figures all run within 2% of the 5% value expected if all assumptions were met.

It would seem then that both empirically and mathematically there can be demonstrated only a minor effect on the validity of probability statements caused by heterogeneity of variance, provided the sizes of the samples are the same. This applies to the F as well as the t test. If however, the sample sizes are different, major errors in interpretation may result if normal curve thinking is used.

SAMPLING FROM IDENTICAL NON-NORMAL DISTRIBUTIONS: (EQUAL VARIANCES)

Let us now proceed to violate the other main assumption, that of normality of distribution from which sampling takes place. At this time we will consider the t distributions arising when both samples are taken from the same non-normal distribution. The distributions shown here, and all subsequent ones, are based upon only 1000 t's, and hence will exhibit somewhat more column to column fluctuation than the preceding distributions.

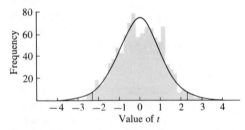

Fig. 7. Empirical distribution of t's from $E(0, 1)5$-$E(0, 1)5$ and theoretical distribution with 8 df.

Figure 7 compares the theoretical t distribution and the empirical distribution obtained from two samples of Size 5 from the exponential distribution—$E(0, 1)5$-$E(0, 1)5$. The fit is fairly close, but the proportion of cases in the tails seems less for the empirical distribution than for the theoretical. By count, 3.1% of the obtained t's exceed the nominal 5%

values—that is, the test in this case seems slightly conservative. If both sample sizes are raised to 15 (distribution not shown here), the corresponding percentage of obtained t's is 4.0%. While this is probably not an appreciably better fit than for samples of Size 5, we shall see later that there are theoretical reasons to suspect that increasing the sample size should better the approximation of the empirical curve by the theoretical no matter what the parent population may be.

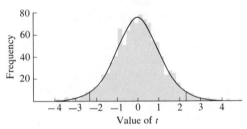

Fig. 8. Empirical distribution of t's from $R(0, 1)5$-$R(0, 1)5$ and theoretical distribution with 8 df.

If both samples are of Size 5 from the same rectangular distribution—$R(0, 1)5$-$R(0, 1)5$—the result is as depicted in Fig. 8. The fit of theoretical curve to empirical data here is as good as any thus far observed. The percentage of obtained t's exceeding the 5% values is 5.1% in this particular case. For the case in which the sample sizes are both 15 (not shown here), the fit is equally good, with 5.0% of the cases falling outside of the nominal 5% bounds.

SAMPLING FROM NON-NORMAL DISTRIBUTIONS: (UNEQUAL VARIANCES)

We may assume that if the variances are unequal, and at the same time the sample sizes are different, the resulting distributions from non-normal populations will be affected in the same way as the distributions derived from normal populations, and for the same reasons. These cases will not be considered.

If sampling is in sizes of 5 from two exponential distributions, one with a variance of 1, and the other of 4, a skewed distribution of obtained t's emerges (not shown here). We shall discover that a skewed distribution of *t*'s generally arises when the sampling is from distributions which are different in degree of skewness or asymmetry. (For an explanation, see discussion of $E(0, 1)5$-$N(0, 1)5$ below.) Apparently, the effect of increasing the variance of the exponential distribution as in the present case—$E(0, 1)5$-$E(0, 4)5$—is to make the negative sample means arising from the distribution with larger variance even more negative than those from the distribution with smaller variance. In terms of percentage exceeding the nominal 5% limits for this case, the value is 8.3%, of which 7.6% comes from the skewed tail. This combination of variances and distribution was not tested with larger samples, but we shall see when comparing exponential and normal distributions that an increase in the sample size decreases the skew of the obtained *t* distribution there. Theoretically, this decrease should occur in almost all cases, including the present one.

The result is much less complicated if, while variances are different, the sampling is from symmetrical rectangular distributions—$R(0, 1)$-$R(0, 4)5$. For this small sample situation, (not illustrated), there occurs a distribution of obtained *t*'s having 7.1% of the values exceeding the nominal 5% points. This is roughly the same magnitude as the corresponding discrepancy from normal distributions. For the normal, it will be recalled that an increase of the sample sizes to 15 decreased the obtained percentage to 4.9%. There is no reason to believe that increasing the size of the rectangular samples would not have the same effect. However, time did not permit the determination of this distribution.

SAMPLING FROM TWO DIFFERENT DISTRIBUTIONS

By drawing the first sample from a distribution having one shape, and by drawing the second from a distribution having another shape (other than shape differences arising from heterogeneity of variance), yet another way has been found to do violence to the integrity of the assumptions underlying the *t* test.

Perhaps the least violent of these happenings is that in which at least one of the populations is normal.

When one sample is from the exponential distribution and the other from the normal, the interesting result shown in Fig. 9 occurs.

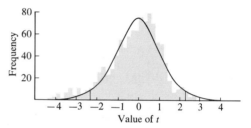

Fig. 9. Empirical distribution of *t*'s from $E(0, 1)5$-$N(0, 1)5$ and theoretical distribution with 8 *df*.

This is the small sample case—$E(0, 1)5$-$N(0, 1)5$. It will be recalled that for skewed distributions the mean and median are at different points. In the exponential distributions, for example, the mean is at the 63rd centile. If samples from the exponential distribution are small, there will be a tendency for the sample mean to be less than the population mean, obviously since nearly two thirds of the scores are below that mean. Since the population mean of the present distributions is 0, the result will be a preponderance of negative sample means for small samples. If the other sample is taken from a symmetrical distribution, which would tend to produce as many positive as negative sample means, the resulting distribution of obtained *t*'s would not balance about its zero point, an imbalance exacerbated by small samples. In Fig. 9, 7.1% of the obtained cases fall outside the 5% limits, with most, 5.6%, lying in the skewed tail. The effect of increasing the sample size to 15 is to normalize the distribution considerably; the resulting curve, Fig. 10, is fairly well approximated by the *t* distribution. One of the tails, however, does contain a disproportionate share of the cases, 4.2% to 0.9% for the other tail, or a total of 5.1% falling outside the nominal 5% limits. Nevertheless, the degree to which the theoretical

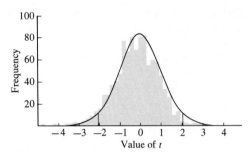

Fig. 10. Empirical distribution of t's from $E(0, 1)15$-$N(0, 1)15$ and theoretical distribution with 28 df.

and empirical distributions coincide under these conditions is striking. It seems likely that if both samples were each of Size 25, the resulting sample distribution of t's would be virtually indistinguishable from the t distribution for 48 df, or the next best thing, the normal curve itself. To test this hypothesis, an additional empirical t distribution based on sample sizes of 25 from these same exponential and normal populations was obtained (not shown here). The results nicely confirm the presumption. Comparison with the usual 5% values reveals 4.6% of the empirical t's surpassing them. Whereas with the smaller samples the ratio of t's in the skewed tail to those in the other tail is roughly 80:20, the corresponding ratio for the larger sample case is 59:41. Clearly, the increase in sample sizes has tended to normalize the distribution of t's.

For these conditions, involving rather drastic violation of the mathmatical assumptions of the test, the t test has been observed to fare well with an adequate sample size. Such a state of affairs is to be expected theoretically. By invoking a few theorems of mathematical statistics it can be shown that if one samples from any two populations for which the Central Limit Theorem holds, (almost any population that a psychologist might be confronted with), no matter what the variances may be, the use of equal sample sizes insures that the resulting distribution of t's will approach to normality as a limit. It would appear from the present results that the

approach to normality is rather rapid, since samples of sizes of 15 are generally sufficient to undo most of the damage inflicted by violation of assumptions. Only in extreme cases, such as the last which involves distributions differing in skew, would it seem that slightly larger sizes are prescribed. Thus it would appear that the t test is functionally a distribution-free test, providing the sample sizes are sufficiently large (say, 30, for extreme violations) and equal.

The distributions arising when sampling is from the normal and the rectangular distributions—$N(0, 1)5$-$R(0, 1)5$ and $N(0, 1)15$-$R(0, 1)15$—would further tend to substantiate this claim. The respective percentages exceeding the 5% nominal values are 5.6% and 4.6% from the empirical distributions for these cases, the distributions of t's being symmetrical and close to the theoretical (not shown).

The only other combination examined in the sampling study is the uninteresting case of exponential and rectangular distributions. This distribution (not shown) is again skewed with the effect of increase of sample size from 5 to 15 to cut down the skew and to decrease the percentage of cases falling outside the theoretical 5% values from 6.4% to 5.6%. For those cases falling outside the nominal 5% values, the ratio is 79:21 for the smaller samples. This is changed to 69:31 for the sample size of 15. Here again it would seem that larger sample sizes would be required to insure the validity of probability statements utilizing the t distribution as a model.

The results of the total study are summarized in Table 1 which gives for each combination of population, variance, and sample size (a) the percentage of obtained t's falling outside the nominal 5% probability limits of the ordinary t distribution, and (b) the percentage of obtained t's falling outside the 1% limits. The combinations are represented symbolically as before. The table is divided into two parts, the first part presenting information on the empirical distributions which are intrinsically symmetrical. The second part is based on the intrinsically nonsymmetrical distributions, additional information in this section of the table being the percentage of obtained *t*'s falling in the larger of the tails. The percentage for the smaller tail may be obtained by subtraction of the percentage in the larger tail from the total.

Table 1. Obtained percentages of cases falling outside the appropriate tabled *t* values for the 5% and 1% level of significance

Symmetric distributions	Obtained percentage at	
	5% level	1% level
$N(0, 1)5-N(0, 1)5$	5.3	0.9
$N(0, 1)15-N(0, 1)15$	4.0	0.8
$N(0, 1)5-N(0, 1)15$	4.0	0.6
$N(0, 1)5-N(0, 4)5$	6.4	1.8
$N(0, 1)15-N(0, 4)15$	4.9	1.1
$N(0, 1)5-N(0, 4)15$	1.0	0.1
$N(0, 4)5-N(0, 1)15$	16.0	6.0
$E(0, 1)5-E(0, 1)5$	3.1	0.3
$E(0, 1)15-E(0, 1)15$	4.0	0.4
$R(0, 1)5-R(0, 1)5$	5.1	1.0
$R(0, 1)15-R(0, 1)15$	5.0	1.5
$R(0, 1)5-R(0, 4)5$	7.1	1.9
$N(0, 1)5-R(0, 1)5$	5.6	1.0
$N(0, 1)15-R(0, 1)15$	5.6	1.1

Asymmetric distributions	Obtained percentage at			
	5% level		1% level	
	Total	Larger Tail	Total	Larger Tail
$E(0, 1)5-N(0, 1)5$	7.1	5.6	1.9	1.9
$E(0, 1)15-N(0, 1)15$	5.1	4.2	1.4	1.2
$E(0, 1)25-N(0, 1)25$	4.6	2.7	1.3	1.1
$E(0, 1)5-R(0, 1)5$	6.4	5.0	3.3	2.5
$E(0, 1)15-R(0, 1)15$	5.6	3.9	1.6	1.2
$E(0, 1)5-E(0, 4)5$	8.3	7.6	1.7	1.7

Certain implications of the table should be discussed. In the Norton study, more severe distortions sometimes occurred with significance levels of 1% and .1% than appeared with the 5% level. The inclusion in Table 1 of the percentages of obtained *t*'s falling outside the nominal 1% values makes possible the comparison of the 1% and 5% results. The 1% values seem to be approximately what would be expected considering that sampling fluctuations are occurring. It was not felt feasible to determine the results for the .1% level since with only 1000 or 2000 cases the number of obtained *t*'s falling outside the prescribed limits was negligible in most cases.

It is possible, however, that the distortions in the apparent level of significance are more drastic for the smaller α values.

All the results and discussion have been limited thus far to the two-tailed *t* test. With notable exceptions, the conclusions we have reached can be applied directly to the one-tailed *t* test as well. The exceptions involve those distributions which are intrinsically *asymmetric* (see Table 1). In these distributions a preponderance of the obtained *t*'s fall in one tail. Depending upon the particular tail involved in the one-tailed test the use of *t* should produce too many or too few significant results when sampling is from a combination of populations from which an asymmetric *t* distribution is expected. It seems impossible to make any simple statements about the behavior of the tails in the general case of asymmetric *t* distribution except to say that such distributions are expected whenever the skew of the two parent populations is different. The experimenter must determine for each particular instance the direction of skew of the expected distribution and act accordingly. Table 1 gives for the intrinsically asymmetric distributions the total percentage of obtained *t*'s falling outside the theoretical 5% and 1% limits and the percentage in the larger tail. From these values can be assessed the approximate magnitude of the bias incurred when a one-tailed test is used in specific situations.

Discussion and Conclusions

Having violated a number of assumptions underlying the *t* test, and finding that, by and large, such violations produce a minimal effect on the distribution of *t*'s, we must conclude that the *t* test is a remarkably *robust* test in the technical sense of the word. This term was introduced by Box (1953) to characterize statistical tests which are only inconsequentially affected by a violation of the underlying assumptions. Every statistical test is in part a test of the assumptions upon which it is based. For example, the null hypothesis of a particular test may be concerned with sample means. If, however, the assumptions under-lying the test are not met, the result may be "significant" even though the population means are the same. If the statistical test is relatively insensitive to violations of the assumptions other than the null hypothesis, and, hence, if probability statements refer primarily to the null hypotheses, it is said to be robust. The t and F tests apparently possess this quality to a high degree.

In this particular context, an important example of a test lacking robustness is Bart-lett's test for homogeneity of variance (4). Box (5) has shown that this test is extremely sensi-tive to non-normality and will under some conditions be prone to yield "significant" results even if variances are equal. For ex-ample, Box tables a number of exact probabili-ties of exceeding the 5% normal theory signi-ficance level in the Bartlett test for various levels of λ_2, the kurtosis parameter, for differ-ent quantities of variances being compared. As an extreme case, if $\lambda_2 = 2$ (i.e., a peaked distribution) with 30 variances being tested, the probability of rejecting the hypothesis at the nominal .05 level is actually .849. If $\lambda_2 = -1$ (i.e., a flat distribution), the proba-bility is .00001. Note that in both these cases, all variances are actually equal. Box, realizing that in the case of equal sample sizes the analysis of variance is affected surprisingly little by heterogeneous variance and non-normality, concludes that the use of the non-robust Bartlett test to "make the preliminary test on variances is rather like putting out to sea in a rowing boat to find out whether condi-tions are sufficiently calm for an ocean liner to leave port!" Apparently, as reported in this same article, other commonly used tests for evaluating homogeneity are subject to the same weakness.

We may conclude that for a large number of different situations confronting the re-searcher, the use of the ordinary t test and its associated table will result in probability state-ments which are accurate to a high degree, even though the assumptions of homogeneity of variance and normality of the underlying

distributions are untenable. This large number of situations has the following general charac-teristics: (a) the two sample sizes are equal or nearly so, (b) the assumed underlying popula-tion distributions are of the same shape or nearly so. (If the distributions are skewed they should have nearly the same variance.) If these conditions are met, then no matter what the variance differences may be, samples of as small as five will produce results for which the true probability of rejecting the null hypothesis at the .05 level will more than likely be within .03 of that level. If the sample size is as large as 15, the true probabilities are quite likely within .01 of the nominal value. That is to say, the percentage of times the null hypothesis will be rejected when it is actually true will tend to be between 4% and 6% when the nominal value is 5%.

If the sample sizes are unequal, one is in no difficulty provided the variances are compen-satingly equal. A combination of unequal sample sizes and unequal variances, however, automatically produces inaccurate probability statements which can be quite different from the nominal values. One must in this case resort to different testing procedures, such as those by Cochran and Cox (9), Satterthwaite (19), and Welch (21). The Welch procedure is interesting since it has been extended by Welch (22) to cover the simple randomized analysis of variance which suffers the same defect as the t test when confronted with both unequal variance and unequal sample sizes. The Fisher-Behrens procedure suggested by many psychologically oriented statistical text-books has had its validity questioned (3) and, hence, is ignored by some statisticians (e.g., 1, p. 82).

If the two underlying populations are not the same shape, there seems to be little difficulty if the distributions are both sym-metrical. If they differ in skew, however, the distribution of obtained t's has a tendency itself to be skewed, having a greater percentage of obtained t's falling outside of one limit than the other. This may tend to bias probability statements. Increasing the sample size has the effect of removing the skew, and, due to the Central Limit Theorem and others, the normal distribution is approached by this maneuver. By the time the sample sizes reach 25 or 30, the approach should be close enough that one can, in effect, ignore the effects of violations of assumptions except for extremes. Since this is so, the *t* test is seen to be functionally non-parametric or distribution-free. It also retains its power in some situations (11). There is, unfortunately, no guarantee that the *t* and *F* tests are uniformly most powerful tests. It is possible, even probable, that certain of the distribution-free methods are more powerful than the *t* and *F* tests when sampling is from some unspecified distributions or combination of distributions. At present, little can be said to clarify the situation. Much more research in this area needs to be done.

Since the *t* and *F* tests of analysis of variance are intimately related, it can be shown that many of the statements referring to the *t* test can be generalized quite readily to the *F* test. In particular, the necessity for equal sample sizes, if variances are unequal, is important for the same reasons in the *F* test of analysis of variance as in the *t* test. A number of the cited articles have demonstrated both mathematically and by means of sampling studies that most of the statements we have made do apply to the *F* test. It is suggested that psychological researchers feel free to utilize these powerful techniques where applicable in a wider variety of situations, the present emphasis on the nonparametric methods notwithstanding.

References

1. Anderson, R. L., & Bancroft, T. A. *Statistical theory in research.* New York: McGraw-Hill, 1952.
2. Bartlett, M. S. The effect of non-normality on the *t*-distribution. *Proc. Camb. Phil. Soc.*, 1935, 31, 223–231.
3. Bartlett, M. S. The information available in small samples. *Proc. Camb. Phil. Soc.*, 1936, 32, 560–566.
4. Bartlett, M. S. Properties of sufficiency and statistical tests. *Proc. Roy. Soc. (London)*, 1937, 160, 268–282.
5. Box, G. E. P. Non-normality and tests on variances. *Biometrika*, 1953, 40, 318–335.
6. Box, G. E. P. Some theorems on quadratic forms applied in the study of analysis of variance problems, I. Effect of inequality of variance in the one-way classification. *Ann. of math. Statist.*, 1954, 25, 290–302.
7. Box, G. E. P. Some theorems on quadratic forms applied in the study of analysis of variance problems, II. Effects of inequality of variance and of correlation between errors in the two-way classification. *Ann. of math. Statist.*, 1954, 25, 484–498.
8. Box, G. E. P., & Andersen, S. L. Permutation theory in the derivation of robust criteria and the study of departures from assumption. *J. Roy. Statist. Soc. (Series B)*, 1955, 17, 1–34.
9. Cochran, W. G., & Cox, G. M. *Experimental designs.* New York: Wiley, 1950.
10. Daniels, H. E. The effect of departures from ideal conditions other than non-normality on the *t* and *z* tests of significance. *Proc. Camb. Phil. Soc.*, 1938, 34, 321–328.
11. David, F. N., & Johnson, N. L. The effect of non-normality on the power function of the *F*-test in the analysis of variance. *Biometrika*, 1951, 38, 43–57.
12. Gayen, A. K. The distribution of the variance ratio in random samples of any size drawn from non-normal universes. *Biometrika*, 1950, 37, 236–255. (a)
13. Gayen, A. K. Significance of difference between the means of two non-normal samples. *Biometrika*, 1950, 37, 399–408. (b)
14. Horsnell, G. The effect of unequal group variances on the *F*-test for the homogeneity of group means. *Biometrika*, 1953, 40, 128–136.
15. Lindquist, E. F. *Design and analysis of experiments in psychology and education.* Boston: Houghton Mifflin, 1953.
16. Norton, D. W. An empirical investigation of some effects of non-normality and heterogeneity on the *F*-distribution. Unpublished doctoral dissertation, State Univer. of Iowa, 1952.
17. Pearson, E. S. The analysis of variance in the case of non-normal variation. *Biometrika*, 1931, 23, 114–133.
18. Quensel, C. E. The validity of the *Z*-criterion when the variates are taken from different normal populations. *Skand. Aktuarietids*, 1947, 30, 44–55.
19. Satterthwaite, F. E. An approximate distribution of estimates of variance components. *Biomet. Bull.*, 1946, 2, 110–114.
20. Welch, B. L. The significance of the difference between two means when the population variances are unequal. *Biometrika*, 1937, 29, 350–362.

21. Welch, B. L. The generalization of Student's problem when several different population variances are involved. *Biometrika*, 1947, 34, 28–35.

22. Welch, B. L. On the comparison of several mean values: An alternative approach. *Biometrika*, 1951, 38, 330–336.

BELA O. BAKER   CURTIS F. HARDYCK
LEWIS F. PETRINOVICH

42 Weak Measurements vs. Strong Statistics: An Empirical Critique of S. S. Stevens' Proscriptions on Statistics[1]

The disagreement between those who belong to what Lubin (6) called the "school of 'weak measurement' theorists" and those who belong to what might be called the school of "strong statistics" has persisted for a number of years with little apparent change of attitude on either side. Stevens, as the leading spokesman for the weak measurement school, has asserted (14) and reasserted (15, 16) the view that measurement scales are models of object relationships and, for the most part, rather poor models which can lead one far astray from the truth if the scores they yield are added when they should only be counted. At least two current statistics texts intended for psychologists (11, 12) present this view as gospel.

Opposing this view, an assortment of statistically minded psychologists—e.g., Lord (5), Burke (3), Anderson (1), McNemar (7), and Hays (4) have argued that statistics apply to numbers rather than to things and that the formal properties of measurement scales, as

such, should have no influence on the choice of statistics. Savage (10), a statistician, has supported this point of view, stating: "I know of no reason to limit statistical procedures to those involving arithmetic operations consistent with the scale properties of the observed quantities." In other words, a statistical test answers the question it is designed to answer whether measurement is weak or strong.

In his widely cited discussion of measurement, Stevens (14) distinguished four classes of scales: Nominal, ordinal, interval, and ratio, and specified the arithmetic operations (and hence the statistics) which are permissible for each scale. Nominal scales consist simply of class names and can be treated only by counting operations and frequency statistics. Ordinal scales are developed by demonstrating that some objects have more of a particular quality than do other objects and representing numerically this order among objects. Lacking units, the numbers of an ordinal scale cannot be added, subtracted, multiplied, or divided, but they can be treated by order statistics such as the median or the rank-order correlation. Interval scales represent equal increments in the magnitudes of an object property by equal numerical increments. An

1. We are grateful to Professor Jack Block, Professor Quinn McNemar, and Miss Mary Epling for their many helpful suggestions throughout this study. We are also indebted to Mrs. Eleanor Krasnow who developed and tested the computer programs used in this study.

From *Educational and Psychological Measurement*, Vol. XXVI, No. 2, 1966. By permission of G. Frederic Kuder.

increase of one unit in any region of an interval scale represents the same increment in the object property as does an increase of one unit in any other region of the scale. Scores from interval scales can be added and subtracted and hence such statistics as the mean, the standard deviation, and the product-moment correlation can be used. Ratio scales add a true zero point to equal intervals and can be multiplied, divided, and treated by subtle statistics which are of little concern to most psychologists.

Although Stevens develops his rationale for relating measurements and statistics almost exclusively in terms of descriptive statistics, he introduces the issue of hypothesis testing somewhat obliquely in his discussions of invariance of results under scale transformations (14, 15). He says, "The basic principle is this: Having measured a set of items by making numerical assignments in accordance with a set of rules, we are free to change the assignments by whatever group of transformations will preserve the empirical information in the scale: These transformations, depending on which group they belong to, will upset some statistical measures and leave others unaffected (15, p. 30)."

If parametric significance tests, such as t or F are used, the permissible transformations are linear. Only then will invariant results be found in comparing groups. An implication of this point of view, which is not made explicit by Stevens, is that if a scale is viewed as a model of object relationships, then any scale transformation is a transformation of those relationships. Hence the problem of invariance of results under scale transformations raises the following question: Can we make correct decisions about the nature of reality if we disregard the nature of the measurement scale when we apply statistical tests?

This aspect of Stevens' position has apparently been ignored by many of his critics. Anderson (1) dismisses out of hand any restriction on the uses of t arising from the nature of the measurements to which it is applied but discusses the question of invari-

ance of results under scale transformations seriously and at length before concluding that: "The practical problems of invariance or generality of results far transcend measurement scale typology" (p. 316).

The aspects of the problem as related to descriptive and inferential statistics are as follows: The problem for descriptive statistics as presented by Stevens (14, 15, 16) concerns the relationship of the value of a particular statistic computed on obtained measurements to the value of the same statistic computed under conditions of perfect measurement. The argument is that the farther the measurement model departs from the underlying properties of the objects being measured, the less accurate the statistics. In other words, this aspect is concerned with precision of measurement.

In making statistical inferences, however, the issue is whether one will arrive at the same probability estimates from different types of measurement scales. Given the condition that a measurement scale may be a very poor model indeed of the properties of the objects under study, the question of the effect of the scale on the sampling distribution of a statistic remains unanswered. Where hypothesis testing is the issue, the appropriate question is: Do statistics computed on measures which are inaccurate descriptions of reality distribute differently than the same statistics computed under conditions of perfect measurement? If not, then a research worker who has nothing better than an ordinal scale to work with may have to face the problem of more precise measurement for descriptive purposes, but at least the probability decisions he may make from his ordinal measurements will not be inappropriate for parametric statistical models.

In view of the importance of the issue raised by Stevens for users of statistics, it is surprising, as Lubin (6) notes, that so few detailed discussions of the problem are available. If Stevens is correct, then psychologists should be disturbed about the state of their research literature. Since it can be safely asserted that most measurements in psychology yield scales which are somewhere between ordinal and interval scales, many psychologists may have been propagating fiction when they have made statistical inferences based on significance tests inappropriate to anything less than interval measurements. If Stevens' position is correct, it should be emphasized more intensively; if it is incorrect, something should be done to alleviate the lingering feelings of guilt that plague research workers who deliberately use statistics such as t on weak measurements.

A test of the issue would seem to require a comparison of the sampling distribution of a statistic computed under conditions of "perfect" measurement with the sampling distribution of the same statistic based on imperfect measurements. Since it is not possible to obtain such "perfect" measurements, this comparison is manifestly impossible. As noted above, however, Stevens has suggested that the main issue is that of invariance of results when measurement scales are transformed. Cast in these terms, the problem can be examined empirically. All that is required is that the sampling distribution of a statistic based on one set of scores be compared with the sampling distribution of the same statistic based on scores which are not "permissible" transformations of the first set. If Stevens is right, these sampling distributions should differ in some important way. If they do not, then the nature of the measurement scale is, within potentially determinable limits, an irrelevant consideration when one chooses an hypothesis testing statistic.

Method

The statistic selected for study was Student's t. Not only is this one of the most commonly used statistics in psychology but it also has the advantage of having been demonstrated empirically to be relatively robust in the face of violations of the assumptions of normality and equality of variances (8, 2).

The first set of scores used—which will be referred to as criterion (unit-interval) scores—comprised the cardinal numbers from 1 to 30. Three populations of 1000 scores each were constructed by assigned frequencies to the unit-interval scores to approximate as closely as possible the expected frequencies for 1) a normal distribution, 2) a rectangular distribution, and 3) an exponential distribution ($f = 1 + 275^{(e - .25 \times)}$).

According to Stevens (14), when one uses the mean or standard deviation the permissible score transformations are linear. And so, to evaluate this proscription, 35 non-linear transformations of the unit-interval scores were constructed. These fell into three subsets, each designed to simulate a common measurement problem in psychology. The rationale for this approach is that an investigator can almost always develop a measuring device that looks as if it yields scores with equal intervals. However, relations among the objects represented by these numbers may not be equal—this is, of course, Stevens' main concern—and consequently by producing non-linear transformations of cardinal numbers, a class of situations is produced directly analogous to the situation that obtains when a measurement scale correctly represents the order among objects but incorrectly represents the magnitude of differences between objects. A statistic such as t, it is argued, cannot be used with such a measuring device, since the operations of addition, subtraction, multiplication, and division are inappropriate—a condition which rather limits the investigator seeking statistical support for his conclusions.

The first set of transformations (1 through 15) was constructed to simulate the situation in which an ordinal scale is achieved but interval sizes vary randomly. This may often be the case when the sum of responses in a keyed direction on a personality inventory is used as a trait measure. The first score of each transformation was the number 1, to which was added a number selected at random within pre-set limits to produce the second score. Another random number was then added to the second score to produce the third number, continuing until 30 scores had been developed. With this technique, the intervals between successive scores could vary randomly from 1 to a pre-selected maximum. In order to examine the effects of the magnitude of interval variations, three different maximum interval sizes were used in the first 15 transformations. Transformations 1 through 5 were constructed with a maximum of 2, allowing the largest interval to be twice as large as the smallest. Transformations 6 through 10 were constructed with a maximum of 10, and transformations 11 through 15 were constructed with a maximum of 25. Therefore, in transformations 11 through 15 one interval potentially could be 25 times as large as another. Figure 1

greater than those represented by equal appearing intervals in the middle of the scale. Each transformation was produced by choosing a number from 1 to a relatively large maximum for the first interval, a number from 1 to a somewhat smaller maximum for the second interval, and so forth, progressively reducing the maximum until the center of the score array was reached, then increasing the maximum at the same rate to the end of the score array. For transformations 16–20, the series of maximum values decreased by one unit steps from a possible maximum of 15 at

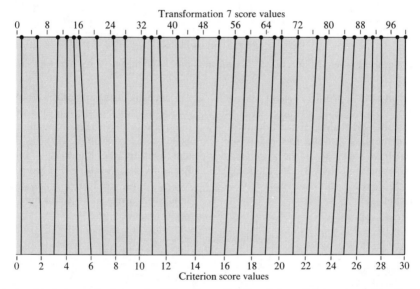

Fig. 1. Relationship between the intervals of Transformation 7 and the unit intervals of the criterion scores.

illustrates the relationship between the scores of transformation 7 and the unit-interval criterion scores. Each preselected maximum value was used to develop five transformations—a precaution which served to cancel out artifacts of sampling for a particular transformation.

The second set of transformations (16 through 25) was devised to simulate the situation which may often occur in the measurement of achievement and ability in which the magnitude of trait differences represented by intervals at the extremes of a scale may be

the beginning of the array to 1 at the center of the array, increasing again by one unit steps to a possible maximum of 15 again at the other end of the array. For transformations 21–25, the maximum was decreased by 3 unit steps from 45 to 3 at the center of the array and back to 45. The type of transformation produced by this procedure is illustrated in Figure 2.

For the third set of transformations (26 through 35), unit intervals were retained for scores ranging from 1 to 15, the remaining 15 intervals being varied randomly. This proced-

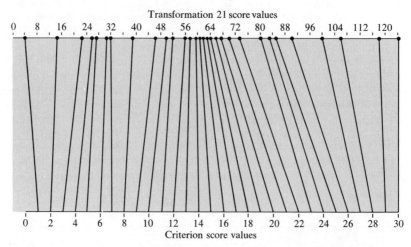

Fig. 2. Relationship between the intervals of Transformation 21 and the unit intervals of the criterion scores.

ure crudely imitates a problem which may be present sometimes in social distance scales or in the Thurstone type scaling of attitude items. For transformations 26–30, the maximum interval size above the center of the score array was 10. For transformations 31–35, the maximum was 25. Figure 3 illustrates this type of transformation.

For each of the populations, the unit-interval scores and the transformations were stored in the memory of an IBM 7090 digital computer as 36 scores for each of 1000 cases, which were identified by the numbers 1 through 1000. Random samples of cases were selected by means of a multiplying random number generator, with some additional features to

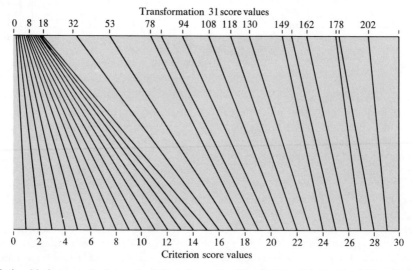

Fig. 3. Relationship between the intervals of Transformation 31 and the unit intervals of the criterion scores.

insure complete randomness and to guard against cycling. The generator sequence was initiated by obtaining a 35 binary digit (bit) number from the clock of the computer. This number was forced to be odd by the insertion of a low-order bit. A tape containing the one million random digits produced by the RAND Corporation (9) was then referenced and a word of ten decimal digits read from this tape. The first half of the 10 digit word, R, was then transformed by the value $8R + 3$. This value served as the initial multiplier for the number obtained from the computer clock. This multiplication produced a 70 bit number, the right 35 bits of which were extracted from the random number. The left bits of the latter were used to obtain an integer in the range 1—1000. This value determined the "case" to be selected from the population. The 35 bit random number was retained and multiplied by $8R + 3$ to obtain the next value from the population.

The second half of the ten-digit number first read from the RAND tape was divided by the quantity $(NA + NB)/2$, where NA and NB are the respective sizes of the pairs of samples drawn. The remainder occurring from this division determined the number of times the value $8R + 3$ was used as a multiplier in generating a random sequence. When the number of values generated equaled the value of the remainder, another ten digit record was read from the RAND tape and the sequence of generation repeated. When samples of size NA and NB had been drawn, t was computed using a standard computing formula.

A total of 36 t values were computed for each pair of samples drawn: One value for the unit-interval or criterion scores and one for each of the 35 transformations of the criterion. This is analogous to sampling from a pool of 1000 subjects with scores on 36 variables, the first variable representing a set of measurements with equal intervals and the remaining 35 variables representing measurement scales standing in varying non-linear relationships to the first set.

The following notation will be used through-out the paper:

N,R,E...............the type of distribution used: Normal, Rectangular, or Exponential

5,5; 15,15; 5,15 ...size of first and second samples

C ....the criterion set of values

T_n.....................the nth transformation

T_{j-k} ....transformations j through k.

The sequence of the notation is as follows: $N,15,15,T_{6-10}$; a normal distribution with sample sizes of 15 and 15 for transformations 6 through 10.

The computations were summarized in three forms: 1) Contingency tables showing the relationship of the criterion t value to each transformation t value for the .01 and .05 significance levels were tabulated. These tables allow the determination of the difference in the percentage of t's reaching given significance levels for a particular transformation and for the criterion scores. 2) Frequency distributions of all sets of t values were tabulated. Figure 4 shows the frequency distributions of t for N, 5, 5, C; N, 5, 5, T_5; N, 5, 5, T_{20}; and N, 5, 5, T_{35}. 3) Pearson correlation coefficients between the criterion t values and each of the transformation t values were calculated over the total number of sample pairs drawn for a given condition. The standard error of estimate was also computed. These statistics provide estimates of the degree to which t's based on transformed scores varied from t's based on unit-interval scores for the same pairs of samples.

Parts (1) and (2) of the computation summaries are directly relevant to the question of the effect of the measurement model on the sampling distribution of t. Part (3) is an attempt to represent the deviation of the various types of "inappropriate" measurement models from a true value (represented by the criterion).

As has been mentioned earlier, three types of distributions—normal, rectangular, and exponential, were used. Three variations in sample size were studied—NA = NB = 5; NA = NB = 15; and NA = 5, NB = 15.

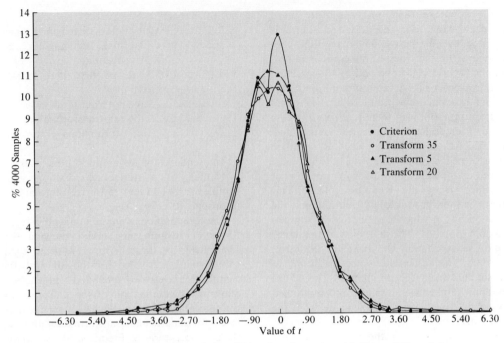

Fig. 4. Empirical sampling distributions of t for 4000 pairs of samples with NA = NB = 5, from a normal distribution for the Criterion and Transformations 5, 20, and 35.

These combinations are identical with those used by Boneau (2) and permit the present results to be compared directly with his.

Results

As a first step, the distributions of t on the criterion measurements for all conditions were compared with the theoretical distributions for the appropriate degrees of freedom. Table 1 contains the percentage of t values falling in

the 5 per cent and 1 per cent regions of the distribution for the criterion scores.

The deviations of the empirical distributions from the expected theoretical values for the normal curve are quite small. The results are very similar to those reported by Boneau (2) [Ch. 41], including the underestimates for the exponential distribution. Somewhat surprisingly, the deviations are reduced only slightly from those reported by Boneau, despite the fact that the present results are based on 4000

Table 1. Per cent of t's based on criterion unit interval scores falling in the 5% and 1% regions of rejection for 4000 random sampling runs

| | Sample Sizes | | | | | |
| | NA = NB = 5 | | NA = NB = 15 | | NA = 5, NB = 15 | |
Population Distribution	5% Level	1% Level	5% Level	1% Level	5% Level	1% Level
Normal	4.8	.8	5.4	1.0	5.3	1.1
Rectangular	5.4	1.6	4.6	.9	5.1	.8
Exponential	3.9	.9	5.1	1.0	4.2	.9

t's as compared to Boneau's 1000.

The results for the first set of transformations, which were constructed to simulate a situation where intervals vary randomly throughout the range of the measuring instrument, are given in Table 2. Since the tabulation of results for individual transformations within and across sets T_{1-5}, T_{6-10}, and T_{11-15} revealed little variation, only mean values for all transformations are given in Table 2. The mean value tabled for each transformation is based on 60,000 t's.

Table 2. Per cent of t's falling in the 5% and 1% regions of rejection when interval sizes vary randomly (4000 samples per condition)

		5% level		1% level	
		Total %	% in Larger tail	Total %	% in Larger tail
N, 5, 5:	C	4.8	2.4	.8	.4
	T_{1-15}	4.8	2.4	.8	.4
N, 15, 15:	C	5.4	3.0	1.0	.5
	T_{1-15}	5.3	2.9	.9	.5
N, 5, 15:	C	5.3	2.7	1.1	.6
	T_{1-15}	5.0	2.6	1.1	.6
R, 5, 5:	C	5.4	3.0	1.6	.9
	T_{1-15}	5.3	3.0	1.6	.9
R, 15, 15:	C	4.6	2.6	.9	.5
	T_{1-15}	4.6	2.5	.9	.5
R, 5, 15:	C	5.1	2.7	.8	.7
	T_{1-15}	5.0	2.6	.9	.7
E, 5, 5:	C	3.9	2.0	.9	.5
	T_{1-15}	3.9	2.0	.8	.4
E, 15, 15:	C	5.1	2.6	1.0	.6
	T_{1-15}	5.2	2.6	1.0	.6
E, 5, 15:	C	4.2	3.8	.9	.9
	T_{1-15}	4.2	3.8	1.0	1.0

Examination of Table 2 indicates that random variations tend to have little effect on the number of t's falling in the 5 per cent and 1 per cent regions of rejection. Columns 1 and 3 contain the total percentages for the 5 per cent and 1 per cent levels of the t distribution for all distributions and sample sizes. For the first group of transformations, the total percentages in the critical regions are very close to the theoretical expectation for a normal distribution. The largest discrepancy present is for E, 5, 5,—a discrepancy of only 1.1 per cent.

Columns 2 and 4, which contain the percentage in the larger tail, show similar minimal variations. If one allows for the effects of sampling and takes the deviations of each transformation from the obtained percentages of the C distribution, the discrepancies become almost nonexistent. The largest deviation is .3 per cent for N, 5, 15. It is evident that random variations in interval sizes, regardless of the magnitude of those variations, have virtually no effect on the percentage of t's reaching conventional significance levels.

One condition reported in Table 2 (E, 5, 15) did result in an asymmetrical t distribution. However, as can be seen by examining the tabled values for E, 5, 15, the C distribution is equally asymmetrical. For E, 5, 15, the majority of the t values reaching the 5 per cent level and all of the t's at the 1 per cent level are in one tail of the distribution. The direction of the skewing is negative, indicating that where large differences between sample means occurred, the higher mean tended to be the mean of the smaller sample. On the basis of this finding, an experimenter would be ill-advised to use a one-tailed test when he is using samples of unequal sizes (at least if the sizes are of the magnitudes used in this study). However, it makes little difference whether there is an interval scale of measurement or not.

The results for the more irregular and extreme transformations (16 through 35) are presented in Table 3. Again, since there was little variation within sets only mean values for transformations 16–25 and transformations 26–35 are presented.

An inspection of Table 3 also permits the conclusion that the magnitude of variations in interval sizes has little effect on the t distribution. At the same time, it is apparent that t is affected more by these types of transformations than was the situation for simple random variation. However, the discrepancies are still far from extreme. In columns 1 and 3 the largest obtained discrepancy is 2.3 per cent for E, 15, 15, T_{26-35} at the 5 per cent level. In columns 2 and 4, the largest discrepancy is again at the 5 per cent level for E, 15, 15, T_{26-35}, a value of 1.1 per cent.

When compared to the 5.1 per cent of t's falling in the 5 per cent region for the E, 15, 15, C distribution, this discrepancy of 2.3 per cent seems rather large. However, it seems slight compared to the discrepancies obtained when more serious violations of the assumptions for

Table 3. Per cent of t's falling in the 5% and 1% regions of rejection when interval sizes vary more in some regions of the scale than in others (4000 samples per condition)

		5% level		1% level	
		Total %	% in larger tail	Total %	% in larger tail
N, 5, 5:	C	4.8	2.4	.8	.4
	T_{16-25}	3.4	1.8	.4	.3
	T_{26-35}	4.2	2.2	.8	.4
N, 15, 15:	C	5.4	3.0	1.0	.5
	T_{16-25}	4.6	2.6	.6	.4
	T_{26-35}	5.1	2.8	.9	.5
N, 5, 15:	C	5.3	2.7	1.1	.6
	T_{16-25}	5.0	2.7	1.0	.6
	T_{26-35}	4.7	3.6	1.0	.9
R, 5, 5:	C	5.4	3.0	1.6	.9
	T_{16-25}	4.9	2.7	1.0	.6
	T_{26-35}	4.4	2.6	.8	.5
R, 15, 15:	C	4.6	2.6	.9	.5
	T_{16-25}	4.6	2.4	.8	.4
	T_{26-35}	4.9	2.8	.8	.4
R, 5, 15:	C	5.1	2.7	.8	.7
	T_{16-25}	4.9	2.6	.8	.6
	T_{26-35}	4.3	3.1	1.1	1.1
E, 5, 5:	C	3.9	2.0	.9	.5
	T_{16-25}	5.2	2.8	1.4	.7
	T_{26-35}	3.3	1.6	.7	.4
E, 15, 15:	C	5.1	2.6	1.0	.6
	T_{16-25}	5.4	2.7	1.2	.6
	T_{26-35}	2.8	1.4	.4	.3
E, 5, 15:	C	4.2	3.8	.9	.9
	T_{16-25}	4.6	3.4	.8	.7
	T_{26-35}	3.8	3.6	.6	.6

the use of t are made. For example, Boneau (2) reported 16 per cent of obtained t's at the 5 per cent level for samples of 5 and 15 drawn from normally distributed populations with unequal variances.

When Table 3 is examined for asymmetry, it is evident that the transformations in which the intervals in one half of a scale stand for substantially smaller variations in the objects being measured than do intervals in the other half of the scale—T_{26-35}—yield seriously skewed distributions of t for all conditions where unequal sample sizes are used. For E distributions, skewing is present for most of the transformations. These transformations provide the only situation where the nature of the scale transformation affected the sampling distribution of t to a more serious degree than could be attributable to the use of unequal sample sizes drawn from an exponential distribution. Even for this condition the effect is quite small. For any real-life situation in which the possibility of such a measurement scale exists, an experimenter should be chary of using t to make a one-tailed test between means based on unequal sample N's. Fortunately, this problem occurs only rarely and when it does occur the use of equal sample sizes will minimize the distortion.

In reviewing the results presented so far, the following generalizations seem warranted:

1. The percentage of t's reaching the theoretical 5 per cent and 1 per cent levels of significance is not seriously affected by the use of non-equal interval measurements.[2]

2. To the extent that there is any influence of the scale transformation on the percentage of t's reaching theoretical significance levels, the influence is more marked when intervals in one broad region of a scale are larger than intervals in another region of the scale than it is when interval sizes vary randomly.

3. If an investigator has a measuring instrument which produces either an interval scale or an ordinal scale with randomly varied interval sizes, he can safely use t for statistical decisions under all circumstances examined in this study. The single exception is that t should not be used to do a one tailed test when sam-

2. It is possible that the effects of the scale transformations used in this study are actually due to changes in the shape of the distributions which the different transformations produced. However, if this is the case, the arguments presented regarding the insignificant effects of the nature of measurement scales on probability statements are strengthened even more.

ples of unequal size have been drawn from a badly skewed population.

4. If a measurement scale deviates from reality in such a fashion that the magnitude of trait differences represented by intervals at the extremes of the scale may be greater than those represented by equal-appearing intervals in the middle of the scale (T_{16-25}), it seems reasonably safe to use t. Unequal sample sizes can even be used if the population is symmetrical, but the proscriptions against using one-tailed tests for unequal sample sizes from exponential populations still apply.

5. If the scale is of the kind represented by the relationship between C and T_{26-35} (in which inequality of units is present in one-half of the distribution only), it is still safe to use t, with a somewhat stricter limitation on the use of one-tailed tests. This arises from the finding that for all population distributions these transformations yielded skewed distributions of t when unequal sample sizes were used.

6. As a maximally conservative empirical set of rules for using t, the following restrictions would seem to be sufficient to compensate for almost any violation of assumptions investigated up to this time:

    a. Have equal sample sizes.

    b. Use a two-tailed test.

7. Returning to the question as originally formulated: Do statistics computed on a measurement scale which is at best a poor fit to reality distribute differently than the same statistics computed under conditions of perfect measurement? The answer is a firm "no," provided that the conditions of equal sample sizes and two-tailed tests are met. The research worker who has nothing better than an ordinal scale to work with may have an extremely poor fit to reality, but at least he will not be led into making incorrect probability estimates if he observes a few simple precautions.

As a final step, a different sort of analysis will be cited. The previous results and discussion related to one aspect of the measurement problem as posed by Stevens (14); a second aspect remains. This concerns the accuracy of the descriptive statistics when the measure-

ment model is a poor fit. Stevens has presented his point of view almost exclusively in terms of descriptive statistics and has tended to use illustrations from descriptive statistics to support his arguments. In the last analysis, this would seem to raise an epistemological question, since it is concerned with the relationship of measurement to a true value which cannot be known. However, evidence as to the correctness of the point of view can be examined from the data of the present study, even though the results are of no help in solving the problems faced by an experimenter who is wondering how to evaluate the validity and the precision of his measuring instrument.

The question of the accuracy of representation can be evaluated by defining the unit interval criterion t values as true measures and the values calculated on the various transformations as those obtained on a measurement model which misrepresents reality. Then the degree of relationship between the values of t calculated on specific samples for C and the values calculated on T_{1-35} can be obtained. This is a correlational question and the results are reported in Table 4.

Columns 1, 3, and 5 contain for each of the distributions the correlations between values of t for each set of transformations and the corresponding values of t for the criterion. The correlations are impressively high. However, because of the broad range of values in the t distribution, the standard errors of estimate in columns 2, 4, and 6 are more informative statistics.

Several points can be noted in connection with Table 4: There is a regular progression in the size of the standard errors of estimate across the sets of transformations used, such that they are smallest for T_{1-15}, and largest for T_{26-35}. These standard errors also become larger as the magnitude of variations in interval size increases, but this is less striking than the differences among types of transformations. Variations in sample sizes and in the shape of the population distribution do not seem to have much influence on the standard errors of estimate; consequently these results seem to

Table 4. Mean* correlation coefficients and standard errors of estimate for
the prediction of t's based on transformed scores from t's based on criterion
Unit-interval scores

	NA = NB = 5		NA = NB = 15		NA = 5, NB= 15	
	Mean	Mean	Mean	Mean	Mean	Mean
Population	r	$s_{y.x}$	r	$s_{y.x}$	r	$s_{y.x}$
Distribution	(1)	(2)	(3)	(4)	(5)	(6)
N: T_{1-5}	.997	.089	.997	.082	.997	.084
T_{6-10}	.996	.111	.995	.100	.995	.104
T_{11-15}	.992	.146	.991	.138	.991	.142
T_{16-20}	.975	.244	.966	.265	.970	.260
T_{21-25}	.968	.271	.964	.274	.966	.278
T_{26-30}	.935	.401	.933	.380	.933	.386
T_{31-35}	.914	.462	.911	.434	.912	.439
R: T_{1-5}	.999	.056	.988	.048	.999	.033
T_{6-10}	.996	.094	.096	.081	.996	.084
T_{11-15}	.994	.117	.994	.088	.988	.104
T_{16-20}	.973	.256	.973	.231	.973	.233
T_{21-25}	.973	.258	.975	.227	.976	.225
T_{26-30}	.948	.368	.943	.339	.944	.348
T_{31-35}	.927	.430	.922	.394	.924	.404
E: T_{1-5}	.994	.121	.993	.113	.992	.117
T_{6-10}	.992	.138	.992	.126	.992	.129
T_{11-15}	.984	.199	.985	.181	.983	.189
T_{16-20}	.970	.283	.946	.342	.951	.324
T_{21-25}	.963	.313	.953	.314	.954	.309
T_{26-30}	.981	.218	.930	.382	.940	.325
T_{31-35}	.966	.288	.885	.483	.922	.405

* Median values do not differ until the third decimal place for the majority
of transformations.

show a specific influence of scale transformations on the values of t. The correspondence
between values of t based on the criterion unit
interval scores and values of t based on transformations decreases regularly and dramatically—from standard errors of estimate on the
order of .08 to standard errors of estimate on
the order of .45—as the departure from linear
transformations becomes more extreme. Here,
then, is a finding consistent with Stevens'
expectations: The value of t determined for a
comparison of samples of non-interval scores
does tend to be different from the value of t
based on interval scores for the same samples
and the discrepancy tends to become greater
as the departure from equal intervals is more
marked.

In conclusion, the views presented by
Stevens (14, 15, 16) and by advocates of his
position such as Senders (11), Siegel (12), and
Stake (13) state that, when one uses t, the

measurement model should have equal intervals representing linear transformations of the
magnitudes of the characteristics being measured, or the statistic will be "upset." This view
may be correct if one considers single specific
determinations of a statistic in a descriptive
sense—this seems to be the significance of the
standard errors of estimate reported in Table
4—but it is incorrect when applied to the
problem of statistical inference.

The present findings indicate that strong
statistics such as the t test are more than
adequate to cope with weak measurements—
and, with some minor reservations, probabilities estimated from the t distribution are little
affected by the kind of measurement scale
used.

References

1. Anderson, N. H. Scales and Statistics: Para-

metric and Nonparametric. *Psychological Bulletin*, 1961, 58, 305–316.

2. Boneau, C. A. The Effects of Violations of Assumptions Underlying the *t* Test. *Psychological Bulletin*, 1960, 57, 49–64.

3. Burke, C. J. Additive Scales and Statistics. *Psychological Review*, 1953, 60, 73–75.

4. Hays, W. L. *Statistics for Psychologists*. New York: Holt, Rinehart and Winston, 1963.

5. Lord, F. M. On the Statistical Treatment of Football Numbers. *American Psychologist*, 1953, 8, 750–751.

6. Lubin, A. Statistics. In *Annual Review of Psychology*. Palo Alto, Calif.: Stanford University Press, 1962.

7. McNemar, Q. *Psychological Statistics*, 3rd ed. New York: Wiley, 1962.

8. Norton, D. W. An Empirical Investigation of Some Effects of Non-Normality and Heterogeneity on the F-Distribution. Unpublished Doctoral Dissertation, State University of Iowa, 1952. Cited in E. F. Lindquist, *Design and Analysis of Experiments in Psychology and Education*. Boston: Houghton Mifflin, 1953.

9. RAND Corporation. *A Million Random Digits*. New York: The Free Press of Glencoe, 1955.

10. Savage, I. R. Non-parametric Statistics. *Journal of the American Statistical Association*, 1957, 52, 331–344.

11. Senders, V. L. *Measurement and Statistics*. London: Oxford University Press, 1958.

12. Siegel, S. *Nonparametric Statistics*. New York: McGraw-Hill, 1956.

13. Stake, R. E. Review of *Elementary Statistics* by P. G. Hoel. *Educational and Psychological Measurement*, 1960, 20, 871–873.

14. Stevens, S. S. Mathematics, Measurement and Psychophysics. In S. S. Stevens (Ed.), *Handbook of Experimental Psychology*. New York: Wiley, 1951.

15. Stevens, S. S. Measurement, Psychophysics and Utility. In Churchman, G. W., and Ratoosh, P. (Eds.), *Measurement: Definitions and Theories*. New York: Wiley, 1959.

16. Stevens, S. S. Review of *Statistical Theory* by Lancelot Hogben. *Contemporary Psychology*, 1960, 5, 273–276.

Current Interpretations

The three articles in this section all present somewhat unusual, current, discussions of correlational techniques. Darlington offers a very sophisticated analysis of multiple regression. Yee and Gage discuss the problem of making causal statements using correlational techniques. Cohen's analysis of multiple regression shows its relationship to analysis of variance and covariance, and the usefulness of these techniques.

RICHARD B. DARLINGTON

43 Multiple Regression in Psychological Research and Practice[1]

A number of common practices and beliefs concerning multiple regression are criticized, and several paradoxical properties of the method are emphasized. Major topics discussed are the basic formulas; suppressor variables; measures of the "importance" of a predictor variable; inferring relative regression weights from relative validities; estimates of the true validity of population regression equations and of regression equations developed in samples; and statistical criteria for selecting predictor variables. The major points are presented in outline form in a final summary.

In recent years, electronic computers have made the multiple regression method readily available to psychologists and other scientists, while simultaneously making it unnecessary for them to study in full the cumbersome computational details of the method. Therefore, there is a need for a discussion of multiple regression which emphasizes some of the less obvious uses, limitations, and properties of the method. This article attempts to fill this need. It makes no attempt to cover thoroughly computational techniques or significance tests,

1. For critical comments on preliminary drafts, the author is indebted to J. Millman, P. C. Smith, and T. A. Ryan, and to his students J. T. Barsis, W. Buckwalter, H. Day, B. Goldwater, and G. F. Stauffer. He is especially grateful to his student C. S. Otterbein, whose editorial and substantive contributions amounted nearly to coauthorship.

From *Psychological Bulletin*, Vol. 69, No. 3, pp. 161–82, 1968. Copyright © 1968 by the American Psychological Association, and reprinted by permission.

both of which are discussed in such standard sources as McNemar (33), Hays (26), DuBois (13), and Williams (46). The discussion of significance tests by Williams is especially complete, as is the presentation of computing directions by DuBois. The latter source also contains many basic formulas of considerable interest. Anderson (1) gives a very complete mathematical presentation of the exact sampling distributions of many of the statistics relevant to multiple regression. Elashoff and Afifi (17) reviewed procedures applicable when some observations are missing. Beaton (3) described a set of elegantly simple computer subroutines which a FORTRAN programmer can use to write quickly almost any standard or special-purpose regression program he may require.

Some of the points made herein are original, some have been derived independently by several workers in recent years, and some surprisingly little-known points were made in print 40 or more years ago.

In general, the dependent or criterion variable will be denoted by X_0, and the independent or predictor variables by X_1, X_2, ..., X_n. The score of person i on variable X_j is symbolized by x_{ij}. The population multiple correlation is denoted by $\bar{R}$, ordinary correlations by ρ, standard deviations by σ. Population regression weights are denoted by β, with β' denoting the corresponding weights when all variables have been adjusted to standard score form. Sample values of these parameters are denoted by $\bar{R}$, r, s, b, and b'.

The purpose of the multiple regression method is to derive weights β_1, β_2, ..., β_n for the variables X_1, X_2, ..., X_n, and an additive constant α, such that the resulting weighted composite $\hat{X}_0$, which is defined by the multiple regression equation

$$\hat{X}_0 = \beta_1 X_1 + \beta_2 X_2 + \beta_3 X_3 + \ldots + \beta_n X_n + \alpha$$
Eq. 1

predicts a specified criterion variable X_0 with a minimum sum of squared errors; thus $\hat{X}_0$ correlates maximally with X_0. This paper deals directly only with the linear additive model,

in which $\hat{X}_0$ is a linear function of the predictor variables. This restriction is more apparent than real, however, since if desired some of the variables in the equation can be curvilinear or configural (interactive) functions of other variables.

Basic Formulas[2]

As described in standard works on the subject, the n multiple regression weights β_1, β_2, β_3, ..., β_n are found by solving a set of n simultaneous linear equations in which these weights are the unknowns. These equations are the so-called *normal equations* of regression theory, although this term does not imply any dependence on an assumption that variables are normally distributed. The known quantities in the normal equations are the standard deviations of the n predictor variables and the criterion variable, and the intercorrelations among these $n+1$ variables. A change in the standard deviation of one of the predictor variables will affect only the beta weight of that one variable, while a change in the correlation between any two variables will generally affect all the beta weights.

After the βs are found, the additive constant α is chosen so as to make the mean of the scores on $\hat{X}_0$ equal to the mean of the scores on X_0. The multiple correlation $\bar{R}$ can then be found in any of several ways, of which the simplest conceptually (though not computationally) is to compute each person's score on $\hat{X}_0$, and then to correlate these scores with X_0.

2. A number of points made in this paper are amplified and proven in a supplementary document by the author entitled "Proofs of Some Theorems on Multiple Regression." Statements in the present section are given as Theorems 4, 6, 10, 11, 12, and 13 of that document. Although the proofs are not original in any important sense of the word, the author has tried to simplify many of the standard proofs to a level readily grasped by students in an intermediate-level course in psychometric theory. The document is available from the American Documentation Institute. Order Document No. 9810 from the ADI Auxiliary Publications Project, Photoduplication Service, Library of Congress, Washington, D.C. 20540. Remit in advance $1.75 for microfilm or $2.50 for photocopies and make checks payable to: Chief, Photoduplication Service, Library of Congress.

If all predictor variables are uncorrelated, then the above-mentioned procedures for computing beta weights and $\bar{R}$ reduce to the simple formulas

$$\beta_j = \rho_{0j}\frac{\sigma_0}{\sigma_j} \qquad \text{Eq. 2}$$

and

$$\bar{R}^2 = \rho_{01}{}^2 + \rho_{02}{}^2 + \rho_{03}{}^2 + \ldots + \rho_{0n}{}^2 \qquad \text{Eq. 3}$$

If we define the "usefulness" of predictor variable X_j as the amount $\bar{R}^2$ would drop if X_j were removed from the regression equation and the remaining variables appropriately reweighted, then Formula 3 shows that the usefulness of X_j equals $\rho_{0j}{}^2$ when predictor variables are uncorrelated.

Results analogous to some of those stated above can be derived for the case in which predictor variables are intercorrelated. Suppose we have a regression equation predicting X_0 from $X_1, X_2, \ldots, X_n$. Consider a second multiple regression equation in which one of the predictor variables X_j $(1 \le j \le n)$ is the dependent variable and the remaining $n-1$ predictor variables $X_1, X_2, \ldots, X_{j-1}, X_{j+1}, \ldots, X_n$ are the predictors. Let the residuals in this second equation (i.e., the set of scores obtained by subtracting each person's score on this regression function from his actual score on X_j) constitute the variable $X_{j(p)}$. The variable $X_{j(p)}$ is uncorrelated with all of the variables used to construct the regression equation predicting X_j. Following Rozeboom (38) and others, $X_{j(p)}$ is termed the component of X_j orthogonal to the other predictor variables, or more simply the orthogonal component of X_j. (We shall later have occasion to denote the component of X_0 orthogonal to *all* the predictor variables—which component is the residual in the regression equation predicting X_0 from those predictor variables—as $X_{0(p)}$. The component of any predictor variable X_j orthogonal to the criterion variable X_0 will be denoted by $X_{j(c)}$. In the present terminology, the partial correlation between two variables X_j and X_k holding m other variables constant is the correlation between

the components of X_j and X_k orthogonal to the other m variables.)[3]

The standard deviation of $X_{j(p)}$ is denoted by $\sigma_{j(p)}$, and the correlation of $X_{j(p)}$ with any variable X_h by $\rho_{h \cdot j(p)}$. Then we can write a formula for β_j which is very similar to Formula 2 but which applies whether the predictor variables are intercorrelated or not:

$$\beta_j = \rho_{0 \cdot j(p)}\frac{\sigma_0}{\sigma_{j(p)}} \qquad \text{Eq. 4}$$

Further, just as the usefulness of X_j equals $\rho_{0j}{}^2$ when predictor variables are uncorrelated, so it equals $\rho_{0 \cdot j(p)}{}^2$ when predictor variables are intercorrelated. There is no formula quite so directly analogous to Formula 3; in general it is *not* true that

$$\bar{R}^2 = \rho_{0 \cdot 1(p)}{}^2 + \rho_{0 \cdot 2(p)}{}^2 + \ldots + \rho_{0 \cdot n(p)}{}^2$$

When $n = 2$, it can be shown that

$$\rho_{0 \cdot 1(p)} = \frac{\rho_{01} - \rho_{02}\rho_{12}}{\sqrt{1 - \rho_{12}{}^2}} \qquad \text{Eq. 5}$$

and that

$$\sigma_{1(p)} = \sigma_1\sqrt{1 - \rho_{12}{}^2} \qquad \text{Eq. 6}$$

Interchanging the subscripts 1 and 2 in Formulas 5 and 6 gives $\rho_{0 \cdot 2(p)}$ and $\sigma_{2(p)}$. Substituting Formulas 5 and 6 in Formula 4 gives the familiar formula

$$\beta_1 = \frac{\rho_{01} - \rho_{02}\rho_{12}}{1 - \rho_{12}{}^2} \cdot \frac{\sigma_0}{\sigma_1} \qquad \text{Eq. 7}$$

for the case in which $n = 2$. Analogously, when $n = 2$,

$$\beta_2 = \frac{\rho_{02} - \rho_{01}\rho_{12}}{1 - \rho_{12}{}^2} \cdot \frac{\sigma_0}{\sigma_2} \qquad \text{Eq. 8}$$

When $n = 2$, the useful relation

$$\bar{R}^2 = \rho_{01}{}^2 + \rho_{0 \cdot 2(p)}{}^2 = \rho_{02}{}^2 + \rho_{0 \cdot 1(p)}{}^2$$

3. Dunlap and Cureton (14) called the correlation between a variable and the orthogonal component of another variable a "semipartial correlation," and McNemar (33, p. 167) called it a "part correlation." Both these terms emphasize its similarity to the partial correlation.

follows directly from the fact that $\rho_{0 \cdot j(\mathrm{p})}{}^2$ equals the usefulness of X_j. This result fits intuitively with Formula 3 since X_1 and $X_{2(\mathrm{p})}$ (or X_2 and $X_{1(\mathrm{p})}$) are uncorrelated variables which contain the same basic information (and thus yield the same prediction of X_0) as X_1 and X_2.

Suppressor Variables

This section describes suppressor variables and criticizes the common belief that dealing with them requires a modification of standard multiple regression procedures. For simplicity, the section assumes that each predictor variable with a nonzero correlation with X_0 is scored in the direction which makes that correlation positive in the population. The scoring direction of variables correlating zero with X_0 can be chosen arbitrarily.

Although various definitions have been given (cf. 21, 29, 33), a suppressor variable is here defined as a variable which, when included in a regression equation in which the variables have been scored as described above, receives a negative weight when the equation is derived in the population. (This definition thus excludes variables whose negative weight is the result of sampling error.) Since a variable correlating zero with X_0 is allowed to be scored in either direction, and since it will receive a negative regression weight when scored in one of those directions if its weight is not zero, then by our definition any variable which correlates zero with X_0 but which receives a nonzero weight can be called a suppressor variable. Contrary to most previous definitions, by the present definition a suppressor variable need not have a low or zero validity, although in practice it usually does.

Since the multiple regression method chooses those weights, whether positive or negative, which maximize the multiple correlation, it necessarily follows that a suppressor variable improves prediction in the population when it is given a negative weight. A typical example in which prediction is improved by assigning a negative weight to a variable might be a situation in which a test of reading speed is used in conjunction with a speeded history achievement test to predict some external criterion of knowledge of history. Since the history test is contaminated by reading speed, assigning a negative weight to the reading-speed test would help to correct for the disadvantage suffered by a student with low reading speed who is competing with faster readers.

To understand more fully the functions of suppressor variables, it is helpful to examine the exact conditions under which negative weights appear. For simplicity, regression equations with only two predictor variables X_1 and X_2, and only the case in which X_2 receives a negative weight, will be considered.

Let $X_{1(\mathrm{e})}$ denote the component of X_1 orthogonal to the criterion variable. $X_{1(\mathrm{e})}$ can be considered to measure the sources of error in X_1, that is, those aspects of X_1 which prevent a perfect prediction of X_0 from X_1. For example, consider a hypothetical modification of the previous example in which reading speed correlates zero with the criterion variable, and is the only source of error in the history test. If the history test were X_1, then $X_{1(\mathrm{e})}$ would measure only reading speed. In real-life cases, $X_{1(\mathrm{e})}$ does not represent a single source of error, such as reading speed, but measures instead a composite of all the sources of error in X_1.

Ordinarily, the variable $X_{1(\mathrm{e})}$ is not directly measurable. However, suppose a second test X_2 were available which correlated perfectly with $X_{1(\mathrm{e})}$; in other words, suppose X_2 were a perfect measure of the sources of error in X_1. (For instance, in our hypothetical example, suppose X_2 was a perfect test of reading speed.) Then, by giving X_2 a negative weight in a regression equation in which X_1 had a positive weight, it would be possible to subtract out, or correct for, or "suppress," those sources of error.

Generally, of course, a second variable X_2 does not correlate perfectly with $X_{1(\mathrm{e})}$. The example should make clear, however, that X_2 can be used in either of two ways, depending on its characteristics: to measure X_0 directly, or to measure $X_{1(c)}$. X_2 should receive a positive weight if used the first way or a negative weight if used the second way. It will be shown that whether X_2 receives a positive or a negative weight, when used in a regression equation with X_1, depends upon the ratio between its abilities to perform these two different tasks; specifically, on the ratio $\rho_{2 \cdot 1(c)} : \rho_{02}$.

In a regression equation with two predictor variables, Formula 8 shows that X_2 receives a negative weight if

$$\rho_{02} - \rho_{01}\rho_{12} < 0 \qquad \text{Eq. 9}$$

Some algebra shows that Inequality 9 is equivalent to

$$\frac{\rho_{2 \cdot 1(c)}}{\rho_{02}} > \frac{\rho_{1 \cdot 1(c)}}{\rho_{01}} \qquad \text{Eq. 10}$$

The algebra here consists of using Formulas 5 and 6 to set

$$\rho_{2 \cdot 1(c)} = \frac{\rho_{12} - \rho_{01}\rho_{02}}{\sqrt{1 - \rho_{01}^2}}$$

and

$$\rho_{1 \cdot 1(c)} = \sqrt{1 - \rho_{01}^2}$$

and then substituting these expressions in Inequality 10, which then simplifies to Inequality 9. These same two formulas can be used to derive an inequality which is similar to Inequality 10, but which some readers will find more meaningful. If both sides of Inequality 10 are squared, then the resulting quantities ρ_{01}^2, ρ_{02}^2, $\rho_{1 \cdot 1(c)}$, and $\rho_{2 \cdot 1(c)}$ equal the proportions of variance in X_1 and X_2 "accounted for" by X_0 and $X_{1(c)}$, respectively, so that the formula is in terms of proportions of variance rather than correlation coefficients. Some readers will prefer this alternative since ratios between proportions of variance are more familiar than ratios between correlation coefficients.

Inequality 10 provides the basis for a clear and simple statement of the algebraic nature of a suppressor variable. The left side of Inequality 10 is the ratio mentioned above, showing the ability of X_2 to measure $X_{1(c)}$ relative to its ability to measure X_0. The right side is an analogous ratio for X_1, showing the ability of X_1 to measure $X_{1(c)}$ relative to its ability to measure X_0. If the ratios on the left and right sides of Inequality 10 are equal, then X_2 cannot usefully supplement X_1 in measuring either X_0 or $X_{1(c)}$, so it receives a zero weight. Normally, X_1 is a better measure of its own sources of error than is X_2, so $\rho_{1 \cdot 1(c)}$, the numerator of the right side, is normally larger than $\rho_{2 \cdot 1(c)}$, the numerator of the left side. Hence the fraction on the right side is normally larger than the fraction on the left. If this occurs, then X_2 is more useful as a measure of X_0 than as a measure of $X_{1(c)}$, so it receives a positive weight. However, if X_2 correlates so highly with $X_{1(c)}$ that the left side of Inequality 10 is larger than the right (as a test of reading speed would correlate highly with the error in the history test in the above example), then X_2 is more useful as a measure of $X_{1(c)}$, and so receives a negative weight.

Inequality 9 shows that in regression equations with two predictor variables, β_2 is never negative if ρ_{02} is greater than or equal to ρ_{01} or if both predictor variables correlate positively with X_0 and negatively with each other. Further, β_2 is always negative if $\rho_{02} = 0$ and ρ_{12} and ρ_{01} are both positive.

When an equation contains more than two predictor variables, any variable X_j is a suppressor if Inequality 10 holds when X_2 is replaced by X_j, and X_1 is replaced by the variable formed by dropping the jth term from the multiple regression equation which uses all n predictor variables. This follows from the fact that if the variable formed in this way were used with X_j in a two-variable regression equation predicting X_0, then clearly the weight of X_j in this equation would equal the weight of X_j in the regression equation computed directly from all n variables. Thus β_j in the n-variable equation would be negative whenever β_j in the two-variable equation was negative, which would occur whenever Inequality 10 holds for that equation.

The multiple regression method considers suppressor relationships in that it chooses the weights, positive or negative, which give the highest multiple correlation. Hence, the observation of negative weights in a sample regression equation, indicating that suppressor variables may be present, does not alone imply that there should be a deviation from standard regression procedures. However, Gulliksen (24, p. 330) stated that negative weights "should lead to a careful scrutiny of the test and a consideration of the reasonableness of such a finding." Although such a scrutiny can often be attempted with confidence in regression equations with two predictor variables, it is difficult for an investigator to reach a conclusion about the reasonableness of a negative weight in a complex, multipredictor situation. For example, consider a three-predictor situation in which $\rho_{01} = \rho_{02} = .15$, $\rho_{03} = .2$, $\rho_{12} = 0$, and $\rho_{13} = \rho_{23} = .7$. Although X_3 is the most valid single predictor and would be assigned a positive weight when used in conjunction with either X_1 or X_2 alone, it can be shown that it is given a negative weight when X_1, X_2, and X_3 are all used together. Yet using X_3 in this way raises the multiple correlation for all three variables to .5, while the highest multiple correlation without negative weights is only .21, using X_1 and X_2.

Thus, suppressor relationships appear in situations in which a "reasonable" interpretation of the relationship is extremely difficult. Relationships among more than three predictor variables are even more complex. Therefore, even if the improvement resulting from using a negative weight were small, it is difficult to imagine an investigator with such faith in his ability to conceive of all possible suppressor situations that he would ignore the improved prediction resulting from the use of a negative weight.

Measures of the "Importance" of a Predictor Variable

The present section deals with five different measures of the "importance" of predictor variables; for variable X_j, the measures are $\rho_{0j}{}^2$; $\beta'_j{}^2$; $\rho_{0 \cdot j(p)}{}^2$, which as we saw above equals the usefulness of X_j; $\beta'_j \rho_{0j}$; and a measure proposed by Englehart (18). It will be recalled that β'_j was defined as the weight given to X_j when all variables have been adjusted to unit variance, and that the usefulness of X_j was defined as the amount $\bar{R}^2$ would drop if X_j were removed from the regression equation and the weights of the remaining predictor variables were then recalculated.

When all predictor variables are uncorrelated, all five of these measures are equivalent. The equivalence of the first four can be verified merely by inspection of Formulas 2 and 3; the fifth will be discussed later. If predictor variables are uncorrelated, each of the five measures also equals the difference (expressed as a proportion of the variance of X_0) between the original variance of X_0 and the variance of X_0 in a subpopulation whose members all have the same score on X_j. (If this latter variance varies across subpopulations, then an average is taken.) Further, if any of the five measures is summed across all the predictor variables in a regression equation, the total is $\bar{R}^2$. Thus it is meaningful and useful to consider $\bar{R}^2$ to be the sum of the proportions of variance in the criterion variable "accounted for by," or "attributable to," or "contributed by" each of the predictor variables. The interpretation is completely analogous to the interpretation of results in analysis-of-variance designs.

In analysis-of-variance designs, the complete independence of all the independent variables is assured by the requirement of equal or proportional cell frequencies—or by the requirement of statistical adjustments, such as those given by Federer and Zelen, (19), designed to produce estimates of the same parameters as those estimated with equal cell frequencies. In multiple regression, however, there is no requirement that predictor variables be uncorrelated. This property gives regression analysis a substantial element of flexibility lacking in analysis of variance. When predictor variables are intercorrelated, however, the five measures of importance are no longer equivalent, so that the term "contribution to variance" suddenly becomes very ambiguous. The different measures of importance do not even necessarily rank order the variables in a regression equation in the same order. For example, consider the case in which $\rho_{01} = .4$, $\rho_{02} = .44$, $\rho_{03} = .3$, $\rho_{12} = .8$, $\rho_{13} = 0$, and $\rho_{23} = .4$. Given these values, standard formulas show that $\bar{R} = .5$. The three β' weights computed from these numbers are, respectively, .4, 0, and .3, and the three decreases in $\bar{R}^2$ used as measures of usefulness are, respectively, .038, 0, and .050. Thus X_1 has the highest β' weight, X_2 is most valid, and X_3 is most useful. Although in this example the variable with the lowest β' weight, X_2, is also the least useful, other examples can be constructed in which this is not true.

The rest of this section attempts to explain what meaning, if any, can be attached to each of the five measures of importance. Of the five, only $\beta'_j \rho_{0j}$ and Englehart's measure total to $\bar{R}^2$ when summed across the variables in a regression equation. Nevertheless, of the five, these two will be shown to be of least interest and value.

SQUARED VALIDITY

Of the five measures, ρ_{0j}^2 or the squared validity, needs the least comment. It is the only one of the five measures unaffected by the choice of the other variables in the regression equation.

BETA WEIGHTS AS MEASURES OF THE
IMPORTANCE OF CAUSAL RELATIONSHIPS

For many purposes, β'_j is of more interest than $\beta'_j{}^2$. In the present discussion, they will be considered equivalent, since either can be computed from the other (provided the sign of the weight is known) and since they rank variables in the same order of importance.

Previous sections showed that beta weights,

like usefulness, are determined solely by the characteristics of the orthogonal component of the variable under consideration. They thus have little relation to validity and are heavily influenced by the nature of the other variables in the regression equation. Beta weights can even change in sign as variables are added to or removed from the equation; one example was given in the section on suppressors, another is given by Kendall (31, p. 74).

It was shown above that β'_j (or $\beta'_j{}^2$) is not a measure of the usefulness of X_j when predictor variables are intercorrelated. The present section describes a particular case in which beta weights are nevertheless of considerable interest as a measure of the "importance" of a variable.

It is true that "correlation does not imply causation." In most cases, an investigator cannot determine whether an observed correlation between two variables X_0 and X_1 is due to the effect of X_0 on X_1, or to the effect of X_1 on X_0, or to some combination of effects which might include the effects of other outside variables on both X_0 and X_1. However, there are cases in which some of these alternatives can be ruled out by the nature of the variables involved; thus, if there is a correlation between snowfall and traffic accidents, it can be assumed that the traffic accidents did not cause the snowfall. If a large enough number of such causal hypotheses can be eliminated, then there are certain situations in which a multiple regression equation can be used to estimate the importance of the remaining causal relationships. Partly because this technique has been used in cases in which it was not wholly appropriate, this section attempts to make explicit the assumptions necessary for the use of the technique.

Consider a situation in which (a) a given dependent variable is affected only by a specified set of measurable variables, (b) the effect of each of these variables on the dependent variable is linear, and (c) the dependent variable has no effect, either directly or indirectly, on any of the independent variables. In such a situation, consider a linear function of the causal variables in which the weight of each variable equals the causal importance of that variable; that is, if increasing X_j by 1 unit increases the dependent variable by g units, then g is the weight of X_j. This linear function will perfectly predict the dependent variable. Since the multiple regression method computes the weights which result in the best prediction of the dependent variable, in this situation a multiple regression equation computed in the population necessarily computes the true causal weights for the set of variables involved in the equation, since these are the only weights which result in perfect prediction. Further, if an investigator has inadvertently included among the predictors a variable which in fact has no effect on the dependent variable, then that predictor variable will receive a weight of zero.

Suppose now that the dependent variable is determined partly by chance factors or by nonchance factors which are uncorrelated with all of the predictors which the investigator uses. It can be shown that the weights in a multiple regression equation are unchanged by the addition of a new predictor variable which is uncorrelated with all the other predictors.[4] Therefore, the best possible prediction of the dependent variable from the causal measures used is still obtained when the weight of each variable equals the true causal effect of that variable on the dependent variable. Hence the population multiple regression weights still equal the true causal weights, although the multiple correlation is less than unity. And since sample beta weights are unbiased estimates of the population beta weights, they can be employed as unbiased estimates of the true causal weights. The method can also be extended to handle curvilinear or interactive effects by including such terms in the regression equation.

Thus, the method assumes:

1. All variables which might affect the dependent variable are either included in the regression equation or are uncorrelated with the variables which are included.

2. Terms are included in the regression equation to handle any curvilinear or interactive effects.[5]

3. The dependent variable has no effect on the independent variables.

Since these assumptions are rarely all fully met, the technique should be used with caution. Nevertheless, when they are met, it provides a technique for rationally inferring causal relationships in complex situations even though experimental manipulation of the independent variables is impossible.

The technique is actually a variant of the method of computing a partial correlation between the dependent variable and each of the independent variables. In the regression technique, however, the emphasis is on regression weights rather than correlation coefficients. The advantage is that the final conclusions are in the form, "Increasing X_j by 1 unit increases the dependent variable by β_j units"; for example, "Every inch of snowfall causes, on the average, 15 additional traffic accidents." This is the most useful form of a statement when the emphasis is on cause and effect.

In any attempt to illustrate the method by an example, valid questions can be raised concerning the applicability of the assumptions listed above to that specific example. However, as an illustration of the technique, consider a study of the effects of different weather conditions on the frequency of traffic accidents. Suppose that each day, in a large city, several measures of weather conditions were recorded, and that the number of traffic accidents in the city each day was also recorded. Suppose then that a multiple regression equation was constructed to predict the number of traffic accidents in a day from the various measures of weather con-

---

4. See Theorem 5 of the document cited in Footnote 2.

5. Configural and curvilinear terms, however, can produce complications in the interpretation of linear terms. See Darlington and Paulus (12) for a more complete discussion.

ditions that day. Despite the fact that weather conditions cannot be manipulated at will, and despite the fact that, say, humidity may be correlated with temperature, the beta weights in this regression equation would give information on the causal importance of each aspect of the weather.

The questions which arise in connection with this example illustrate the types of questions which must be considered in any use of the technique. For example, in connection with Assumption 1 above, we must ask: (a) "Does temperature have a positive beta weight because vacations come in the summer, and people drive more during vacations?" (This could be handled by, say, using number of accidents per vehicle mile as the dependent variable.) (b) "Does an aspect of the weather which has not been recorded, but which correlates with some measures which were recorded, affect accidents?" (This would result in spuriously high beta weights for these recorded measures.) Similar questions arise concerning the appropriateness of Assumption 2, although Assumption 3 seems to hold for this example.

Whenever a causal relationship is established in any branch of science, there is always the possibility of investigating the causal relationships which mediate those relationships found. This is true of the present technique. Thus, if hot weather is found to increase accidents, there remains for future investigators the task of discovering whether this is mediated by the effect of heat on the alertness of drivers, on the reliability of brakes, or on other factors. This consideration, however, does not lessen the value of the original finding.

The method has been developed far beyond the limits indicated here. More complete discussions by social scientists of this and related techniques can be found in Simon (39), Blalock (4), Monroe and Stuit (34), Dunlap and Cureton (14), and Burks (6). The method was first developed by Wright (47) in the biological sciences, where it is known as "path analysis." Recent general discussions of the method were given by Wright (48) and by Turner and Stevens (41). At least one of these should be read by anyone planning to use the technique. Detailed recent discussions of particular aspects of path analysis have been given by Wright (49, 50) and by Turner, Monroe, and Lucas (42). These and the more general articles also give references to further literature in the area. They also discuss in detail techniques applicable when some of the independent variables are themselves affected by other independent variables. The simple technique outlined above still applies in this situation, but the weight given to each independent variable measures only the direct causal effect which that variable has on the dependent variable, ignoring effects which operate indirectly through the effect which the independent variable has on other independent variables.

USEFULNESS

When the focus is on the prediction of X_0, rather than causal analysis, usefulness is clearly the measure of greatest interest. Usefulness actually has a closer relationship to a partial correlation coefficient than does β'_j; it can be shown that dividing the usefulness of X_j by $1 - \bar{R}^2$ gives the squared partial correlation between X_0 and X_j, holding all other variables constant. Since $1 - \bar{R}^2$ is constant for a given regression equation, it follows that the usefulnesses of the predictor variables in a regression equation are proportional to these squared partial correlations.

It follows directly from Formula 4 that β'_j equals the validity of the orthogonal component of X_j (i.e., the square root of the usefulness of X_j), divided by the standard deviation of the same orthogonal component (when all the original variables are expressed in standard-score form). Thus, if two variables are equally useful, the one with the larger β' weight has the orthogonal component with the smaller variance.

The hypothesis that a predictor variable has zero usefulness in the population is equivalent to the hypothesis that the variable has a population beta weight of zero, so the significance tests of these two hypotheses are the same. The parametric test of this hypothesis is an F test, described in McNemar (33, p. 284) and elsewhere. The F value given by this test equals $r_{0 \cdot j(p)}^2$ (which is the sample usefulness of the variable in question), multiplied by the fraction $(N - n - 1)/(1 - R^2)$. This fraction is, of course, constant for all the variables in a given regression equation. Hence the F statistic is equivalent to usefulness as a measure of the relative importance of the variables in a given regression equation. If a worker has access to a computer program which computes this F value for each predictor variable (if the test available is a t test, then t^2 equals F), then he can readily find each variable's usefulness by dividing F by the above fraction.

$\beta'_{j\rho 0 j}$

It can be shown that $\bar{R}^2$ can be calculated from β' weights by the formula[6]

$$\bar{R} = \beta'_1 \rho_{01} + \beta'_2 \rho_{02} + \ldots + \beta'_n \rho_{0n}$$

This formula has suggested to several writers (7, 27, and personal communications from several sources) that $\beta'_j \rho_{0j}$ must be a measure of the "importance" of X_j, since it totals to $\bar{R}^2$ when summed across all the variables in the regression equation, and all measures of importance have this property when predictor variables are uncorrelated. Ward (43) raised a question concerning the value of the measure; in defense, Hoffman (28) called it the unique measure of the "independent contribution" of X_j. Ward's position will be restated and elaborated, since the present position is in basic agreement with it.

Although it is the province of an author to assign a name like "measure of independent contribution" to any statistic he proposes, this particular name has accumulated a good deal of "surplus meaning" by virtue of the

6. See Theorem 9 of the document cited in Footnote 2.

powerful properties which it has when predictor variables are uncorrelated, as in analysis-of-variance designs, where its meaning is highly specific. Partly as a review, the following is a list of meanings which "independent contribution" has when predictor variables are uncorrelated:

1. The squared validity of X_j.
2. The usefulness of X_j.
3. $\beta'_j{}^2$.
4. The amount the variance of the regression equation would drop if X_j were removed from the equation, expressed as a proportion of σ_0^2.
5. The amount the covariance between the regression equation and X_0 would drop if X_j were removed, expressed as a proportion of σ_0^2.
6. The increase in the variance of $X_{0(p)}$ when X_j is removed from the equation, expressed as a proportion of σ_0^2.
7. The average difference, expressed as a proportion of σ_0^2, between σ_0^2 and the variance of X_0 in subpopulations in which X_j is held constant.

This list attempts to include all of the major properties which most readers consciously or unconsciously associate with the term "independent contribution." It is thus of considerable interest to note that $\beta'_{j\rho 0j}$ has none of these properties. As a minor exception, $\beta'_{j\rho 0j}$ has Property 5 if the remaining variables in the regression equation are not reweighed after removal of X_j, but this is not a property of any particular interest.

Although all of the measures in the above list do sum to $\bar{R}^2$ when predictor variables are uncorrelated, this fact alone does not justify the use of a measure, simply on the grounds that it sums to $\bar{R}^2$ even when predictor variables are intercorrelated. It would be better to simply concede that the notion of "independent contribution to variance" has no meaning when predictor variables are intercorrelated. The meaninglessness of $\beta'_{j\rho 0j}$ as a measure of importance is further underscored by the fact that it can be zero, or even negative, in cases in which X_j contributes substantially to the prediction of X_0.

Englehart assigned a "contribution to variance" not only to each predictor variable, but also to the joint effect of each pair of predictor variables. He based his system on the formula

$$\bar{R}^2 = \beta'_1{}^2 + \beta'_2{}^2 + \ldots + \beta'_n{}^2 + 2\beta'_1\beta'_2\rho_{12} + 2\beta'_1\beta'_3\rho_{13} + \ldots + 2\beta'_{n-1}\beta'_n\rho_{(n-1)n}$$

Each of the first n terms in this sum is labeled the "contribution to variance" of the corresponding predictor variable, while each of the last $[n(n-1)]/2$ terms is called the contribution of the "joint effect" of two variables. This analysis was accepted by McNemar (33, p. 176).

The criticisms of this measure are similar to those of $\beta'_j\rho_{0j}$; the measure has none of the most important properties that a "contribution to variance" has when variables are uncorrelated. The concept of the "joint contribution to variance" of two predictor variables might connote to some readers a measure of the amount that $\bar{R}^2$ would drop if the two predictor variables were somehow made uncorrelated. This connotation would be incorrect; in fact, if β'_j, β'_k, and ρ_{jk} are all positive, so that the "joint contribution to variance" of X_j and X_k is positive in Englehart's system, then $\bar{R}^2$ would actually *increase* if ρ_{jk} were zero.

Inferring Relative Regression Weights from Relative Validities

This section briefly mentions a series of papers which deal with a problem, or set of problems, which is not clearly defined. Although these papers have not traditionally been considered to be closely related to regression theory, they are mentioned briefly here since a regression solution can be proposed for at least one of the problems with which they deal. All of these papers deal in some fashion with the relationship between the weight of a variable in a weighted average of several variables, and the "importance" of the variable to that composite. The weights of the variables in the composite may have been chosen by any subjective or objective method. This freedom in the method of assigning weights distinguishes these papers from those mentioned in the previous section, which assume that regression weights are used. For all of the measures of importance referred to in the present section, increasing the weight of a variable increases its importance.

Some of these papers (8, 37) simply propose statistical measures of importance, calling the proposed measure the "effective weight" or "contribution to variance" of the variable. (In every case, the latter term is subject in large part to the same criticism made of the term in the previous section.) Others (16, 29, 45) go one step further, first adopting one particular measure of importance, and then showing how the variables should be weighted so that all of the variables are equally important, or, more generally, how the variables should be weighted so that the measures of importance of the different variables are proportional to some specified set of numbers.

These methods, then, are intended to be used for weighting variables in situations in which regression equations cannot be derived because the criterion variable is not easily observable, even though it exists in some meaningful sense. Although all of these papers give careful descriptions of the statistical properties of the resulting composite, none gives an example of a practical situation in which the composite can be shown to have optimum properties. Most of the papers state that the procedure for specifying the desired relative sizes of the measures of importance would vary across situations. This statement, though true, has been allowed to obscure the fact that not one of the papers gives even the slightest hint, even for one situation, how one should go about specifying these values. In other words, none of the papers makes a convincing case for the practical value of the particular measure of importance proposed.

In approaching the present problem, it would seem that the first question to be asked is what a layman or a psychologist is likely to mean when he tells a psychometrician that he wants several variables to be weighted so that they are, for example, "equally important." Most commonly, (though certainly not always), he probably means that he estimates the variables to correlate equally with some specified but unobservable criterion variable. In this case, use can be made of the property of multiple regression equations—obvious from an inspection of the normal equations of regression theory—that the relative weights of the predictor variables in a multiple regression equation can be determined from a knowledge of only the relative (rather than absolute) sizes of the correlations of the predictor variables with a criterion variable. That is, if the validities of all the predictor variables in a multiple regression equation are multiplied by the same constant and the beta weights are then recomputed using the new validities and the old matrix of predictor intercorrelations, the relative sizes of the weights will be unchanged; each weight will simply be multiplied by the same constant by which the validities were multiplied.

This fact enables the estimation of the optimum relative weights of several predictor variables even when the criterion variable is not directly observable, provided there is some estimate of the relative validities of the variables. For example, suppose several observers are estimated to be equally accurate raters of some trait on which subjects are to be ranked. Suppose the ratings by these observers are available, and the problem is to find the optimum relative weights for a weighted average of the raters. A problem of this type was described by Dunnette and Hoggatt (15). A solution to this problem could proceed as follows. An arbitrarily chosen number can be entered into a multiple regression computer program as the common validity of the raters, along with the ob-served standard deviations and intercorrelations of the raters, and along with an arbitrarily chosen value for the standard deviation of the criterion variable. The weights computed by the regression program are then the weights used to form a composite variable. If the user has entered into the program accurate estimates of the relative validities of the different variables, then this composite is optimum in the obviously important sense that it correlates higher with the unobservable "criterion" variable than any other composite using different relative weights.

The technique thus makes explicit the measure of importance (i.e., simple validity) which one should use in specifying the relative importance of the different variables. The reader should be cautioned that the technique does not apply—at least in the simple form outlined above—to another common situation in which the validity of each predictor variable is estimated from the correlation of that variable with other predictor variables, rather than from external data as in the above example.

In using the technique, the arbitrarily chosen validities should not be set so high that they are inconsistent with the observed intercorrelations of the variables. For example, if two variables correlate zero with each other, it can be shown that they cannot both correlate .9 with the same criterion variable. Setting validities so high that such an inconsistency appears does not distort the relative weights computed by the program, but will usually produce one of two otherwise puzzling results (depending on the computer program used): The program will fail to run, or it will compute and print a value of $\bar{R}$ above unity.

Estimates of the Validity of Regression Equations

ESTIMATING THE VALIDITY OF THE POPULATION REGRESSION EQUATION

Let the term "population regression equation" refer to the equation developed in the entire population using predictor variables X_1, $X_2, \ldots, X_n$ to predict X_0; the validity of this equation is measured by the population multiple correlation $\bar{R}$. Likewise, let the term "sample regression equation" refer to an equation using the same variables which is developed in any random sample from that population; the validity of this equation in that same sample is measured by the sample multiple correlation R.

Normally, a sample multiple correlation is higher than the corresponding population multiple correlation. In the extreme instance in which a regression equation using one predictor variable is developed in a sample of only two individuals, the sample multiple correlation is unity in all but trivial cases, no matter what the population correlation is. In general, the same result occurs whenever the number of predictor variables n is one less than the sample size N. If n is greater than or equal to N, then the solution is indeterminate; infinitely many sets of weights will yield sample multiple correlations of unity.

It is often useful to describe the validity of a regression equation in terms of its mean square error; this quantity is the mean of the squared differences between each person's true criterion score and the prediction of that score made by the regression equation.

The expected value of the mean square error in a sample of size N in which a regression equation is developed is equal to $(N-n-1)/N$ times the mean square error in the population of the population regression equation. Therefore, the reciprocal of this fraction times the sample mean square error is an unbiased estimator of the population mean square error. Since the latter mean square error equals the population variance of the component of X_0 orthogonal to the predictors, it is denoted by $\sigma_{0(p)}^2$, as mentioned earlier. Similarly, the sample mean square error is

$$s_{0(p)}^2 = \frac{1}{N} \sum_i (x_{i0} - \hat{x}_{i0})^2$$

where $\hat{x}_{i0}$ is the predicted score of person i on X_0, as made by the sample regression equation. Thus, the formula for an unbiased estimator of $\sigma_{0(p)}^2$ is

$$\hat{\sigma}_{0(p)}^2 = \frac{N}{N-n-1} s_{0(p)}^2 \qquad \text{Eq. 11}$$

An examination of the derivation of this estimator (20, p. 111) shows it to be unbiased even if none of the usual assumptions of linearity, homoscedasticity, and normality holds, although without these assumptions little can be said about its efficiency.

A special case of Formula 11 is the case in which $n = 0$. In this case, the prediction of any individual's criterion score is the sample mean, so that the sample mean square error is the sample variance of the criterion variable. By the same reasoning, the population mean square error is the population variance of the criterion variable. Hence, the familiar formula which states that $N/(N-1)$ times the sample variance gives an unbiased estimate of the population variance is simply the special case of the previous formula in which $n = 0$.

The population mean square error is related to the multiple correlation by the formula

$$\bar{R} = \sqrt{1 - (\sigma_{0(p)}^2 / \sigma_0^2)} \qquad \text{Eq. 12}$$

which is merely the translation into present notation of a familiar formula taught in most undergraduate statistics courses. Wherry (44) suggested that $\bar{R}$ could be estimated by substituting into this formula the estimates of $\sigma_{0(p)}^2$ and σ_0^2 described in the previous two paragraphs. He further pointed out that the ratio between these two estimates is a function of the sample multiple correlation. The resulting formula can be found in McNemar (33, p. 184) and elsewhere.

Although the Wherry formula is based on unbiased estimators of σ_0^2 and $\sigma_{0(p)}^2$, in itself it is not an unbiased estimator of $\bar{R}$ in the strict statistical sense, contrary to McNemar (33, p. 184) and others. However, this is no grounds for criticism of the formula, since it has long been known that any unbiased estimator of $\bar{R}$ has properties which make it clearly inferior to certain biased estimators. By definition, an estimator is unbiased only if the mean of an infinite number of estimates from independent random samples equals the parameter estimated, no matter what the value of that parameter is. When $\bar{R}$ is less than 1, no estimate of $\bar{R}$ based on finite samples can be perfect, that is, yield exactly correct estimates of $\bar{R}$ in every sample. Therefore, if $\bar{R} = 0$, an estimator which is unbiased must be one which can yield negative estimates in some samples. But this means that a statistic, in order to be an unbiased estimator of $\bar{R}$, must be able to assume values which the parameter estimated cannot assume, since $\bar{R}$ is greater than or equal to zero. Clearly, whenever an estimate of $\bar{R}$ is negative, the estimate can be improved by estimating $\bar{R}$ to be zero, since zero is always closer to the true $\bar{R}$ than is the negative estimate. But although this modification of the estimation procedure is obviously an improvement, it no longer yields an unbiased estimate of $\bar{R}$. Therefore, unbiased estimators of $\bar{R}$ are clearly not the best estimators. For similar reasons, unbiased estimators of $\bar{R}^2$ are of no practical interest. These points were made by Olkin and Pratt (36), who nevertheless developed an unbiased estimator of $\bar{R}^2$.

ESTIMATING THE VALIDITY OF A SAMPLE REGRESSION EQUATION

Lord (32) and Nicholson (35) have pointed out that the Wherry formula has often been misinterpreted as an estimator of the true validity (i.e., the validity in the population) of a multiple regression equation developed in a sample. Actually, it overestimates this validity. The Wherry formula estimates, instead, the validity of the *population* regression equation, which was the equation developed in the entire population rather than in a sample. This equation, by definition, has a higher validity in the population than any other linear equation using the same predictor variables. In general, the weights in a sample regression equation will not be exactly equal to the weights in the population equation. The sample regression equation will then necessarily have a lower validity in the population than will the population regression equation. Thus, the Wherry formula generally overestimates the population validity of a sample regression equation, because it actually estimates a parameter (the validity of the population regression equation) which is higher than this validity.

The same distinction must be made if the validities of the two types of regression equation are measured in a second (cross-validation) random sample from the population. If any regression equation, based either on the entire population or on a random sample from that population, is applied to a cross-validation sample, then the expected mean square error of that equation in the cross-validation sample equals the mean square error of that equation in the population. Since the regression equation developed in a sample does not predict as well in the population as does the population regression equation, it would therefore also not be expected to predict as well in a random cross-validation sample from the population.

Hence, three different m   square errors must be distinguished. The smallest, and normally the easiest to observe, is the sample mean square error of the equation developed in that same sample. The second and next smallest is the population mean square error of the equation developed in the entire population; this equals the expected mean square error of that equation in any random sample. The third and largest is the mean square error of a sample regression equation in the population, which equals the expected mean square error of such an equation in a cross-validation sample. The Wherry formula is based on a formula which estimates the second of these three mean square errors from the first, while a prediction of cross-validity requires predicting the third from the first. In his original article, Wherry failed to distinguish between the second and third of these mean square errors, and the resulting confusion still appears in even the most recent standard sources, such as Guilford (22, p. 401) and Guion (23, pp. 163–164). Since the Wherry formula was thus often misused to attempt to predict the cross-validity of a sample regression equation, it was often observed to overestimate this quantity (i.e., to underestimate the mean square error).

Lord and Nicholson, working independently, found that an unbiased estimator of the population mean square error of a regression equation developed in a sample of size N is

$$\frac{N+n+1}{N-n-1} s_{0(p)}{}^2 \qquad \text{Eq. 13}$$

In their derivations, Lord and Nicholson assumed that the conditional distributions of X_0 are normal, have a common variance, and are linearly related to the predictor variables. They further assumed that the scores observed on the predictor variables are fixed by the investigator, rather than sampled randomly from a population (the usual case in psychology). If we replace the assumption of fixed scores by the assumption of random sampling, and replace the other assumptions by the assumption that scores on all variables form a multivariate normal distribution, then the estimator comparable to Formula 13 is

$$\frac{N-2}{N-n-2} \cdot \frac{N+1}{N-n-1} s_{0(p)}{}^2 \qquad \text{Eq. 14}$$

This estimator gives still larger estimates of the mean square errors than does Formula 13, except in the trivial case in which $n = 0$, in which instance the two estimates are identical. Formula 14 is an algebraic rearrangement of a formula given by Stein (40, p. 427). An independent derivation by the present author, which is longer but which requires less mathematical competence to follow, is given under Theorem 18 of the document cited in Footnote 2.

Unfortunately, there is as yet no practical means of establishing a confidence interval around estimates computed from either Formula 13 or 14; empirical work suggests that their standard errors might be quite large.

An extremely important property of Formulas 13 and 14 is that the estimated true validity of a sample multiple regression equation is very low (and the mean square error very high) when the number of predictor variables is large in relation to the number of people in the sample on which the equation was derived. This is often observed in practice. For example, Guttman (25, p. 360) constructed a regression equation with 84 predictor variables using 136 subjects, and observed a correlation with the criterion variable of .73 in the initial sample and .04 in a cross-validation sample. Thus, it is often better to use fewer predictor variables, or to use a different prediction method altogether, than to use a regression equation with an extremely large number of variables. For example, using the same data, Guttman observed a cross-validity of .20 using a regression equation with 21 variables, and a crossvalidity of .31 for a simple item-analytic technique.

RELATION BETWEEN THE MEAN SQUARE ERROR AND THE CORRELATION COEFFICIENT

The points to be made in this section are relevant to measures other than multiple regression equations, even though they will be phrased in regression terms.

Formula 12 shows the well-known means of translating the mean square error of a population regression equation into the coefficient of correlation between the regression equation and the criterion variable. However, when the mean square error of a *sample* regression equation is computed in a cross-validation sample or in the population as a whole, neither Formula 12 nor any other formula provides an exact translation of that mean square error into a coefficient of correlation between the regression equation and the criterion variable. This is because two regression equations can have different mean square errors yet correlate equally with the criterion variable. Suppose that two sample regression equations are based on the same predictor variables, and that the weights within the first equation have exactly the same relative sizes as the weights within the second. Then the two equations will correlate equally with the criterion variable. But if the actual sizes of the weights, or the size of the additive constant a, differ between the two equations, then the two equations will have different mean square errors in the population or in a cross-validation sample.

Just as two regression equations with different mean square errors may correlate equally with the criterion variable, parallel reasoning shows that two equations with the same mean square error may have different correlations with the criterion variable. Thus a cross-validity mean square error computed in a second sample, or estimated by Formula 13 or 14, cannot be translated exactly into a correlation coefficient by formulas analogous to Formula 12. If N is large, however, the familiar formula for translating a mean square error into a correlation coefficient should give a good approximation.

When a regression equation or other measure is used to select the m individuals estimated to be highest on the criterion variable and m is fixed by the situation, then the value of the measure depends only upon the relative, not absolute, scores of the individuals on that measure. Since the correlation coefficient likewise depends only on relative scores, it follows that, in this situation, the correlation between the measure and the criterion variable gives a more realistic statement of the value of the measure than does the mean square error. On the other hand, when m is not predetermined, whether a person is selected depends upon his absolute score on the measure rather than upon the relationship of that score to the scores of other individuals. In this situation, the value of a measure is a function of the actual difference between a person's estimated and true criterion scores; therefore, the mean square error is a more appropriate index of the value of the measure than is the correlation coefficient. For this reason, Formulas 13 and 14 are most useful in a situation in which the number of people to be selected by a measure is flexible rather than predetermined. (None of this is meant to imply, however, that either the multiple correlation coefficient or the mean square error is *proportional* to the value of a test battery, as value is measured in decision theory terms.)

Statistical Criteria for Selecting Predictor Variables

Formulas 13 and 14 show the desirability of selecting a small number of predictor variables for use in a regression equation when v, the total number of available variables, is large. This section discusses several methods which have been proposed for doing this. All methods discussed below involve complex computational manipulations, such as inverting the $v \times v$ correlation matrix of predictor variables. Although modern computers use approximate methods to perform these calculations, the calculations are so complex that either the computational time or the rounding errors increase rapidly as v increases. As a very rough rule, when v is larger than approximately 50–100, item-analytic methods discussed by Darlington and Bishop (11) are preferable to any of the methods discussed below, both because they are simpler computationally and because tests constructed by those methods have been demonstrated to perform better on cross-validation when the number of people in the test-construction sample is small. Roughly speaking, the methods discussed below are of most interest when $10 < v < 50$, but may be of value when $5 < v < 100$.

If an investigator wishes to predict a criterion variable by a regression or least squares technique, and he has available v possible predictor variables, he can use in the equation all v variables (so that n, the number of predictor variables used in the regression equation, is equal to v). Or, he can discard all v predictor variables (so that $n = 0$) and use the sample mean of the criterion variable as the prediction of each person's criterion score. Or, he can use a regression equation with less than v predictors (so that $v > n > 0$). Since he can choose independently whether to include or exclude each of the v variables, he is faced with 2^v possible alternative sets of predictor variables, plus sets formed by lumping together several variables and then entering them in a regression equation as one variable.

In general, it is impractical to compute all of the 2^v or more possible regression equations and then estimate the validity of each equation, so it is necessary to follow some simpler procedure in choosing a final regression equation. The remainder of this section discusses several such procedures.

SELECTING VARIABLES TO MINIMIZE SAMPLING ERRORS OF BETA WEIGHTS

If the regression of X_0 on the predictor variables is linear and if the conditional distributions of X_0 have a common standard deviation, then the sampling distribution of each sample beta weight b_j has mean β_j (hence b_j is an unbiased estimator of β_j) and a conditional standard deviation

$$\sigma_{0(p)}/\sqrt{N}\,s_{j(p)} \qquad \text{Eq. 15}[7]$$

An estimate of Expression 15, using the estimate of $\sigma_{0(p)}^2$ given by Formula 11, is computed by most standard multiple regression computer programs. If we can also assume normality of the conditional distributions of

---

7. Although this expression as a whole is a population value, it contains the sample value $s_{i(p)}$ This usage will be new to many psychologists, although it is standard practice in some branches of statistical theory. Briefly, the expression as a whole is the standard deviation of the sampling distribution of b_j *in those samples which have a given value of $s_{j(p)}$*, rather than in all samples. This point is further clarified in the discussion at the beginning of Part II of the document cited in Footnote 2. Some of the points made briefly in the remainder of the present paragraph are also expanded there.

X_0 (or if N is large enough so that the central limit theorem applies), then dividing $b_j - \beta_j$ by this estimate of Expression 15 yields a statistic with a t distribution with $N - n - 1$ df. When β_j is set equal to zero, this test is equivalent to the F test mentioned earlier. Although many texts fail to mention it, Bartlett (2, esp. pp. 277–278) has shown that use of both Expression 15 and the t test is appropriate when the sample values on the predictor variables are determined by the random sampling procedure common in psychology, as well as in the case (more commonly discussed by statisticians) in which those values are fixed by the investigator.

Because the quantities N and $\sigma_{0(p)}$ in Expression 15 are the same for all the variables in any one regression equation, the standard errors of the several b_js in the equation are inversely proportional to the values of $s_{j(p)}$, which are the observed standard deviations of the orthogonal components of the various predictor variables. The quantity $s_{j(p)}$ is generally large if X_j has low correlations with the other predictor variables and small if X_j is highly correlated with the other predictors; therefore, the weights of the variables which have the lowest correlation with other predictor variables are generally the weights which are least subject to sampling errors.

Cureton (9, pp. 12–15; 10, p. 691) referred to the number of variables which must be removed from a set of predictor variables in order to leave the remaining variables reasonably uncorrelated with each other as the number of "approximate linear restraints" in the set. He recommended that variables be removed or combined so as to eliminate the approximate linear restraints, in order to maximize $s_{j(p)}$ for each j and thus minimize the sampling errors of beta weights in the regression equation. His recommendation was apparently accepted by Guilford (2, p. 404). It will be shown, however, that Formulas 13 and 14 raise considerable doubt as to the value of this strategy.

Consider a situation with three predictor variables, X_1, X_2, and X_3. Suppose the initial-sample validity of the regression equation using X_1 and X_2 equals the initial-sample validity of the equation using X_1 and X_3, but suppose that r_{12}^2 is lower than r_{13}^2. In this situation, an investigator following Cureton's recommendation would prefer using the former of the two equations, since the estimated standard errors of the beta weights are lower in that equation, even though the initial-sample validities of the two equations are the same.

On the other hand, when Formula 13 or 14 is used to estimate the true validity of a regression equation, intercorrelations of the predictor variables are ignored except insofar as they affect the initial-sample validity. Hence, in the above example, the predicted cross-validities of the two regression equations would be the same, despite the differences in the estimated sampling errors of the beta weights caused by the difference between r_{12}^2 and r_{13}^2.

We thus have the paradoxical situation that the sizes of the errors in estimates of beta weights do not enter into the estimation of the true validity of a regression equation.

The solution to this paradox lies in the nature of the correlation between the two sample beta weights within the same equation (i.e., the correlation we would observe if we drew infinitely many equal-sized independent random samples from the population, computed two regression weights b_j and b_k in each sample, and then correlated b_j with b_k across the samples). In a regression equation with n variables, the correlation between any two weights b_j and b_k equals -1 times the partial correlation between X_j and X_k, partialing out the other $n-2$ predictor variables.[8] This correlation is defined as the correlation between the com-

ponents of X_j and X_k orthogonal to the other $n-2$ predictor variables. In the present example, in which $n = 2$, there are no other predictor variables; hence, the correlation between b_1 and b_2 is $-r_{12}$. Thus in this example, if r_{12} is positive, the correlation between the two sample beta weights is negative. Since sample beta weights are unbiased estimates of the corresponding population weights, this means that if r_{12} is positive, an overestimation of one beta weight will tend to be found in the same sample with an underestimation of the other beta weight. Further, the higher the value of r_{12}, the more probable it is that this relationship exists.

This fact becomes important when considered in conjunction with the effect of different combinations of errors in the two beta weights on the validity of the regression equation. When two predictor variables are positively correlated, then, if an error is made in estimating one beta weight, the adverse effect of this error on validity can be lessened by an error in the opposite direction in estimating the other beta weight. The higher the correlation between the two variables, the greater is the ability of errors in opposite directions to compensate for each other in the prediction of criterion scores, since the predictors are increasingly "substitutable" for each other.[9] In the extreme case in which two variables of equal variance correlate perfectly, any two pairs of beta weights with the same sum are completely equivalent to each other. For example, in this extreme instance, weights of .8 and $-.2$, of .3 and .3, and of $-.1$ and .7 are all equivalent since each pair sums to .6.[10]

Hence, when r_{12} is positive, the sampling errors of the two beta weights are larger than if $r_{12} = 0$, but the errors tend to be in

---

8. This statement assumes linearity and homoscedasticity but not normality. The statement is exactly correct only if values on the predictor variables are fixed by the experimenter; if instead they are sampled randomly (the most common case in psychology), then we use, instead of all samples, the subset of samples with given values of the predictor variables. See Theorem 16 of the document cited in Footnote 2.

9. The last two statements follow directly from a formula proven by Guttman (25, p. 305). It is given without proof as Theorem 17 of the document cited in Footnote 2.
10. The truth of this statement is unaffected by the fact that standard methods of deriving multiple regression weights break down when two predictor variables are perfectly correlated.

opposite directions and such errors tend to compensate for each other in a manner lacking when $r_{12} = 0$.

Errors in beta weights also tend to compensate for each other when r_{12} is negative. Again, in the extreme case in which $r_{12} = -1$, the compensation is perfect. Thus, it is precisely in those situations in which errors in the estimates of beta weights tend to be largest that the adverse effect of these errors on validity is minimized by the pattern in which the errors tend to occur. This is true for regression techniques with any number of variables.[11] Therefore an investigator seeking to choose which of several regression equations has the highest true validity need not concern himself directly with sampling errors of beta weights. He should simply choose the equation for which Formula 13 or 14 predicts the lowest cross-validation mean square error, based on the number of individuals in the initial sample, the number of predictor variables in an equation, and the initial-sample validity (expressed in terms of the initial-sample mean square error).

The laws described above also explain the paradoxical but common finding that when predictor variables are highly correlated, regression equations developed in two different random samples from the same population often have widely different weights, yet both equations predict about equally well in both samples. In a typical example of this effect in operation, a psychologist using the Graduate Record Exam Verbal Aptitude Test and the Miller Analogies Test to predict a criterion of success in graduate school found that the regression equation developed in one half of his sample gave a high positive weight to the GRE and a near-zero weight to the MAT, while the equation developed in the other half of his sample did exactly the opposite, giving the MAT a high positive

11. These few paragraphs are an attempt to reconcile Formulas 13 and 14 with facts which at first seem to contradict them, using the simplest case of two predictor variables. A more rigorous development of the reasoning presented would simply amount to proofs of those formulas.

weight and the GRE a near-zero weight. Yet each equation worked almost as well in the other half of the sample as in the half in which it was originally derived.

REMOVING VARIABLES WITH SMALL BETA WEIGHTS

It was shown above that the predictor variables with the smallest β' weights in a population regression equation are not necessarily those whose removal would cause the smallest drop in the population validity of that equation. The same relationship clearly holds between initial-sample beta weights and initial-sample validity.

Formulas 13 and 14 show that when two regression equations have the same number of predictor variables, the one which has the higher initial-sample validity has the higher estimated true validity. Since removing variables with the smallest beta weights is not the most efficient way to achieve the highest possible initial-sample validity after the removal of a given number of predictor variables, it follows that this is also not the best way to maximize true validity.

STEPWISE REGRESSION

The foregoing discussion has made it clear that the only statistics relevant to selecting predictor variables from a larger number of variables are the initial-sample validity, N, and n for each of the possible regression equations formed from different combinations of the variables. The technique of stepwise regression, for which computer programs are widely available, has the desirable property that it uses only these statistics.

This technique selects variables for a regression equation one at a time. Selecting first the most valid predictor variable, it then selects that variable which when combined with the first is the most useful—that is, the one which adds the most to the multiple correlation and which thus yields the best two-predictor equation among those equations which contain the first variable selected. The extent to which the multiple correlation would be increased by a variable is determined by computing the validity of the orthogonal component or some mathematically equivalent statistic for the predictor variable being considered. The technique then selects by the same criterion the variable which combines with the first two variables to produce the best three-predictor equation. Subsequent variables are selected in a similar manner. Variables can also be removed if they are found to be no longer useful.

The process can be stopped when the initial-sample validity of the equation approaches that computed using all available variables, or when adding the most useful remaining variable produces no statistically significant increase in the multiple correlation by the significance test mentioned earlier. Significance tests are not normally appropriate for this purpose, however, since addition of a variable to a regression equation does not normally require a definite rejection of the hypothesis that fewer variables would suffice. Perhaps the best strategy is to use Formula 13 or 14 to evaluate each of the regression equations calculated by a stepwise regression computer program, and then to select the one equation which appears best by this criterion. Of course, Formula 13 and 14 will then underestimate the mean square error of the equation so selected for the same reason that the correlation between a test and a criterion variable can be expected to shrink if the test was selected from a large number of tests on the basis of this correlation.

FACTOR ANALYSIS OF PREDICTOR VARIABLES

Another technique for reducing the number of predictor variables is to factor analyze the set of all available predictors and then use some of the resulting factors in a regression equation in place of the original variables. This section discusses the conditions under which this procedure or variations of it are

likely to improve the prediction of the criterion variable.

If the number of factors extracted equals the original number of predictor variables, then it can be shown that the multiple regression equation constructed to predict the criterion variable from the factors is equivalent to the comparable equation constructed from the original variables. The two equations will make identical predictions for any individual since the weight given to each original variable in the equation based on factors exactly equals the weight given that same variable in the regression equation based on the original variables.[12] Therefore, any improvement resulting from the use of factors as predictors can occur only when the number of factors used is smaller than the number of original predictor variables.

Because of this, often only the few factors which account for the most variance are used (cf. 30, pp. 437–444). However, from a purely mathematical standpoint, it could conceivably happen that the factor which accounts for the least variance in the predictor variables could correlate perfectly with the criterion variable, and all other factors could correlate zero with the criterion. Therefore, if factor analysis is a possibility, it is important to consider, from the nature of the variables being factored, whether this or a similar result is likely to occur.

When the variables being factored contain substantial error variance, it is well known that this error tends to be concentrated in the factors which account for the least variance, with a resultant increase in the reliability and therefore the validity of the other factors. In such a situation, the strategy of using in a regression equation only the several factors which account for the most variance would have much to recommend it.

The situation is different when highly reliable variables, such as age, sex, or census data, are used. In such situations, it could happen that factors which account for very

12. See the discussion under Theorem 11 of the document cited in Footnote 2.

little variance in the predictor variables are highly useful in predicting the criterion. For example, if two of the original variables are highly correlated, such as subject's age and age of the subject's next younger sibling (assuming he has one), a factor consisting of the difference between these two scores would "account for" very little variance in the original two variables. Yet this difference might well have had an important effect on the subject's childhood and therefore might correlate more highly with an external criterion than, say, a factor consisting of the sum of the two ages, which accounts for far more variance in the original predictor variables. In such situations, two alternative strategies are especially worthy of consideration: stepwise regression (discussed above), and stepwise regression using all of the factors rather than the original variables. When factors are uncorrelated, it follows from Formula 3 that the latter procedure simply involves selecting the factors most highly correlated with the criterion variable. Both these strategies have the desirable property that only the usefulness of each predictor variable is considered in the selection of variables, and this property is not shared by any strategy which considers only the factors which account for the most variance in the original set of predictor variables. An empirical comparison of the two stepwise methods have been made by Burket (5).

Summary

BASIC FORMULAS

The beta weight and usefulness of a predictor variable in a multiple regression equation are expressed simply in terms of the properties of the component of the variable orthogonal to the other predictor variables.

SUPPRESSOR VARIABLES

A variable receives a negative weight in a regression equation if the ratio between its correlation with the error in the rest of the equation, and its correlation with the criterion variable, exceeds a certain amount.

The relations possible among sets of variables are so complex that when a variable with a positive correlation with the criterion variable receives a negative weight in a regression equation, it is generally very difficult or impossible to determine, from the content of the variables, whether the negative weight is "unreasonable".

MEASURES OF THE "IMPORTANCE" OF A PREDICTOR VARIABLE

When the predictor variables in a multiple regression equation are intercorrelated, the "contribution to variance" of a predictor variable cannot be interpreted in the same way that it can be interpreted when predictor variables are uncorrelated. In the latter case, the phrase has essentially the same meaning it has in analysis-of-variance designs.

If the usefulness of a predictor variable is defined as the amount that the squared multiple correlation would drop if the variable were removed, then rank ordering the predictor variables in a regression equation gives different orders depending on whether the ranking is by validity, by usefulness, or by the absolute value of the beta weight. This is true even if all variables have the same standard deviation.

From the sizes of the weights in a multiple regression equation predicting a specified dependent variable from several independent variables, it is sometimes possible to measure the size of the "effect" which each of the independent variables has on the dependent variable.

Two measures of "importance," which sum to $\bar{R}^2$ when summed across all variables in a regression equation, have little practical value.

INFERRING RELATIVE REGRESSION WEIGHTS FROM RELATIVE VALIDITIES

The relative sizes of the weights in a regression equation can be computed from the relative validities (correlations with the criterion variable) of the predictor variables, even if the actual validities are unknown. This provides an exact solution to a common practical problem.

ESTIMATES OF THE VALIDITY OF REGRESSION EQUATIONS

The Wherry formula estimates the validity of the multiple regression equation developed in a population from the validity of an equation developed in a sample.

Statistics which give strictly unbiased estimates of a population multiple correlation coefficient are of no practical interest.

The Wherry formula has been used widely but incorrectly to estimate the cross-validity of a regression equation developed in a sample. Two alternative formulas are the correct formulas for this situation.

These alternative formulas produce extremely low estimates of cross-validity when the number of predictor variables is large in relation to the number of cases used in developing the regression equation. This agrees with the results of empirical cross-validation studies. Therefore, cross-validity is sometimes enhanced by using fewer predictor variables or by using a different prediction method altogether.

Estimates of the true validity of a sample regression equation can be expressed either as correlation coefficients or as mean square errors. Unfortunately, estimates in one form cannot always be readily converted to the other form, despite the well-known formula relating the two in other situations. The correlation coefficient is more useful in "fixed quota" situations, and the mean square error is more useful in "flexible quota" situations.

STATISTICAL CRITERIA FOR SELECTING PREDICTOR VARIABLES

The method of "approximate linear restraints" is not the most effective method of selecting predictor variables, because of the highly paradoxical relationship between the validity of a regression equation and the sampling errors of beta weights in the equation.

The same analysis explains the fact that regression equations developed in two different random samples from the same population often have surprisingly different beta weights, yet in any one sample the two equations make very similar predictions and thus have very similar validities.

The method of removing from a regression equation variables with low beta weights is not the most effective method, because such variables are not necessarily those whose removal produces the smallest drop in the multiple correlation.

Stepwise regression and extensions thereof are defended.

Under certain conditions, factor analysis can be used to develop a few factors which contain most of the valid variance in a set of predictor variables; under other conditions this procedure is not recommended.

References

1. Anderson, T. W. *Introduction to multivariate statistical analysis.* New York: Wiley, 1958.
2. Bartlett, M. S. On the theory of statistical regression. *Proceedings of the Royal Society of Edinburgh*, 1933, 53, 260–283.
3. Beaton, A. E. The use of special matrix operators in statistical calculus. (Research Bulletin No. 64–51) Princeton, N. J.: Educational Testing Service, 1964.
4. Blalock, H. M., Jr. *Causal inferences in non-experimental research.* Chapel Hill: University of North Carolina Press, 1964.
5. Burket, G. R. A study of reduced rank models for multiple prediction. *Psychometric Monographs*, 1964, No. 12.
6. Burks, B. S. On the inadequacy of the partial and multiple correlation technique. *Journal of Educational Psychology*, 1926, 17, 532–540, 625–630.
7. Chase, C. I. Computation of variance accounted for in multiple correlation. *Journal of Experimental Education*, 1960, 28, 265–266.
8. Creager, J. A., & Valentine, L. D., Jr. Regression analysis of linear composite variance. *Psychometrika*, 1962, 27, 31–38.

9. Cureton, E. E. Approximate linear restraints and best predictor weights. *Educational and Psychological Measurement*, 1951, 11, 12–15.

10. Cureton, E. E. Validity. In E. F. Lindquist (Ed.), *Educational measurement*. Washington, D.C.: American Council on Education, 1951.

11. Darlington, R. B., & Bishop, C. H. Increasing test validity by considering interitem correlations. *Journal of Applied Psychology*, 1966, 50, 322–330.

12. Darlington, R. B., & Paulus, D. H. On the use of interaction terms in multiple regression equations. Paper presented at the meeting of the Educational Research Association of New York State, Albany, November, 1966. (Available from the author.)

13. DuBois, P. H. *Multivariate correlational analysis*. New York: Harper, 1957.

14. Dunlap, J. W., & Cureton, E. E. On the analysis of causation. *Journal of Educational Psychology*, 1930, 21, 657–679.

15. Dunnette, M. D., & Hoggatt, A. C. Deriving a composite score from several measures of the same attribute. *Educational and Psychological Measurement*, 1957, 17, 423–434.

16. Edgerton, H. A., & Kolbe, L. E. The method of minimum variation for the combination of criteria. *Psychometrika*, 1936, 1, 183–188.

17. Elashoff, R. M., & Afifi, A. Missing values in multivariate statistics—I. Review of the literature. *Journal of the American Statistical Association*, 1966, 61, 595–604.

18. Englehart, M. D. The technique of path coefficients. *Psychometrika*, 1936, 1, 287–293.

19. Federer, W. T., & Zelen, M. Analysis of multifactor classification with unequal numbers of observations. *Biometrics*, 1966, 22, 525–552.

20. Graybill, F. A. *An introduction to linear statistical models*. Vol. 1. New York: McGraw-Hill, 1961.

21. Guilford, J. P. *Psychometric methods*. (2nd ed.) New York: McGraw-Hill, 1954.

22. Guilford, J. P. *Fundamental statistics in psychology and education*. (4th ed.) New York: McGraw-Hill, 1965.

23. Guion, R. M. *Personnel testing*. New York: McGraw-Hill, 1965.

24. Gulliksen, H. *Theory of mental tests*. New York: Wiley, 1950.

25. Guttman, L. Mathematical and tabulation techniques. Supplementary Study B. In P. Horst, *Prediction of personal adjustment*. (Bulletin No. 48) New York: Social Science Research Council, 1941.

26. Hays, W. L. *Statistics for psychologists*. New York: Holt, Rinehart & Winston, 1963.

27. Hoffman, P. J. The paramorphic representation of clinical judgment. *Psychological Bulletin*, 1960, 57, 116–131.

28. Hoffman, P. J. Assessment of the independent contributions of predictors. *Psychological Bulletin*, 1962, 59, 77–80.

29. Horst, P. Obtaining a composite measure from a number of different measures of the same attribute. *Psychometrika*, 1936, 1, 53–60.

30. Horst, P. *Prediction of personal adjustment*. (Bulletin No. 48) New York: Social Science Research Council, 1941.

31. Kendall, M. G. *A course in multivariate analysis*. London: Griffin, 1957.

32. Lord, F. M. Efficiency of prediction when a progression equation from one sample is used in a new sample. (Research Bulletin No. 50–40) Princeton, N. J.: Educational Testing Service, 1950. (Discussed by H. E. Brogden, Statistical theory and research design. *Annual Review of Psychology*, 1954, 5, 381.)

33. McNemar, Q. *Psychological statistics*. (3rd ed.) New York: Wiley, 1962.

34. Monroe, W. S., & Stuit, D. B. Correlation analysis as a means of studying contributions of causes. *Journal of Experimental Education*, 1935, 3, 155–165.

35. Nicholson, G. E., Jr. The application of a regression equation to a new sample. Unpublished doctoral dissertation, University of North Carolina, 1948. (Condensed in G. E. Nicholson, Jr., Prediction in future samples. In I. Olkin et al. (Eds.), *Contributions to probability and statistics*. Stanford: Stanford University Press, 1960.)

36. Olkin, I., & Pratt, J. W. Unbiased estimation of certain correlation coefficients. *Annals of Mathmatical Statistics*, 1958, 29, 201–211.

37. Richardon, M. W. Supplementary Study D. In P. Horst, *Prediction of personal adjustment*. (Bulletin No. 48) New York: Social Science Research Council, 1941.

38. Rozeboom, W. W. Linear correlations between sets of variables. *Psychometrika*, 1965, 30, 57–71.

39. Simon, H. A. *Models of man: Social and rational. Mathematical essays on rational human behavior in a social setting*. New York: Wiley, 1957.

40. Stein, C. Multiple regression. In I. Olkin et al. (Ed.), *Contributions to probability and statistics*. Stanford: Stanford University Press, 1960.

41. Turner, M., & Stevens, D. The regression analysis of causal paths. *Biometrics*, 1959, 15, 236–258.

42. Turner, M., Monroe, R. J., & Lucas, H. L., Jr. Generalized asymptotic regression and nonlinear path analysis. *Biometrics*, 1961, 17, 120–143.

43. Ward, J. H., Jr. Comments on "The paramorphic representation of clinical judgment." *Psychological Bulletin*, 1962, 59, 74–76.

44. Wherry, R. J. A new formula for predicting the shrinkage of the coefficient of multiple correlation. *Annals of Mathematical Statistics*, 1931, 2, 440–457.

45. Wilks, S. S. Weighting systems for linear functions of correlated variables when there is no dependent variable. *Psychometrika*, 1938, 3, 23–40.

46. Williams, E. J. *Regression analysis*. New York: Wiley, 1959.

47. Wright, S. Correlation and causation. *Journal of Agricultural Research*, 1921, 20, 557–585.

48. Wright, S. The interpretation of multivariate systems. In O. Kempthorne et al. (Eds.), *Statistics and mathematics in biology*. Ames: Iowa State College Press, 1954.

49. Wright, S. Path coefficients and path regressions: Alternative or complementary concepts? *Biometrics*, 1960, 16, 189–202.

50. Wright, S. The treatment of reciprocal interaction, with or without lag, in path analysis. *Biometrics*, 1960, 16, 423–445.

A. H. YEE   N. L. GAGE

44 Techniques for Estimating the Source and Direction of Causal Influence in Panel Data[1]

Techniques for estimating the source and direction of causal influence in panel data are described and applied to illustrative data on teachers' and pupils' interpersonal attitudes. The techniques are Lazarsfeld's 16-fold table, Campbell's cross-lagged panel correlation, and the present authors' frequency-of-shift-across-median and frequency-of-change-in-product-moment. The latter method seems preferable because it permits treatment of continuous data, analysis of all cases, and a necessary distinction between the source and direction of causal influence.

Contemporary scientists seem uncertain as to the value of causal analysis, especially in the social sciences. Explicit discussions of causality rarely occur. But, as Nagel (19) observed, "though the *term* may be absent, the *idea* for which it stands continues to have wide currency," as "when scientists distinguish in various inquiries between spurious and genuine correlations [p. 12]." Simon (26) also noted

1. The authors thank Donald T. Campbell, Donald C. Pelz, Philip J. Runkel, Joan E. Sieber, Julian Stanley, and M. C. Wittrock for advice and encouragement on preliminary drafts, but absolve them of responsibility for any shortcomings of the present version.

the common reference to causality in scientific writing, despite its "generally unsavory epistemological status [p. 11]."

In the natural sciences causal connections may be perceived in the tangible or visible mechanisms underlying the connections. Natural scientists also have the advantage of freedom to control and manipulate the matter they investigate: they can burn, catalyze, hybridize, electrolyze, break apart, boil, vivisect, bombard, and subject to acid tests almost as they please. Lacking such freedom, social scientists must place greater reliance upon statistical treatments than upon direct manipulation.

From *Psychological Bulletin*, Vol. 70, No. 2, pp. 115–26, 1968. Copyright © 1968 by the American Psychological Association, and reprinted by permission.

Recent statements by social psychologists indicate increasing concern with causal relationships. For example, Gerard and Miller (11) noted in their review that "The study of the determinants and consequences of mutual attraction is a focus for a good deal of research in social psychology [p. 294]." Terms implying causality—such as, determine, influence, produce, affect, effect, modify, and attract—occur frequently in the literature. Occasionally, a direct reference to causality may be found; for example, Andrews (2) studied the business organization as the "causal link" between a nation's achievement concern and its economic development. Causal connections must be exploited, of course, when social-psychological research findings are used in efforts to improve individuals and society, as in the programs of the "Great Society" and investigations into the causes of civil disorders. Greater precision in connecting theory and methods has led to more explicit use of causal inference in the social sciences (16).

In recent years sociologists (e.g., 5), political scientists (e.g., 1), and psychologists (e.g., 24), among others, have given increased attention to statistical methods for investigating causal relationships. Faris (9, p. 23) noted that

the research equipment of sociology contains a rich and rapidly growing body of techniques for the extraction of causal generalizations from the data ... most important ... is the fund of statistical methods, which can uncover regularities in masses of data too bewildering in their complexity to give up their secrets to any kind of personal skill or intuition. ... These statistical, and related formal logical methods, employed in connection with modern high-speed computers, promise exponential progress in scientific knowledge of human and social behavior.

Similarly, McGuire (18, p. 134) recommended that courses in experimental design and statistics for social psychologists "give more attention to techniques that allow us to tease out causal directions among covariants in situations where we do not have the resources to manipulate one of the factors."

One category of techniques for causal analysis consists of those that can be applied to panel data, that is, data collected on the same two or more variables on the same individuals at two or more points in time. This paper reviews two techniques of this kind—the 16-fold table (15) and Campbell's cross-lagged panel correlation technique (7)—presents two new ones, and applies all four to the same data on relationships between teachers' and pupils' attitudes.

Causal Relationships in Social Interaction

Social psychology is largely the study of social interaction, in which the action of one person is a response to that of a second person, whose next response is in turn influenced by that of the first. "The actions of each are at once a *result* of and a *cause* of the actions of the other [14, p. 4]." Thus, influence flows in both directions as interacting individuals mutually determine the nature and outcome of the interpersonal behavior event.

In this framework, the "warmth" of a teacher toward his class may be regarded as at once a cause and an effect of the liking of the pupils for their teacher. The following questions can then be raised: Does teacher warmth tend to make the pupils like their teacher better? Or does teacher warmth make the pupils *less* favorably disposed toward their teacher? Or does the influence actually flow in the opposite direction, so that pupils' liking of their teacher increases teacher warmth? Or, finally, does the pupils' favorable attitude toward their teacher *decrease* teacher warmth?

These are four possible combinations of the source and direction of influence between persons in social interaction. These possibilities can characterize any human relationship. For example, Bell (4) questioned the assumption that influence always flows from parent to child and presented evidence that children's characteristics influence parent behavior. The methods considered in this paper make possible the testing of alternative hypotheses concerning the source and direction of influence between characteristics and behaviors of inter-acting persons in any relationship. The methods are also useful in determining the relative strength of two influences *within* a set of persons, as the illustrative data for Lazars-feld's (15) method, discussed in a following section, indicate. Finally, the methods may be considered applicable to variables of any kind —economic, political, demographic, etc.— where the source and direction of causal influence are to be estimated.

Given paired measurements of two variables that may be causally related, one can compute correlations. With repeated measures, or panel data, one can compute test-retest and same-occasion correlations. These correlations may suggest the operation of causal influence in some direction when (*a*) the correlations be-tween the variables increase (or decrease!) over time; and (*b*) there is marked stability in one variable and marked instability in the other. But, suggestive as such results may be, infer-ences of causal direction from such correla-tional results alone are suspect; other inde-pendent variables may be influencing the relationship. Suppose it is assumed, however, that no other independent variable is as potent as the two interacting variables in producing what Zeisel (30) has designated as "true" correlations "which reflect a direct causal con-nection [p. 205]." Then the four previous questions may be raised: Does one variable affect the other more than it is affected by the other? Or less? Does an increase in the value of one variable increase the value of the other? Or decrease it?

The Data on Teacher-Pupil Relationships

These questions can be illustrated with data from a recent study (28) of teachers' attitudes toward pupils (*T*) and pupils' attitudes toward their teacher (*P*). Here it is possible that *T* is determining *P*, or that *P* is determining *T*. In many studies of teacher-pupil interaction (e.g., 8; 10, p. 65; 25, p. 432; 27), it has been sug-

gested that the direction of influence is an open question.

In Yee's study, teachers' attitudes toward children and teacher-pupil relationships were measured with the Minnesota Teacher Attitude Inventory (MTAI); pupils' attitudes toward their teacher were measured with the 100-item "About My Teacher" inventory developed by Beck (1964). Pretests of these attitudes were made as early in the school year as adminis-trators would allow, mostly during the second week of school. Posttests were made about 5 months later, after considerable interaction between teachers and pupils. Thus, the post-test measures represented teachers' and pupils' interpersonal attitudes that had evolved from initial attitudes. Corrected split-half and Horst (13) coefficients in the high .80's indicated substantial reliability of the teachers' scores and pupils' class means, respectively.

Results were obtained not only for the total group but also for various subgroups based on classifications of teachers by years of teaching experience and of pupils by social class back-ground. In addition to total scores, subscores based on factor analyses of the teacher and pupil attitude measures were analyzed. Hence, 720 correlations between *T* and *P* for all classi-fications were obtained. This report, however, deals only with results for (*a*) the total group of 212 teacher-class pairs and the two sub-groups based on whether the modal pupils' social class background was lower class or middle class, and (*b*) total MTAI and "About My Teacher" scores.

First, Lazarsfeld's 16-fold table technique is described in terms of the intrapersonal opinion data to which he applied it. Then Campbell's cross-lagged panel correlation technique is described, applied to the authors' own data, and referred to problems with that technique noted by Campbell and also by the authors. Finally, two methods developed by the authors—the frequency-of-shift-across-median technique and the frequency-of-change-in-product-moment technique—are de-scribed. In each section, the merits of the various techniques are examined.

Lazarsfeld's 16-Fold Table Technique

The 16-fold table technique was described in two writings (15, 17). Unfortunately, the published treatment of 1954 omitted and glossed over crucial features which may be found in the earlier mimeographed paper. In 1948 Lazarsfeld wrote:

Now let us consider for a moment what we mean by saying that the attitude A has an "effect" on, or is the "cause" of the attitude B. We mean two things: First of all, the attitude A will tend to *generate* the attitude B; that is, if a person has the attitude A but not the attitude B, he will tend to aquire the attitude B: the attitude pattern A$\bar{\text{B}}$ (where $\bar{\text{B}}$ denotes the lack of B, or non-B) will tend to change to AB, and conversely, the pattern $\bar{\text{A}}$B will tend to change to $\bar{\text{A}}\bar{\text{B}}$; secondly, the attitude A will tend to *preserve* the attitude B; that is, there will be fewer changes from AB to A$\bar{\text{B}}$ than we would expect from chance variations in the attitude B, that is, the attitude pattern AB will tend to be stable, and conversely, the attitude pattern $\bar{\text{A}}\bar{\text{B}}$ will also tend to be stable [15, p. 4].

In this passage, Lazarsfeld described four possibilities—two that do not change, AB → AB, $\bar{\text{A}}\bar{\text{B}}$ → $\bar{\text{A}}\bar{\text{B}}$, and two that change in the "congruent" direction, that is, that raise the correlation between the attitudes, so that A$\bar{\text{B}}$ → AB, $\bar{\text{A}}$B → $\bar{\text{A}}\bar{\text{B}}$. But, given A as cause and B as effect, there are two additional possibilities, AB → $\bar{\text{A}}$B and AB → A$\bar{\text{B}}$, which represent possible change in the "incongruent" direction, that is, change that lowers the correlation between attitudes; these possibilities are not mentioned. Let us employ Lazarsfeld's own analogy to illustrate these possible causal relationships; in this analogy, A = consump-

tion of vitamins and B = good health. One can find logical grounds for asserting that vitamin consumption while enjoying good health (AB) can change incongruently to the situation when vitamins may not be consumed but good health continues ($\bar{\text{A}}$B). Also, the AB situation can change incongruently to the situation where vitamin consumption continues but good health does not (A$\bar{\text{B}}$), especially when the wrong kind of vitamins or too many vitamins are consumed.

Although his illustration could be misleading, his method (15) did not overlook the possibilities of incongruent influence. Lazarsfeld wanted to see which variable, party allegiance or attitude toward Willkie, was "cause" and which was "effect" in the 1940 presidential campaign. The two variables correlated highly at the time of the first interview (r = .53) and even higher at the time of the second (r = .67); data for the study are summarized in Table 1.

In Table 1, we see that Lazarsfeld took account of what he called "divergent" cases, namely, those where $(+ +) → (+ -)$ or $(- +)$, and those where $(- -) → (+ -)$ or $(- +)$, which we have termed incongruent cases. Nevertheless, Lipset et al. (17, p. 6) concentrated only on the response patterns of people who "harmonized" their attitudes between the two interviews, that is, those where $(+ -) → (+ +)$ or $(- -)$ and those where $(- +) → (+ +)$ or $(- -)$. In our terminology, these would be instances of congruent intrapersonal influence. Having only the 1954 description of the technique before him, a

Table 1. Concurrent change in vote intention and personal liking for Willkie

		Second interview				
Interview		$+ +$	$+ -$	$- +$	$- -$	*Total*
	Republican (+) for Willkie (+)	129	3	1	2	135
	Republican (+) against Willkie (−)	11	23	0	1	35
First interview	Democrat (−) for Willkie (+)	1	0	12	11	24
	Democrat (−) against Willkie (−)	1	1	2	68	72
	Total	142	27	15	82	266

Note.—From Lipset et al. (17, p. 1161). All entries represent the first and second sets of responses from the same *S*s; e.g., 3 in Row 1. Column 2 represents the same *S*s who were Republican (+) for Willkie (+) in the first interview but Republican (+) against Willkie (−) in the second interview.

reader could easily be misled to consider only cases of congruent change.

In his 1948 paper, Lazarsfeld (15, p. 6) described a method of analyzing his data as follows: "A good measure of the relative strength of the two attitudes, then, will be the number of adjustments toward 'vote intention' beyond the expected chance value, plus the excess beyond the expected chance value of losses of adjustment away from 'Willkie opinion.'" He offered the following index for the relative strength of two variables:

$$I_{A,B} = \frac{8\left(\dfrac{\Delta_H}{N_H} + \dfrac{\Delta_H}{N_V}\right)}{N}$$

Where, as restated by us, with more concise notation:

$I_{A,B}$ is an index for the relative strength of two variables A and B, in causal relationship

$$\Delta_H = N_{(-+\to--)}N_{(+-\to++)} \\ - N_{(-+\to++)}N_{(+-\to--)},$$

or net change toward congruence, where the first variable is the cause

$$N_H = N_{(-+\to--)} + N_{(+-\to++)} \\ + N_{(-+\to++)} + N_{(+-\to--)},$$

or the sum of the four Ns in the Δ_H elements

$$\Delta_V = -[N_{(--\to+-)}N_{(++\to-+)} \\ - N_{(--\to-+)}N_{(++\to+-)}],$$

or negative amount of net change toward incongruence where the second variable is the cause

$$N_V = N_{(--\to+-)} + N_{(++\to-+)} \\ + N_{(--\to-+)} + N_{(++\to+-)},$$

or the sum of the four Ns in the Δ_V elements,

$N =$ total cases in study.

As Lazarsfeld (15, pp. 6–7) explained this method:

In the ideal case, $\dfrac{\Delta_H}{N_H}$ and $\dfrac{\Delta_V}{N_V}$ will have the same sign: they will both be positive if the first variable (in the present example "vote intention") is stronger, and both negative if the second variable (in the present example "Willkie opinion") is stronger. Their relative magnitude will depend on the comparative frequency of adjustment and maladjustment cases, that is, on whether the correlation between the two variables has been increasing or decreasing in the interval between the two interviews.

Unfortunately, the 1954 publication merely stated that "The details of this index will be omitted here; suffice it to say that the index takes into account the stability of each variable separately and that the more change in one variable is influenced by change in another, the larger the index will be [17, p. 1161]." Lazarsfeld's method takes into account both "adjustment," or congruent, cases (Δ_H), and "non-adjustment," or incongruent, cases (Δ_V).

In an appendix by William L. Robinson, Lazarsfeld (15, p. vi) presented a significance test which requires computation of the variance of $\dfrac{\Delta}{N}$ and the mean deviation of $I_{A,B}$.

Chi-square appears to offer greater power and to be simpler to compute and interpret. Applying chi-square tests to Lazarsfeld's data in Table 1 shows that party allegiance caused "Willkie opinion" to change; that is,

$$27 > 4$$

or

$$N_{(++\to+-)} + N_{(+-\to++)} + N_{(-+\to--)} + \\ + N_{(--\to+-)} > N_{(++\to-+)} + N_{(+-\to--)} + \\ + N_{(-+\to++)} + N_{(--\to+-)}$$

$$(\chi^2 = 15.6, \quad p < .0001)$$

Furthermore, party allegiance caused "Willkie opinion" to change toward congruity; that is,

$$22 > 2$$

or

$$N_{(+-\to++)} + N_{(-+\to--)} \\ > N_{(+-\to--)} + N_{(-+\to++)}$$

$$(\chi^2 = 15,04, \quad p < .0001)$$

Finally, party allegiance did not cause "Willkie opinion" to change significantly toward incongruity; that is,

$$5 > 2$$

or

$$N_{(+ + \to + -)} + N_{(- - \to - +)}$$
$$> N_{(+ + \to - +)} + N_{(- - \to + -)}$$

$$(\chi^2 = .57, \quad p, \quad \text{nonsignificant})$$

Despite its ingenuity, the 16-fold table technique has limitations. First, it is applicable only to dichotomous variables. Second, it has no readily understood metric, such as the value of r. And, as Campbell (6) has pointed out, "regression becomes a plausible rival hypothesis when the item marginals are extreme and differ for the two variables [p. 241]."

Campbell's Cross-Lagged Panel Correlation Technique

In an attempt to extend Lazarsfeld's reasoning to continuous data, Campbell (7) offered the "cross-lagged panel correlation technique." The method was later discussed in greater detail by Campbell (6) and has been noted by Blalock (5, pp. 191–192), Pelz and Andrews (21), and McGuire (18).

Campbell (6, pp. 235–236) argued that cross-lagged series can differentiate between opposing interpretations of the causal relationship between two variables:

Where two data series correlate, . . . the direction of causation may be equivocal. . . . In such a situation, r_{CnEn+1} should be greater than r_{Cn+1En}, where C stands for cause, E for effect. These cross-lagged series correlations can frequently differentiate the relative plausibilities of competing causal interpretations. When both variables are on both sides of the comparison, i.e., when relative correlation magnitude is used rather than the absolute level of r_{nEn}, secular trends of long-term cycles are controlled. . . . Our criterion becomes $r_{C1E2} > r_{C2E1}$.

Campbell cited the following illustrative question: "Does lack of parental love cause children to be behavior problems, or does a difficult child cause parents to love less?" In

Yee's (28) data, the comparable question is: Do unsympathetic and unfavorable attitudes of the teacher toward pupils cause her pupils to develop a dislike for their teacher, or do hostile, aggressive pupils cause the teacher to develop unfavorable and unsympathetic attitudes toward pupils?

Using the cross-lagged technique, one would infer that pupils' attitudes P tend to influence teachers' attitudes T if $r_{P_1T_2} > r_{T_1P_2}$. One would infer that teachers' attitudes influence pupil attitude if $r_{T_1P_2} > r_{T_2P_1}$. But these two inferences are not the only possible ones. The first finding could result not only from greater pupil influence toward raising the correlation between teachers' and pupils' attitudes (which we term influence toward *congruity*), but also from greater teacher influence toward *incongruity* (i.e., toward lowering the correlation between teachers' and pupils' attitudes). In that event, teachers' influence may be greater than pupils' but in an incongruent direction. But it is impossible to ascertain this possibility from the cross-lagged r's because the latter confound, or prevent us from distinguishing between, the source and direction of influence of the two correlated variables.

This unexpected problem in the use of the cross-lagged technique was also found independently by Rozelle (22), who noted that there were *four* competing hypotheses, namely, A increases B, B increases A, A decreases B, and B decreases A. Later, Rozelle and Campbell (23, p. 12) concluded that "The apparent power of the technique is now seen as much less than in previous estimates, even though under some conditions the confounded pair can be separately examined."

Frequency-of-Shift-Across-Median (FSM) Technique

Prior to our study of Lazarsfeld's 16-fold table technique, we developed one of our own that turned out to be highly similar, except that it entailed trichotomizing rather than dichotomizing each variable. The trichotomies consist of scores (*a*) above the median, (*b*) at the median, and (*c*) below the median. The matrix shown in Figure 1 provides for all possible types of shifts in paired trichotomous measures from pre- to posttest. This matrix forms the basis for what we termed the fre-

quency-of-shift-across-median technique. In applying this technique, we determined the frequencies of teacher-class pairs that shifted between first and second testings in the various ways shown in Figure 1. Such shifts could be interpreted as (*a*) raising or lowering (i.e.,

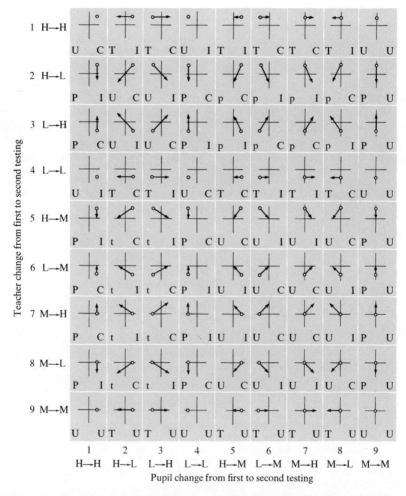

Fig. 1. Possible resolutions and nature of influence in the relationship of teachers' and pupils' attitudes. (Arrows both in the margins and in the cells denote direction of change in relationship to the medians of teachers' and pupils' measures; lack of arrow denotes no change. H = above median; L = below median; M = on median; T = teacher is dominant influence; *P* = pupils are dominant influence; *U* = uncertain influence; t = teacher causes pupils to change more than pupils cause teacher to change; p = pupils cause teacher to change more than teacher causes pupils to change; C = continuation in or change toward state of congruity; and I = continuation in or change toward state of incongruity. Whether cells in Row 9 and Column 9 are states of congruity or incongruity cannot be determined.)

shifting toward congruity or incongruity, respectively) the correlation between teachers' and pupils' attitudes, and (b) indicating whether the teacher or the pupils exerted the influence toward change. Table 2 presents interpretations of the 81 possible shifts between pre- and posttest.

As is shown in Table 2, the source of influence operating in each of the 81 resolutions was judged to be the teacher (T) or the pupils (P) on the basis of which participant in social interaction changed less in relation to the pre- and posttest medians. For example, if the teacher remained stable and pupils changed from below-the-pupils'-median to above-the-pupils'-median, then teachers' influence would be considered the cause of pupils' change. Cells in which it could not be determined whether

teachers' or pupils' influence was operating were considered "uncertain"; such a case would be one where both teachers and pupils remained in the H-H cell on both testing occasions.

Table 2 also indicates whether the teachers' and pupils' attitudes shift toward congruent (C) or incongruent (I) states. If a cell showed teachers and pupils moving to or remaining in resolutions where their attitudes were similar (both above or both below the median), then that cell was considered "congruent." If a cell showed teachers' and pupils' attitudes moving to or remaining in resolutions where their attitudes were dissimilar (one above and the other below the median), then that cell was considered "incongruent." Whether some teacher-class pairs, such as those falling exactly

Table 2. Nature of influence in 81 possible resolutions in the cause-effect relationship of teachers' and pupils' attitudes

Category type	Nature of influence	Cells*
TC	Teacher influence to increase correlation (Teacher stays high, pupils move higher. Teacher stays low, pupils move lower.)	1.3, 1.6, 1.7, 4.2, 4.5 4.8, 5.2, 6.3, 7.3, 8.2
TI	Teacher influence to lower correlation (Teacher stays high, pupils move lower. Teacher stays low, pupils move higher.)	1.2, 1.5, 1.8, 4.3, 4.6 4.7, 5.3, 6.2, 7.2, 8.3
PC	Pupil influence to increase correlation (Pupils stay high, teacher moves higher. Pupils stay low, teacher moves lower.)	2.4, 2.5, 2.8, 3.1, 3.6 3.7, 5.4, 6.1, 7.1, 8.4
PI	Pupil influence to lower correlation (Pupils stay high, teacher moves lower. Pupils stay low, teacher moves higher.)	2.1, 2.6, 2.7, 3.4, 3.5 3.8, 5.1, 6.4, 7.4, 8.1
UC	Uncertain influence, no change from pretest to posttest; teacher and pupils continue in state of congruity.	1.1, 4.4
	Uncertain influence, teacher and pupils change in same direction, i.e., staying in state of congruity.	2.2, 3.3, 5.5, 5.8, 6.6 6.7, 7.6, 7.7, 8.5, 8.8
UI	Uncertain influence, no change from pretest to posttest; teacher and pupils continue in state of incongruity.	1.4, 4.1
	Uncertain influence, teacher and pupils change in opposite directions, i.e., staying in state of incongruity.	2.3, 3.2, 5.6, 5.7, 6.5 6.8, 7.5, 7.8, 8.6, 8.7
TU	Uncertain teacher influence causing pupils to change.	9.2, 9.3, 9.5, 9.6, 9.7 9.8
PU	Uncertain pupil influence causing teacher to change.	2.9, 3.9, 5.9, 6.9, 7.9 8.9
UU	Uncertain influence, no change from pretest to posttest; teacher and pupils continue in uncertain state.	1.9, 4.9, 9.1, 9.4, 9.9

* Cell designations from Figure 1: first numbers represent teachers' row and second numbers represent pupils' column.

on pre- and posttest medians (Row 9 and Column 9), shifted in congruent or incongruent directions could not be determined; these were judged "uncertain."

To summarize, the 9×9 table of 81 possible resolutions is based on the relationships of the teachers' and pupils' pre- and posttest attitudes to their medians, and two logical interpretations are made for each resolution: (a) whether it is caused by the teacher, the pupils, or an uncertain influence, and (b) whether it leads to a state of congruity, incongruity, or an uncertain attitude adjustment. Frequencies in each cell of the 9×9 table are tabulated and then summarized in the 3×3 schema shown in Table 3.[2]

Table 3. Schema for summarizing frequencies in Table 2

Source of influence	Direction of influence		
	Congruity	Incongruity	Uncertain
Teacher	TC	TI	TU
Pupil	PC	PI	PU
Uncertain	UC	UI	UU

The following hypotheses refer to the frequencies of teacher-class pairs reflecting the various sources and directions of influence indicated in Table 3.

H_1: Teacher-class pairs showing teacher influence toward either congruity or incongruity are more frequent than those showing pupil influence toward either congruity or incongruity. That is,

Teacher Influence (TC + TI + TU)
> Pupil Influence (PC + PI + PU)

H_2: Teacher-class pairs showing teacher influence toward congruity are more frequent than those showing pupil influence toward congruity. That is,

Teacher Influence toward Congruity (TC)
> Pupil Influence toward Congruity (PC)

2. Descriptions and listings of the Fortran programs (CDC 1604 computer) for the FSM and FCP techniques may be obtained by request from A. H. Yee. H. Albert Napier, William Geeslin, and Leslie Shroyer provided programming and data-processing assistance.

H_3: Teacher-class pairs showing teacher influence toward incongruity are more frequent than those showing pupil influence toward incongruity. That is,

Teacher Influence toward Incongruity (TI)
> Pupil Influence toward Incongruity (PI)

These hypotheses can be tested with chi-square, adjusted with Yates' correction for continuity, one-tailed with $df = 1$ (12, pp. 228–230, 237–239).

Frequency-of-Change-in-Product-Moment (FCP) Technique

In depending on shifts in relation to the medians, the FSM technique requires disregarding the many cases (about 60% in the present study) that do not change in relation to the medians from pre- to posttest. The frequency-of-change-in-product-moment (FCP) technique was developed in part to overcome this problem. It entails putting every teacher-class unit into one of the four categories of influence—TC, TI, PC, or PI—by the following procedure:

1. Convert the raw scores for teachers' and pupils' pre- and posttest attitudes to standard scores on the basis of their respective means and standard deviations. That is, determine $z = (x - \bar{x})/s$ for every score.

2. For each class, ascertain whether the cross-product of its posttest z scores is more positive or negative than the cross-product of its pretest z scores. If the cross-product of posttest z's, $z_{T_2}z_{P_2}$, is algebraically greater than $z_{T_1}z_{P_1}$, the direction of change is considered to be congruent; that is, the interaction between the teacher and her class makes the overall correlation more positive. If the cross-product of posttest z's is algebraically lower than that of pretest z's, the direction of change is considered to be incongruent; that is, the interaction between the teacher and her class makes the overall correlation more negative. This manner of assessing direction of influence is, of course, based on the defining formula for the product-moment correlation coefficient:

$$r = \frac{\Sigma z_x z_y}{N-1}$$

In short,

If $z_{T_1} z_{P_1} < z_{T_2} z_{P_2}$, classify as an instance of congruent change.

If $z_{T_1} z_{P_2} > z_{T_2} z_{P_1}$, classify as an instance of incongruent change.

3. For each class, examine the cross-lagged z products, $z_{T_1} z_{P_2}$, and $z_{P_2} z_{T_1}$. When direction of change is congruent, the variable whose premeasure is part of the more positive product is considered to be the source of the influence. When direction of influence is incongruent, the variable whose premeasure is part of the more negative product is considered to be the source of the influence. That is,

If change is toward congruency, and
if $z_{T_1} z_{P_2} > z_{T_2} z_{P_1}$, then T is source of influence;
if $z_{T_1} z_{P_2} < z_{T_2} z_{P_1}$, then P is source of influence.
If change is toward incongruency, and
if $z_{T_1} z_{P_2} > z_{T_2} z_{P_1}$, then P is source of influence;
if $z_{T_1} z_{P_2} < z_{T_2} z_{P_1}$, then T is source of influence.

Results

Table 4 presents the results obtained with the cross-lagged, FSM, and FCP techniques. Findings with the 16-fold table technique will be discussed with results from the FSM technique.

RESULTS WITH THE CROSS-LAGGED PANEL CORRE-LATION TECHNIQUE

All three pairs of cross-lagged r's indicated greater pupil influence than teacher influence; that is, $r_{P_1 T_2} > r_{T_1 P_2}$. The greatest difference between cross-lagged r's occurred in the subgroup with lower-class pupils. Although none of the differences was statistically significant, according to the formula developed by Olkin (20), the predominant source of causal influence, judged on the basis of the cross-lagged technique, was the pupils.

But the question now arises: Did pupil attitude influence teacher attitude in the congruent direction? Or did teacher attitude influence pupil attitude in the incongruent direction?

According to Campbell's earlier view (6, pp. 239–240), if r's between teachers' and pupils' second measures ($r_{T_2 P_2}$) are higher than those between the first measures ($r_{T_1 P_1}$), then it may be inferred that there is some causal connection of unspecified direction. Thus, a partial answer may be found in the following same-occasion correlations: for the total sample, $r_{T_1 P_1} = .19$, $r_{T_2 P_2} = .17$; for the lower-class subsample, $r_{T_1 P_1} = .23$, $r_{T_2 P_2} = .21$; and for the middle-class subsample, $r_{T_1 P_1} = .04$, $r_{T_2 P_2} = .05$. Thus, the same-occasion r's did not increase from pre- to posttest. Hence, the possibility arises that pupil influence causing congruent teacher change is weaker than the alternative of teacher influence causing incongruent pupil change.

We are assuming from past evidence that the interaction of teachers and pupils in hundreds of classroom encounters significantly influences their attitudes. Such interaction can either raise or lower the correlation between teachers' and pupils' attitude measures. And the results of applying the cross-lagged technique are inadequate to portray such possibilities.

RESULTS WITH THE FREQUENCY-OF-SHIFT-ACROSS-MEDIAN TECHNIQUE

In Table 4, we see that the test of H_1 with the FSM technique yielded significant results favoring teacher influence in the lower-class subsample ($\chi^2 = 4.78, p < .02$). The difference between the results on H_1 for the lower-class and middle-class subsamples is striking. For the lower-class pupils, the frequencies for (TC + TI) and (PC + PI) are 28 and 13, respectively; for the middle-class pupils, they are 22 and 18.

The results for H_2 and H_3 show that the teachers' significant influence on lower-class pupils is in the direction of incongruence; that is, for H_3, TI > PI, or $16 > 5$ ($\chi^2 = 4.76$, $p < .02$). When it is recalled that the largest difference between cross-lagged r's shown in

Table 4. Summary of results from the three techniques

Teacher-class group	r's						Frequency-of-shift-across-median frequencies*						Chi-squares†			Frequency-of-change-in-product-moment frequencies				Chi-squares		
	T_1T_2	P_1P_2	T_1P_1	T_2P_2	T_1P_2	P_1T_2	TC	TI	PC	PI	UC	UI	H_1	H_2	H_3	TC	TI	PC	PI	H_1	H_2	H_3
Total $n = 212$	.79	.69	.19	.17	.10	.20	29	22	27	20	66	48	.09	.02	.02	56	65	45	46	3.97‡	.99	2.92‡
Lower class $n = 110$	.76	.62	.23	.21	.08	.25	12	16	8	5	40	29	4.78*	.45	4.76*	33	38	21	18	8.74‡	2.24	6.45‡
Middle class $n = 102$	.80	.71	.04	.05	.02	.06	8	14	12	6	29	33	.23	.45	2.45	28	25	24	25	.09	.17	.02

* No cases found for TU, PU, or UU.
† H_1: (TC+TI) > (PC+PI); H_2: TC > PC; H_3: TI > PI.
‡ $p < .05$.

Table 4 was that for the lower-class subgroup, where $r_{P_1T_2} > r_{T_1P_2}$, or $.25 > .08$, it is evident that the FSM results indicate the *source* as well as the *direction* of influence for those teacher-class pairs that shift position in relation to the median attitude.

The FSM technique is very similar to Lazarsfeld's 16-fold table technique. If one compares the 16-fold table (Table 1) with the 81-cell table of the FSM method (Figure 1), it can be seen that the 16 cells in the upper-left corner of Figure 1 resemble those of the 16-fold table. Since most of the FSM frequencies were found in these 16 cells and few were tabulated in the other 65 cells in Figure 1, results of the two techniques should be equivalent.

RESULTS WITH THE 16-FOLD TABLE TECHNIQUE

When the 16-fold table technique is applied to the illustrative problem

Δ_c, or change toward congruity

$$= N_a N_b - N_c N_d$$

Where,

N_a = number of classes where teachers exert congruent influence, or TC, and pupils shift from + to −

N_b = number of classes where teachers exert congruent influence, or TC, and pupils shift from − to +

N_c = number of classes where pupils exert congruent influence, or PC, and teachers shift from + to −

N_d = number of classes where pupils exert congruent influence, or PC, and teachers shift from − to +

Δ_I or change toward incongruity

$$= -[N_e N_f - N_g N_h]$$

Where,

N_e = number of classes where pupils exert incongruent influence, or PI, and teachers shift from + to −

N_f = number of classes where pupils exert incongruent influence, or PI, and teachers shift from − to +

N_g = number of classes where teachers exert incongruent influence, or TI, and pupils shift from + to −

N_h = number of classes where teachers exert incongruent influence, or TI, and pupils shift from − to +

In the subgroup with lower-class pupils, the frequencies are:

$N_a = 6$, $N_b = 6$, $N_c = 4$, $N_d = 4$, $N_e = 2$,
$$N_f = 3, N_g = 9, N_h = 7$$
$\Delta_c = (6)(6) - (4)(4) = 20$
$\Delta_I = -[(2)(3) - (9)(7)] = 57$

Both Δ_c and Δ_I show teachers' influence to be stronger, especially in Δ_I. This finding accords with the FSM and FCP results given in Table 4.

RESULTS FROM THE FREQUENCY-OF-CHANGE-IN-PRODUCT-MOMENT TECHNIQUE

Frequencies from the FCP technique for all three hypotheses, as shown in Table 4, indicate that teacher influence occurred more often than pupil influence. Significant chi-square results support H_1 and H_3 for the total group and the lower-class subgroup, but not for the middle-class group. The results for the middle-class subgroup are consistent with those obtained by the cross-lagged method, inasmuch as the near-zero r's for this subgroup could have resulted from the finding that influences of opposite direction and source were approximately equal in frequency. Also consistent are the FSM results showing statistically insignificant differences between competing frequencies.

Although the H_2 results for the total group and lower-class subgroup are not significant, the frequencies for TC are greater than those for PC. The significant H_1 results for the lower-class subgroup ($\chi^2 = 8.74$, $p < .001$) reflect the combined effect of greater teacher-congruent frequencies in H_2 and the strikingly greater teacher-incongruent frequencies in H_3 (TI = 38, PI = 18, $\chi^2 = 6.45$, $p < .01$). But all the results for the middle-class subgroup are nonsignificant. Similar results were obtained from the FSM technique, and both sets of results are consistent with those obtained with the cross-lagged technique for the lower-class subgroup. Significant H_1 and H_3 results for the total sample reflect the combination of both subgroups' frequencies. Refer to Yee (1968) for greater discussion of FCP results.

Discussion

First, some interpretation of incongruent teacher influence of the kind revealed in these data should be attempted. Such influence means that teachers with relatively high initial MTAI scores tended to make their pupils have less favorable attitudes later in the school year, and vice versa. Perhaps high MTAI-scoring teachers tried to substitute "warmth" for instructional effectiveness, and their pupils eventually resented their ineffectiveness, while the opposite trends occurred in the classes of low MTAI-scoring teachers. But, of course, additional data on other variables would be needed to test this interpretation.

At any rate, the results obtained with the cross-lagged technique support the contention of Rozelle and Campbell (23) that analyses of causal influence in panel data must consider incongruent as well as congruent outcomes. While results with the cross-lagged panel correlation technique are equivocal, the 16-fold table, FSM, and FCP techniques appear to be consistent in the objective estimates of source and direction of influence which they yield.

The FSM technique resembles the 16-fold table technique, for the majority of frequencies found by both methods in the illustrative problem were tabulated and interpreted similarly. By providing for the consideration of more types of shift, however, the FSM technique offers the potential advantage of handling a wider range of outcomes than is possible with the 16-fold table technique. The FSM method relies upon those cases that shift relative to the arbitrary criterion of the median; its results indicate causal source and direction for the cases that shift most.

The FCP method, in using all cases, has an advantage over the FSM method; in being applicable to continuous data, it has an advantage over both the FSM and 16-fold table methods; and in revealing both source and direction of influence it has an advantage over the cross-lagged panel correlation method. Analyses of other panel data, in which measures of two correlated variables are obtained on two or more occasions, should be made to explore the utility of the FCP method in testing causal hypotheses. Pending further experience with and analysis of this technique, the authors recommend its use in preference to the others.

References

1. Alker, H. R., Jr. Causal inference and political analysis. In J. Bernel (Ed.), *Mathematical applications in political science, II.* Dallas, Texas: The Arnold Foundation, Southern Methodist University, 1966.
2. Andrews, J. D. W. The achievement motive and advancement in two types of organizations. *Journal of Personality and Social Psychology*, 1967, 6, 163–168.
3. Beck, W. H. Pupils' perceptions of teacher merit: A factor analysis of five hypothesized dimensions. Unpublished doctoral dissertation, Stanford University, 1964.
4. Bell, R. Q. A reinterpretation of the direction of effects in studies of socialization. *Psychological Review*, 1968, 75, 81–95.
5. Blalock, H. M., Jr. *Causal inferences in non-experimental research.* Chapel Hill: University of North Carolina Press, 1964.
6. Campbell, D. T. From description to experimentation: Interpreting trends as quasi-experiments. In C. W. Harris (Ed.), *Problems in measuring change.* Madison: University of Wisconsin Press, 1963.
7. Campbell, D. T., & Stanley, J. C. Experimental and quasi-experimental designs for research on teaching. In N. L. Gage (Ed.), *Handbook of research on teaching.* Chicago: Rand McNally 1963. (Also published as a separate: *Experimental and quasi-experimental designs for research.* Chicago: Rank McNally, 1966.)
8. Della Piana, G. M., & Gage, N. L. Pupils' values and the validity of the Minnesota Teacher Attitude Inventory. *Journal of Educational Psychology*, 1955, 45, 167–178.
9. Faris, R. E. L. The discipline of sociology. In R. E. L. Faris (Ed.), *Handbook of modern sociology.* Chicago: Rand McNally, 1964.

10. Flanders, N. A. *Teacher influence, pupil attitudes, and achievement.* Document No. OE-25040, 1965, Washington, D.C.: United States Government Printing Office.

11. Gerard, H. B., & Miller, N. Group dynamics. *Annual review of psychology*, 1967, 18, 287–332.

12. Guilford, J. P. *Fundamental statistics in psychology and education.* (4th ed.) New York: McGraw-Hill, 1965.

13. Horst, P. A generalized expression of the reliability of measures. *Psychometrika*, 1949, 14, 21–32.

14. Krech, D., Crutchfield, R. S. & Ballachey, E. L. *Individual in society.* New York: McGraw-Hill, 1962.

15. Lazarsfeld, P. F. Mutual effects of statistical variables. New York: Columbia University, Bureau of Applied Social Research, 1948. (Mimeo.)

16. Lerner, D. (Ed.) *Cause and effect.* New York: Free Press, 1965.

17. Lipset, S. M., Lazarsfeld, P. F., Barton, A. H., & Linz, J. The psychology of voting: An analysis of political behavior. In G. Lindzey (Ed.), *Handbook of social psychology.* Vol. 2. Cambridge, Mass.: Addison-Wesley, 1954.

18. McGuire, W. J. Some impending reorientations in social psychology: Some thoughts provoked by Kenneth Ring, *Journal of Experimental Social Psychology*, 1967, 3, 124–139.

19. Nagal, E. Types of causal explanation in science. In D. Lerner (Ed.), *Cause and effect.* New York: Free Press, 1965.

20. Olkin, I. Correlations revisited. In J. C. Stanley (Ed.), *Improving experimental design and statistical analysis.* Chicago: Rand McNally, 1967.

21. Pelz, D. C., & Andrews, F. M. Detecting causal priorities in panel study data. *American Sociological Review*, 1964, 29, 836–848.

22. Rozelle, R. M. An exploration of two quasi-experimental designs: The cross-lagged panel correlation and the multiple time series. Unpublished master's thesis, Northwestern University, 1965.

23. Rozelle, R. M., & Campbell, D. T. More plausible rival hypotheses in the cross-lagged panel correlation technique. Evanston: Northwestern University, Department of Psychology 1966. (Mimeo.)

24. Runkel, P. J. Appendix Q: An index of influence by one individual on another for multiple-item, non-homogeneous instruments. In J. T. Hastings, P. J. Runkel, & D. E. Damrin, *Effects on use of tests by teachers trained in a summer institute.* Vol. 2. Cooperative Research Project No. 702, 1961, University of Illinois, Urbana, United States Department of Health, Education and Welfare, Office of Education.

25. Ryans, D. G. Assessment of teacher behavior and instruction. *Review of Educational Research*, 1963, 33, 415–441.

26. Simon, H. A. *Models of man: Social and rational.* New York: Wiley, 1957.

27. Withall, J. & Lewis, W. W. Social interaction in the classroom. In N. L. Gage (Ed.), *Handbook of research on teaching.* Chicago: Rand McNally, 1963.

28. Yee, A. H. *Factors involved in determining the relationship between teachers' and pupils' attitudes.* Cooperative Research Project No. 5-8346, 1966, University of Texas, Contract OE-6-10-077, United States Department of Health, Education and Welfare, Office of Education.

29. Yee, A. H. The source and direction of causal influence in teacher-pupil relationships. *Journal of Educational Psychology*, 1968, 59, in press.

30. Zeisel, H. *Say it with figures.* (Rev. ed.) New York: Harper, 1957.

JACOB COHEN

45 Multiple Regression as a General Data-Analytic System[1]

Techniques for using multiple regression (MR) as a general variance-accounting procedure of great flexibility, power, and fidelity to research aims in both manipulative and observational psychological research are presented. As a prelude, the identity of MR and fixed-model analysis of variance/covariance (AV/ACV) is sketched. This requires an exposition of means of expressing nominal scale (qualitative) data as independent variables in MR. Attention is given to methods for handling interactions, curvilinearity, missing data, and covariates, for either uncorrelated or correlated independent variables in MR. Finally, the relative roles of AV/ACV and MR in data analysis are described, and the practical advantages of the latter are set forth.

If you should say to a mathematical statistician that you have discovered that linear multiple regression analysis and the analysis of variance (and covariance) are identical systems, he would mutter something like, "Of course—general linear model," and you might have trouble maintaining his attention. If you should say this to a typical psychologist, you would be met with incredulity, or worse. Yet it is true, and in its truth lie possibilities for more relevant and therefore more powerful exploitation of research data.

That psychologists would find strange the claimed equivalence of multiple regression (MR) and the fixed-model analysis of variance (AV) and covariance (ACV) is readily understandable. The textbooks in "psychological" statistics treat these matters quite separately,

with wholly different algorithms, nomenclature, output, and examples.

MR is generally illustrated by examples drawn from the psychotechnology of educational or personnel selection, usually the prediction of some criterion (e.g., freshman grade point average) from predictors (e.g., verbal and quantitative score, high school rank). The yield is a multiple correlation (R) and a regression equation with weights which can be used for optimal prediction. The multiple R and the weights are subjected to significance testing, and conclusions are drawn about the effectiveness of the prediction, and which predictors do and do not contribute significantly to the prediction.

By way of contrast, AV and ACV are generally illustrated by pure research, manipulative experiments with groups subjected to different treatments or treatment combinations. Means and variances are found and main effect, interaction, and error mean squares computed and compared. Conclusions are drawn in terms of the significance of differences in sets or pairs of means or mean differences. More analytic

1. The author is also grateful to the members of the Society of Multivariate Experimental Psychology for their constructive response when this material was presented at their annual meeting in Atlanta, Georgia, November 1966. This work profited greatly from detailed critiques supplied by Robert A. Bottenberg and Joe H. Ward, Jr., but since not all their suggestions were followed, they share no responsibility for any defects in the result.

From *Psychological Bulletin*, Vol. 70, No. 6, pp. 426–43, 1968. Copyright © 1968 by the American Psychological Association, and reprinted by permission.

yield of one or both of these systems is sometimes presented, but the above is a fair description of the respective thrusts of the two methods, and they are clearly different.

The differences are quite understandable, but the basis for this understanding comes primarily from the history and sociology of behavioral science research method and not from the essential mathematics. MR began to be exploited in the biological and behavioral sciences around the turn of the century in the course of the study of *natural* variation (Galton, Pearson, Yule). A couple of decades later, AV and ACV came out of the structure of (agronomic) experimentation, that is, of *artificial* or experimentally manipulated variation, where the treatments were carefully varied over the experimental material in efficient and logically esthetic experimental designs. The chief architect here was R. A. Fisher. These historical differences resulted in differences in tradition associated with substantively different areas and value systems in the psychological spectrum (cf. 2).

Yet the systems are, in the most meaningful sense, the same.

One of the purposes of this article is to sketch the equivalence of the two systems. In order to do so, it is necessary to show how nominal scales ("treatment," religion) can be used as "independent" variables in MR; the same is shown for "interactions." It is also necessary to demonstrate how multiple R^2 (and related statistics) can be computed from fixed-model AV and ACV output. Once the case is made for the *theoretical* equivalence of the two systems, the *practical* advantages of MR will be presented, which, given the foregoing, will be seen to constitute a very flexible general system for the analysis of data in the most frequently arising circumstance, namely, where an interval scaled or dichotomous (dependent) variable is to be "understood" in terms of other (independent) variables, however scaled.

A word about originality. Most of the material which follows was "discovered" by the author, only to find, after some painstaking library research, that much of it had been anti-cipated in published but not widely known works (chiefly 1; 9). Thus, no large claim for originality is being made, except for some of the heuristic concepts and their synthesis in a general data-analytic system realized by means of MR.

The Equivalence of the Systems: Nominal Scales as Independent Variables in MR

Some of the apparent differences in MR and AC/ACV lie in their respective terminologies. The variable being analyzed (from AV and ACV) and the criterion variable (from MR) are the same, and will be called the dependent variable and symbolized as Y. The variables bearing on Y, variously called main effect, interaction, or covariate in AV and ACV (depending on their definition and design function), and predictor variables in MR will be called independent variables, and symbolized as X_i ($i = 1, 2, \ldots k$). Each X_i consumes *one* degree of freedom (*df*). In complex problems (e.g., factorial design, curvilinear analysis), it is convenient to define sets of the X_i, each such set representing a single research variable or factor.

In the conventional use of MR, the X_i are ordered quantitative variables, treated as equal interval scales. Thus, in a study of the prediction of freshman grade point average (Y), one might have X_1 = verbal aptitude score, X_2 = quantitative aptitude score, X_3 = percentile rank in high school graduating class, and X_4 = Hollingshead socio-economic status index. Thus, $k = 4$, and the question of sets need not arise (or, they may be thought of as four sets, each of a single variable). But what if one wanted to include *religion* among the X_i? Or alternatively, if the entering class were to be assigned randomly to four different experimental teaching systems, how would experimental group assignment be represented? More generally, how does one accommodate a purely nominal or qualitative variable as an independent variable in MR?

Imagine a simple situation in which a dependent variable Y is to be studied as a function of a nominal scale variable G, which has four "levels": groups G_1, G_2, G_3, and G_4. For concreteness, Y and G may be taken as having the following alternative meanings:

Research Area	Y
Social Psychology	Attitude toward United Nations
Clinical Psychology	Suggestibility
Physiological Psychology	Retention

Formally, what is being posited is the assignment, not necessarily equally, of each of n cases into (four) mutually exclusive and exhaustive groups, no matter whether G is an organismic, naturally occurring variable or one created by the experimenter's manipulative efforts on randomly assigned subjects.

The expression of group membership as independent variables in MR can be accomplished in several ways, all equivalent in a sense to be later described. The intuitively simplest of these is "dummy" variable coding (1; 15).

DUMMY VARIABLE CODING

Table 1 presents various coding alternatives for the rendition of membership in one of four groups. Columns 1, 2, and 3 represent a dum-

The G Set: G_1, G_2, G_3, G_4

Religion:	Protestant
	Catholic
	Jewish
	Other

Diagnosis:	Paranoid Schizophrenia
	Nonparanoid Schizophrenia
	Compulsive Neurosis
	Hysterical Neurosis

Treatment:	Drug and Frontal Lesion
	Drug and Control Lesion
	No Drug and Frontal Lesion
	No Drug and Control Lesion

my variable coding scheme. It involves merely successively dichotomizing so that each of $3(=g-1)$ of the $4(=g)$ groups is distinguished from the remainder as one aspect of G. For example, on X_1 all subjects in G_1 are scored 1 and all others, without differentiation, are scored 0. Thus, this variable by itself carries only some of the information in the G variable as a whole, for example, Protestant versus all other, or Paranoid Schizophrenia versus all other. However, the three variables coded as in Columns 1, 2, and 3 together exhaust the information of the G variable. One might think

Table 1. Illustrative coding for a nominal scale

Nominal scale variable	|—Columns—|														
	1 X_1*	2 X_2	3 X_3	4 X_1	5 X_2	6 X_3	7 X_1	8 X_2	9 X_3	10 X_1	11 X_2	12 X_3	13 X_1	14 X_2	15 X_3
G_1	1	0	0	1	1	0	1	1	1	5	25	125	1	-7	0
G_2	0	1	0	1	-1	0	1	-1	-1	0	0	0	-1	-1	0
G_3	0	0	1	-1	0	1	-1	1	-1	-4	16	-64	-4	$\frac{1}{2}$	24
G_4	0	0	0	-1	0	-1	-1	-1	1	6	36	216	1	$\frac{1}{6}$	-1

* Independent variable.

that a fourth independent variable, one which distinguishes G_4 from all others, would be necessary, but such a variable would be redundant. In the usual MR system which uses a constant term in the regression equation, it requires no more than $g-1$ independent variables (no matter how coded) to represent g groups of a G nominal scale. A fourth X_i here is not only unnecessary, but its inclusion would result in indeterminacy in the computation of the MR constants. This is an instance of a more general demand on the set of independent variables in any MR system: no independent variable in the set may yield a multiple R with the remaining independent variables of 1.00. This constraint on the independent variables (in matrix algebraic terms, the demand that their data matrix be nonsingular or of full rank) would be violated if we introduced a fourth variable, since, in that case, any of the four X_i would yield $R = 1.00$ when treated as a dependent variable regressed on the other three. In terms that are intuitively compelling, one can see that members of G_4 are identified uniquely on the X_1, X_2, X_3 vector as 0, 0, 0, that is, as not G_1, not G_2, and not G_3, thus not requiring a fourth dichotomous X_i. G_4 is not being slighted; on the contrary, as will be shown below, it serves as a reference group. Any group may be designated for this role, but if one is functionally a control or reference group, so much the better.[2]

Before we turn to a consideration of X_1, X_2 and X_3 as a set of variables, let us consider

2. It is of interest to note that information about the "omitted" group, here G_4 (more generally, G_0), is readily recovered. The value for the correlation of the dichotomy for that group with *any* variable Z (r_{Z0}) is a simple function of the r's of the other variables with Z (r_{Zi}) and the standard deviation of the X_i, namely

$$r_{Z0} = \left(- \sum_{i=1}^{g-1} r_{Zi}\sigma_i \right)/\sigma_0$$

where

$$\sigma_1 = [n_i(n-n_i)/n^2]^{\frac{1}{2}}, \quad \text{similarly for } \sigma_0.$$

When all groups are of the same size, this simplifies to

$$r_{Z0} = - \sum_{i=1}^{g-1} r_{Zi}$$

This relationship will hold whatever the nature of Z; it need not even be a real variable,—it will hold if Z is a factor in the factor-analytic sense, unrotated or rotated, with the r_{Zi} being factor loadings.

them separately. Each can be correlated with the dependent variable Y. A set of artificial data was constructed to provide a concrete illustration. For $n = 36$ cases, a set of three-digit Y scores was written, the cases assigned to four groups and coded for X_i as described. The resulting product moment r's (point-biserial) were $r_{Y1} = -.5863$, $r_{Y2} = .0391$, and $r_{Y3} = .4965$. When squared, the resulting values indicate the proportion of the Y variance each distinction accounts for: $r^2_{Y1} = .3437$, $r^2_{Y2} = .0015$, and $r^2_{Y3} = .2465$. Thus, for example, the Protestant versus non-Protestant variable accounts for .3437 of the variance in Attitude toward the United Nations dependent variable, as represented in the sample.

Whether the .3437 value can be used as an estimator of the proportion of variance which G_1 versus remainder accounts for *in the population* of naturally occurring G depends on the way G was sampled. If the n cases of the sample were obtained by randomly sampling from the population as a whole so that the proportion of G_1 cases in the sample, n_1/n reflects their population predominance, .3437 estimates the proportion of variance in the natural population. However, if G was sampled to yield equal n_i in the g groups (or some other nonrepresentative numbers), the .3437 value is projectible to a similarly distributed artificial population. The statistical purist would abjure the use of r or r^2 (and R or R^2) in such instances, but if one understands that the parameters being estimated are for populations whose X_i characteristics are those of the sample, no inappropriate errors in inference need be made, and a useful analytic tool becomes available.

Although the separate r^2_{Yi} are analytically useful, our purpose is to understand the operation of X_1, X_2, X_3 as a set, since it is as a set that they represent G as the four-level nominal scale. The r^2_{Yi} cannot simply be added up to determine how much Y variance G accounts for, since dummy variables are inevitably correlated with each other. Mutually exclusive assignment means that membership in one group G_i necessarily means nonmembership in any other, G_j, hence a negative relationship. The product moment r (i.e., the phi coefficient) between such dichotomies, that is, between G_i and G_j or X_i and X_j when expressed in dummy variable form, is

$$r_{ij} = -\sqrt{\frac{n_i n_j}{(n-n_i)(n-n_j)}} \qquad \text{Eq. 1}$$

where n_i, n_j are the sample sizes of each group, and n is the total sample size over all g groups. When sample sizes are all equal, the formula simplifies to

$$r_{ij} = -\frac{1}{g-1}, \qquad \text{Eq. 2}$$

that is, the negative reciprocal of one less than the number of groups; thus, in our running artificial example, if we assume the four groups equal in size, the phi coefficients among the X_i dichotomies are all $-1/3$.

The fact that the independent variables representing group membership are correlated with each other poses no special problem for MR, which is designed to allow for this in whatever guise it appears. But it does alert us to the fact that the proportions of Y variance given by the r^2_{Yi} are overlapping. If we now compute the multiple R^2 using X_1, X_2, and X_3 as independent variables, the value we find in the artificial data is $R^2_{Y \cdot 123} = .4458$. This is interpreted as meaning that G (religion, diagnosis, or treatment group membership) accounts for .4458 of the variance in the dependent variable Y, and in the exact sense ordinarily understood.

IDENTITY WITH ANALYSIS OF VARIANCE

Consider the more familiar AV analysis of these data. The Y scores can be assembled into the four G groups and a one-way AV performed. This yields the usual sums of squares for between groups ($B\ SS$), for within groups ($W\ SS$), and their total ($T\ SS$). If we determine the proportion of $T\ SS$ which $B\ SS$ constitutes, we have η^2 (eta square), the squared correlation ratio. This statistic has, as its most

general interpretation, the proportion of variance of the dependent variable accounted for by G-group membership, or, equivalently, accounted for by the group Y means. (Unfortunately, tradition in applied statistics textbooks and courses has focused on a narrow, special-case interpretation of η as an index of curvilinear correlation. For a broader view, see 3, pp. 104–105 and 12, pp. 312–325 and, particularly, 353–357.)

If we compute $\eta^2_{Y \cdot G}$ for the artificial data, we find

$$\eta^2_{Y \cdot G} = \frac{B\ SS}{T\ SS} = \frac{12127.0}{27205.6} = .4458 \quad \text{Eq. 3}$$

Thus, our MR coding procedure yields an $R^2_{Y \cdot 123}$ exactly equal to $\eta^2_{Y \cdot G}$, interpretable as the proportion of Y variance for which G accounts. The parallel goes further. It is demonstrable that the "shrunken" or df-corrected R^2 (10, pp. 184–185) is identically the same as Kelley's "unbiased" squared correlation ratio, epsilon-square (3, p. 105; 4; 12, pp. 319–322).

Furthermore, if one tests either of these results for significance, one obtains identically the same F ratio, for identically the same df:

For the $R^2_{Y \cdot 123}$, using the standard formula (e.g., 10, p. 283)

$$F = \frac{R^2_{Y \cdot 123 \cdots k}/k}{(1-R^2_{Y \cdot 123 \cdots k})/(n-k-1)}$$

$$= \frac{R^2_{Y \cdot 123 \cdots k}/(g-1)}{(1-R^2_{Y \cdot 123 \cdots k})/(n-g)}$$

$$= \frac{.4458/(4-1)}{(1-.4458)/(36-4)} = 8.580, \qquad \text{Eq. 4}$$

for numerator (regression) $df = k = g-1 = 3$ and denominator (residual or error) $df = n-k-1 = n-g = 32$.

The significance of η^2 is, of course, the significance of the separation of the G groups' Y means, that is, the usual AV F test of the between-groups mean square (MS):

$$F = \frac{\text{between } G \text{ groups } MS}{\text{within } G \text{ groups } MS} = \frac{(B\ SS)/(g-1)}{(W\ SS)/(n-g)}$$

$$= \frac{(12127.0)/(4-1)}{(15078.6)/(36-4)} = \frac{4042.33}{471.21} = 8.580,$$

Eq. 5

for numerator (between G groups) $df = g-1 = 4-1 = 3$, and denominator (within G groups, or error) $df = n-g = 36-4 = 32$.

These F ratios must be identical, since $B\,SS = (R^2 y_{.123...k})$ (total SS), and $W\,SS = (1 - R^2 y_{.123...k})$ (total SS). Formula 4 differs from Formula 5 only in that the total SS has been cancelled out from numerator and denominator.

The formulas help clarify the identity of the two procedures. We obtain another perspective on why $3(= g-1)$ independent variables carry all the group membership information for $4(= g)$ groups, —there are only 3 df "associated with" G group membership. By either the MR or AV route, the total SS (or variance) of Y has been partitioned into a portion accounted for by G group membership (or by G group Y means), and a portion not so accounted for (i.e., within group, residual, or "error"), the latter, by either route, based on $n-g\ df$.

Conceptually, the F ratios can be understood to be the same because they are testing null hypotheses which are mathematically equivalent, even though they are traditionally differently stated:

MR: H_0: Population $R^2 y_{.123} = 0$
AV: H_0: Population $m_1 = m_2 = m_3 = m_4$
    $= m$

If the AV H_0 is true, then knowledge of group membership and the use of group means leads to the same least squares prediction of the Y value of a given case as no knowledge, namely, the grand mean, thus one can account for none of the variance in Y by such knowledge, hence $R^2 y_{.123} = 0$, and conversely.

A full MR analysis also yields the regression coefficients and constant for the regression equation:

$$\hat{Y} = B_1 X_1 + B_2 X_2 + \ldots + B_k X_k + A \quad \text{Eq. 6}$$

where $\hat{Y}$ is the least-squares estimated ("predicted") value of Y, the B_i are raw score partial regression coefficients attached to each X_i, and A is the regression constant or Y-intercept, that is, the estimated value of Y when all X_i are set at zero. (Its computation is accomplished by including a "unit vector" with the X_i; see 5.)

In any MR problem, a B_i coefficient gives the amount of the effect in Y expressed in Y units which is yielded by a unit increase in X_i. But since as dummy variables the X_i are coded $0-1$, a unit increase means 1, membership in the group, rather than 0, nonmembership in the group. Solving for the values of the general regression Equation 6 for the artificial data, and using dummy variables, we obtain:

$$\hat{Y} = -30.34 X_1 - .56 X_2 + 21.22 X_3 + 84.12$$

Since group membership is all-or-none, the B_i values give the *net* consequence of membership in G_i relative to G_4 for groups G_1, G_2, and G_3. Thus,

$$\hat{Y}_1 = \bar{Y}_1 = -30.34(1) - .56(0)$$
$$+ 21.22(0) + 84.12 = 53.78$$

$$\hat{Y}_2 = \bar{Y}_2 = -30.34(0) - .56(1)$$
$$+ 21.22(0) + 84.12 = 83.56$$
$$\hat{Y}_3 = \bar{Y}_3 = -30.34(0) - .56(0)$$
$$+ 21.22(1) + 84.12 = 105.34$$

And G_4 has not been slighted, since, substituting its scores on X_1, X_2, and X_3, we find:

$$\hat{Y}_4 = \bar{Y}_4 = -30.34(0) - .56(0)$$
$$+ 21.22(0) + 84.12 = 84.12.$$

Thus, one can understand that "B_4," the "missing" reference group's weight, is always zero, and that therefore $\hat{Y}_4 = A$. The exact values of the B_i will vary, depending on which group is taken as the reference group (i.e., is coded 0, . . ., 0), but the differences among the B_i's will always be the same, since they are the same as the differences between the group Y means. That is, whichever the reference group, the separation of the B_i's in the example will be the same as that among the values -30.34,

$-.56$, $+21.22$ and 0. (For example, if G_1 is taken as the reference group, the new B_i are 0, 29.78, 51.56, and 30.33, and the regression constant $A = \bar{Y}_1 = 53.78$.)

Not only are the B_i meaningful, but also the multiple-partial correlations with the criterion, that is, the correlation of Y with X_i, partialing out or holding constant all the other independent variables, which for the sake of notational simplicity, we designate p_i. With dummy variable coded X_i, p_i can be more specifically interpreted as the correlation between Y and the dichotomy made up of membership in G_i versus membership in G_0, the reference group. The p_i thus give, in correlational terms, the relevance to Y of the distinction between each G_i and the reference group.

Furthermore, the p_i, B_i, and β_i (the standardized partial regression coefficient) can be tested for significance by means of t (or equivalently, F with numerator $df = 1$). Indeed, the null hypothesis is the same for all three,—the respective population parameter equals zero. But for a given X_i, if any one of the three is zero, all are zero, and the value of t is identical for all three tests. For the artificial data, the results are

	X_1	X_2	X_4
B_i	-30.34	$-.56$	$+21.22$
β_i	$-$ .478	$-.009$	.344
p_i	$-$ .464	$-.010$	.344
t_i	$-$ 2.96	$-.05$	2.07

Thus, the G_1-G_4 distinction and also the G_3-G_4 distinction with regard to Y are significant (two tailed .01 and .05, with 32 df) while the G_2-G_4 is not. These are identically the results one would obtain for t tests between the respective Y means, using the within-group mean square (with 32 df) as the variance estimate.

The reader, having been shown the MR-AV identities, may nevertheless react, "O.K., that's interesting, but so what?" Other than the provision of correlational (or regression) values, no advantage of MR over AV is claimed for this problem. But if there were other independent variables of interest (main effects,

either nominal, ordinal, or interval; interactions; covariates; nonlinear components; etc., whether or not correlated with G or each other), their addition to the G variable could proceed easily by means of MR, and not at all easily in an AV/ACV framework. This possibility is the single most important advantage of the MR procedure, and will receive further attention below.

To summarize, dummy variable coding of nominal scale data yields the multiple R^2 and F test (proportion of variance accounted for by group membership and an overall significance test) and the group Y means, but also information on the degree of relevance to Y of membership in any given group, G_i, relative to the remainder (r_{Yi}), and to a reference group in terms of either regression weights (B_i or β_i) or correlation (p_i), as well as specific significance tests on the relevant null hypotheses. The importance of dummy variable (or other nominal scale) coding lies not so much in its use when only a single nominal scale constitutes the independent variables, but rather in its ready inclusion with other independent variables in MR.

Contrast Coding

Another system for representing nominal data can be thought of as contrast or "issues" coding. Here, each independent variable carries a contrast (in the AV/ACV sense) among group means. Each subject is characterized for each contrast according to the role he plays in it, which depends upon his group membership. With all contrasts so represented, the MR analysis can proceed.

As an example, reconsider the representation of the G variable. We can contrast membership neither G_1 or G_2 versus membership in either G_3 or G_4. This could be substantively interpreted as, for example, majority versus minority religions, schizophrenic versus neurotic, or drug versus no-drug treatment condition. The coding or scoring of this issue may be rendered as in Column 4 in Table 1: the value 1 is assigned the subjects in G_1 and G_2 and the value -1 to those in G_3 and G_4, as is done in the computation of orthogonal contrasts in AV (e.g., 6). Actually, any two different numbers can be used to render this issue by itself, but there are advantages for some purposes in using values which sum to zero. The simple correlation between the dependent variable and this X_1 is a point-biserial correlation (as were the dummy variable correlations) whose square gives directly the proportion of Y variance attributable to the G_1, G_2 versus G_3, G_4 distinction. For the artificial data, the r^2_{Y1} = .2246 ($r_{Y1} = -.4739$). This is a meaningful value which gives the size of the relationship in the sample. This r_{Y1} can be tested for significance, and confidence limits for it (or for r^2_{Y1}) can be computed by conventional procedures.

Other issues or contrasts can be rendered as independent variables. For example, a second issue which may be rendered is the effect on Y of the G_1 versus G_2 distinction, ignoring G_3 and G_4. A third issue may be the analogous G_3 versus G_4 distinction, ignoring G_1 and G_2. These are rendered, respectively, in Columns 5 and 6 in Table 1. Each yields an r and r^2 with the criterion which is interpretable, testable for significance, and confidence boundable.

Beyond the separate correlations of these three contrast variables, there is the further question of what their *combined* effect is on Y. We compute the $R^2_{Y.123}$ and F and obtain *exactly* the same values as when the arbitrary or dummy variable coding was used, .4458 and 8.580 (for the artificial data). This follows from the fact that the three independent variables satisfy the nonsingularity condition, that is, no one of them gives a multiple R with the other two of unity. This is a necessary *and sufficient* condition for *any* coding of $g-1$ independent variables to represent G (see next section).

As before the partial statistics, that is, the p_i, B_i and β_i and the common t test of their significance are also meaningful. If the independent variables all correlate zero with each other, the β_i will equal their respective r_{Yi}. That this must be the case can be seen from the fact that each r^2_{Yi} represents a *different*

portion of the Y variance whose sum is the multiple $R^2_{Y.123}$ and thus the relationship $R^2_{Y.123} = \Sigma r_{Yi}\beta_i = \Sigma r^2_{Yi}$ must hold. The X_i as presented in Columns 4, 5, and 6 will be mutually uncorrelated if and only if the group sample sizes are equal. If they are not equal, the correlations among the X_i will be nonzero, which means that the contrasts or issues posed to the data are not independent. Such would be the case, in general, in the example if it were religion or diagnosis which formed the basis for group membership, and the actual natural population randomly sampled. Given unequal n_i for the four samples, although it is possible to make the three contrasts described above mutually uncorrelated, the coding of Columns 4, 5, and 6 does not do so. The scope of this article precludes discussion of the procedures whereby contrasts are coded so as to be uncorrelated. We note here merely that although it is always possible to do so, it is not necessarily desirable (see below).

Since, in AV terms, the between-groups SS can be (orthogonally) partitioned in various ways, there are sets of contrasts other than the set above which can be presented in the coding. A particularly popular set is that automatically provided by the AV factorial design. If the four groups of this example are looked upon as occupying the cells of a 2×2 design (an interpretation to which the physiological example of drug versus no drug, frontal lesion versus control lesion particularly lends itself), each of the usual AV effects can be represented as X_i by the proper coding. The first is the same as before, and contrasts G_1 and G_2 with G_3 and G_4, for example, the drug-no-drug main effect, reproduced as Column 7 of Table 1. The second main effect, for example, frontal-control lesion, contrasts G_1 and G_3 with G_2 and G_4 and is given by the coding in Column 8. This latter X_2 gives r_{Y2}, the (point-biserial) r for (e.g.) site of lesion with the dependent variable (e.g.) retention, and r^2_{Y2} is the proportion of Y variance accounted for by this variable.

The remaining df is, as the AV has taught us, the interaction of the two main effects, for example,   Drug–No-Drug $\times$ Frontal-Control

Lesion. It can always be rendered as a multiplicative function of the two single df aspects of the main effects. Here, it is simply coded as the product of each group's "scores" on X_1 and X_2 (given as Column 9 in Table 1): $1 \times 1 = 1$, $1 \times -1 = -1$, $-1 \times 1 = -1$, and $-1 \times -1 = 1$. Rendering the interaction as X_3, one can interpret it as carrying the information of that aspect of group membership which represents the *joint* (note, *not* additive) effect of the drug and frontal lesion conditions. Its (point-biserial) r_{Y3} is an expression in correlational terms of the degree of relationship between Y and the *joint* operation of drug and lesion site. r^2_{Y3} gives the proportion of Y variance accounted for by this joint effect.

In the example, these three issues are *conceptually* independent, thus it would be desirable that the X_i be uncorrelated, that is, $r_{12} = r_{13} = r_{23} = 0$. The coding values given in Columns 7, 8, and 9 of Table 1 will satisfy this condition if (and only if) the sample sizes of the four cells are equal. (If not, other coding, not discussed here, would be necessary.)

The conceptual independence of the issues arises from the consideration that they are both manipulated variables. When this is the case, it is clearly desirable for them to be represented as mutually uncorrelated, since then the $\beta_{Yi} = r_{Yi}$ and the $R^2_{Y.123}$ is simple a sum of the separate r^2_{Yi}. Thus, the total variance of Y accounted for by group membership is unambiguously partitioned into the three separate sources. Further, the factorial AV F test values of each of the separate (one df) effects is *identical* with the t^2 of the analogous MR partial coefficients (β_i, B_i, or p_i).

However, whether one wishes to represent the issues as uncorrelated depends on whether they are conceptually independent and the differing n_i are a consequence of animals randomly dying or test tubes being randomly dropped on the one hand, or whether they carry valid sampling information about a natural population state of affairs. Assume Y is a measure of liberalism-conservatism and reconsider the problem with the groups reinterpreted as G_1: low education, low income

($n_i = 160$), G_2: low education, high income ($n_2 = 20$), G_3: high education, low income ($n_3 = 80$), and G_4: high education, high income ($n_4 = 100$). These unequal and disproportional n_i carry valid sampling information about the univariate and bivariate distributions of education and income as defined here, the product moment r_{12} (phi) between them (coded as in Columns 7 and 8) equalling .4714. They may also be correlated with their interaction. One would ordinarily not wish to render these effects as uncorrelated, since the resulting X_i would be quite artificial, but rather by the coding given in Columns 7, 8, and 9, where, again, X_3 is simply the X_1X_2 product.

Note that whether the X_i are correlated or uncorrelated, or whether the n_i are equal or unequal, *all* of these coding systems yield the same $R^2_{Y.123}$ and associated F.

Two systems of rendering nominal scale (group membership) information into independent variables have been described: dummy variable coding and contrast coding. They result in identically the same multiple R^2 (and associated F) but different per independent variable partial statistics which are differently interpreted. Either involves expressing the nominal scale of g levels (groups) into $g - 1$ independent variables, each carrying a distinct aspect of group membership whose degree of association and statistical significance can be determined.

NONSENSE CODING

It turns out, quite contraintuitively, that if one's purpose is merely to represent G so that its R^2_Y and/or its associated F test value can be determined, it hardly matters how one codes X_1, X_2, ..., X_{g-1}. *Any* real numbers, positive or negative, whole or fractional, can be used in the coding subject only to the nonsingularity constraint, that is, no X_i may have a multiple R of 1.00 with the other independent variables.

Consider, for example, the values of Columns 10–12 of Table 1. The numbers for X_1 in Column 10 were obtained by random entry into a random number table and their signs by coin flipping. Column 11 for X_2 was constructed by squaring the entries in Column 10, and Column 12 for X_3 by cubing them. Powering the X_1 values assures the satisfaction of the nonsingularity constraint. Now, using these nonsense "scores" to code G and the same Y values of the artificial example, we find the *same* $R^2_{Y\cdot123}$ of .4458 with associated $F = 8.580$!

Or, alternatively, the coding values of Columns 13, 14, and 15 were obtained by haphazard free association with a quick eyeball check to assure nonsingularity. They, too, yield $R^2_{Y\cdot123} = .4458$ and $F = 8.580$.

Why these, or any other values satisfying nonsingularity will "work" would require too much space to explain nontechnically. Ultimately, it is a generalization of the same principle which makes it possible to score a dichotomy with *any* two different values (not only the conventional 0 and 1) and obtain the same point-biserial r^2 against another variable.

Of course, the statistics per X_i, that is, r_{Yi}, p_i, B_i, β_i, are as nonsensical as the X_i. But the regression equation will yield the correct group means on Y, and, as noted, R^2 and its F remain invariant. Thus, with the aid of an MR computer program and a table of random numbers (or a nonsingular imagination), one can duplicate the yield of an AV.

Apart from its status as a statistical curiosity, of what value is the demonstration that one can simulate an AV by means of an arbitrarily coded MR analysis? Not much, taken by itself. However, despite this disclaimer, it should be pointed out that for most investigators, the yield sought from the AV of such data is the significance status of the F test on the means, which the MR provides; the latter also "naturally" yields, in R^2, a statement of proportion of variance accounted for. True, this is identically available from the AV in η^2, but this is not generally understood and computed. The MR approach has the virtue of calling to the attention of the investigator the existence of a rho (relationship) value and its distinction from a tau (significance test) value

(3, pp. 101–106), an issue usually lost sight of in AV contexts (but, see 7, pp. 325–333).

But if it hardly matters how we score G and still get the same $R^2_{Y\cdot123}$ and F ratio, we can score it in some meaningful way, one which provides analytically useful intermediate results, that is, by dummy variable or contrast coding. For other approaches to nominal scale coding, see Bottenberg and Ward (1) and Jennings (8).

Aspects of Quantitative Scales as Independent Variables

As noted in the introduction, psychologists are familiar with the use of quantitative variables as independent variables in MR. This, indeed, is the only use of MR illustrated in the standard textbooks. Thus, given duration of first psychiatric hospitalization as the dependent variable Y, and as independent variables: age (X_1), Hollingshead SES Index (X_2), and MMPI Schizophrenia (*Sc*) score (X_3), the psychologist knows how to proceed. But MR provides opportunities for the analysis of quantitative independent variables which transcend this very limited approach.

CURVILINEAR REGRESSION

From the enlarged conceptual framework of the present treatment of MR, we would say that this analysis is concerned with the *linear* aspects of age, SES, and *Sc*. There are other functions or aspects of these variables which can be represented as independent variables.

It has long been recognized that curvilinear relationships can be represented in linear MR by means of a polynomial form in powered terms. The standard Equation 6

$$\hat{Y} = B_1X_1 + B_2X_2 + \ldots + B_kX_k + A$$

is linear in the X_i. If the X_i are $X_1 = Z$, $X_2 = Z^2$, $X_3 = Z^3$, ... $X_k = Zk$, the equation is *still* linear in the X_i, even though not linear in Z. The result of this strategem is that nonlinear regression of Y on Z can nevertheless be represented within the linear *multiple* regression framework, the "multiplicity" being used to represent various aspects of nonlinearity, the quadratic, cubic, etc. The provision of any given power u of Z, that is, Z^u allows for $u - 1$ bends in the regression curve of Y or Z. Thus Z^1 or Z provides for $1 - 1 = 0$ bends, hence a straight line, Z^2 provides for $2 - 1 = 1$ bend, Z^3 for 2 bends, etc. In most psychological research, provision for more than one or two bends will rarely be necessary.

It is the same strategem of polynomial representation further refined to make these aspects orthogonal to each other, which is utilized in the AV, also a linear model, in trend analysis designs.

A note of caution must be injected here. Such variables as Z, Z^2, and Z^3 are in general correlated, indeed, for score-like data, usually highly so. Table 2 presents some illustrative data. In this example, the correlations are .9479, .8840, and .9846. For reasons of ordinary scientific parsimony, unless one is working with a strong hypothesis, we normally think of them as a hierarchy: how much Y variance does Z account for? (.5384) If Z^2 is added to Z as a second variable, how much do both together account for? (.5949) The difference represents the increment in variance accounted for by making allowance for quadratic (parabolic) curvature. In the example, it is a very small amount,—.0115. If to Z and Z^2 we add Z^3, the multiple $R^2_{Y \cdot 123}$ becomes .5956, an increment over $R^2_{Y \cdot 12}$ of only .0007. Each of these separate increments, or the two combined can be tested for significance. In general, any increment to an $R^2_{Y \cdot A}$ due to the addition of B can be tested by the F ratio:

$$F = \frac{(R^2_{Y \cdot A, B} - R^2_{Y \cdot A})/b}{(1 - R^2_{Y \cdot A, B})/(n - a - b - 1)} \quad \text{Eq. 7}$$

with $df = b$ and $(n - a - b - 1)$, where

$R^2_{Y \cdot A, B}$ is the incremented R^2 based on $a + b$ independent variables, that is, predicted from the combined sets of A and B variables,

$R^2_{Y \cdot A}$ is the smaller R^2 based on only a independent variables, that is, predicted from only the A set,

a and b are the number of original (a) and added (b) independent variables, hence the number of df each "takes up."

This F test of an increment to R^2 is much more general in its applicability than the present narrow context, and its symbols have been accordingly given quite general interpretation. It is used several times later in the exposition, in other circumstances where, because of correlation among X_i, it provides a basis for judging how much a set of independent variables contributes *additionally* to Y variance accounting. Since what is added is independent of what is already provided for, this is a general device for partitioning R^2 into orthogonal portions. Since the size of such portions depends on the *order* in which sets are included, the hierarchy of sets is an important part of the investigator's hypothesis statement. The generality of Formula 7 is further seen in that Formula 4 is actually a special case of Formula 7, where $R^2_{Y \cdot A}$ is zero because no X_i are used (hence $a = 0$) and $R^2_{Y \cdot B}$ is the R^2 based on b ($= k$) df which is being tested, that is, an increment of R^2 from zero.

Either set may have one or more independent variables. Thus, to test the increment of Z^2 to Z alone, assuming total $n = 36$,

$$F = \frac{(.5949 - .5384)/1}{(1 - .5949)/(36 - 1 - 1 - 1)} =$$
$$= \frac{.0115}{.4051/33} = .934$$

with $df = 1$ and 33 (a chance departure).
To test the pooled addition of both Z^2 and Z^3 to Z,

$$F = \frac{(.5956 - .5834)/2}{(1 - .5956)/(36 - 1 - 2 - 1)} =$$
$$= \frac{.0122/2}{.4044/32} = .483$$

with $df = 2$ and 32 (also a chance result).

The need for caution arises in that if one studies the results of the regression analysis which uses Z, Z^2 and Z^3, where the solution of the partial (regression or correlation) coefficients is simultaneous, not successive, the three variables are treated quite democratically. Each is partialed from the others without favor or hierarchy. Since such variables are highly correlated, when one partials Z^2 and Z^3 from Z, one is robbing Z of Y variance which we think of as rightfully belonging to it. Table 2 gives the p_i of the three predictors when one treats them as a set. The values are smaller (reflecting the mutual partialing), and may be negative (reflecting "suppression" effects). Because the p_i are so small, they may well be nonsignificant (as they are here), even though r_{YZ} is significant and any of the other variables may yield a significant increment. Thus, the significance interpretation of the regression of a set of polynomial terms simultaneously may be quite misleading when the usual hierarchical notions prevail.

This results in $g-1$ independent variables, each a segment of the Z range. The resulting $R^2_{Y \cdot G}$ is the amount of Y variance accounted for by Z (curvilinearly, if such is the case) and the Y means for the g intervals, computable from the resulting raw score regression equation, can be plotted graphically against the midpoints of the class intervals of Z to portray the function.

A more elegant method is the transformation (coding) of the Z values to *orthogonal* polynomials. This has the advantages in that the resulting X_i terms representing linear, quadratic, cubic, etc., components of the polynomial regression are uncorrelated with each other; thus each contributes a separate portion of the Y variance capable of being tested for significance. Unfortunately, this method be-

Table 2. Illustrative data on polynomial multiple regression

| | | Correlations (r) | | Cumulative | | |
Variable	Y	Z	Z^2	R^2	Increment	p_i
$Z \ (= X_1)$	.7638			.5834	.5834	.1399
$Z^2 (= X_2)$	.7582	.9479		.5949	.0115	−.0116
$Z^3 (= X_3)$	.7268	.8840	.9846	.5956	.0007	.0419

On the other hand, if the analyst's purpose is to portray a polynomial regression fit to an observed set of data, he can solve for the set simultaneously and use the resulting MR equation. For the data used for Table 2, the regression Equation 6 is:

$$Y = 11.70X_1 - .50X_2 + .25X_3 + 55.90$$

the values being the B_i regression coefficients and constant, and the X_i successively Z, Z^2, and Z^3. One can substitute over the range of interest of Z and obtain fitted values of Y for purposes of prediction or of graphing of the function.

There are other means whereby curvilinear relationships can be handled in an MR framework. Briefly, one can organize an independent variable Z into g class intervals (ordinarily, but not necessarily equal in range) and treat the resulting classes as groups, coding them by the dummy variable technique described above.

comes computationally quite cumbersome unless the Z values are equally spaced and with equal n_i per interval. The latter is the usual case when Z is an experimentally manipulated variable, where the standard trend analysis designs of the AV can be used (6).

Finally, although the first few powers of a polynomial is a good *general* fitting function, in some circumstances, such transformations of Z as log Z, $1/Z$, or $Z^{\frac{1}{2}}$ may provide a better fit. Draper and Smith (5) provide a useful general reference for handling curvilinearity (and other MR problems).

JOINT ASPECTS OF INTERACTIONS

Given two independent variables, $X_1 = Z$ and $X_2 = W$, one may be interested in not only their separate effects on Y, but also on their joint effect, over and above their separate effects. As noted above (Contrast Coding), where this was discussed in the narrow context of a 2×2 design, this joint effect is carried by a third independent variable, a score defined for each subject by the product of his Z and W scores, that is, $X_3 = ZW$. This variable contains this joint effect, which is identically the (first-order) interaction effect of AV, or the "moderator" effect of Saunders (13). This identity is quite general, so that a triple interaction is carried by a triple product, say ZWV, etc. Furthermore, the above are all interactions or joint effects of *linear* aspects of the variables. The more complex interactions of nonlinear aspects, such as the linear by quadratic, or quadratic by cubic, made familiar by advanced treatments of AV trend analysis (16, pp. 273–278), would be represented by products of powered variables, for example, ZW^2, Z^2W^3, each a single independent variable.

The presentation of joint effects as simple products in MR requires the same caution as in the polynomial representation of a single variable. (Indeed, a powered variable can be properly understood as a special case of an interaction, for example, Z^2 contains the Z by Z interaction.) If one uses simultaneously as independent variables $X_1 = Z$, $X_2 = W$, $X_3 = ZW$, the correlations of Z with ZW, and W with ZW will ordinarily not be zero, may indeed be large, and the partial coefficients for Z and W (β, B, p) will have lost to ZW some Y variance which properly is theirs (just as Z would be robbed of some of its Y variance by Z^2 and Z^3). The problem is solved as in the polynomial regression analysis: Find $R^2_{Y \cdot 123}$, the variance proportion accounted for by all three variables; then find $R^2_{Y \cdot 12}$, the amount accounted for *without* the interaction. The increment is tested for significance by the F ratio of Formula 7.

This, too, generalizes. In more complex systems, involving either more variables and higher order interactions or interactions among polynomial aspects (or both), one forms a hierarchy of sets of independent variables and tests for the significance of increments to R^2 by means of the same F ratio (Formula 7). For example, if one has three variables Z, W,

and V, represented both linearly and quadratically with all their interactions, one possible way of organizing the variables is by means of the following sets:

$A: Z, W, V$
$B: ZW, ZV, WV$
$C: ZWV$
$D: Z^2, W_2, V_2$
$E: Z^2W, ZW^2, Z^2V, ZV^2, W^2V, WV^2$
$F: Z^2W^2, Z^2V^2, W^2V^2$
$G: Z^2W^2V^2$

One would then test $R^2_{Y \cdot AB} - R^2_{Y \cdot A}$, $R^2_{Y \cdot ABC} - R^2_{Y \cdot AB}$, etc., each by the F ratio for increments. When a set containing more than one variable is significant, one can "break out" each variable in it and test its increment for significance by the same procedure. Of course, one can elect to make all sets contain only one variable, but the number of resulting tests (in the example there would be 20) brings with it an increased risk of spuriously significant results over the complete analysis. This strategy parallels that of the AV, where the avoidance of this risk is implicit. In a 4×5 factorial design AV, for example, the interaction involves a single mean square based on $3 \times 4 = 12$ df which is tested by a single F test. One ordinarily does not test each of these 12 effects separately unless the set as a whole is significant. The principle, of course, obtains even for the main effects, involving sets of 3 and 4 df, where each set normally is tested "wholesale."

Other combinations and priorities of the X, Y, and Z variables are, of course, possible. This operation involves formulating hypotheses about what constitutes a relevant class of independent variables and the priorities of these classes. It depends not only on mechanical variance-stealing considerations, but also on substantive issues in the research and the judgment of the investigator.

Although the discussion in this section has been concerned with interactions among quantitative variables, the principles of forming interaction variables hold also for nominal variables, and for mixtures of variables. Let an "aspect" of a research variable such as religion or IQ be one of the X_i of the set which represent it. Then, for example, if the interaction of u aspects of one variable U and v aspects of another variable V are desired, one may form a total of uv interaction X_i, by multiplying each of the u aspects by each of the v aspects. Each of the resulting uv independent variables is a single (one df) variable which represents a specific aspect by aspect joint or interaction effect. Either U or V may be nominal or quantitative. Where nominal, their aspects may be dummy variables or contrasts; where quantitative, the aspects may be powered polynomial terms or missing data dichotomies (see below). One can thus generate such single interaction X_i as "majority-minority religious group by authoritarianism," "experimental group D versus control group by quadratic of stimulus intensity," etc. It is both convenient and enlightening to have each such joint aspect separately and unambiguously (but not necessarily orthogonally) represented in the set of independent variables. Their individual increment to R^2 and significance can then be determined.

Perhaps as important as being able to represent the interaction X_i in specific detail is the availability of the option *not* to represent some or all of them. The textbook paradigms for factorial design AV lead data analysts to dutifully harvest all possible interactions of all possible orders up to the highest, whether or not they are meaningful or interpretable or, if interpretable, communicable. There emanate from psychology departments many silent prayers to the spirit of R. A. Fisher that high-order interactions will not prove significant! Obviously, one need not (indeed cannot) analyze for all possible aspects including joint aspects of variables if for no other reason than the rapid loss of df for estimating error. The need to "specify the model," that is, the set of X_i to be studied in MR has the salutary effect of requiring an incisive prior conceptual analysis of the research problem. This goes hand in hand with the flexibility of the MR system, which makes readily possible the representation of the research issues posed by the investigator (i.e., multiple regression in the service of the ego!), rather than the canned issues mandated by AV computational routines.

MISSING DATA

In nonexperimental, particularly survey, research, it frequently occurs that some subjects are missing data on one or more (but not all) of the independent variables under study. Typically, the data are not missing randomly, but for reasons frequently related to values for other independent variables, and particularly to values for the dependent variable under study. For example, in a study of factors associated with the rehabilitation of drug addicts, reported weekly wages on last job is used as an independent variable, among others. Some respondents claim they do not recall or refuse to respond. As another example, consider a retrospective study of the school records of adult mental retardates where the recorded IQ is abstracted for use as an independent variable but found missing in some cases. In neither of these cases can one prudently assume that the mean of these cases on the X_i in question, other X_i, and, particularly, Y is the same as that for the cases with data present. The practice of excluding cases lacking some of the data has the undesirable properties of analyzing a residual sample which is unrepresentative to an unknown degree of the population originally sampled, as well as the loss of information (viz., the *fact* of data being missing) which may be criterion relevant.

MR provides a simple method for coping with this problem. Each such variable has *two* aspects, its value (where present) and whether or not the value *is* present. Accordingly, two independent variables are constructed: X_1 is the value itself, with the mean of X_1 for those cases where it is present entered for the cases where it is missing, and X_2 is the missing data aspect, a dummy variable dichotomy coded 0–1 for absent-present. These two aspects contain all the information available in the variable. Moreover, as scored, $r_{12} = 0$, hence X_1 and X_2 are each contributing an independent portion of the Y variance.

Actually, *any* value entered for the missing data in X_1 will "work" in the sense of accounting for Y variance, that is, the $R^2_{Y.12}$ will be the same. The use of the mean will uniquely result in $r_{12} = 0$, which may be advantageous interpretively. For some purposes, this advantage may be offset by using some (or any) other value, obviating the necessity of a prior computation of the mean.

The researcher, normally sensitive about tampering with data, may find the prospect of "plugging" empty spaces in his data sheet with means singularly unappealing. He may even correctly point out that this will have the effect of reducing r_{Y1} from what r_{YX} is for the subsample having X values present. In rebuttal, it must be pointed out that the subsample is not representative of the originally defined population, and the method proposed can be thought of as reflecting the fact that the population studied contains missing data, and fully incorporates this fact as positive information.

Analysis of Covariance

Viewed from the perspective of the MR system, the fixed-model ACV turns out to be a rather minor wrinkle, and not the imposing parallel edifice it constitutes in the AV/ACV framework. A covariate is, after all, nothing but an independent variable, which, because of the logic dictated by the substantive issues of the research, assumes priority among the set of independent variables as a basis for accounting for Y variance. Consider a research in educational psychology in which the Y variable is some performance measure in children, X_1 is midparental education, X_2 is family income, and G carried by the set X_3, X_4, X_5 represents some differential learning experience in four intact classes. This situation is a "natural" for ACV (assuming its assumptions are reasonably well met). One would think of it as studying the effect of learning experience

or class membership on Y, using X_1 and X_2 as covariates. Thus considered, we are asking how much variance in Y (and its significance) the variables X_3, X_4, and X_5 account for, *after* the variance due to X_1 and X_2 is allowed for, or held constant, or "partialed out" (the terms being equivalent). The form of the MR analysis to accomplish this purpose is directly suggested. Find $R^2_{Y.12345}$, the proportion of Y variance all independent variables account for. Then find $R^2_{Y.12}$, the proportion of Y variance attributable to the covariates education and income. Their difference is the increment due to group membership, which is tested for significance by the F test of Formula 7 used in a different design context above. Note that no problem arises if the four groups are defined by a 2×2 factorial. If X_3, X_4, X_5 are coded as in Columns 7, 8, 9 in Table 1 to represent the two main effects and their interaction, the respective ACV significance tests are performed by (Formula 7) F ratio tests of the increments $R^2_{Y.12345} - R^2_{Y.1245}$ (for the main effect represented by X_3), $R^2_{Y.12345} - R^2_{Y.1235}$ (for the main effect represented by X_4) and $r^2_{Y.12345} - r^2_{Y.1234}$ (for the interaction or joint effect). Note that X_1 and X_2 are always included in the debited R^2, because of their priority in the issues as defined. This principle is readily generalized to designs of greater complexity.

That a covariate is nothing but another independent variable except for priority due to substantive considerations is evident when one considers a study formally almost identical to the above, now, however, done by a social psychologist. Since there are four different classes and four different teachers, the classes ipso facto have had different learning experiences. But this research is concerned with the effects of parental education and income on the performance criterion, with group membership now the contaminant which must be removed, hence the covariate. Using the same set up and data, he would find $R^2_{Y.12345} - R^2_{Y.345}$ as the combined effect of education and income, $R^2_{Y.12345} - R^2_{Y.2345}$ as the net effect of education (i.e., over and above that of income as well as the covariates of class membership), and

$R^2_{y.12345} - R^2_{y.1345}$ for the net effect of income, each F-testable as before. Thus, one man's main effect is another man's covariate.

The MR approach to ACV-like problems opens up possibilities for statistical control not dreamed of in ACV. We have just seen how purely nominal or qualitative variables (class membership) can serve as covariates. Beyond this, we can apply other principles which have been adduced above: (a) Any aspects of data can, by appropriate means, be represented as independent variables. (b) Any (sets of) independent variables can serve as covariates by priority assignment in variance accounting. Thus, for example, one can make provision for a covariate being nonlinearly related to Y (and/or to other independent variables) by writing a polynomial set of independent variables and giving the set priority; or, one can carry two variables *and* their interaction as a covariate set; or, one can even carry as a covariate a variable for which there are missing data by representing the two aspects of such a datum as two independent variables and giving them priority. Finally, one can combine the priority principle with those of contrast coding to achieve analytic modes of high fidelity to substantive research aims.

The ACV assumption that the regression lines (more generally, surfaces) of the covariate (U) on Y have the same slopes (more generally, regression parameters) between groups (V) is equivalent to the hypothesis of no significance for the set of uv interaction independent variables. This hypothesis can be F-tested as a Set B following the inclusion of U as Set A, using Formula 7.

Discussion

In the introduction it was argued that MR and AV/ACV are essentially identical systems, and so they are, at least in their theory. In the actual practice of the data-analytic art, many differences emerge, differences which generally favor the MR system as outlined above.

Before turning to these differences, a closer look at their similarity in regard to statistical assumptions is warranted. This article has concerned itself only with the fixed-model AV/ACV, wherein it is assumed that inference to the population about the independent variables is for just those variables represented (and not those variables considered as samples) and that values on these variables are measured without error. This means that in a MR whose set of X_i include quantitative variates (e.g., scores), the population to which one generalizes, strictly speaking, is made up of cases having just those X_i values, only the Y values for any given combinations of values for the X_i varying; moreover, the Y distribution (and only this distribution) is assumed normal and of equal variance for all the observed combinations of X_i values. These seem, indeed, to be a constraining set of assumptions. However, the practical effect on the validity of the generalizations which one might wish to draw is likely to be vanishingly small. It seems likely that the substantive generalizations made strictly for the particular vectors of X_i values in the rows of the basic data matrix of the sample would hold for the slightly differing values which the population would contain if the sampling is random. As for the normality and variance homogeneity assumptions for Y, the robustness of the F test under conditions of such assumption failure is well attested to (for a summary, see 3, pp. 114–116). Particularly when reasonably large samples are used, itself desirable to assure adequate statistical power, no special inhibition need surround the drawing of inferences from the usual hypothesis testing, certainly no more so than in AV.

A discussion of the practical differences between MR and AV is best begun with a consideration of the nature of classical fixed-model AV. Its natural use is in the analysis of data generated by experimental manipulations along one or more dimensions (main effects), resulting in subgroups of observations in multifactor cells, treatment combinations. Each main effect is paradigmatically a set of qualitative distinctions along some dimension. These dimensions are conceptually independent of each other, and since they are under the control of the designer of the experiment, the data can, in principle, be gathered in such a way that the dimensions are actually mutually orthogonal in their representation in the data. (This condition is met by the proportionality of cell frequencies in all two dimensional subtables.) This also results in interactions being orthogonal to each other and to the main effects. Thus, the paradigm is of a set of batches (one batch per AV main effect or interaction) of qualitative independent variables, all batches mutually orthogonal.

Now, under such conditions, one *can*, as illustrated above, analyze the data by MR, but there is no advantage in so doing. The AV can be seen as a computational shortcut to an analysis by the linear model which analyzes by batches and capitalizes on the fact that batches are orthogonal. Thus, the classical fixed factorial AV is a special simplified case of MR analysis particularly suited to neat experimental layouts, where qualitative treatments are manipulated in appropriate orthogonal relationships. Later refinements allows for quantitative independent variables being exploited by trend analysis designs, but these, too, demand manipulative control in the form of equally spaced intervals in the dimension and equal sized samples per level if the computational simplicity is to be retained.

These designs are quite attractive, not only in their efficiency and relative computational simplicity, but also in the conceptual power they introduced to the data analyst, for example, interactions, trend components. They were presented in excellent applied statistics textbooks. Inevitably, they attracted investigators working in quite different modes, who proceeded to a Procrustean imposition of such designs on their research.

A simple example (not too much of a caricature) may help illustrate the point. Dr. Doe is investigating the effects of Authoritarianism (California F scale) and IQ on a cognitive style score (Y), using high school students as subjects. He is particularly interested in the F $\times$ IQ interaction, that is, in the possibility that r_{YF} differs as a function of IQ level. He

gives the three tests, and proceeds to set up the data for analysis. He dichotomizes the F and IQ distributions as closely as possible to their medians into high-low groups and proceeds to assign the Y scores into the four cells of the resulting 2×2 fixed factorial design. He then discovers that the number of cases in the high-low and low-high cells distinctly exceed those in the other two, an expression of the fact that F and IQ are correlated. He must somehow cope with this disproportionality (nonorthogonality). He may (*a*) throw out cases randomly to achieve proportionality or equality; (*b*) use an "unweighted means" or other approximate solution (14, pp. 385–387); or (*c*) "fit constants by least squares" (14, pp. 388–391; 16, pp. 224–227), which is, incidentally, an MR procedure.

Clearly, this is a far cry from experimentally manipulated qualitative variables. These are, in fact, naturally varying correlated quantitative variables. This analysis does violence to the problem in one or both of the following ways:

1. By reducing the F scale and IQ to dichotomies, it has taken reliable variables which provide graduated distinctions between subjects over a wide range, and reduced them to two-point (high-low) scales, squandering, much information in the process. For example, assuming bivariate normality, when a variable is so dichotomized, there is a reduction in r^2_{YX}, the criterion variance it accounts for, and hence in the value of F in the test of its significance, of 36%. This wilful degradation of available measurement information has a direct consequence in the loss of statistical power (3, pp. 95–101, 118).

2. The throwing out of cases to achieve proportionality clearly reduces power, but, even worse, distorts the situation by analyzing as if IQ and F scale score were independent, when they are not. Other approximations suffer from these and/or other statistical deficiencies or distortions.

If Dr. Doe uses the MR-equivalent exact-fitting constants procedure, he has still given up computational simplicity, and, of course, the measurement information due to dichotomization. If he seeks to reduce the latter and also allow for the possibility of nonlinearity of Y on X_i regressions by breakdown of IQ and/or F scale into smaller segments, say quartiles, his needs for equality of intervals and cases will be frustrated, and he will not be able to find a computational paradigm, which, in any case, would be very complicated. It seems quite clear that, however considered, the conventional AV mode is the wrong way to analyze the data.

On the other hand, the data can be completely, powerfully, and relevantly analyzed by MR. A simple analysis would involve setting $X_1 = $ IQ, $X_2 = $ F scale score, $X_3 = $ (IQ)(F). By finding $R^2_{Y \cdot 123} - R^2_{Y \cdot 12}$ and testing it for significance (or equivalently, by testing the significance of p_3), he learns how much the interaction contributes to Y variance accounting and its significance. Determinations of the values of r^2_{Y1}, r^2_{Y2}, $R^2_{Y \cdot 12}$, $R^2_{Y \cdot 12} - r^2_{Y1}$, and $R^2_{Y \cdot 12} - r^2_{Y2}$ and testing each for significance fully exploits the information in the data at this level. If he believes it warranted, he can add polynomial terms for IQ and F score and their interaction in order to provide for nonlinearity of any of the relationships involved.

Another practical difference between MR and AC/ACV is with regard to computation. The MR procedure, in general, requires the computation and inversion of the matrix of correlations (or sums of squares and products) among the independent variables, a considerable amount of computation for even a modest number of independent variables. It is true that *classical* AV, whose main effects, interactions, polynomial trend components, etc., are mutually orthogonal, capitalizes on this orthogonality to substantially reduce the computation required. Whatever computational reduction there is in AV or MR depends directly on the orthogonality of the independent variables, which we have seen is restricted to manipulative experiments, and is by no means an invariant feature even of such experiments.

However, given the widespread availability of electronic computer facilities, the issue of the *amount* of computation required in the analysis of data from psychological research dwindles to the vanishing point, and is replaced by problems of programming. The typical statistical user of a typical computer facility requires that a computer program which will analyze his data be available in the program library. Such programs will have been either prepared or adapted for the particular computer configuration of that facility. Unfortunately, it is frequently the case that the available AV program or programs will not analyze the particular fixed AV design which the investigator brings. Some AV programs are wanting in capacity in number of factors or levels per factor, some will handle only orthogonal designs, some will handle only equal cases per cell, some will do AV but not ACV, some of those that do handle ACV can handle only one or two covariates. Many will not handle special forms of AV, for example, Latin squares.

On the other hand, even the most poorly programmed scientific computer facility will have at least one good MR program, if for no other reason than its wide use in various technologies, particularly engineering. All the standard statistical program packages contain at least one MR program. Although these vary in convenience, efficiency, and degree of informativeness of output, all of them can be used to accomplish the analyses discussed in this article. In contrast to the constraints of AV programs, the very general MR program can be particularized for any given design by representing (coding) those aspects of the independent variables of interest to the investigator according to the principles which have been described.

A note of caution: as we have seen, given even a few factors (main effects of nominal variables or linear aspects of quantitative variables), one can generate very large numbers of distinct independent variables (interactions of any order, polynomials, interactions of polynomials, etc.). The temptation to represent many such features of the data in an analysis must be resisted for sound research-philosophical and statistical reasons. Even in researches using a relatively large number of subjects (n), a small number of factors (nominal and quantitative scales) can generate a number of independent variables which exceed n. Each esoteric issue posed to the data costs a df which is lost from the error estimate, thus enfeebling the statistical power of the analysis.

This, ultimately, is the reason that it is desirable in research that is to lead to *conclusions* to state hypotheses which are relatively few in number. This formulation is not intended to indict exploratory studies, which may be invaluable, but by definition, such studies do not result in conclusions, but in hypotheses, which then need to be tested (or, depending on the research context, cross-validated). If one analyzes the data of a research involving 100 subjects by means of MR, and utilizes 40 independent variables, what does one conclude about the 4 or 5 of them which prove to have partial regression weights "significant" at the .05 level? Certainly not that *all* of them are real effects, when one realizes that an overall null hypothesis leads to an expectation that 5% of 40, or 2 are expected by change. But which two?

A reasonable strategy depends upon organizing a hierarchy of sets of independent variables, ordered, by sets, according to a priori judgments. Set A represents the independent variables which the investigator most expects to be relevant to Y (perhaps all or some of the main effects and/or linear aspects of continuous variables). These may be thought of as *the* hypotheses of the research, and the fewer the better. Set B consists of next order possibilities (perhaps lower order interactions and/or some quadratic aspects). These are variables which are to be viewed less as hypotheses and more as exploratory issues. If there is a Set C (perhaps some higher order interactions and/or higher degree polynomials), it should be thought of as unqualifiedly exploratory. (If there are covariates in the design, they, of course, take precedence over all these sets, and

would enter first.) The "perhaps" in the parenthetical phrases in this paragraph are included because it is *not* a mechanical ordering that is intended. In any given research, a central issue may be carried by an interaction or polynomial aspect while some main effect may be quite secondary. In most research, however, it is the simplest aspects of factors which are most likely to occupy the focus of the investigator's attention. However, the decision as to what constitutes an appropriate set depends on both research-strategic issues that go to the heart of the substantive nature of the research, and subtle statistical issues beyond the scope of this article. The latter are discussed by Miller (11, pp. 30–35).

The independent variables so organized, one first does an MR analysis for Set A, then Sets A + B, then Sets A + B + C. Each additional set is tested for the increment to R^2 by means of the F test of Formula 7. A prudent procedure would then be to test for significance the contribution of any *single* independent variable in a set only if the set yields a significant increment to R^2. A riskier procedure would be to dispense with the latter condition, but then the results would clearly require cross-validation.

References

1. Bottenberg, R. A., & Ward, J. H., Jr. *Applied multiple linear regression.* (PRL-TDR-63-6) Lackland AF Base, Texas, 1963.
2. Cattell, R. B. Psychological theory and scientific method. In R. B. Cattell (Ed.), *Handbook of multivariate experimental psychology.* Chicago: Rand McNally, 1966.
3. Cohen, J. Some statistical issues in psychological research. In B. B. Wolman (Ed.), *Handbook of clinical psychology.* New York: McGraw-Hill, 1965.
4. Cureton, E. E. On correlation coefficients. *Psychometrika*, 1966, 31, 605–607.
5. Draper, N., & Smith, H. *Applied regression analysis.* New York: Wiley, 1967.
6. Edwards, A. E. *Experimental design in psychological research.* (Rev. ed.) New York: Rinehart, 1960.
7. Hays, W. L. *Statistics for psychologists.* New York: Holt, Rinehart & Winston, 1963.

8. Jennings, E. Fixed effects analysis of variance by regression analysis. *Multivariate Behavioral Research*, 1967, 2, 95–108.

9. Li, J. C. R. *Statistical inference*. Vol. 2. *The multiple regression and its ramifications*. Ann Arbor, Mich.: Edwards Bros., 1964.

10. McNemar, Q. *Psychological statistics*. (3rd ed.) New York: Wiley, 1962.

11. Miller, R. G., Jr. *Simultaneous statistical inference*. New York: McGraw-Hill, 1966.

12. Peters, C. C., & Van Voorhis, W. R. *Statistical procedures and their mathematical bases*. New York: McGraw-Hill, 1940.

13. Saunders, D. R. Moderator variables in prediction. *Educational and Psychological Measurement*, 1956, 16, 209–222.

14. Snedecor, G. W. *Statistical methods*. (5th ed.) Ames: Iowa State College Press, 1956.

15. Suits, D. B. Use of dummy variables in regression equations. *Journal of the American Statistical Association*, 1957, 52, 548–551.

16. Winer, B. J. *Statistical principles in experimental design*. New York: McGraw-Hill, 1962.

Index